RADIOACTIVITY IN MAN

Second Symposium

RADIOACTIVITY IN MAN

Second Symposium

Whole Body Counting and Effects of Internal Gamma Ray-Emitting Radioisotopes

A Symposium

Sponsored by Northwestern University Medical School and the American Medical Association

Edited by

GEORGE R. MENEELY, M.D.

General Chairman

and

SHIRLEY MOTTER LINDE

Symposium Coordinator

CHARLES C THOMAS • PUBLISHER

Springfield • Illinois • U.S.A.

Published and Distributed Throughout the World by

CHARLES C THOMAS • PUBLISHER

Bannerstone House

301-327 East Lawrence Avenue, Springfield, Illinois, U.S.A.

Natchez Plantation House

735 North Atlantic Boulevard, Fort Lauderdale, Florida, U.S.A.

*With THOMAS BOOKS careful attention is given to all details of
manufacturing and design. It is the Publisher's desire to present books
that are satisfactory as to their physical qualities and artistic possibilities
and appropriate for their particular use. THOMAS BOOKS will be true
to those laws of quality that assure a good name and good will.*

Printed in the United States of America

I-1

CONTRIBUTORS

ERNEST C. ANDERSON, *University of California, Los Alamos, New Mexico*

INGVAR O. ANDERSSON, *AB Atomenergi, Studsvik, Tystberga, Sweden*

JAMES B. AUSTIN, *U. S. Steel Corporation, Pittsburgh, Pennsylvania*

C. O. T. BALL, *Vanderbilt University School of Medicine, Nashville, Tennessee*

ALLEN D. BASS, *Vanderbilt University School of Medicine, Nashville, Tennessee*

M. C. BELL, *University of Tennessee, Knoxville, Tennessee*

E. H. BELCHER, *Postgraduate Medical School, London, England*

D. V. BECKER, *Cornell Medical Center, New York, New York*

D. BINOPOULOS, *Alexandra Hospital, Athens, Greece*

WILLIAM H. BLAHD, *Veterans Administration Center, Los Angeles, California*

F. J. L. BLASINGAME, *American Medical Association, Chicago, Illinois*

RICHARD C. BOZIAN, *Vanderbilt University School of Medicine, Nashville, Tennessee*

FRANCIS S. BRADLEY, *University of Pittsburgh, Pittsburgh, Pennsylvania*

I. BRANN, *Karolinska Hospital, Stockholm, Sweden*

L. T. BROWN, *U. S. Naval Hospital, Bethesda, Maryland*

G. L. BROWNELL, *Massachusetts General Hospital, Boston, Massachusetts*

H. DAVID BRUNER, *U. S. Atomic Energy Commission, Washington, D. C.*

J. S. BURKLE, *U. S. Naval Hospital, Bethesda, Maryland*

JOHN CARDARELLI, *Evans Memorial Hospital, Boston, Massachusetts*

BENEDICT CASSEN, *University of California School of Medicine, Los Angeles, California*

S. H. COHN, *Brookhaven National Laboratory, Upton, New York*

BILL COLEMAN, *Veterans Administration Hospital, Oklahoma City, Oklahoma*

C. CONSTANTINIDES, *Vanderbilt University School of Medicine, Nashville, Tennessee*

W. COOK, *Veterans' Administration, Iowa City, Iowa*

E. P. CRONKITE, *Brookhaven National Laboratory, Upton, New York*

WILLIAM J. DARBY, *Vanderbilt University School of Medicine, Nashville, Tennessee*

PHILLIP N. DEAN, *University of California, Los Alamos, New Mexico*

ROBERT K. DORTON, *St. Louis School of Medicine, St. Louis, Missouri*

CHARLES L. DUNHAM, *U. S. Atomic Energy Commission, Washington, D. C.*

WILLIAM H. ELLETT, *Massachusetts General Hospital, Boston, Massachusetts*

ROBERT J. EPSTEIN, *Argonne National Laboratory, Argonne, Illinois*

JOHN L. FERGUSON, *Vanderbilt University School of Medicine, Nashville, Tennessee*

JACK FOOKS, *U. S. Public Health Service, Cincinnati, Ohio*

GEORGE W. GAFFNEY, *U. S. Public Health Service, Washington, D. C.*

SEBASTIAN GENNA, *Boston University School of Medicine, Boston, Massachusetts*

B. I GRIFFIN, *General Electric Company, Richland, Washington*

E. A. GUSMANO, *Brookhaven National Laboratory, Upton, Long Island, New York*

D. B. HALE, *University of California, Los Alamos, New Mexico*

ROBERT H. HANKLA, *Vanderbilt University School of Medicine, Nashville, Tennessee*

WARREN HANSEN, *U. S. Public Health Service, Cincinnati, Ohio*

W. C. HANSON, *General Electric Company, Richland, Washington*

ALAN R. HARBERTSON, *Atomic Energy Commission, Idaho Falls, Idaho*

J. W. HARGUS, *U. S. Naval Hospital, Bethesda, Maryland*

ROBERT C. HARTMANN, *Vanderbilt University School of Medicine, Nashville, Tennessee*

LEONARD D. HEATON, *U. S. Army, Washington, D. C.*

H. C. HEINRICH, *Universitat Hamburg, Hamburg, Germany*

ROBERT M. HEYSSEL, *Vanderbilt University School of Medicine, Nashville, Tennessee*

GERALD J. HINE, *Veterans Administration Hospital, Boston, Massachusetts*

N. G. HOLMBERG, *Karolinska Hospital, Stockholm, Sweden*

RICHARD B. HOLTZMAN, *Argonne National Laboratory, Argonne, Illinois*

HUGH H. HUSSEY, *American Medical Association, Chicago, Illinois*

P. I. JAGGER, *Boston Veterans Administration Hospital Service, Boston, Massachusetts*

ROBERT D. JORDAN, *U. S. Naval Hospital, Bethesda, Maryland*

GERALD KARCHES, *U. S. Public Health Service, Cincinnati, Ohio*

ALEXANDER KAUL, *Max-Plank-Institut, Frankfort, Germany*

JAMES G. KEREIAKES, *University of Cincinnati College of Medicine, Cincinnati, Ohio*

JOSEPH A. KING, *Vanderbilt University School of Medicine, Nashville, Tennessee*

JERRY M. KOPLOWITZ, *Veterans Administration Center, Los Angeles, California*

ROBERT LAGEMANN, *Vanderbilt University, Nashville, Tennessee*

ALAIN LANSIART, *Commissariat a l'Energie Atomique, Gif-Sur-Yvette (S.-&-O.) France*

GERARD R. LAURER, *New York University, New York, New York*

MARIANNE LEDERER, *Veterans' Administration Center, Los Angeles, California*

KURT LIDEN, *University of Lund, Lund, Sweden*

RAY D. LLOYD, *University of Utah, Salt Lake City, Utah*

GORDON M. LODDE, *Army Research Medical Laboratory, Fort Knox, Kentucky*

A. ROSS LORIMER, *Vanderbilt University School of Medicine, Nashville, Tennessee*

C. C. LUSHBAUGH, *University of California, Los Alamos, New Mexico*

N. S. MACDONALD, *University of California, Los Angeles, California*

BASIL MALAMOS, *University of Athens, Athens, Greece*

C. J. MALETSKOS, *Massachusetts Institute of Technology, Cambridge, Massachusetts*

W. F. MARLOW, *U. S. Atomic Energy Commission, Washington, D. C.*

HAROLD MAY, *Argonne National Laboratory, Argonne, Illinois*

WILLIAM A. MCCARTHY, *Victoreen Instrument Company, Cleveland, Ohio*

L. CLIFFORD MCKEE, *U. S. Naval Hospital, Oakland, California*

WERNER MEHLHORN, *Vanderbilt University School of Medicine, Nashville, Tennessee*

ETHELWYNNE U. MENEELY, *Houston, Texas.*

GEORGE R. MENEELY, *University of Texas M. D. Anderson Hospital and Tumor Institute, Houston, Texas*

O. M. MEREDITH, *Lockheed Missiles and Space Division, Palo Alto, California*

JORMA K. MIETTINEN, *University of Helsinki, Helsinki, Finland*

J. MONAHAN, *Argonne National Laboratory, Argonne, Illinois*

YNGVE NAVERSTEN, *University of Lund, Lund, Sweden*

R. R. NEWELL, *U. S. Naval Radiological Defense Laboratory, San Francisco, California*

J. H. NICHOLS, *U. S. Naval Hospital, Bethesda, Maryland*

ERICH OBERHAUSEN, *Universitat des Saarlandes, Hamburg, Germany*

BETTY O'CONNOR, *Veterans Administration Hospital, Oklahoma City, Oklahoma*

SATORU OHTANI, *Japanese Atomic Energy Research Institute, Tokai-mura, Ibaraki-ken, Japan*

CHARLES O. ONSTEAD, *Universitat des Saarlandes, Hamburg, Germany*

MASAO OSHINO, *Japanese Atomic Energy Research Institute, Tokai-mura, Ibaraki-ken, Japan*

H. EARL PALMER, *General Electric Company, Richland, Washington*

DANIEL R. PATRICK, *Veterans Administration Hospital, Oklahoma City, Oklahoma*

ELAINE PATRICK, *Veterans Administration Hospital, Oklahoma City, Oklahoma*

RICHARD E. PETERSON, *Veterans Administration Hospital, Iowa City, Iowa*

ALEXANDER PFAU, *Max-Plank-Institut, Mariensee, Germany*

DAVID C. PRICE, *Toronto General Hospital, Toronto, Canada*

SOL RABOY, *Argonne National Laboratory, Argonne, Illinois*

B. RAJEWSKY, *Max-Planck-Institut, Frankfort, Germany*

B. V. RAMA SASTRY, *Vanderbilt University School of Medicine, Nashville, Tennessee*

STELIOS REGAS, *Metrix, Incorporated, Deerfield, Illinois*

PETER REIZENSTEIN, *Karolinska Hospital, Stockholm, Sweden*

WILLIAM B. RIVKIN, *Nuclear Industries, Inc., Chicago, Illinois*

C. J. ROBINSON, *Postgraduate Medical School, London, England*

W. C. ROESCH, *General Electric Company, Richland, Washington*

PAANO ROINE, *University of Lund, Lund, Sweden*

HOWARD L. ROLF, *Vanderbilt University School of Medicine, Nashville, Tennessee*

JOHN RUNDO, *United Kingdom Atomic Energy Authority, Berkshire, England*

EUGENE L. SAENGER, *University of Cincinnati College of Medicine, Cincinnati, Ohio*

THORNTON SARGENT, *University of California, Berkley, California*

REMIGIUS SCARPATETTI, *International Atomic Energy Agency, Vienna, Austria*

GUNNAR SEVELIUS, *Veterans Administration Hospital, Oklahoma City, Okla.*

PHILIP SHEVICK, *Nuclear Chicago Corporation, Chicago, Illinois*

B. C. SINCLAIR-SMITH, *Vanderbilt University School of Medicine, Nashville, Tennessee*

L. L. SKOLIL, *San Diego State University, San Diego, California*

W. S. SNYDER, *Oak Ridge National Laboratory, Oak Ridge, Tennessee*

SUSUMU SUGURI, *Japanese Atomic Energy Research Institute, Tokai-Mura, Ibaraki-Ken, Japan*

FRANK SWANBERG, *Hanford Laboratories, Richland, Washington*

PETER J. TALSO, *Loyola University Stritch School of Medicine, Chicago, Illinois*

B. T. TAYLOR, *Atomic Energy Research Establishment, Berkshire, England*

LUTHER L. TERRY, *U. S. Public Health Service, Washington, D. C.*

GEORGE E. THOMA, *St. Louis University School of Medicine, St. Louis, Missouri*

C. C. TRAIL, *Argonne National Laboratory, Argonne, Illinois*

WILHELM VON DÖBELN, *Gymnastika Centralinstitutet, Stockholm, Sweden*

V. W. WALTER, *Metrix, Incorporated, Deerfield, Illinois*

RAYMOND L. WEILAND, *Vanderbilt University School of Medicine, Nashville, Tennessee*

E. V. WEINER, *Veterans Administration Hospital, Iowa City, Iowa*

EDWARD S. WEISS, *Division of Radiological Health, U. S. Public Health Service, Washington, D. C.*

H. N. WELLMAN, *U. S. Public Health Service, Cincinnati, Ohio*

ROBERT W. WOOD, *Division of Biology and Medicine, U. S. Atomic Energy Commission, Washington, D. C.*

BOYCE W. WORTHLEY, *University of Adelaide, Adelaide, South Australia*

KAZUO YANAGISHITA, *Japan Atomic Energy Research Institute, Tokai-mura, Ibaraki-ken, Japan*

CHAIRMEN

ALBERT BEHNKE, *2865 Jackson Street, San Francisco, California*

JOSEF BROZEK, *Lehigh University, Bethlehem, Pennsylvania*

BELTON A. BURROWS, *Boston University, Boston, Massachusetts*

JOHN A. D. COOPER, *Northwestern University Medical School, Chicago, Illinois*

ROBERT A. DUDLEY, *International Atomic Energy Agency, Vienna, Austria*

MERRIL EISENBUD, *New York University, New York, New York*

ROBLEY EVANS, *Massachusetts Institute of Technology, Cambridge, Massachusetts*

PAUL F. HAHN, *U. S. Public Health Service, Washington, D. C.*

S. ALLAN LOUGH, *U. S. Atomic Energy Commission, Washington, D. C.*

CHARLES E. MILLER, *Argonne National Laboratory, Argonne, Illinois*

RUSSELL H. MORGAN, *Johns Hopkins Hospital, Baltimore, Maryland*

E. ERIC POCHIN, *University College Hospital Medical School, London, England*

ALEXANDER P. REMENCHIK, *Hines Veterans Administration Hospital, Hines, Illinois*

FOREWORD

CAPT. ALBERT R. BEHNKE

U. S. Navy, Retired

THE BRILLIANCE of scientific achievement may obscure the far-sighted and discerning administrative effort which makes possible the multidisciplinary endeavor requisite in radiation biology. Noteworthy since World War II is the cooperative effort between military installations and universities. The enlightened policies and generous support afforded by the Office of Naval Research was a pioneer military effort to expand basic investigation particularly in fields which required sophisticated, costly and at times heavy equipment. In turn, the A.E.C. supported laboratories under university cognizance to provide facilities for the training of and investigations by both civilian and officer personnel.

A striking example of military-university effort is an outstanding communication in the symposium by Drs. Oberhausen and Onstead on the relationship of total body potassium content with age and sex. This investigation involving an examination of 10,000 normal persons over two and one-half years focusses attention upon acceleration of research effort which is possible through military-university endeavor.

Several years ago at the Naval Radiological Defense Laboratory, Boling *et al.* determined the exchangeable potassium, chloride and total body water on a sizeable number of men, chiefly military personnel. In the effort to compare total body potassium obtained from radioisotope dilution with K^{40} estimates, it was necessary to transport a few subjects from San Francisco to the University of California at Los Alamos where "human counter" studies confirmed the validity of data obtained by radically divergent procedures. Subsequently the collaboration of Allen,

Anderson and Langham in a joint investigation by the U. S. Army Medical Research and Nutrition Laboratory at Fitzsimons Army Hospital and the Los Alamos laboratories were responsible for a classical contribution relating body potassium to body composition and age. Recently it was possible at the Radiological Defense Laboratory to make the critical examination of the K^{40} and cesium content of a large number of adolescents under observation in a multiparameter longitudinal study conducted by the School of Public Health at the University of California.

The exigency for meaningful radiobiologic research calls for multiparameter examinations, both morphologic and functional. The limitations attending measurement alone of K^{40}, total body water or body density are painfully apparent. In the military it is possible to study some parameters under carefully controlled conditions with respect to functional state and to employ techniques utilizing radioisotopes and other procedures not feasible or permissible in the university laboratory separated from clinical facilities.

The consummation of a comprehensive, definitive quantitative study on a group of subjects may require the cooperation of several laboratories each having unique facilities or adequate test experience. In the logistics of such an operation air and other forms of transportation are essential. Despite a few outstanding examples of military-university endeavor, there is no formal administrative setup to facilitate mass transportation and examination of subjects in several laboratories. At times, security consideration, petty administrative strictures, circumscribed outlook and even chauvinism have barred productive research involving cooperative effort. One would look therefore to the creation of a central research administrative office charged with expediting multidisciplinary, multiparameter investigation of subjects in military-university laboratories engaged in radiobiologic investigation.

FOREWORD

Josef Brozek

Research Professor
Lehigh University

THE PRINCIPLE of "successive approximations" in the understanding and mastery of reality is the very essence of science. It is particularly appropriate to our thinking about the progress in research on body composition and the potential contribution of K^{40} determinations in the intact body.

The human body is heterogeneous. The aim of "somatolytic" techniques is to separate and measure relatively homogeneous compartments. Let's think at first in terms of the anatomically separable components. The first step is to break down the gross body weight (W) into its adipose (A) and its non-adipose or residual component (R_1), a more homogeneous "lean" body mass.

$$W = A + R_1$$

Historically, the densitometric approach to body composition has been based on just such a two component model. The principal point is that the separation and removal of the adipose component from the non-adipose component yields the first approximation to a relatively homogeneous body compartment, more homogeneous than the gross body weight.

The second step might involve a further splitting up of the R_1 component into a skeletal fraction (S) and the remainder (R_2).

$$R_1 = S + R_2$$

Similarly, we might wish to subdivide the R_2 component into the muscular fraction (M) and the remainder (R_3).

$$R_2 = M + R_3$$

Broadly speaking, R_3 is the visceral component. For some purposes, especially for research on energy metabolism at rest, it might be useful to separate from R_3 a component representing the central nervous system (N).

$$R_3 = N + R_4$$

Finally, R_4 might be split into thoracic and abdominal viscera (V) and a remainder (R_5) primarily representing skin and ligaments.

$$R_4 = V + R_5$$

Historically, Matiegka's 1921 model of body composition estimated on the basis of somatic measurements was tridimensional, or, if we take into account the necessary remainder, quadridimensional.

$$W = M + D + O + R$$

where   M = muscles
            D = skin plus subcutaneous adipose tissue
            O = the skeleton ("ossa")
            R = the remainder

Behnke's 1941 model had two components, with the body weight divided, densitometrically, into excess fat (with a density of 0.94) and the non-fat or lean body mass.

$$W = \text{"F"} + L$$

Fat was estimated from body density (or, to be historically accurate, from specific gravity), while the lean compartment was obtained by subtraction (L = W − "F").

In the hydrometric system of somatolysis, the initial model also had two components, only the components were biochemically more definite. One component was defined as fat (ether extract, F); the other component, as the fat-free weight (Ff).

$$W = F + Ff$$

The fat-free component was calculated on the basis of determinations of total body water; fat was obtained by subtraction. While the densitometric and the hydrometric systems differed in operation, they were interlocking as far as basic assumptions were concerned.

Genuine progress will involve not so much an increase in the precision or ease of measuring—even though this is of great significance for the application of the somatolytic methods—as the development of techniques for measuring *directly* some additional and important body compartments, principally body fat and body mineral (or at least bone mineral).

Gas dilution appears to be a promising approach for body fat determination (Lesser and Zak, 1963), at least for purposes of basic laboratory research, including validation of the biological constants used in the equations for the estimation of body composition on the basis of indirect methods.

Knowing the fat content, we could split the fat-free compartment into its fluid (total body water) and solid phase. In turn, the solid phase could be view as consisting of a protein and a mineral compartment. The proteins could be usefully separated into those contributed by the muscles and by the viscera.

F. D. Moore and co-workers (1963) made significant advances along these lines, although their model of body composition was somewhat different. Moore's interest is focused on quantitatively studying the cell mass—intracellular water plus intracellular solids—by combining information derived from K^{42} and urinary creatinine excretion. The approach exemplifies well the application of the principle of successive approximations.

There is also progress in combining the methods. Let's consider body fat. There are at least three questions we can ask:

How much fat is there in the body as a whole?

How is the fat distributed between the subcutaneous and internal compartment?

How is the subcutaneous fat distributed over the body surface?

The third question, important as it is, deals with body shape and may be neglected here. The second question, we believe, should not be neglected, since in aging and in disease the two phases may change independently. So it is worthwhile to subdivide the body fat compartment by combining the somatometric and densitometric or hydrometric approaches, in parallel to the separation of the fat-free body weight into components increasing in homogeneity.

FOREWORD

Belton A. Burrows

Associate Professor of Medicine
Boston University Medical Center

REGULATION OF SODIUM metabolism is an important aspect of the management of many patients with diseases involving abnormalities of fluid and electrolyte balance, such as congestive heart failure, liver or kidney disease, or various endocrine disorders associated with changes in blood pressure. Sodium balances have been carefully determined for study purposes on a limited number of patients, but the expense and difficulties of the balance method have precluded its use for purely clinical purposes.

It has been recognized for many years, since the initial studies of Meneely and co-authors, that repetitive measurements of body sodium by the isotope dilution technique using short-lived isotopes was medically feasible, but the logistics and expense of obtaining such isotopes again discouraged clinical use of this method.

With body counting of the long-lived Na^{22}, it is now possible to obtain exchangeable sodium measurements repetitively for up to three or four months after the injection of a single tracer dose. To establish the validity of such measurements, it has been necessary to evaluate the possible contribution of slowly exchanging bone sodium to the exchangeable sodium values.

In five normal subjects given 15 μc Na^{22} and studied by Jagger *et al.* with measurements of body radioactivity and serum sodium specific activity, changes in sodium intake from 1-2 meq to 181-359 meq daily resulted in a significant increase in calculated exchangeable sodium. There was no discernible contribution of a slowly exchanging sodium pool to these measurements.

There was prolonged retention (2.6 year biological half life) of a small fraction (less than 1%) of the tracer dose, consistent with its incorporation into bone. Almost identical exchangeable sodium values were obtained with Na^{24} at twenty-four hours as with Na^{22} at two to three months in one normal and two edematous patients. It was concluded that long term sodium balances were feasible with this technique in that changes in the values would accurately reflect changes in the metabolically active sodium pool. An additional group of patients with edema from various metabolic disorders associated with disturbances of sodium metabolism has been studied for periods of two to three months to evaluate the possible influence of a slowly exchanging sodium pool on exchangeable sodium measurements. Evidence for such a pool was not obtained. Again in a limited number of patients there was no evidence of a significant fraction of Na^{22} being present three to four years after the tracer dose.

FOREWORD

JOHN A. D. COOPER

Dean of Sciences
Northwestern University

THE INCREASING complexity and cost of instrumentation required by modern medical scientists poses problems for a university in making facilities available for faculty members in different disciplines. Separate instruments cannot be provided individuals who use them only a fraction of the time available. For instruments required in the measurement of radioactivity, this problem has often been solved by the creation of a radioisotope laboratory to provide services and facilities to the departments in a medical school or to an entire medical center. Although it was possible in the early days of the use of radioisotopes in medicine to bring almost all of the equipment into such a central location, the present widespread use of radioactive materials as investigative tools has changed the concepts of such a laboratory. Only the large and expensive instruments can be centralized if research activities are not to be impaired. Commonly used equipment must be available to the investigator in the same way as he has access to a spectrophotometer or a pH meter.

The centralization of equipment always poses problems regarding the supervision of its use and allocation of time to users. Unless a single individual feels the responsibility for maintenance and care of the equipment, it often deteriorates through improper use and failure to provide required repairs and maintenance. For this reason, one person should be given the responsibility for the instrument. Usually this person can also assign time for use of the instrument and provide the necessary instruction in its operation. Where the requests of users far exceed the available time, problems often arise. In this case a "users committee" made up of knowledgeable faculty members probably assures the most effective and equitable use.

For very large facilities, such as whole body counters, consideration can be given to establishing a separate laboratory under the direction of an individual reporting directly to the dean of the medical school. This removes the facility from relationship to a single department and helps assure its availability to all departments. The director of such a laboratory is usually a faculty member of one of the departments and for academic affairs is responsible in the usual manner to the chairman of that department. He must, however, act as a representative of the dean's office in carrying out his duties and responsibilities with regard to the laboratory. In many instances, faculty members whose research involves considerable use of such a faculty are appointed as members of the laboratory and thus have a double responsibility—one to the department chairman in academic matters and the other to the laboratory director for research facilities. A part of funds available for the research support of the members of the laboratory can be made available to the laboratory director for his use in maintaining the facilities and replacing equipment as it becomes obsolete.

Funds for the maintenance of such specialized equipment usually come from university sources or through equipment grants from government agencies or foundations. The university has responsibility to provide funds required for its continuing use. Often, nominal charges can be made against the research funds of users to make the operation partially or fully self sustaining.

Common facilities are often more effective on paper than in actual practice. Their success in supplying the needs of investigators rests with the competence and tact of the supervising individual and the good will of the users.

FOREWORD

Robert A. Dudley

International Atomic Energy Agency
Vienna

READERS OF THIS volume may be interested in some worldwide statistics concerning whole body counters and their use. A picture is provided in the directory of total body radioactivity monitors which has been compiled by H. Mehl and which is shortly to be published by the International Atomic Energy Agency. There are now roughly 100 major installations of this type in use, and their number has been increasing exponentially with a two to three year doubling period. (In addition many simpler systems are in existence where modest sensitivity suffices, e.g., in hospitals.) Slightly less than half are in the U.S., and about the same number are in Europe. However, several laboratories on all the other inhabited continents are either operating already or actively planning such facilities.

For shielding, about two thirds of these laboratories use steel, most often of 15 to 20 cm. thickness. Lead and water are the next most common materials.

For detection systems about three quarters use NaI(TI) crystals connected to multichannel pulse height analyzers. Most of the rest employ either liquid or plastic scintillation detectors. The crystals are divided into three rough size groups of approximately equal population: 8 in. D by 4 in., 5 in. D by 4 in. and smaller. Usually a single crystal is used, although multiple crystal systems are also quite popular.

The most common measurement geometry involves the suspension of the subject who is seated in the "standard chair" — although detailed examination has revealed that few if any laboratories use conditions identical with those of any other laboratory.

xix

The use reported most commonly (about 90% of reporting laboratories) is the monitoring of radionuclides incorporated unintentionally in persons occupationally exposed. Other popular uses are the measurement of K^{40} and Cs^{137} burdens and of radium and thorium burdens, the development of techniques and the analysis of foodstuffs and other samples. Contamination rather than metabolism has been at the focus of attention.

Regarding current trends, it is clear that special requirements call for special instruments and techniques, and therefore that no one system is likely to supplant all others. Most observers do see, nevertheless, a growing popularity for the idea which they themselves favor. Thus biased, I believe that shielding in the form of steel rooms is continuing to predominate. However, many laboratories not requiring the ultimate in sensitivity may be satisfied with much less massive shields: either thinner or concentrated predominantly around the detector. NaI(Tl) crystals continue as the most popular detector. However, they are more and more commonly used in techniques emphasizing uniformity of sensitivity over the body (e.g., some type of scanning) rather than in those for which sensitivity varies appreciably over the body (e.g., the "standard chair"). It appears that techniques are now available for reducing to insignificance the long troublesome instrumental instabilities which have distorted scintillation spectra and complicated their analysis. In the use of whole body counters it is likely that more attention will be given to metabolic studies when techniques are in wider use whose sensitivity is less affected by redistribution of the activity in the body.

FOREWORD

Professor of Industrial Medicine
New York University Medical Center

THE SUBJECT OF radioactivity in man is receiving increasing attention and is being studied with a variety of new tools that make it possible to quantitate both artificially produced radionuclides and natural radionuclides.

Total body counting is perhaps the best known of the new tools for estimating human radioactivity. There are obvious advantages to a technique which permits identification of radionuclides *in vivo*, and this is certainly the method of choice for research directed at understanding the kinetic behavior of trace elements in the human body whether they occur naturally as with potassium or artificially as with Cs^{137}, I^{131} and Fe^{59}.

In vivo techniques of measuring human radioactivity make it possible to study trace element metabolism in normal and diseased persons with a facility not before possible. Measurements of this kind have been limited in the past few years because, understandably, the first of the total body counters were located in laboratories that were not always directly related to centers of clinical research. However, there is now a trend toward construction of such facilities at medical centers, and the application of these techniques to medical research should soon be exploited to a degree not before possible.

The use of *in vivo* techniques of radionuclide estimation in industrial hygiene continues to be hampered by the fact that many of the important radionuclides cannot be measured easily by these methods. This is because such nuclides as Sr^{90}, Pu^{239}, U^{235} and U^{238} do not emit gamma rays, and such electromagnetic rays as are produced are found at the low energy portion of the spectrum where measurements are made more difficult by the high background from Compton scattering. However, it is possible with anticoincidence techniques and thin crystals to reduce the background in the Compton scatter region, and future research may make it possible to utilize *in vivo* counting for these nuclides.

The elaborate systems that have been constructed for *in vivo* counting, consisting of heavy shields, large sodium iodide crystals and expensive multichannel analyzers, are necessary in those laboratories undertaking the basic research that is necessary to develop the techniques and to define their lower limits of sensitivity. The full assortment of equipment is also necessary for those laboratories that must work at very low levels. Unfortunately, a complete facility of this kind is very expensive, and the numbers of such installations may always be relatively limited. However, for many purposes the high degree of sensitivity is not required. *In vivo* counting techniques may in some instances be quite feasible without the elaborate shielding that has been used in most laboratories. Demonstration by the Hanford group of the feasibility of counting Cs^{137} in the field using shadow shields is a trend in this direction. Similarly, while many laboratories may be unable to afford the complete total body counter that will make it possible to measure a thyroid iodine burden of the order of 15 or 20 pc, it should be recognized that the newly developed techniques include not only better shielding, but better crystal geometries and better gamma-ray resolution. Relatively inexpensive adaptations of these innovations can be provided for a small fraction of the cost of a total installation. For example, a small shadow shield, a single channel analyzer and a small sodium-iodine crystal can probably be used to detect as little as 200 or 300 pc in the thyroid. Thyroid uptake measurements thus could be made by administering about 1,000 pc of I^{131}, resulting in a dose that is a small fraction of the dose received when more conventional techniques are used.

The greatest value of *in vivo* counting techniques may be that they will make it possible to calibrate other techniques of bioassay such as breath and urine measurements. Thus, although total body counting has been used extensively in recent years for estimating the radium and mesathorium content of subjects with abnormally high body burdens, there is no reason in principle why one could not revert to the simple techniques of breath radon or thoron analysis. In the case of many other nuclides, studies of urinary excretion as a function of time coupled with total body counting techniques should give us additional information that will considerably enhance the value of urine analysis for estimating body burdens of many radionuclides.

FOREWORD

Robley D. Evans

Professor of Physics
Massachusetts Institute of Technology

"PHYSICIAN" and "physicist" are adjoining words in most English dictionaries, and happily this juxtaposition has been extended to the clinic and the laboratory. The results of research teamwork between them have been far reaching, especially in the last few decades.

In the teaching of physics a broad foundation of fundamental principles is emphasized, reaching back to such basic truths as the conservation of energy and the conservation of momentum. Out of such basic principles there arise many specialized truths and finally entire disciplines, — such as electrical engineering, optics, acoustics, hydraulics, and nuclear engineering. Each of these finds areas of fruitful application in the life sciences and in the healing arts. Electrical engineering has contributed greatly to our knowledge of nerve impulses and brain waves, optics has contributed to vision, acoustics has contributed to hearing, hydraulics to blood flow, and nuclear physics and engineering to areas of metabolism diagnosis and pathology.

Many instruments and techniques from the physics laboratory have found some of their most valuable applications in the medical sciences, for example, the optical microscope, x ray, electron microscope, radioactive tracers and radiation therapy, and improvements and advances in physics instrumentation quickly have found new areas of usefulness in the medical sciences. The Geiger-Muller counters provided, by about 1930, a substantial improvement over electroscopes in the sensitivity of gamma-ray detection. They were quickly applied to problems in quantifying internal deposits of radium in humans, especially in luminous dial painters. Over two decades later, when sodium iodide scintillators and multichannel analyzers were developed for studies in nuclear physics, these quickly were applied to the measurement of internal radioactivity in man, and they provided such an increase in sensitivity that for the first time the natural K^{40} radiation from normal humans could confidently be quantified.

Faraday is credited with the remark that a physicist is a scientist "who can saw with a file, or file with a saw." In terms of fundamental mechanism both are simply abrading tools, specialized for distinct applications, but identical in basic principle. The teamwork between physicists and physicians has led to many instruments, techniques and procedures which superficially look distinct, but which in fact are variants in application of one or a few fundamental principles. This conference on Radioactivity in Man contains many examples of the fruitful teamwork between the physical and the life sciences and of the varied application of a few fundamental principles and methods of physics.

FOREWORD

Paul F. Hahn

Chief, Research Grants Staff
Division of Radiological Health
U. S. Public Health Service

A s one who has never had the opportunity to use the whole body counting technique, my first reaction is envy. Study of iron metabolism using Fe^{59} some fifteen to twenty-five years ago entailed several drawbacks. The laboratory procedure took at least two full days of exacting and tedious manipulations. It was necessary to assume that all the absorbed iron was converted to circulating hemoglobin and to estimate a total circulating red cell mass on a basis of body weight, thus injecting assumptions into the final calculation. In iron deficiency anemia, this was probably justifiable, but in other states there was considerable question as to how valid such assumptions were. With the total body gamma counter a single reading some days after administration of the tagged iron preparation furnishes the answer in about one half hour. There is no comparison between the simplicity, directness and over-all reliability of these two approaches.

It was learned early with the former technique that the need for iron in some manner determined the amount of uptake by the body. This is a peculiarity in the metabolism of this element and to my knowledge does not hold true in the metabolism of any other element. It had been shown earlier by chemical methods alone by McCance and Widdowson that excretion of iron was negligible following the parenteral administration of the element. These two basic findings showed that iron constituted a "one-way element." Such observations would have been relatively simple and direct had total body counters of a gamma-emitting iron isotope been available in the 1930's. Other problems relating to the relative absorption of ferrous and ferric iron and to absorption during infection and pregnancy and hemachromatosis which were studied with the more arduous methods could have been conducted with efficiency and dispatch.

Many other opportunities still present themselves for study by the modern methods. Further investigation of the pros and cons of the mucosal block theory, the postulation of the ferritin mechanism of iron uptake as first proposed by us in 1943 and the related problem concerned with multiple feedings of the element at various intervals can be studied conveniently in this manner. Little imagination is necessary to suggest applications of total body counting as a means of studying the metabolism of this and many other elements with the distinct possibility of serendipitous findings.

Monitoring of chelation programs would be highly simplified without resort to balance studies by the usual tedious procedures. Most early work on iron metabolism involved balance techniques. These were disagreeable and time consuming and were subject to considerable error, in part due to the formation of insoluble phosphates and phytates and inaccuracies inherent in the analytical procedures themselves.

Necessary precautions in the use of trace elements must, of course, still be observed. In particular carrier-free materials must be used with a great deal of circumspection. One must be sure that the use of the amounts of carrier studied are within the physiological range of mechanisms involving saturation phenomena such as would exist if the ferritin-apoferritin complex were being investigated.

At the turn of the century our knowledge of iron metabolism was in a very imperfect state. Now, radioactive isotopes, particularly those from the reactor rather than the cyclotron, have led to a much more complete understanding of the mechanisms involved in the metabolism of this critically important element about whose pathways so little is yet known. Formerly, when using the best available chemical procedures, I could only account for 60 percent of iron administered intravenously, even though

such unlikely tissues as fat and hair were included in an effort to
track down this elusive element.

One general criticism has been leveled at the current uses
of total body counters. Scientific review committees have found
a lack of imagination in proposals for this sophisticated instrumentation process. It is to be fervently hoped that the judi-
cious employment of the several score of such instruments now
available will result in the elucidation of many unknown mechanisms of absorption, retention, reutilization and excretion of the
many elements with which we are concerned.

FOREWORD

Charles E. Miller

Argonne National Laboratory

A NYONE BUILDING A whole body counter is immediately faced with the problem of deciding which type of counter will most nearly meet his requirements. Should he construct a 4π liquid scintillation counter patterned after the Los Alamos Scientific Laboratory Humco II, one that utilizes three plastic scintillation counters such as developed by P. J. R. Burch of the University of Leeds or one that utilizes from one to seven NaI(Tl) crystals arranged in some suitable geometrical pattern? Although the same shielded room can be used for all three, the electronic systems and detectors are so different and so expensive that once one is committed to a given system, it is not economically feasible to abandon it in favor of another system.

For some types of measurements, the requirements immediately and obviously indicate the advantages of one type of whole body counter over the other types. For instance a 4π liquid scintillation counter would be indicated if the purpose were to survey a large population on a routine basis or to perform a large number of whole body retention studies with a particular isotope. However, the NaI(Tl) crystal should be selected if it is necessary to identify the radioactive materials present in persons contaminated with a variety of isotopes or if the problem is to study the distribution of radioactive materials within the body.

The problem arises when one attempts to select a whole body counter with which to measure accurately the quantity of a specific radioactive material in a particular person. The inherent error present in any whole body counter measurement as a result of the various distributions of the isotope within the body has not been determined for the various types of counters. Most of the

whole body counters have been calibrated either by placing
point sources in presdwood, water or plastic phantoms or by
mixing the isotopes into water or sugar phantoms shaped to approximate the body. The calibration factors thus obtained are
only approximate since they do not duplicate conditions in the
body. Until these inherent errors in measurements with the
various types of whole body counters are accurately determined,
it is not possible to recommend a particular counting system for
quantitative measurements of K^{40} or any other gamma-emitting
isotope.

The magnitude of this inherent error can only be determined
by giving known amounts of selected isotopes to numerous people of different body types, collecting all of the excreta so that
the amount of each isotope present at any time is known and
then measuring these people in the various types of whole body
counters. Such experience obtained by giving K^{42} to humans has
demonstrated that it is not sufficient to study simply a small
sample of, say, six people of the same age and size. To be meaningful, the sample should include at least thirty people of widely
differing body sizes. Also, the same people should be measured
in the different types of counters if the data are to be used to compare the advantage of one counter over those of another.

FOREWORD

RUSSELL H. MORGAN

Chairman of Radiology
Johns Hopkins Hospital

WHENEVER MAN EMBARKS upon a new technology which involves both hazard and benefit, he is immediately faced with a series of problems on how to reduce the hazard while, at the same time, using the technology as fully as possible. An example of this may be found in the history of the events which followed the discovery of the x ray. It was excitingly evident to a great many workers within weeks after Roentgen's discovery that the x ray would have a profound influence on the diagnosis and treatment of disease. X-ray machines were quickly put together and placed in operation in a rapidly increasing number of hospitals throughout the world. Since the x ray was new, its dangers were not anticipated.

Within a few years, however, it became evident that the physicians who used fluoroscopic techniques were developing pathological changes of their hands. It was the practice of these physicians to test their fluoroscopic equipment each day by placing their hands in the x-ray beam and observing the quality of the image on the fluoroscopic screen.

When the hazards of x rays were recognized, methods of radiation protection were quickly devised. After these methods were thoroughly tested, a series of radiation standards were then developed for the guidance of individuals who might be exposed to ionizing radiation in their daily work. There standards were formulated quite unofficially by physicists and physicians with an interest in radiology.

With the increase in the size of the population which might potentially be exposed to ionizing radiation following the development of the nuclear sciences and with the increase in the size of the scientific community concerned with the benefits and hazards of ionizing radiation, there has arisen a need for formulaization of radiation standards at an official government level. In 1959, the Federal Radiation Council was established for this purpose. The council, with representation from all government agencies concerned with ionizing radiation, has acted to provide the federal guidance needed by the nation on radiation standards. The creation of the council seems an important and necessary step for the protection of the public from excessive exposure to ionizing radiation.

The decisions of the council, of course, are determined largely by the information it is able to gain from the scientific community on the biological effects of ionizing radiation, methods of protection and the exposure levels to which man is exposed in his daily life. It is the last of these factors with which we are concerned in this symposium.

FOREWORD

E. Eric Pochin

Director, Department of Clinical Research
University College Hospital Medical School, London

FOR MANY radionuclides, it has hitherto been difficult or impossible to estimate with confidence the irradiation of the whole body or of any organ or tissue of the body that would result from a given intake of the nuclide. It has been no easier to quote reliable mean values for the excretion rates which would correspond with particular body contents or which would occur at a particular time after a single intake. Too often the values that have had to be used for protection purposes have needed to be based on scanty, if any, human data or on results found in other species or even on analogy with values applicable to other elements of broadly similar chemical behavior.

It needs little effort, or knowledge of physiology, to illustrate dissimilarities of metabolism between chemically "similar" elements or between mammalian species; and the differences in metabolic turnover or disposal rates of an element among individual healthy human subjects may be considerable.

It is one of the stimulating aspects of work of the type reported at this symposium that reliable data are beginning to accumulate as to the distribution constants and rate factors for various elements when given by specified routes and in known chemical forms and that these data are based upon sizeable groups of normal human subjects, so that some estimate can be obtained of mean values and of their precision. The tapestry is far from complete — a few patches only are adequately woven onto the basic sketch. It is, however, encouraging that the relevant information is being obtained and, I think, urgent that any available opportunities should be taken to secure and report reliable data on further elements, or elements given in different chemical form or under different metabolic conditions.

The symposium has illustrated many of the factors involved and the importance of relating them to each other — the measured whole body content of a nuclide, its blood levels in identified chemical state, respiratory, urinary or fecal excretion rates, differences in concentration in different organs—at any one time or as a function of time after a single dose—nonuniformity of concentration within a single organ and migration between different parts of the body. Iodine is becoming fairly well documented in these respects, with good normal mean values for many of its sites of concentration and turnover rates between different tissues or different chemical forms, although unexpected sites of significant selective concentration still keep cropping up. Calcium and strontium are coming into the same category, and the long term handling of radium; so are sodium and potassium, and iron is not far behind. Even for some of these, however, the evidence is still necessarily rather "acute," and the possibilities of small compartments of slow turnover and a high dose commitment cannot properly be excluded. Much more quantitative knowledge is needed on the analysis, or more over-all description, of the total turnover of even these elements from their earliest transient circulatory levels to their latest and longest retentions. And that leaves about ninety other elements.

INTRODUCTION

J UST OVER thirty years ago, when instruments sensitive enough
to measure small numbers of gamma rays were developed, it
was recognized that elements in humans which emitted gamma
radiation could be measured from outside the skin. The new
method of estimating body content of an element was soon used
in persons who had accumulated large burdens of radium.

Since then, the sensitivity, precision and accuracy of whole
body counting have been progressively improved. Now, even the
body content of the naturally occurring radioactive isotope of
potassium (K^{40}) can be estimated with an uncertainty of only a
few per cent. Human experimentation can be done with certain
isotopes which otherwise would exceed permissable levels. Reliable measurements of minute human body burdens of fallout
Cs^{137} at levels of just a few micro microcuries per kilogram are
routine. When one recalls that a micro microcurie of radioactivity undergoes only about two disintegrations per minute, it is evident these methods are remarkable indeed.

It is these methods that are of such widespread medical, industrial, military and ecological interest that were focussed on at
this Second Symposium on Radioactivity in Man held at Northwestern University on September 5, 6 and 7, 1962.

Some forty-six papers were presented, covering virtually
every facet of whole body counting. Nearly all of the active
whole body counting laboratories in the world were represented.
Besides representatives from the United States, there were Canadian, Australian, English, Scottish, Norwegian, Swedish, Danish,
Finnish, German, Austrian, French, Dutch, Belgian, Japanese and
Greek representatives who participated.

Sessions were divided into several special categories: on instrumentation, technique and calibration; on potassium and body
composition; on cobalt metabolism, iron metabolism and the

metabolism of fission products. There was a session on social and industrial aspects of radioactivity and a special evening session to discuss estimation of Cs^{137} burdens in humans and problems of interlaboratory calibration.

There have been only three other public meetings at which whole body counters and the uses made of them have been discussed in breadth and depth. The first was at the University of Leeds, England, in 1956; the second at Vanderbilt University, Nashville, Tennessee in 1960, and the third at the International Atomic Energy Agency in Vienna, Austria in 1961. The reader with a serious interest in whole body counting would do well to consult the proceedings of these meetings as well as the 1962 review article by Marinelli, Miller, May and Rose.

This symposium was sponsored by Northwestern University Medical School and the American Medical Association. It was made possible by grants from the Division of Radiological Health of the U. S. Public Health Service and the United States Steel Foundation. It was also supported by the Division of Biology and Medicine of the Atomic Energy Commission and the Army Medical Research and Development Command.

We wish to thank all the individuals, institutions and agencies who cooperated and contributed to making possible this Second Symposium on Radioactivity in Man.

Many individuals cooperated in developing the symposium, their assistance ranging from an expression of good wishes to a great deal of hard work on program selection and preparation, planning arrangements and resolving miscellaneous administrative problems. Sincere thanks are due to: Fred G. Armstrong, James B. Austin, Con O. T. Ball, Lionel Bernstein, F. J. L. Blasingame, Austin M. Brues, H. David Bruner, Donald B. Charleston, Arthur R. Colwell, John A. D. Cooper, Ralph E. De Forest, Charles L. Dunham, David P. Earle, C. Larkin Flanagan, Paul F. Hahn, J. W. G. Hannon, Robert J. Hasterlik, Hugh H. Hussey, Jr., J. E. Rose, Jacques L. Sherman, Leif Sorenson, Peter J. Talso, Jack Towne, Samuel N. Turiel, John B. Youmans, and Richard H. Young.

We wish also to express our thanks to Alexander P. Remenchik who served as a scientific advisor in editing the manuscript and to Frances L. Nyberg who assisted with the editing.

George R. Meneely
General Chairman and Editor
Shirley Motter Linde
Symposium Coordinator and Editor
Ethelwynne U. Meneely
Symposium Secretary

PREFACE

James B. Austin

Vice-President, Research and Technology
U. S. Steel Corporation

Some twenty years ago, in a remarkable acknowledgment appended to her biography of Willard Gibbs, Muriel Rukeyser wrote: "One of the reasons that I wrote this book is that I needed to read it." She also stated that: "This book has relied on information and attitudes from many sources." Although this second symposium volume is not the work of a single author, Miss Rukeyser's remarks are strikingly apposite. For the aim of many of the contributors must have been to provide a book which they, and other participants in the meeting, needed to read. Moreover, such a book could only be written by drawing on "information and attitudes from many sources."

As has been amply demonstrated in this symposium, the subject of Radioactivity in Man is growing ever more important. The use of active materials in research and in theory is increasing. More and more concern is being expressed over the possible hazards arising from accidental or unavoidable exposure to radiation whether in a laboratory or over a broad area by radioactive fallout. And beyond the immediate questions in radiobiology and medicine lie a number of more nebulous problems in sociology and law. It is high time that we began to devote more attention to these areas. But as Lord Kelvin once pointed out, one does not really know much about a subject until he can make some measurements on it. It is in this respect that instrumental techniques can provide a key to future progress.

Whole body counting is, in itself, a complicated procedure, but evaluating the significance of the results is even more complex. One is tempted to compare the situation to that of the well-known blind men examining the elephant, but this would be unfair to those who are working in the field because they certainly are not blind. The difficulty lies in the fact that the elephant is so enormous that those studying the trunk, even in a fairly sophisticated way, just cannot be expected to obtain comparable data on the tail. To do any kind of justice to the subject it is necessary, as has been done here, to bring together different viewpoints and data of various kinds. It is in this sense that this volume has been written so that it may give the person who needs to read it a better and more complete description of this scientific elephant.

This symposium also offers a felicitous example of "information and attitudes from many sources." For it is rare, indeed, these days to find a project which succeeds in enlisting on an international scale the whole-hearted support of so many diverse groups. In this instance, science as represented broadly by several universities and research institutes, government in the form of a number of agencies, industry, the medical profession directly and through the American Medical Association, and the public have all cooperated to make this conference possible and have worked to assure its success.

This leads one to wonder what there is about the subject which generates such a wide appeal. It is certainly not any associated political or economic issue. Nor can it be solely intellectual curiosity, or a search for new methods of diagnosis or therapy, or the prevailing glamour attached to super-gadgetry, though each of these may be responsible to some extent. Rather, I suspect, it is founded chiefly on something more subtle — that malaise which affects us all when we face in ignorance a situation which may have unpleasant consequences for us. It is a sort of feeling of insecurity in facing the unknown. Anyone in any of the groups represented in the discussions can readily imagine a situation in which he may be involved in one way or another, by accident or design, in an exposure to active material. The possibility of resulting somatic or genetic damage, about which much has been hinted but far too little is known, makes us all so uncomfortable that we seek company in our misery. It is this feeling, coupled with a sense of responsibility to start doing some-

thing about it, which accounts, I believe, in large part for the
response to the symposium program.

The basic community of interest does not, of course, mean
that everyone will agree with everything that was said at the
symposium. This, however, is all to the good, because progress
in science often comes most rapidly from disagreements and
arguments which drive the investigators back to the laboratory
to check, to search for improved data and to fill in existing gaps
in our knowledge. So the best outcome of these discussions would
be the rapid accumulation of more, and more realiable, information. In this connection, I cannot resist the temptation to quote
once more from Miss Rukeyser: "The best I can hope for this
or any other work is that it will be taken up and outdone as soon
as possible." To which I can only add, apropos the present
volume, a devout "Amen."

PREFACE

Charles L. Dunham

Director, Division of Biology and Medicine

and

H. David Bruner

Chief, Medical Branch
Division of Biology and Medicine
U. S. Atomic Energy Commission

THIS SECOND SYMPOSIUM on Radioactivity in Man was held at a rather critical point in the course of development of this potentially productive area of biomedical research.

Since the whole body counter as a measuring instrument seems to be reliable and well developed, the next question is whether enough imagination and ingenuity have been employed in making use of it. The papers presented at this symposium are representative of the kinds of investigations which the whole body counter is useful for pursuing, but it must be left to the individual to decide whether the investigations up to now are mostly all of the same pattern and whether the existing counters have been used as intensively as the device warrants. Some features of the equipment need improvement, and a better knowledge is needed of the significance of the perturbations introduced by the sample or subject being measured. Fortunately, progress is being made along both lines.

Gamma emitters can be used in at least three areas with whole body counting procedures. For example, diagnostic efforts may be made more effective in some cases by studying the behavior of appropriate labeled compounds in health and disease. Metabolic studies almost certainly will become a more profitable application of whole body counting. Perhaps less certain of realization, but extremely important from a practicing health physics standpoint, is a solution to the problem of estimating organ dose from radionuclides deposited in the body. It may prove possible to identify the radiations emerging from a given region of the body and equate this to organ content of radioisotope and radiation dose to the organ, as with iodine in the thyroid. Hopefully, one might go one step further and fractionate the total body content to radiation doses for all the major organs of the body.

It will be noted that we have, as with the electron microscope, the curious circumstances of the measuring instrument having been developed in an advanced form prior to there having been a keen long-time awareness of the kinds of information it can produce. Because of this reversal of the common sequence, it may be unfair to suggest that the compentency of the machine has been only partially capitalized on, but to those interested in the general subject of internal emitters in man, the pace of development does seem to have been slow.

New as it is, the technique of whole body counting is here to stay. Many applications of it will be explored and finally abandoned; others will prove of permanent benefit and will strengthen our armamentarium of methods useful in biology and medicine. Meanwhile, symposia such as this one are important.

PREFACE

LEONARD D. HEATON
The Surgeon General
U. S. Army

MAN HAS carried radioactive carbon in his skeleton for at least
50,000 years; this we know, for it can be measured in his remains. This may seem a short time when looking at life on Earth,
but it is sufficient indication that radioactivity, life and man have
been at least somewhat compatible for that portion of man's history responsible for his existence as we know it today.

Radiation is as inseparable from life as water. All radiation
is not harmful, for life has evolved not only in spite of, but, in
part, because of radiation. We know with equal certainty that
radiation can be very dangerous, in fact, as unfailing in causing
death as life itself. Somewhere between these extremes are aspects of radioactivity which can be of great benefit to mankind.

Through our present knowledge and equipment, we are gain-
ing an intimate insight into the workings of what we think of now
as the ultimate building blocks of matter, the atoms and molecules. Hazards not previously conceived will be brought to
light. Past and present fears will be set aside as having no basis
in fact. New processes will introduce more and different isotopes
into the life stream, and means will be sought to render them useful or harmless.

The discovery of the principles of radioactivity by Becquerel
just over a half century ago and then the ability to produce and
sustain controlled nuclear fission have set off a series of events
which are having increasing effect on the entire world, from the
lowly ooze at the bottom of the ocean with its increasing concentration of radionuclides to the possibility of vast devastation of
man and his supporting life through nuclear weapons. Today
with better means of medical diagnosis, increased amounts and

xliii

quality of foods, improved quality control in metals, detection of metabolic change in bone, control of insects, therapy of malignancy, pollution of the atmosphere, contamination of fish, and concentrated energy in untold amounts, a most interesting chapter is being written in the medical aspects of radioactivity in man.

The long term preservation of foods by irradiation opens doors to new concepts of the utilization and distribution of foods on a world-wide basis not possible before. The fundamental problems of starvation faced by segments of the world's population and the tremendous potential of the utilization or irradiated foods as a weapon in battle for world peace are of great concern to all of us. The U. S. Army Medical Service continues its active participation in the field of wholesomeness of irradiated foods and in studies of low level radioactivity through its whole body counting program.

PREFACE

Hugh H. Hussey

Director, Division of Scientific Activities
American Medical Association

and

F. J. L. Blasingame

Executive Vice-President
American Medical Association

THE SUBJECT OF radiation has generated more opinion, contradiction and controversy among physicians and scientists today than almost any other subject — and raised more questions. Are we radiating ourselves or future generations into oblivion? Will atomic fallout shorten our lives, deform our offspring, give us a cancer? Is our food being poisoned? Do x rays and radiation therapy do more harm than good?

It is not possible to get absolute answers to these questions for we haven't built up a sufficient mass of knowledge yet. Radiation and radioactivity have been known in the laboratory and the clinic since the turn of the century, but detailed studies of the effects on man and his germplasm are fairly recent. Not until the threat of extinction flared up in the atomic fireball was there any sense of urgency.

Physicians and biophysicists have recently developed some new guidelines that give a somewhat less forbidding hue to life with nuclear reactions than the gloom prophicies of a decade ago. Some of the "hard facts" about radiation have been found to be neither hard nor fact.

Any use of radiation is inescapably linked with unknowns and imponderables. Ever since Wilhelm Conrad Roentgen discovered the x ray in 1895, man has been finding new uses for it and new dangers from the penetrating energy which it can deliver to tissue. At long last he has begun to stockpile his knowledge with the ultimate view not of self-liquidation, but of self-improvement.

As far as medicine and science are concerned, while we cannot afford to ignore radiation, neither can we allow ourselves to be terrified and ineffectual in coping with it.

America's physicians have a responsibility to advance scientific knowledge. The American Medical Association, because of its traditional role in medicine, has both the responsibility and the opportunity to make a unique contribution to medical research.

As a part of that responsibility we have joined in sponsorship of scientific assemblies such as the Second Symposium on Radioactivity in Man. The A.M.A. is particularly pleased that this international symposium had the combined support of organized medicine, medical education, private industry, the armed forces and the federal government. With speakers and auditors gathered from all corners of the world, it is truly a combined effort of the best scientific minds to pool knowledge and continue the search for the answers to the many unknowns in the field of radioactivity in man.

PREFACE

LUTHER L. TERRY

The Surgeon General
U. S. Public Health Service

THE ASPECT OF radioactivity in man which involves the inter-relationships between scientists, government and the people is as complex and important as the scientific questions.

Not only in radiological health, but in many other important health problems, such disparate factors as economics, mass psychology, agriculture, labor and industry may play a major role in the decisions which government officials must make. This is markedly true in health hazards arising from or intensified by advancing technology, industrialization and the transition from a primarily rural to a predominantly urban society. These so-called environmental health problems differ from classic public health problems—primarily communicable diseases—in several major respects.

First, cause and effect relationships are not fully delineated. We may suspect strongly, for example, that low level chronic exposure to ionizing radiation or to atmospheric hydrocarbons can cause neoplastic disease in man—but we cannot always prove it. Even if we could, it would be virtually impossible to establish valid dose-effect relationships in humans for many of the known or suspected causes of various kinds of cancer. Even where cause and effect relationships are widely known and the efficacy of a control measure clearly demonstrated, it is difficult to obtain complete protection for the populations at risk. The task becomes harder when we cannot demonstrate unequivocally that a specific health hazard exists.

A further complication with which we must be concerned is that of the genetic effects which radiation is known to cause and

which may accompany certain other agents involved in environmental health. Here again we lack firm dose-effect data.

A second characteristic which sets apart most of this group of
emerging health problems is that the procedures, apparatus and
products which create the hazard may also confer certain public
benefits. An outstanding example is the diagnostic x ray which
makes more of a contribution to health each year at the same
time that it increases the individual and population exposure to
radiation. Another is the enormous increase in pesticide usage
which brings more plentiful food crops, while simultaneously
creating human health hazards which science is only beginning to
identify.

Directly related to this beneficent aspect of many causative
factors of environmental health hazards are the enormous invest-
ments—public and private, social and financial—in the factories,
refineries, vehicles, reactors, defense weapons, x-ray machines
and other apparatus, goods and services required to satisfy the
demands of the times in which we live.

A characteristic that most of these problems share is the
benefit versus risk judgments that must be made and the subsequent actions which must be taken by governments rather than
individuals. Such judgments are relatively easy for the public
to understand when alternate risks are within the range of common knowledge, i.e., hazardous heart surgery versus the more
hazardous congenital heart defect or the risk of rabies vaccine
versus the risk of the disease itself. When both sides of the risk
balance are uncertain, or when the individual or social benefits
of accepting an assumed risk are not clearly defined, public policy
decisions become increasingly difficult to make and to explain to
the public.

All public health problems require public policy decisions.
This is an evolutionary process which often lags behind new
scientific knowledge. There must be acceptance by the public of
the need for a public policy. This acceptance is reflected in
voluntary action by the public or by enactment and enforcement
of local, state or federal laws and regulations. The various elements of our social order such as industry, agriculture and

branches of government adapt to the public policy, which may take many years. The job of the public official eventually becomes primarily that of administration within an established framework of standards, laws and regulations.

This evolutionary process was acceptable during the formative years of public health as a science and a major responsibility of government. A lengthy evolutionary period for some of our newer environmental health problems may not be acceptable. Entire national populations may be exposed, and in the case of environmental radiation the total world population may be at risk.

Faced with the uncertainties of the effects of these agents, responsible government agencies must err on the side of prudence and make public policy judgments now rather than later. Among these judgments is the decision as to what kinds and how much research should be conducted to fill the gaps in our knowledge. Decisions must be made with the knowledge we already have as to how much exposure can be permitted to a potentially hazardous agent. These standards must be related to reasonably reliable data on exposure sources, to amounts received by various population groups in the past, and to present and probable future exposures.

From these judgments we proceed inevitably to the question of control measures—either source control, vector control or prophylactic measures administered to the exposed groups when exposure standards have been exceeded. Control measures require research, demonstration and application. This requires people and money.

Each of these phases and facets involves some degree of understanding and acceptance on the part of special groups within the public. Federal and state legislative bodies must pass necessary legislation and appropriate sufficient funds. Schools and universities must adjust their curricula to train the technologists, engineers and scientists needed. Scientific investigators must decide whether the research problems are of sufficient importance and interest to justify their attention, and if so, whether research funds can be obtained.

The roles of the various governmental agencies which may be concerned with the problem need to be decided by legislatures or chief executives.

Industrial, agricultural, labor and other important interests may be at stake in all of these actions and considerations. Their voices must be heard, and their cooperation secured. Appropriate professional organizations must be consulted, and certain courses of action agreed upon.

Finally, there must be general public acceptance of the need for the funds, laws, regulations and restrictions which may accompany official research and control efforts. Such acceptance is best based upon full understanding of the biological, technical and social issues involved. And here we have in the case of radioactivity in man perhaps our most difficult area of communication. The terminology and scientific principles of the complexity of balancing risk and benefit against hazard are almost beyond lay comprehension.

Although much still remains unknown and undone, real progress has been made toward defining and coming to grips with the radiation problem. This symposium is concrete evidence of progress on the research and communication fronts. Other important questions concerning how man can live and prosper in a changing environment may well draw on our experience with radiation for guidelines toward their ultimate solution.

CONTENTS

INSTRUMENTATION, TECHNIQUE AND CALIBRATION

COBALT METABOLISM

IRON METABOLISM

MISCELLANEOUS TOPICS

METABOLISM OF FISSION PRODUCTS

SOCIAL AND INDUSTRIAL ASPECTS OF
INTERNAL RADIOISOTOPE BURDENS

RADIOACTIVITY IN MAN

Second Symposium

SESSION I, SEPTEMBER 5

INSTRUMENTATION, TECHNIQUE and CALIBRATION

Chairman: JOHN A. D. COOPER

1

GAMMA RAY SPECTROSCOPY
WITH A SCINTILLATION SPECTROMETER
HAVING AN ANTICOINCIDENCE ANNULUS[1]

J. MONAHAN, S. RABOY and C. C. TRAIL

Argonne National Laboratory
Argonne, Illinois

INTRODUCTION

A CAPTURE GAMMA RAY spectroscopy program at Argonne National Laboratory required a detector with high efficiency and good resolution. In addition the multiple effects from pair production and Compton scattering usually present in scintillation spectrometers had to be reduced. Since the counter was to be used in the high radiation background of the reactor floor at CP-5, a thick shield of paraffin, boron carbide and lead was necessary to reduce this background. To keep the weight of this shield manageable, the space available to the counter was limited. To meet these conditions, an anticoincidence spectrometer was designed, in which the auxiliary detector was NaI (Tl) in the shape of a hollow cylinder.

This approach had been suggested by Albert (1), by Roulston and Naqvi (2) and by Bell and co-workers (3,4). Their scheme is to surround the principal detecting crystal with another detector in anticoincidence. Thus, if all the energy of the gamma ray is not lost in the center crystal, the escaping quanta may be detected by the surrounding detector and the event will be discarded by the electronics. Albert surrounded a 0.5 in. cube of NaI(Tl) with chunks of NaI in an oil bath. The efficiency of his system is limited to the efficiency of the 0.5 in. cube of NaI(Tl).

[1]This work was performed under the auspices of the U. S. Atomic Energy Commission.

The light collection properties of the anticoincidence detector seem to be relatively poor because of the many chunks of NaI(Tl) and the use of too few photomultiplier tubes.

Roulston and Naqvi used a 10 by 10 in. cylinder of plastic phosphor for the anticoincidence shield. A 1 by 1 in. cylinder of NaI(Tl) was mounted on a 1.5 in. photomultiplier, and the assembly was inserted into a hole in the plastic phosphor. The source to be studied is placed inside the hole with the NaI(Tl) crystal. These authors report that the Compton distribution from the 1.114 Mev gamma rays of Zn^{65} was reduced by a factor of 2.5.

The system developed by Bell and his co-workers has a high efficiency for gamma detection since the detecting crystal is a cylinder, 4.75 in. in diameter and 5.5 in. high. This crystal was placed in a well in an anticoincident system consisting of a liquid scintillant filling a spherical tank with a diameter of about 28 in. The light pulses from this liquid were detected by four 5 in. photomultipliers; a fifth photomultiplier with a cylindrical tank of liquid scintillant to close the well and completely surround the detecting crystal was optional. Such a system is very efficient for radioactive sources placed in the well of the center crystal. It is also possible to work with a beam of gamma rays which reach the detector through the well in the anticoincident system.

The difficulty of working with small pulse heights from the liquid scintillator is made worse by the difficulties of light collection in such a large solution. Furthermore, even a minimal lead shield around such a large system would be heavy and expensive.

APPARATUS

The principal detecting crystal of our system is a cylinder about 2.4 in. in diameter and 6 in. long. It is optically coupled to a Dumont 6292 photomultiplier. The second crystal, which is to detect degraded photons resulting from the Compton scattering in the main crystal or annihilation radiation escaping from the main crystal, is a hollow cylinder, 12 in. long, with an outside diameter of 8 in. and an inside diameter of 2.5 in. Six photomultipliers are coupled to one face of the hollow cylinder (Fig. 1).

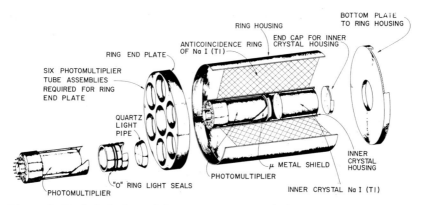

Figure 1. Exploded view of the apparatus. Signals from the outer cylinder are placed in anticoincidence to those from the inner cylinder.

For the Cs^{137} gamma rays, this crystal gives an instrumental line width of 18 to 25 percent, depending upon the location of the source (18 percent if the source is near the end of the crystal away from the photomultipliers; 25 percent if the source is near the photomultipliers).

The signals from the center crystal were fed through conventional linear amplifiers to a 256 channel pulse height analyzer of the type designed by Schuman and McMahon (5). The spectra are stored as punched paper tape suitable for analysis by the ANL digital computer, GEORGE. The six photomultipliers on the anticoincident ring feed their signal through a common pre-amplifier and a linear amplifier to an anticoincidence gate of the 256 channel analyzer. A pulse corresponding to an event of 30 kev or more in the hollow cylinder is large enough to prevent the analysis of a pulse from the center crystal.

Several tests were made with the center crystal at various positions inside the cylinder. Best results were obtained with the crystal at the middle, and it is of interest to discuss qualitatively what response one would expect from this arrangement.

Small angle Compton events occurring soon after the gamma ray enters the center crystal will be suppressed because the degraded photon will have to penetrate a large part of the center crystal. Processes yielding degraded photons at slightly larger angles will also be suppressed because these photons have to pass through the anticoincidence cylinder at an oblique angle. If the degraded photon is emitted at an angle greater than 90°, then its energy must be less than 511 kev, and thus there is a high probability of an interaction with the ring. Very large angle processes will permit the degraded photon to escape detection, and the central crystal will yield a distribution of pulses corresponding to the angular aperture in the outer cylinder. This distribution will occur at pulse heights corresponding to the Compton edge in conventional scintillation spectrometers.

In the event that a pair is created, the subsequent annihilation quanta are emitted in opposite directions. If the quanta strike the ring, each has a 15 percent probability of passing through the crystal without being detected; so there is a 2 percent probability that neither quantum will be detected. Similar arguments apply to the case in which the annihilation quanta are emitted along the axis of the cylinder. If the annihilation occurs near one end of the center crystal, the one quantum can escape through the hole, but the other must penetrate the full 6 in. of the center crystal.

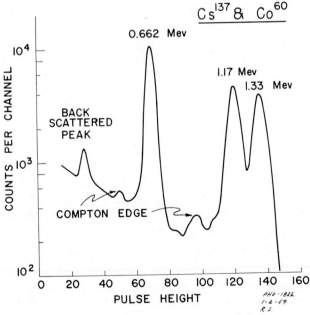

Figure 2. Response of the spectrometer to Co^{60} and Cs^{137} gamma rays.

RESULTS

The response of the spectrometer has been studied for gamma ray energies up to 7.1 Mev. In Figure 2 the spectrum of the gamma rays from Co^{60} and Cs^{137} is presented. The ratio of the counting rate in the 1.17 Mev peak of Co^{60} to the rate in the valley between the peaks is about 6:1. With a new center crystal we recently obtained a peak-to-valley ratio of 15.1. The peak in Figure 2 at pulse height 97 results from large angle Compton scattering of the gamma rays of Co^{60} with the degraded photon escaping through the aperture of the outer cylinder as discussed. The peak at 50 represents the Compton edge of the 0.662 Mev gamma ray of Cs^{137}.

Figure 3 shows the response of this apparatus to the 2.75 and 1.37 Mev gamma rays from Na^{24} with and without the anti-

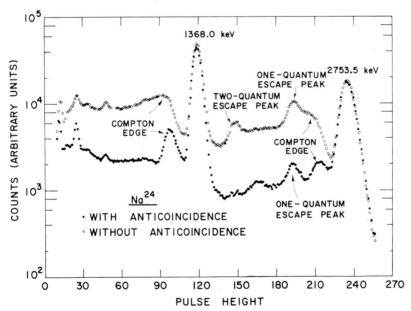

Figure 3. The gamma ray spectrum from Na^{24} with and without the anti-coincidence annulus. The spectra have been normalized at the 2.75 Mev peak and the ordinate is approximately the number of counts.

coincidence annulus. The anticoincidence annulus reduces the spectrum from Compton scattering of the 2.75 Mev gamma ray by about four. The spectrum obtained with the anticoincidence annulus shows a Compton edge which results from back-scattered radiation escaping through the entrance aperture. A 1 quantum escape peak is evident at pulse height 195, but no 2 quantum escape peak is present. A peak at pulse height 165 is presumably from a radioactive contaminant in the source. Figure 4 shows the background observed when the anticoincidence apparatus is surrounded with 2 in. of lead. The crystals, their photomulti-

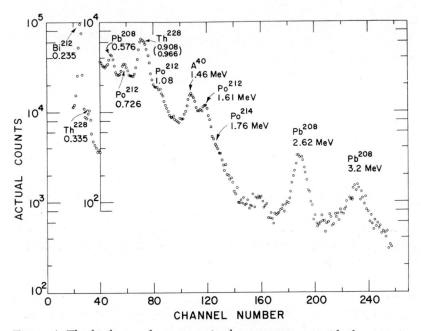

Figure 4. The background spectrum in the spectrometer with the anticoincidence annulus functioning and 2 in. of lead surrounding the crystals, photomultipliers and preamplifiers. The data were obtained in about 23 hrs.

pliers and the preamplifiers were inside the lead shield. The energy scale has been determined with the 898.4 and 1835.5 kev lines of Y^{88} on the assumption that the apparatus has a linear energy response. This assumption has been found to be good to a few percent over the range used.

Figure 5 shows the background spectrum obtained when the lead was removed from the apparatus. A prominent line, which

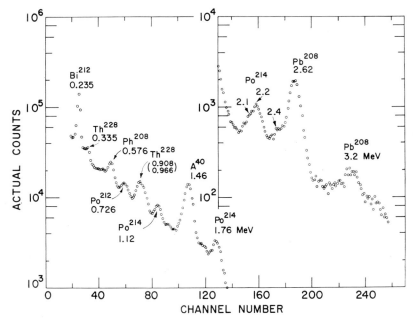

Figure 5. The background spectrum obtained as in Figure 4, but with no lead around the spectrometer. The data were collected in about 26 hrs.

we attribute to the decay of K^{40} to A^{40}, appears at 1.4 Mev. The intensity of the line with the 2 in. lead shield is 7.5 ± 1.0 percent of the intensity without the shield.

The gamma ray at 2.6 Mev is the well known line from the β-decay of Tl^{208} to Pb^{208} in the thorium decay series. In this case the calculated transmission of the shield is 8 percent, while the ratio of intensities is 20 ± 2 percent. We conclude that some thorium is contained in the packaging, photomultiplier, associated circuitry and shielding, rather than in the outer crystal or center crystal.

A detailed analysis of the sources of the backgrounds has been published (6).

We found that the decay from K^{40} and the U^{238} series originates in the room surroundings, and the activity from the Th^{232} series originates in the immediate vicinity of the NaI crystal (such as from the package). The results are consistent with the assumption of no radioactivity within the crystal itself.

In the course of our studies of gamma ray spectra obtained with this scintillation spectrometer, a method of analysis (7) which describes a full energy peak in terms of a Gaussian function was developed. This analysis permits full utilization of the statistical accuracy of the data. From the parameters of the Gaussian, it is possible to determine the position of the mean and the area of the full energy peak. The calculations in the analysis include estimates of the errors associated with the values of these parameters.

From the mean position of a given peak, it is possible to determine the energy of the corresponding gamma ray in terms of the energies of a set of "standard gamma rays." The calculated relative standard deviation in the values of gamma ray energy determined in this manner is about 0.1 percent (8,9). These error estimates are internally consistent in that reasonable statistical agreement is achieved between the values of a gamma ray transition energy measured in two completely independent ways. The area of the peak gives a measure of the intensity of the gamma ray.

The analysis of the data begins with a calculation by a chi-squared minimization procedure which determines the parameters of the Gaussian function that describes the full energy peak. This function is given by

$$F(x_j) = \alpha_1 \exp\left[-\frac{(\alpha_2 - x_j)^2}{\alpha_3{}^2}\right] + \alpha_4$$

$F(x_j)$ is the number of counts in channel x_j, and α_1, α_2, α_3 and α_4 are, respectively, the peak height, mean position, width and residual background of the spectrum in the neighborhood of the full energy peak. The residual background parameter α_4 is necessary to describe a photopeak in the presence of a higher energy photopeak from the same source. The room background and the influence of other gamma rays are subtracted from the observed spectrum(7) to obtain the measured values $F(x_j)$. We have used this technique to determine the lifetimes of some radioactive sources (10). A spectrum (Fig. 6) from Cl^{38} was prepared by irradiating MgCl in the ANL CP-5 reactor.

Table I lists a typical set of parameters which were computed for one run with a $MgCl_2$ source. The first column identifies the gamma ray, and the next four columns give the calculated values

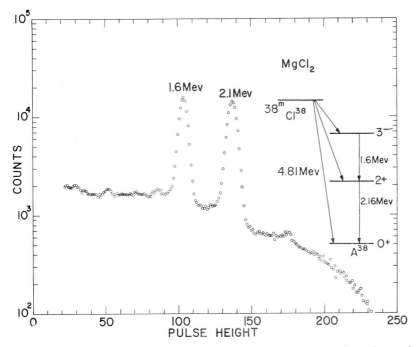

Figure 6. Typical spectrum of MgCl₂. Second run of sequence, data obtained in 5.7 min.

TABLE I.

TYPICAL SET OF PARAMETERS FOR THE GAUSSIAN FUNCTION $\alpha_1 \exp [-(\alpha_2\text{-}x_j)^2/ \alpha_3{}^2] + \alpha_4$ WHICH DESCRIBES THE FULL ENERGY PEAKS OF THE GAMMA RAYS FROM A^{38} AS DETERMINED FROM A χ^2 MINIMIZATION CALCULATION.

E (Mev)	α_1 (Counts)	α_2 (Channel)	α_3 (Channel)	α_3 (Counts)	χ^2 Calc.	Exp.
2.1	13 191 ± 197	137.005 ± 0.020	4.25 ± 0.08	809 ± 217	15	8
1.6	13 847 ± 139	103.623 ± 0.023	3.74 ± 0.06	1317 ± 127	18	7

of the parameters α_j together with the estimated standard deviations obtained from the analyses. These error estimates have been adjusted to allow for the difference between the expected and calculated values of chi squared (last two columns).

The observed area n_v of the photopeak for the v th run is given in terms of the Gaussian parameters as $\sqrt{\pi}\ \alpha_1\ \alpha_3$.

The corrected values $n_v{}^\circ$ of the intensities were substituted in the exponential decay law and the values of N (the initial intensity) and λ (the decay constant) were calculated by the least-squares method, the uncertainty estimates obtained in the analysis of the Gaussian being used as reciprocal weights for the individual data points. The standard deviation associated with the calculated value of the half life was normalized to external consistency, so that the expected and calculated values of chi-square were equal.

Table II lists the present results for the half lives of Cl^{38}, K^{42} and Na^{24}, which agree with the results obtained in other

TABLE II
MEASURED HALF LIVES

Radioactive Source	Chemical Form	Half Life
Cl^{38}	$MgCl_2$	37.12 ± 0.18 min.
Cl^{38}	NaCl	37.53 ± 0.60 min.
K^{42}	KF	12.47 ± 0.07 hr.
Na^{24}	NaF	15.05 ± 0.05 hr.

laboratories by different methods. These methods include 4π beta counting in gas counters, measurements with ionization chambers and electroscopes discharged by β rays. The analyses included graphical techniques and weighted and nonweighted least-squares analyses for equal time intervals.

Although we have used this apparatus only for experiments in nuclear physics, we feel that the instrument and the calculation procedures can be useful in any investigation needing quantitative determination of gamma ray activity.

REFERENCES

1. Albert, R. D.: *Rev. Sci. Instr.*, *24*:1096, 1953.
2. Roulston, K. I., and Naqvi, S.I.H.: *Rev. Sci. Instr.*, 27:830, 1956.
3. Bell, P. R.: *Science, 120*:625, 1954.
4. Davis, Bell, P.R., Kelley, and Lazar: *IRE Trans. Nucl. Sci.*, NS-3:82 (Nov.) 1956.
5. Schuman, R. W., and McMahon, J. P.: *Rev. Sci. Instr.*, 27:675, 1956.

6. Raboy, S., and Trail, C. C.: *Nucl. Instr. Methods,* 9:145, 1960.

7. Julke, R. T., Monahan, J. E., Raboy, S., and Trail, C. C.: Argonne National Laboratory Report. ANL-6499 (unpublished).

8. Monahan, J. E., Raboy, S., and Trail, C. C.: *Nucl. Phys.,* 24:400, 1961.

9. Monahan, J. E., Raboy, S., and Trail, C. C.: *Phys. Rev., 123*:1373, 1961.

10. Monahan, J. E., Raboy, S., and Trail, C. C.: *Nucl. Instr. Methods,* (to be published).

2

LOW LEVEL IN VIVO MEASUREMENT OF I^{131} IN HUMANS

GERARD R. LAURER AND MERRIL EISENBUD

New York University
New York, New York

INTRODUCTION

THE FIRST published indication of the possible presence of radio-iodine in milk during periods of nuclear weapons' testing came with the observations by Van Middlesworth (1) in 1953 of I^{131} in cattle thyroids during tests in Nevada. Comar *et al.* (2) reported *in vitro* measurements of I^{131} in human and cattle thyroids from early 1955 throughout late 1956, and Lewis (3,4) later made estimates based on published reports of the radioiodine content of milk of the dosage to the thyroids of infants and children in the United States from weapons' testing before 1958.

Because of the short half life of I^{131} (8 days), this radionuclide disappeared from the environment shortly after the establishment of the testing moratorium in 1958, and no new data became available until 1961 when the Russians resumed nuclear testing.

In the intervening years, gamma spectrometric techniques have been improved and have become more generally available. When the Soviets resumed testing in 1961, it seemed feasible to develop an *in vivo* procedure for the measurement of I^{131} in human thyroids. This paper will describe the techniques we developed and the methods by which they were calibrated.

METHOD OF MEASUREMENT

The low level equipment at the New York University Environmental Radiation Laboratory includes a whole body counter with 7 in. thick walls fabricated out of battleship armor plate. The detection and counting apparatus used for the thyroid measurements are two 3 by 3 in. NaI(Tl) crystals in conjunction with a 400 channel analyzer and associated read-out apparatus. The crystals are placed at an angle of 90° so that the flat faces are against the neck on either side of the cricoid cartilage. The sides of the crystals are shielded by wrapping them in ⅛ in. of lead.

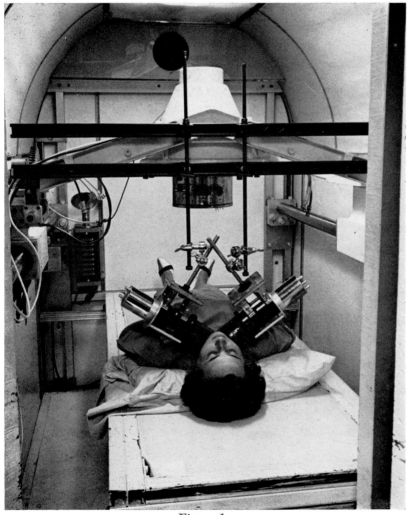

Figure 1.

We have made measurements with the subject lying on a cot (Fig. 1) and seated in a tilting chair. We prefer the tilting chair geometry because it enables us to make a simultaneous measurement of the whole body burdens of Cs^{137} and K^{40} using an 8 by 4 in. crystal. For these measurements the 400 channels of the analyzer are split into two quadrants of 200 channels each using a mixer amplifier. The supine position is preferable for sedated patients or for small children who can be immobilized by standard methods of restraint.

The two methods required different calibration procedures, each of which will be described.

CALIBRATION

To compute the thyroid I^{131} burden in a subject whose gamma ray spectrum includes a given number of counts in the I^{131} region, an equation of the following form must be solved:

$$\text{T.B.}_{I131} = \frac{1}{S}\left[\overset{I^{131}}{\sum}\text{cpm} - f_{Cs/I}\left(\overset{Cs^{137}}{\sum}\text{cpm} - f_{I/Cs}\overset{I^{131}}{\sum}\text{cpm} - f_{K/Cs}\overset{K^{40}}{\sum}\text{cpm} \right) - f_{K/I}\overset{K^{40}}{\sum}\text{cpm} \right]$$

where

$$\text{T.B.}_{I131} = \text{thyroid } I^{131} \text{ burden in picocuries (pc)}$$
$$S = \text{sensitivity factor (cpm/pc)}$$
$$\text{cpm} = \text{gross cpm minus background cpm summed over the energy regions indicated}$$
$$f_{Cs/I}, f_{I/Cs} = \text{fractional Compton scatter coefficients}$$
$$f_{K/Cs}, f_{K/I}$$

The fractional Compton scatter coefficient, $f_{A/B}$, times the net counts under the photopeak of A gives the Compton contribution in the region of the photopeak of B.

The various factors in the equation were quantitated using several procedures. The first measurements shortly after the resumption of Soviet testing were made on cadavers of New York residents who died suddenly and whose I^{131} burden was due to diet. Measurements were first made *in situ* and then compared with measurements made after the thyroid was dissected at autopsy. This provided us with useful relationships for preliminary evaluation of our *in vivo* data, but the problems of quantitating the contribution to the I^{131} region of Compton scatter from Cs^{137} and K^{40} required that our calibration be refined by studies using a masonite phantom.

Measurement of the radioiodine burden of the dissected thyroids was calibrated with a dilute carrier solution of known I^{131}. The radioactivity of the sample was determined by plating triplicate samples on copper disks, evaporating them to dryness and then counting in an internal flow counter. In this type of counter for a weightless source of small diameter, the geometry factor is 0.50, there is no loss by absorption and the backscatter factor is 1.52 (5).

Using 10 ml. of the standard solution a sensitivity factor in cpm/pc was obtained for the measurements of dissected thyroids on the 8 by 4 crystal. Since the counting efficiency remained constant over a circle of 3 cm. radius, no correction factor was necessary for thyroid size.

Estimates of the various scatter factors, i.e., $f_K/_I$, $f_K/_{Cs}$, $f_{Cs}/_I$, were obtained with the use of small sources of K^{40} and Cs^{137} placed at various points along the long axis of a masonite phantom with the crystals in position as during a subject measurement. The factors obtained are merely the ratio of the net counts under the full energy peak of the contributing isotopes to the net counts in the energy region of the isotope to whose spectrum the scatter is contributed, e.g., $f_K/_{Cs}$ = (net cpm in cesium region/net cpm under K^{40} peak) using a K^{40} source with no cesium present.

Measurements using the masonite phantom body and a water-filled 3 in. diameter polyethylene bottle, which was used as a mock neck, indicated the background with scattering and absorbing materials to be the same as the subject-free background.

Application of these scatter factors to the K^{40} and Cs^{137} counts from the cadaver measurements yielded an estimate of the net I^{131} cpm due to the thyroid alone before dissection. These

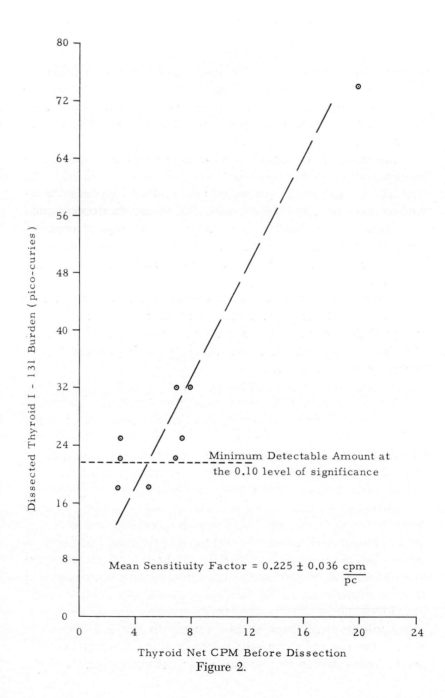

Figure 2.

counts were then compared to the thyroid burden in picocuries as obtained after dissection (Fig. 2).

There is a scarcity of points over 25 pc. The line was put in, nevertheless, to indicate the general trend of the points. If there were no errors involved in estimating the Compton scatter coefficients and no error due to counting statistics, the points should fall on a line, although not necessarily on a straight line. With the amount of data that was available and the small I^{131} burden involved in most of the cases, the spread is considered reasonable.

The *in vivo* sensitivity factor, S, was obtained by taking the ratio of the net counts due to I^{131} in the thyroid of the cadaver to the thyroid burden of I^{131} in picocuries as obtained for the excised thyroid in all nine cadavers. The mean sensitivity factor arrived at for *in vivo* thyroid measurements using the prone geometry was 0.225 ± 0.036 cpm/pc of I^{131}.

These measurements represent body sizes ranging from a three month old infant weighing approximately 15 lbs. to a subject of approximately 230 lbs. The data would seem to indicate that there is no correction necessary for body size and weight when the subject is supine.

TILTING CHAIR CALIBRATION

The tilting chair geometry had been calibrated for Cs^{137} and K^{40} previously, and it was only a matter of convenience to calibrate for the iodine measurements. However, this necessitated the redetermination of the various scatter factors since they change with different types of geometry.

A phantom was prepared by filling a suit of long underwear with brown rice and wrapping it with surgical tape to secure the proper proportioning of the rice within the various sections of the body. The head was an Air Force high altitude helmet filled with rice, which has approximately the same amount of potassium (2 gm./kg.) as man.

From repeated measurements of the phantom in the tilting chair position, we obtained the scatter factors for K^{40}, $f_K/_I$ and $f_K/_{Cs}$. However, the rice phantom could not be used for the Cs^{137} scatter factor calibration because so little of this radionuclide was present. Fortunately, we had already measured several laboratory personnel and other volunteers in the tilting chair position before the appearance of any I^{131} from the U. S. series. We estimated $f_{Cs}/_I$ by subtracting their K^{40} contributions to the Cs^{137} and I^{131} regions of their spectrums by utilizing the K^{40} scatter factors obtained from the phantom measurements and then taking the ratio of the net counts in the I^{131} region to the net counts in the Cs^{137} region. If no I^{131} counts were present, then the net counts above zero in the iodine region should be the Cs^{137} Compton scatter contribution, and the ratio of these counts to the Cs^{137} photopeak counts is the scatter factor $f_{Cs}/_I$.

Measurements were made on twenty-one subjects to test the validity of the various scatter factors. The total contribution to the I^{131} region of each was calculated by multiplying the net counts obtained in the K^{40} and Cs^{137} regions of the spectrums of each by the scatter factors obtained. The values so obtained were then compared to the apparent contribution as shown by the actual net counts in the I^{131} region obtained after subtraction of background. The I^{131} burden of these subjects was presumed to be zero, since I^{131} was known to be absent in foods in the New York City area, as well as in dissected thyroids obtained daily from the Office of the Medical Examiner.

The differences obtained between the apparent or calculated contributions are shown in Table I. A "t" test to test the hypothesis that the mean of these differences was not significantly different from zero proved to be significant at the 0.01 level. The four differences consistently positive by more than five were four men over 6 ft. tall and weighing over 200 lb. Another "t" test performed on the other seventeen points excluding the last four proved to be not significant. The mean of the differences was not different from zero for these seventeen points at the 0.01 level of significance. Hence, the scatter factors obtained were accepted as correct with the provision that they may not apply to persons of above average stature. The scatter factors may not be constant, but may in fact be a function of some body parameter such as height or weight or both. To secure this information, however, will require many more measurements.

Having obtained the scatter factors, there remained the

TABLE I

COMPTON CONTRIBUTION TO I^{131}(0.364 MEV) REGION OF GAMMA SPECTRUM
FROM MEASUREMENTS OF 21 SUBJECTS

	Apparent	Calculated	Difference
1.	32.1	32.4	− 0.3
2.	31.4	28.6	+ 2.8
3.	29.9	30.1	− 0.2
4.	31.4	29.4	+ 2.0
5.	27.6	26.3	+ 1.3
6.	29.8	31.0	− 1.2
7.	23.8	23.7	+ 0.1
8.	30.9	30.4	+ 0.5
9.	32.2	33.3	− 1.1
10.	27.8	29.1	− 1.3
11.	32.0	29.9	+ 2.1
12.	34.3	29.3	+ 4.8
13.	27.8	27.7	+ 0.1
14.	25.6	26.7	− 1.1
15.	31.3	27.6	+ 3.7
16.	30.4	31.0	− 0.6
17.	28.3	27.7	+ 0.6
18.	32.2	27.1	+ 5.1
19.	31.7	26.6	+ 5.1
20.	34.1	28.6	+ 5.5
21.	41.5	36.0	+ 5.5

problem of measuring the sensitivity factor, cpm/pc I^{131}. Two glass mock thyroids were used, 40 cc. and 25 cc., filled with a standard solution of I^{131} and counted in place in the throat of the phantom. Measurements were made to study the effect due to differences in size of thyroids and to differences in the depth of the thyroid in the throat. The mean sensitivity factor was 0.223±0.010 cpm/pc. This represented an error of approximately 7 percent at the 0.10 level of significance, in good agreement with the first calibration factor of 0.225±0.036 cpm/pc.

Using the second sensitivity factor of 0.223±0.010 cpm/pc as the more accurate of the two calibration figures, the minimum detectable activity for this measurement at the 0.1 level of significance is 21.5±1.6 pc. This figure is for a background of 53 cpm for 30 min. of counting.

The mock thyroid measurements in the phantom led to the determination of the factor $f_I/_{Cs}$. This correction is relatively small, being approximately 2 c/m at 100 pc I^{131}.

SUMMARY

Two calibration procedures for the *in vivo* measurement of I^{131} in human thyroids were developed. Measurements can be made in either the supine or tilting chair geometries. Observations must be corrected for the Compton contributions to the I^{131} region of the spectrum from K^{40} and Cs^{137}. The sensitivity factor, expressed as counts per minute per picocurie was found to be 0.223 ± 0.01 for the tilting chair geometry and 0.225 ± 0.036 for the supine position, using two 3 by 3 in. crystals and 30 min. counting time.

REFERENCES

1. Middlesworth, L. Van: *Nucleonics, 12*:56, 1954.
2. Comar, C. L., Trum, Bernard F., Kuhn, U. S. G. III, Wasserman, R. H., Nold, M. M., and Schooley, J. C.: *Science, 126*:16, 1957.
3. Lewis, E. B.: Hearings before the Joint Congressional Committee on Atomic Energy on Fallout from Nuclear Weapons Tests, 1552, 1959.
4. Lewis, E. B.: *Proc. Nat. Acad. Sci.*, U. S. 45:894, 1959.
5. Price, Wm. J.: *Nuclear Radiation Detection.* McGraw-Hill, 1958.

3

A MOBILE WHOLE BODY COUNTER

Wilhelm Von Döbeln

Gymnastiska Centralinst
Stockholm, Sweden

A booth open at the top with inner dimensions of 1.6 by 0.64 by 0.88 meters (height) and a wall thickness of 8 cm. is made of lead bars. The case serves as a shield for a chair and a gamma ray detector and is placed in a wagon with wooden walls and roof. Preliminary data of the physical characteristics of this equipment are presented and discussed.

At the International Atomic Energy Agency Symposium on Whole Body Counting in Vienna in 1961, Bo Lindell from Radiofysiska Institutionen, Stockholm, presented data for "open booth" body counter. In this counter the iron shield is open in one horizontal direction. The subject is placed in this shield sitting upright facing the opening. In front of the subject is a crystal shielded in all directions except the one facing the subject. The arrangement enables qualitative measurements, but because of the geometry, quantitative measurements on humans are not possible.

The fact that the equipment weighed only 6,500 kg. and produced good results stimulated us to build a mobile whole body counter of a similar design.

A wagon with wooden walls and roof, was built for transporting the counter. It had a load capacity of 6,000 kg. and a floor area of 2 by 5 meters.

The subject and detector were shielded by 190 lead bars, each 80 by 8 by 4 cm. and weighing about 29 kg. An open booth was built in the middle of the wagon, with walls 8 cm. thick. The inner dimensions of the case were 1.6 by 0.64 by 0.96 meter.

A chair was placed in the booth so that the subject was semirecumbent. A detector was placed in standard position over the hips of the subject at 60 cm. from the bottom of the lead case.

The shielding characteristics of the equipment were measured with a 4 by 4 in. NaI crystal and a nuclear data 256 channel pulse height analyzer.

When the crystal is placed in the booth and is covered completely with a shield of 8 cm. of lead, the total number of counts is 400 per minute.

When the crystal is placed in position for measuring a test subject without any additional shield, the total number of counts is over 5,000 per minute. As expected, most of the increase in comparison with the result with a completely shielded crystal falls in the low energy region. In all channels over 1 Mev the increase is less than 100 percent. This means that quantitative measurements in this region of human subjects should be possible. A normal test subject was measured in the region of the K^{40} peak. Over four 40 kev channels, the background is 30 counts per minute, while 50 counts are obtained with the test subject. This means that a measuring time of 100 min. would be required for obtaining a statistical error of less than 5 percent with one 4 by 4 in. crystal.

The reported results are obtained when the counter is placed so that the crystal does not count any of the surrounding brick buildings. If this happens, the background in the high energy region is increased considerably.

Before more experience is obtained with the equipment described, no final conclusions with respect to its usefulness are justified. It raises, however, the question whether a complete shield is always necessary when gamma spectrometry is needed. It might be an acceptable solution for many needs to place a shield of the type described in a wooden penthouse on the top of a hospital building. One advantage of the type equipment described is that in measuring patients no complications due to claustrophobia may arise.

4

ENVIRONMENTAL I^{131} IN CHILDREN

H. N. Wellman, Warren Hansen,

Gerald Laurer, Gerald Karches and Jack Fooks

U. S. Public Health Service
Cincinnati, Ohio

During June and July 1962, the U. S. Public Health Service initiated a study of I^{131} from environmental sources in man because of concern over the unique role of this radioisotope in the exposure of the population to fallout. The investigation will hopefully lead to an eventual capability to assess exposure from environmental radionuclides in man whenever an indication is manifest.

A group of ten children from metropolitan St. Louis, Missouri was studied to attempt a total evaluation of the passage through them of I^{131} from fresh fission product debris. Fresh food products and pertinent environmental media (air, water and dust) were measured and analyzed by multichannel gamma spectroscopy for contributions to the intake of radioiodine. Also, 24 hr. urine volumes were calculated from creatinine determinations with gamma spectroscopy analysis of semiquantitative daily urine aliquots for I^{131}. Each child's thyroid content of I^{131} was measured by means of dual 3 by 2 in. NaI (Tl) crystals and gamma spectroscopy in a low background steel room midway and at the end of the study. Each child's PBI was normal. In addition to this "balance study," the parents and another group of twelve children from Kansas City were investigated for their content of I^{131}.

The data indicate that almost all of the accumulated I^{131} may be accounted for by the consumption of fresh milk. Other fresh food products and environmental media contributed minimal amounts to the accumulation of this radionuclide. However, the measured thyroid I^{131} levels are lower than would be expected on the basis of daily accumulation calculations, assuming this exponential model:

q_2 = fractional uptake $\times$ pc ingested + $q_1 \times e^{-\lambda t}$

Where

q_1 = Thyroid content at T_1

q_2 = Thyroid content a T_2

fractional uptake = 0.3 (or 30%)

t = 1 day

$\lambda = \dfrac{0.693}{Teff}$

Teff = 7.6 days

The calculated I^{131} content of the thyroid would have fallen within the range of error for the thyroid counts, if one were to assume no appreciable I^{131} accumulation in the children's glands at the onset of the investigation, June 20, 1962. However, such an assumption would be untenable, for significant levels of radioiodine were detected in St. Louis for the thirty day period prior to study of the children. Individual milk consumption data and market levels of I^{131} were used to estimate the probable thyroid accumulation during the thirty day period prior to the study. Actual thyroid counts in a whole body counter were consistently lower than predicted with the classical model by a factor of about two (Fig. 1). Thus, one may speculate that all of the necessary parameters describing thyroid function are not included in the model. More plausibly, because of the consistent ratio between both sets of thyroid counts and anticipated levels, it may be that I^{131} uptake from environmental media is less than 30 percent, possibly on the order of 15 percent. Urine I^{131} levels tend to follow ingestion.

Thyroid counts of adults and Kansas City children were, in general, higher than those found in the experimental group, but no other data were collected with which to correlate these counts.

SUMMARY

Partial balance data and thyroid measurements for environmental I^{131} were obtained for a group of ten children over thirty days. Measured thyroid I¹³¹ levels were lower than calculated values by a factor of two. This is an initial study to assess the feasibility of future field studies to relate radiation exposure in man to exposure from environmental sources.

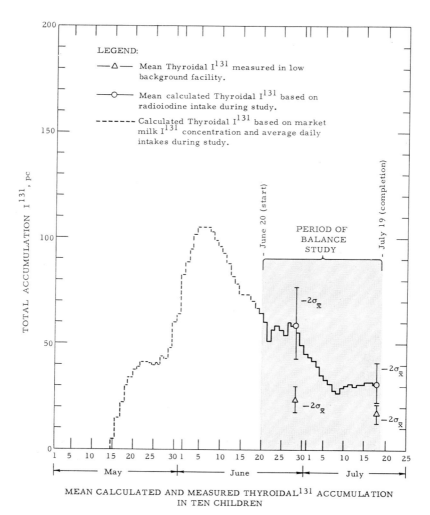

MEAN CALCULATED AND MEASURED THYROIDAL¹³¹ ACCUMULATION
IN TEN CHILDREN

Figure 1. Measured levels of I¹³¹ in the children's thyroids are compared with levels calculated by the commonly used exponential model. A statistically significant difference with p = 0.005 is seen between the two sets of measured and calculated values.

DISCUSSION

Chairman: JOHN A. D. COOPER

Northwestern University
Chicago, Illinois

A. ROSS LORIMER: Stimulated by preliminary reports of Dr. Eisenbud's study in New York, we began a series of weekly counts on adults in Nashville, Tennessee.

We had to use a 4 by 8 in. crystal with a minimal detectable amount of 80 pc. We had counts on twelve persons prior to the resumption of American nuclear testing and at weekly intervals since that time. With these twelve we have found no accumulation of iodine in the thyroid above 80 pc from the American fallout tests.

GERALD LAURER: In the United States series we had the same results, although not completely zero. The highest burden we recorded during the whole series was on myself, and it was about 35 to 40 pc.

CHAIRMAN JOHN A. D. COOPER: Are there any from other countries who have had experience recently in counting iodine burdens as a result of the tests, who would like to give comparative data?

VOICE: At U.C.L.A. we have been examining thyroids of adults and newborn infants, as well as of stillborn, and have found no radioactive iodine that we consider significant. Our lower level for thyroids that have been obtained at autopsy is about 20 $\mu\mu$c. For newborn infants in a plastic bassinette, it is perhaps 100 $\mu\mu$c. We have obtained nothing above that.

RAY D. LLOYD: At the University of Utah in July, 1962 we measured thyroid I^{131} burdens in several people one month after the Nevada tests. We also made milk counts at the farms where these people were residing and obtained about the same results

30

that Dr. Wellman reported. It appeared that the uptake was about one half of what we would expect using a 30 percent relation.

Our limit of sensitivity was probably somewhere around 100 pc per thyroid. The highest iodine burden was in a man with about 10,000 pc.

HENRY WELLMAN: One child from Kansas City had as high as 190 $\mu\mu$c in the gland. One of the mothers of the children had 470 in her thyroid. One of the things we were trying to do was to get people from areas where the levels are known to be high, and then attempt correlations with accurate intake data.

VOICE: At the Colorado Department of Public Health we measured about twenty employees with our whole body counter and found no increase in counts over the thyroid, although there wasn't too much in the milk either — perhaps 50 to 100 $\mu\mu$c per liter.

MERRIL EISENBUD: It would appear that over the past year we have observed that adults seem to accumulate more radioactive iodine in their thyroids than do children in a quart of milk in the diet. The adults have as much as twice that of the children. This simply may mean that the uptake rate may be less than we believe it to be.

HENRY WELLMAN: It may be, too, that the children have a much higher turnover rate.

H. EARL PALMER: In confirmation of what Dr. Eisenbud found in November, 1961, after the Russian tests, we measured thyroid burdens of iodine in several people who drank milk, but the uptake in the children was much less than in the adults. Since that time we haven't been able to detect any significant amounts of iodine in the thyroids.

HENRY WELLMAN: Even though the level is higher in adults, we still have to keep in mind that the concentration may be greater in children on a basis of 1 gm. of thyroid.

VOICE: We measured ten thyroids at autopsy and found average values of 100 pc in the thyroid from October 1 to November 1, 1961, in adults in western Germany. In the spring of 1962, autopsy material showed no more activity.

HENRY WELLMAN: We have been monitoring thyroids in

Cincinnati, too, since November of last year. In December we found one child with leukemia who had had a load of 1,300 $\mu\mu$c. The literature shows no increase uptake in leukemia. There were several children who had about 400 $\mu\mu$c in their glands last December. During the recent testing we occasionally got a thyroid that had a small amount of iodine in it, but the levels weren't nearly what they were during the Russian testing.

E. A. GUSMANO: At Brookhaven National Laboratory we had about the same result. During the Russian testing we found 50 to 100 $\mu\mu$c in the average adult. However, in the current testing we measured fifteen adults' thyroids and found nothing significant.

CHAIRMAN COOPER: Has there been any experience among others on attempts to make measurements at low levels in mobile equipment such as that which Dr. Von Döbeln has commented on? This kind of study is much easier if the counter can be taken into the areas and the counts made.

ALAN R. HARBERTSON: At the A.E.C. National Reactor Testing Station, we have been working with two crystals mounted on plywood on a cassette holder with the two 3 in. crystals separated so that one is at the gut level and the other at the thyroid. With this system, which is unshielded, I can pick up about 0.1 μc of Cs^{134}. There is about 100 times more sensitivity with our 4 by 8 in. in a large iron vault shielded with 11 in. of iron.

The apparatus appears promising for people who don't want to put a lot of money into shielding for picking up less than MPC values.

CHAIRMAN COOPER: Would this be applicable to improving the mobility of some counting systems?

C. C. TRAIL: I would think so. The scintillation counter that I described, however, is 100 lb. of sodium iodide. Perhaps some consideration should be given to taping the end of the annulus to permit the kind of geometry necessary to study the thyroid. Replacing the annulus with a small piece of plastic scintillator in general has been completely unsatisfactory because of its low sensitivity to gamma radiation.

HENRY WELLMAN: One physicist in Cincinnati has tried this with a plastic scintillation counter.

STELIOS REGAS: At Metrix, Inc., we have studied the problem of mobile counting facilities and have concluded that there are two possible approaches to a mobile whole body counter.

One possibility, at least for the United States, is simply installing a full-facility steel room and all the necessary apparatus in a trailer truck. The only limitation is state laws limiting the amount of weight per axle of the trailer, and there are whole body counters in operation which are below the most stringent limitations.

The second possibility is to build a tank and then use free-flowing lead shot, which can be transported in a separate facility in small containers and then loaded on location. This requires a little more time.

Dr. Trail, what are the dimensions of those crystals in the anticoincidence apparatus you described? Second, assuming a large sodium iodide crystal is not very possible, would it be possible that the advantages obtained by improving the peak-to-value ratio are compensated for by the rather limited geometric efficiency due to the size of the crystal?

C. C. TRAIL: The annulus is 8 in. in diameter and 12 in. long. The inner crystal is 2.5 in. in diameter and 6 in. long.

In answer to the second part of the question, I just don't know. If one can use the annulus to reduce the background enough, then he can stand a loss and counter it because he has a better definition of the peak.

I suggest that some effort be made just to check this type of apparatus out and look at low counting rates and see if one can make this sacrifice. If money is no object, there is no reason why the inner crystal cannot be made quite a bit larger. As the techniques progress, then the outer readings can be made correspondingly larger.

FRANCIS S. BRADLEY: Is this annulus available from any of the crystal manufacturers?

C. C. TRAIL: There are some well known crystal manufacturers in the country who sell this commercially.

ALAN R. HARBERTSON: Is the annulus a solid crystal with a hole bored through it, or is it made up of sections of crystal put together?

C. C. TRAIL: The annulus discussed this morning was made of three crystals each 8 in. in diameter and 4 in. long. Recently we made a second one which was composed of two crystals each 8 in. in diameter and 6 in. long. Whether or not these can now be made in one unit, I don't know.

SESSION II, SEPTEMBER 5

INSTRUMENTATION, TECHNIQUE and CALIBRATION,

Continued

Chairman: CHARLES E. MILLER

5

RADIONUCLIDES IN RADIATION PROCESSED FOODS[1]

Raymond L. Weiland, Robert H. Hankla,
E. U. Meneely and George R. Meneely*

*Vanderbilt University School of Medicine
Nashville, Tennessee*

EARLY STUDIES, primarily under sponsorship of the Atomic Energy Commission, indicated the feasibility of the preservation of food for human consumption by using ionizing radiation to prevent the spoilage produced by living micro-organisms. Unfortunately, it has not been proven that irradiated foods have no ill effects on the consumer. For this reason the U. S. Army Quartermaster Corps has been conducting an extensive program designed to determine if radiation preservation of food is practical. One phase of the program is the examination of irradiated foods for radioactivity induced by irradiation. Such induced radionuclides may be harmful if they increase the level of radioactivity in the food by a detectable amount above that occurring naturally. The low level whole body counter at Vanderbilt University has been used in this phase of the project.

Different foods were irradiated using several irradiation sources. In general, raw meat was vacuum sealed in an ordinary commercial tin can and was then radiated by Co^{60} gamma rays, spent reactor fuel rods or electron beams of 8, 11, 12, 13, 14, 16 or 24 Mev energy. Doses were about 5 megarads.

For the gamma ray analysis, the sample consisted of fifteen No. 10 cans or eighty-five No. 2 cans, providing a sample of about 90 lb. This size sample was selected because it approaches the

[1] Supported by Army Medical Research and Development Command, U. S. Public Health Service, and U. S. Atomic Energy Commission.

*Now at University of Texas, Houston, Texas.

size of a human on which we had accumulated much data with the Vanderbilt whole body counter. Analysis of the pure beta-emitting isotopes was performed by Tracerlab, Inc. on similar batches of food sent to them each time a batch arrived at Vanderbilt.

The steel room was adapted for use in counting food samples in No. 10 cans (Fig. 1). The lower shelf holds seven cans; the

Figure 1. No. 10 can counting geometry.

upper shelf holds eight cans. A template mounted on each shelf assures reproducible geometry, and the crystal is suspended into the middle of this array. A similar arrangement was devised for the eighty-five No. 2 cans (Fig. 2). The No. 2 size samples were irradiated by Stanford's Mark IV accelerator; the No. 10 size cans were irradiated by the linear accelerator operated by General

Figure 2. No. 2 can counting geometry.

Atomic at San Diego. At the conclusion of each irradiation, the samples were shipped to Vanderbilt and to Tracerlab by air express.

In order to calibrate the whole body counter for this arrangement, No. 10 and No. 2 cans were filled with accurate quantities of K^{40}, Zn^{65} or Cs^{137}. Additional cans were filled with distilled water for background studies. Figure 3 shows the resulting cali-

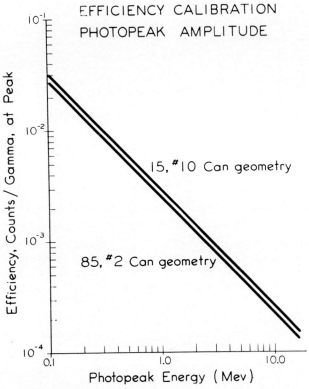

Figure 3. Efficiency calibration for food samples.

bration curve. Two types of samples and geometries used did not cause the counting efficiencies to differ greatly from each other, although it is not necessary that the two be alike. These curves were used subsequently in analyzing the microcurie quantities induced in the food samples. The K^{40} standard was prepared by mixing an accurately weighed quantity of potassium chloride in a large plastic container and then filling the fifteen No. 10 cans and eighty-five No. 2 cans with this solution. Similarly, the zinc and cesium standards were prepared after first calibrating the solutions against National Bureau of Standards calibrated sources.

We had originally intended to use and retain nonirradiated meat for our controls or background measurements. However, the first shipment of nonirradiated pork began to spoil within a few days after arrival because it had not been irradiated and had not been thermally processed. All future control samples are being cooked inside the can.

All samples and controls were counted from 600 to 900 min., producing a standard counting error of about 3 percent. Figure 4 shows a comparison between the fifteen cans of non-

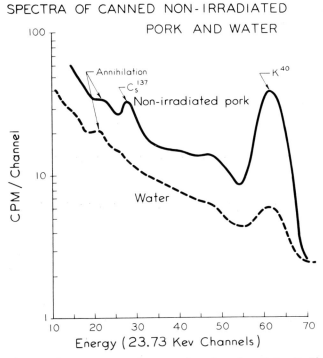

Figure 4. Spectra comparison of nonirradiated pork and distilled water.

irradiated pork and fifteen cans of distilled water. The room background (the background reading obtained with no sample or water present) produced a spectrum identical to the one shown for distilled water. By subtracting the water spectrum from the gross nonirradiated pork spectrum, the net gamma ray spectrum is obtained (Fig. 5). This is similar to a spectrum obtained from

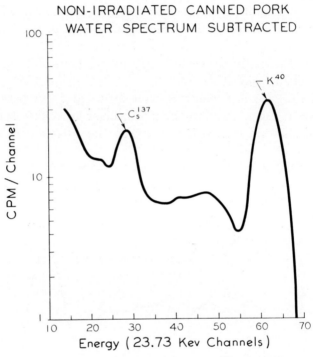

Figure 5. Net spectrum of nonirradiated pork.

whole body counts on normal humans. After integrating the appropriate photopeaks and multiplying these counting rates by the calibration factors obtained from the efficiency graph, it was found that this 90 lb. sample of nonirradiated pork contained 1.56 nc of Cs^{137} and 72 nc of K^{40} (equivalent to about 85 gm. of potassium). Both of these readings are in close agreement to those reported for human whole body counts. The spectrometer was maintained at the 23.73 kev per channel calibration, and every effort was made to keep zero energy in channel zero. This produced a full scale energy range of 3 Mev for these investigations, since we only use 128 of the 256 available channels.

At the outset we wondered about possible can-to-can variability in the homogenized foods which would affect geometrical arrangement and accuracy of results, since calibration depended upon a completely homogeneous distribution of the food within each can. We counted each can of nonirradiated pork for 30 min., and integrated the spectra over the energy range of 475 kev to 2.75 Mev. The fifteen cans gave no evidence of can-to-can variability, and the meat was sufficiently homogeneous within the limits of instrument drift. The standard counting error was not a problem. The line shown for 2 σ_n is based on calculation of the average counting rate, while 2 σ_x is the experienced standard error of the mean, which involves counting error, instrument drift and errors caused in preparation of the samples.

The first batch of irradiated food to be measured consisted of fifteen No. 10 cans of pork, irradiated with Co^{60}. Immediately we discovered a large Co^{60} photopeak which could be removed by merely washing the outside of the unopened cans. Obviously the sample had been contaminated by the irradiation agency. A cotton wipe obtained from the place of irradiation verified this conclusion.

A new batch of Co^{60} irradiated pork, noncontaminated, was obtained and counted in the steel room for 900 min. Except for the slight misalignment of the two spectra, it is clear that Co^{60} irradiation process did not cause increased gamma radioactivity in the sample.

Figure 6 shows similar results obtained from an eighty-five No. 2 can array of 8 Mev electron-irradiated pork. Ham, beef, chicken and bacon, irradiated with 5 megarads from Co^{60} or 8 and 11 Mev electrons, showed similar results. After subtracting the spectrum of a nonirradiated sample from one which had been irradiated, it was necessary to study statistically the "difference spectrum," which quite often could be negative rather than positive. If this unaccounted final residual spectrum was significant in terms of the sensitivity implied by the inherent experimental uncertainties, the excess was quantitated in terms of unknown nuclides expressed in equivalent microcuries of Ra^{226}. To do this, a radium source obtained from the Bureau of Standards was counted, and the entire spectrum was integrated over the energy

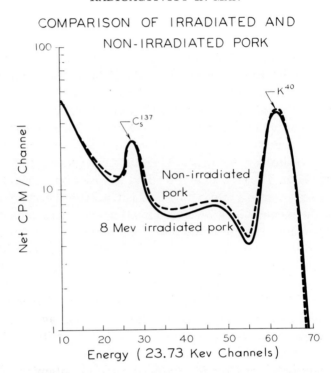

Figure 6. Spectra comparison of 8 Mev irradiated and nonirradiated pork.

range of 475 kev to 2.75 Mev. The residuals from stripped spectra were then multiplied by this radium calibration factor, when no well defined photopeaks were recognized. This technique of equating spectrum differences in terms of "radium equivalence" in a more rational method and can be thought of as evaluating the possible presence of unknown radionuclides. With "radium equivalence" the radiation is a complex mixture of gamma rays and there is Compton distribution associated with each. Such analysis of integral counting data is probably better than any arbitrarily chosen factor for converting counts per minute into hypothetical disintegrations per minute.

The samples showed no significant or recognizable photopeaks in the net spectrum, i.e., the resulting spectrum obtained after stripping the nonirradiated from the irradiated. The integrated residual spectrum was then converted to radium equivalence, and a value of 8.36 × 10⁻⁹ μc/cc. was obtained on the bacon sample. This is more than an order of magnitude below the maximum permissible concentration of unknown radionuclides in water given for unanalyzed samples by the International Commission on Radiological Protection. The calculation should not be taken for any other purpose than to show the significance which might be attached to a burden of a few counts per minute. It is obviously of no significance. It should be kept in mind that the realistic appraisal of the low level gamma counting method used in this study is not actually this sensitive. It would serve only to detect about 2 × 10⁻⁸ μc/cc. Possibly 10⁻⁷ is a more conservative figure. Another way to show the nonsignificance of a residual of a few counts per minute is to note that negative residuals of the same order of magnitude were frequently encountered. Thus, it may be said that the gamma analysis of Co⁶⁰ and low energy electron irradiated pork, ham, beef, chicken and bacon reveals no evidence of induced radioactivity.

For electron irradiation energies higher than 11.2 Mev, induced gamma activity was detected. Quantitative statements as to the radioactive nuclides to be found in food or tissue as a result of electron or photon irradiation are at best difficult to make, owing to the lack of precise knowledge pertaining to the atomic composition of food. Animal tissue, on a weight basis, is approximately 90 percent water, which in turn is 11 percent hydrogen. Approximately 1 in 5,000 natural hydrogen molecules is a deuterium molecule. Deuterium, which has a low photoneutron threshold, represents a fairly appreciable constituent of tissue. One may therefore expect radioactive nuclides to be formed by photoneutrons from deuterium. In the main, the threshold energy for photoneutron production is greater than about 8 Mev.

In order to reach the food, the irradiating beam must first pass through the can in which the food is sealed. It can therefore be expected that radioactivity will be induced in the can itself.

Figure 7 shows the results obtained after counting a 16 Mev electron-irradiated pork sample. Time zero was 130 hr. after ir-

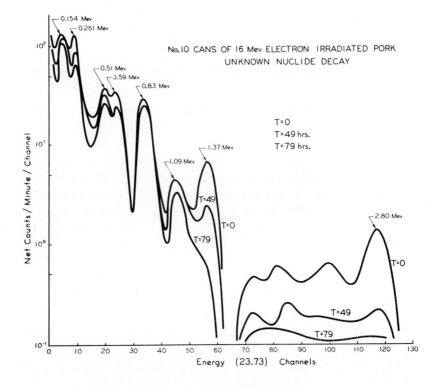

Figure 7. Net spectra of 16 Mev irradiated pork.

radiation. Irradiation energies of 12, 13 and 14 Mev were also analyzed, but only to the extent of observing that there were no induced photopeaks different from those observed in the 16 Mev irradiation. Because of the complexity of the spectrum, it was obvious that a series of spectra would have to be obtained to follow the decay of each photopeak to determine the half lives for identification purposes. Only 3 of 12 spectra taken are shown. In each instance the counting time was 400 min. This covered a total interval of 1,600 hr. after irradiation. Each photopeak was first considered as a single nuclide, and the decay was determined. The Comptons due to each higher energy photopeak had to be determined and subtracted prior to determining the decay. Figure 8 shows our conclusions as to the identification of the isotopes in high energy irradiation pork. To identify radioactive

16 Mev Electron Irradiated Pork Preliminary Identification

Energy (Mev)	Half-Life	No: cpm at T = O 2/12/61	Identification (? ?)
0.154	4.66±0.13 d	212.3±13.5	Rh-101m, Pt-193m
0.273	1.53±0.01 d	212.9± 1.7	Ba-133m
0.5	8.39±0.33 d	45.4± 1.75	Ag-106
0.59	11.11±0.05 d	72.6± 0.45	Nd-147, Ir-190
0.83	197.0 ±10.2 d	165.0± 0.70	
1.09	80.88±29.5 d	17.5± 2.8	Sc-46, Ta 182
1.38	19.72± 5.6 hr	7.1± 0.6	Na-24
2.78	15.37± 0.64hr	17.1± 0.5	Na-24

Figure 8. 16 Mev electron irradiated pork preliminary identification.

isotopes by gamma ray spectroscopy, one must consider not only the energy and decay characteristics, but also, and often more revealing, the feasibility of production under the prevailing conditions of irradiation. For example, before tagging a photopeak with a label according to its energy and half life, one must explain the presence or absence of other photopeaks from the same nuclide, the existence or nonexistence of daughter nuclides, the presence or absence of other nuclides which were transmitted by the same reaction from other stable isotopes of the parent, the existence or nonexistence of other nuclides transmitted from the parent by competing reactions and the availability of the proposed parent in the irradiated sample. All of these items were carefully considered before preparing this final list.

It is apparent that irradiation energies below approximately 12 Mev do not alter the radiation hazard of food from that which existed before irradiation. Above 12 Mev, and specifically at 16 Mev irradiation of pork with a dose of 5.6 megarad, activity is induced in a 90 lb. sample, which is equivalent to about 0.7 μgm. of Ra^{226}, 130 hr. after irradiation.

6

DETERMINATION OF BLOOD VOLUME DISTRIBUTION BY WHOLE BODY COUNTING

GUNNAR SEVELIUS, DANIEL R. PATRICK, BETTY O'CONNOR, ELAINE PATRICK AND BILL COLEMAN

Veterans Administration Hospital

Oklahoma City, Oklahoma

MODEL EXPERIMENTS show that volumes as low as 300 ml. may be determined with good accuracy.

We would like to report a whole body counting technique that can be used generally to estimate blood volume distribution in most portions of the body. The technique is fast, simple and atraumatic. Distribution changes may be followed during redistribution of the blood volume without re-injecting the tracer substance.

I would like to illustrate the principle by describing our experiments to investigate the accuracy and the limitations of the technique. On a table along an isodosic circular line with a radius of about 7½ ft., we placed glass beakers with equal amounts of equally concentrated solution of radioiodinated serum albumin.

The six containers were placed at intervals along this isodosic sector line in front of an uncollimated, but well shielded, scintillation detector containing a 5 by 5 in. plastic crystal. The counts were recorded on a scaler. First the counts were recorded for the radioactivity in all bottles. Then we shielded each bottle in turn with 1 in. of lead and registered the counts for the radioactivity in all bottles except the particular one being shielded. The percentage of counts excluded by the covered bottle was calculated. The percentage of radioactivity multiplied by the total volume of fluid in all bottles would yield the volume in the shielded container. The total volume of fluid was 6 liters, with each beaker containing 1 liter of radioactive fluid. The estimation of the volume in each container by radioisotope technique is shown in Table I. The percent deviations from 1,000 ml. yields an estimation of the accuracy of the technique.

TABLE I

Beaker	1	2	3	4	5	6
Known Volume	1000	1000	1000	1000	1000	1000
Calc. Volume	962	1014	998	1026	1010	960
% Deviation	−3.80	+1.01	−0.20	+1.03	+1.01	−4.00

In order to investigate how small a volume it would be possible to determine by this technique, we used different volumes of fluid in each container and again placed them at the same isodosic line and repeated the experiment. We found that volumes greater than 1,000 ml. could be determined with great accuracy, volumes 250 to 500 ml. with relatively good accuracy, and 100 ml. or less with no accuracy (Table II). We did not use any discriminator, and it is possible a greater accuracy could be achieved if

TABLE II

Beaker	1	2	3	4	5	5
Known Volume	1000	3000	2000	500	250	100
Calc. Volume	1058	3058	2020	536	300	170
% Deviation	+1.06	+1.03	+1.01	+6.72	+16.72	+41.18

we had used a pulse height analyzer. Despite no analyzer, the reproducibility of 3 min. counts for a source only double the background had only 3.5 percent deviation from the mean.

These model experiments illustrate the principle. Our first step is to determine the total blood volume by conventional method or radioisotope dilution. We thereafter place the subject along the isodosic line and make a whole body count. Next we shield the region of the body we are interested in with lead and determine the percentage of radioactivity excluded. The percentage of the traced blood excluded times the total blood volume yields the blood pool under the shielded area.

To place a person along an isodosic line caused some difficulty initially. The patient is placed on his left side with his back and knees along the line, letting the isodosic line pass through his bone structure from the head through the vertebral column

and through the long bones of the legs. The patient was lying
on his left side so the liver would be in his superior flank and
could be outlined. The tracer substance used was 200 μc of radioiodinated serum albumin; the counting time, 3 min. To shield
the different regions of the body we used lead bricks, but I am
sure there could be an easier way of doing the job. After a whole
body count was recorded, we shielded the head, then the thorax
and then the legs below the knees in order to estimate the volume
of blood in each region.

We found the blood pool in the chest was 40 ± 2 percent
(Table III). This agrees with values for central blood volume

TABLE III

	Whole Body Counting	Dye Dilution
Thorax	41.2%	40 %
Head	6.3%	2.7%
Leg (Resting)	9.8%	11.2%
Leg (After Exercise)	12.5%	

reports by Nowy, who reports a mean value in normals of 45 percent. His value was derived by dye dilution with injection of the
tracer in one arm and sampling from the opposite. Such a technique would include the volume of blood in the upper arms. Nylin, using the same technique but with labeled erythrocytes,
showed a mean value of 35 percent; Eich, using iodinated albumin, got 42 percent for corresponding blood pool.

Not many reports are available on the blood pool in the
legs. Karpeles and Huff, using standard and surface counting,
got 11.2 percent of total blood volume in both lower legs, which
agrees very well with our results. We found an increase of blood
pool in the legs after exercise from 9.8 percent to 12.5 percent.

For the head, there are no reports on blood pool comparable
with our figures. Nylin has for the brain a blood pool of mean
2.7 percent, but this is for the brain only. Twice that, as we report for the total head, we do not feel is out of line.

SUMMARY

A new technique for determination of blood volume distribution in the body is reported. The technique yields values for

chest and legs which compare with those determined by older more conventional methods. We found the blood pool in the chest constitutes 40 percent, the blood volume of the head 6 percent, the blood in the lower legs 10 percent of the total blood volume.

REFERENCES

1. Nylin, G., and Celander, H.: Determination of blood volume in the heart and lungs and the cardiac output through the injection of radiophosphorus. *Circulation, 1*:76, 1960.
2. Warren, G. V.: Central blood volume as a factor in the regulation of the circulation, abstracted. *Circulation, 181*:793, 1958.
3. Nowy, H., and Frings, H. D.: Correlation between output and central blood volume in persons with normal hearts. Z. *Kreislaufforsch. 47*:986, 1958.
4. Karpeles, L. M., and Huff, R. L.: Blood volume of representative portion of the musculoskeletal system in man. *Circulat. Res., 3*:483, 1955.
5. Eich, Robert H., Chaffee, W. R., and Chodos, R. B.: Measurement of central blood volume by external monitoring. *Circulat. Res. 9*:626, 1961.

7

A PROGRESS REPORT ON THE MEASUREMENT OF PLUTONIUM IN VIVO

B. T. Taylor and J. Rundo

Atomic Energy Research Establishment
Berkshire, England

INTRODUCTION

SCINTILLATION GAMMA RAY spectrometers using crystals of NaI(Tl) may be used to measure the human body content of almost any radionuclide which emits penetrating gamma rays at a level below the maximum permissible for occupational exposure (1). A notable exception to this is the case of Pu^{239}, the gamma ray emission from which is far too trivial to be detectable even when this toxic material is present *in vivo* at ten times the maximum permissible level of 0.04 μc. It is necessary instead to detect the uranium L x rays which have an intensity of 4 percent per α-disintegration and energies 13.6, 16.9 and 20.2 kev. The x rays are strongly absorbed, the half value thickness in soft tissue being about 0.6 cm., and in bone about 0.03 cm. It would appear that skeletally deposited plutonium is unlikely to be measured via its radiation external to the body. The problem is then the determination of the content of puncture wounds or of specific organs, such as the lungs. Techniques for the measurement of plutonium puncture wounds have been described by Roesch and Baum (2) and by Gale, Peaple and Richards (3), and remarkable sensitivity can be achieved. We have been investigating the possibility of measuring plutonium in human lungs, and this paper reports the progress we have made up to mid-1962. It is noteworthy that the maximum permissible lung burden for insoluble Pu^{239} is only 0.016 μc; this value, which is not included in the recommendations, of Committee II of the I.C.R.P., can be derived from the appropriate data by conventional methods.

There are two possible types of detector for this work: the thin sodium iodide crystal and the gas-filled proportional counter. Sodium iodide crystals as thin as 0.025 cm. have an efficiency of greater than 90 percent at these energies. Comparable efficiencies can be obtained with proportional counters by a suitable choice of filling gas, counter dimensions and pressure. A large detector area is clearly desirable, and this has generally been easier to achieve with proportional counter windows than with thin sodium iodide crystals. The latter present certain difficulties in efficient light transfer to the photomultiplier cathode when manufactured with diameters of more than about 5 in. We chose the proportional counter for our work because we felt that the superior energy resolution would be useful in the interpretation of measurements and because many large proportional counters with very low background counting rates have been used in

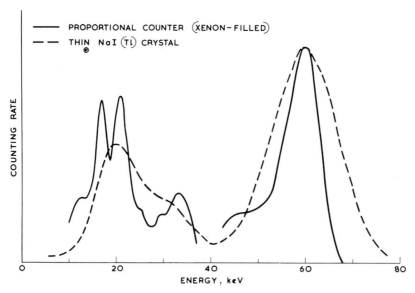

Figure 1. Spectra of x and gamma rays from Am^{241} as measured with a thin crystal of NaI(Tl) and with a small xenon-filled proportional counter.

radiocarbon dating. The improvement in energy resolution with the proportional counter is illustrated by the spectra (Fig. 1) of the 60 kev gamma ray and neptunium L x rays emitted by Am^{241}

as detected by a thin sodium iodide crystal and by a small xenon-filled proportional counter with beryllium window. The ability to resolve the three L x rays together with the large differences in the absorption coefficients in tissue at the three energies means that an effective depth estimation may be possible from the relative peak areas.

PROPORTIONAL COUNTER AND ANTICOINCIDENCE SYSTEM

Figure 2. Proportional counter (P1) for measuring Pu^{239} *in vivo*.

The counter (Fig. 2) is constructed from a lucite cylinder, 15 cm. long with an internal diameter of 14 cm. A thin film of aluminum is evaporated on the inner surface to form the cathode with a connection through the wall to an external earth. The central wire of 0.0025 cm. diameter Inconel is fixed at one end through a lucite end plate to the high voltage plug. The other end assembly consists of a lucite window and support for the central wire. Both ends are attached to the cylinder with screws, and the window is demountable. With a window thickness of 0.15 cm. lucite, 80 percent of the 13.6 kev x rays are transmitted, while any K^{40} β-particles emerging from the body are largely absorbed. The curves in Figure 3 demonstrate the differences in absorption

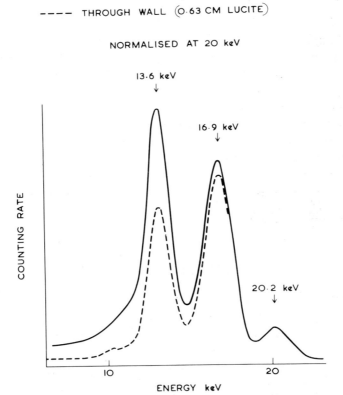

239Pu SPECTRA WITH PROPORTIONAL COUNTER

Figure 3. Spectra of L x rays from Pu[239] measured with counter P1.

at the three x ray energies by quite small thicknesses of absorber, in this case the 0.15 cm. window and the 0.63 cm. wall. There is an obvious application to the measurement of Pu^{239} in wounds. Lucite was chosen as the main constructional material as it has been reported to be free from radioactive contaminants present in many metals (4). Metals also emit characteristic x rays excited by cosmic radiation which may contribute to the background.

The performance of the counter has been studied using it as a flow counter with a mixture of 90 percent argon plus 10 percent methane. Under these conditions the calculated efficiencies for a 15 cm. path length are 58 percent, 34 percent and 21 percent for the 13.6 kev, 16.9 kev and 20.2 kev x rays.

Anticoincidence methods have been used to eliminate contributions to the background resulting mainly from the flux of cosmic μ mesons. At sea level this flux is about 1 min.$^{-1}$ cm. $^{-2}$ of horizontally projected area. Originally we used a ring of G.M. counters, but this system has several disadvantages in this application, and we now use a well-shaped plastic scintillator shield viewed by five photomultipliers. The thickness of phosphor is 5 cm. on top and about 6.5 cm. at the sides of the well. The connector from the proportional counter to preamplifier passes through a 1 cm. diameter hole in the phosphor. After further amplification, the counter pulses are fed into a 100 channel pulse amplitude analyser of the Hutchinson and Scarrot type. Pulses from the phosphor are amplified and formed into 50 μ sec. square pulses of sufficient amplitude to operate the anticoincidence circuit of the analyser.

COUNTER PERFORMANCE

The energy resolution of the counter was determined using a source of Sr^{85} which emits Rb K x rays of energy 13.4 kev. The best value we observed was 11.0 percent, which is close to the theoretical minimum of about 10 per cent based on the statistical fluctuations in the number of initial electrons generated by each photon and number of ion pairs. To obtain this resolution it was necessary to remove impurities from the gas by passing it through a trap of activated charcoal cooled to $-78°C$. These impurities probably arise from the plastic flow tubes which have been used. In routine use a resolution of about 15 percent was obtained.

The initial investigations of the counter background were made in small lead shields 10 cm. thick. A decrease of 10 counts per minute (cpm) in the total background was observed when an additional 0.3 cm. steel was placed around the counter. This was probably due to the absorption in the steel of lead L x rays excited by cosmic radiation, the iron K x rays of 6.4 kev being largely absorbed in the counter wall.

Using the anticoincidence array of G.M. counters, the μ-meson component of the background was determined as 175 cpm (counter axis horizontal) at a barometric pressure of 760 mm. Hg, and it showed a slope of -2% per cm. Hg. The usefulness of obtaining pressure correlations was shown when the anti-coincidence background was examined. In the upper curve of Figure 4, this is plotted as a function of the barometric pressure, and it shows a slope of about -6% per cm. Hg, which we interpret as being due to the detection of a neutron component by proton recoil from the wall of the counter or from the methane. The cosmic neutrons are mainly responsible for the production of secondary neutrons in materials, and both vary by -10% per cm. Hg. We have largely eliminated the neutron component of the background by the use of the plastic phosphor anticoincidence shield. Backgrounds obtained using pure argon, however, are lower than with the usual argon plus methane mixture, which may be due to the detection of a small residual neutron component in the methane, rather than to the presence of C^{14} in the methane which is derived from dead carbon. The lowest background values achieved in the energy range 10 to 22.5 kev are 1.44 ± 0.04 cpm with argon and 1.79 ± 0.04 cpm with argon plus methane. The background variations using argon were not statistically significant, but with argon plus methane there may be a small variation with barometric pressure, which is difficult to determine at this level (lower curve of Figure 4). The lowest integral background above 4 kev using argon was 3.71 cpm, or 1.65 cpm per liter of counter volume. This compares favorably

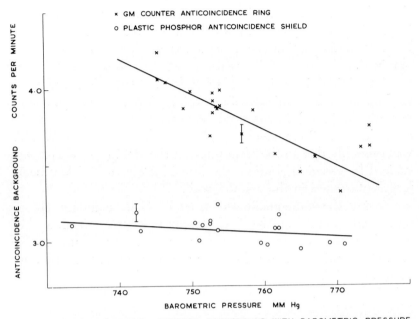

VARIATION OF PROPORTIONAL COUNTER BACKGROUND WITH BAROMETRIC PRESSURE

Figure 4. Variation of anticoincidence background of counter P1 with barometric pressure. For the GM anticoincidence shield the threshold was
about 6 kev, while for the plastic phosphor shield, values of the background
in the energy range 4 to 28 kev are plotted.

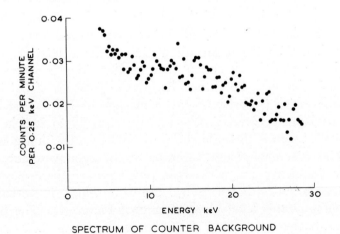

SPECTRUM OF COUNTER BACKGROUND

Figure 5. Spectrum of background of counter P1 in a small lead shield
(4,000 min. counting time).

with the values reported for other low background counters, and a reduction by a factor of two would appear to be difficult to achieve. The spectrum of the background in a small shield is shown in Figure 5; the counting rate in the energy range 4 to 28 kev was 2.79 cpm, and at this low level good statistical precision is difficult to achieve even in a measurement of 4,000 min.

Background counting rates in a shield large enough to accommodate a human subject have been higher. The background spectrum plotted as the lower histogram in Figure 6 represents a total rate of 5.18 cpm, of which 2.53 cpm were in the energy range 10 to 22.5 kev.

Using a standardized source of Pu^{239} at a distance of 10 cm. from the counter window, the response was 910 cpm per μc Pu^{239}. There is some uncertainty in this value due to the presence in the standard of some Am^{241} and Pu^{238}, both of which emit low energy x rays.

RESPONSE FROM HUMAN SUBJECTS

We have not had an opportunity yet to measure a subject with a lung burden of Pu^{239}. A few measurements on normal subjects have been made to study the response of the counter to radiations from K^{40} and Cs^{137}. The two subjects had similar K and Cs^{137} contents of about 145 gm. and 6mμc, respectively. Measurements were made with the proportional counter over the chest of the subjects. One of these spectra is plotted as the upper histogram of Figure 6. In the energy range 10 to 22.5 kev, the mean increase in the background due to the presence of the subject was 1.9 ± 0.2 cpm. A phantom of distilled water in the subject position produced no significant change in the background.

CALIBRATION METHODS

The difficulties of calibration for Pu^{239} in the lungs are mainly due to the high absorption of the x rays in body tissues, differences in chest wall thickness between individuals and our lack of knowledge of the actual distribution of the inhaled material in the lungs.

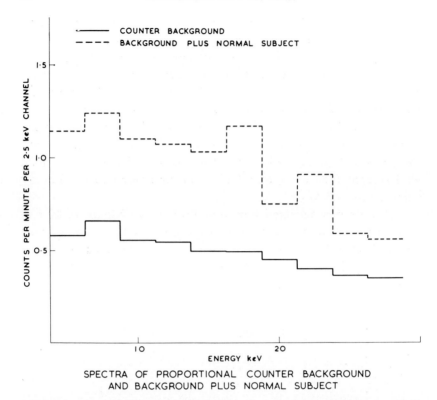

SPECTRA OF PROPORTIONAL COUNTER BACKGROUND
AND BACKGROUND PLUS NORMAL SUBJECT

Figure 6. Spectra of background counter Pl in a large shield and of the
total response with the counter close to the chest of a normal subject.

Two methods of calibration have been reported by Roesch and
Palmer (5), using an animal subject and a "Remcal" phantom;
good agreement between these was found. We investigated the
possibilities of two different methods both involving human subjects. The first makes use of the emission of thorium L x rays by
U^{235}. The energies of these x rays are 13.0 kev, 15.9 kev and 19.0
kev, slightly lower than the uranium L x rays. The determination
of lung burdens of U^{235} is possible with the use of large sodium
iodide crystals by detection of the 186 kev and 90 kev quanta.
If the relative intensities of x ray emission of U^{235} and Pu^{239} are
known, then a subject with a measured U^{235} burden may be used
as an equivalent source of Pu^{239}. We made a comparison of
standardized sources of Pu^{239} and U^{235} at a distance of 10 cm.

from the window of the proportional counter. With our counter, 1 mg. of U^{235} gives about the same x ray counting rate as 0.105 μc Pu^{239} when both sources are counted through 2.54 cm. lucite.

Recently, four proportional counter measurements were made on a subject with a lung burden of 0.5 mg. U^{235}. This content was determined with a 9 by 6 in. sodium iodide crystal placed under the mid-point of the sternum of the supine subject. Three of the proportional counter measurements were made with the window close to the chest, two opposite the right lung and one opposite the left lung. The other measurement was at the back, opposite the right lung. Each measurement was 50 min. long. In order to reduce the scatter due to statistical fluctuations, the counting rates observed in all four measurements were summed (Fig. 7). In all four measurements the observed count-

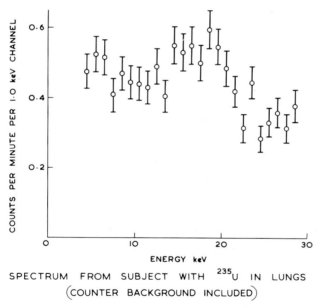

SPECTRUM FROM SUBJECT WITH ^{235}U IN LUNGS
(COUNTER BACKGROUND INCLUDED)

Figure 7. Sum of four spectra (including counter background) obtained from the lungs of a subject containing U^{235}.

ing rate in the energy range of 14 to 21 kev was higher than in the range of 7 to 14 kev, the maximum being at about 19 kev. In the spectra from normal subjects the reverse was found. In order to obtain the net counting rate due to U^{235}, it is necessary to estimate the contribution not from U^{235} in the energy range of 14 to 21 kev. This was attempted by two methods. The first is by comparison with spectra from normal subjects in the same energy range. The observed rates were 3.74 ± 0.16 cpm for the U^{235} subject and 3.11 ± 0.14 cpm for the normal subjects, indicating a rate of 0.63 ± 0.21 cpm from the U^{235}. The second method involves a prediction of the contribution not from U^{235} in the 14 to 21 kev range from the observed counting rate in the 7 to 14 kev range. The justification of the method is based on measurements of the response of the counter to phantoms containing K^{40} and Cs^{137} in solution. These spectra have shown that the counting rate in the 14 to 21 kev range is 10 percent lower than in the 7 to 14 kev range. The method does not involve any prediction of absolute counting rates from phantom measurements, which we have not yet attempted. The net U^{235} counting rate obtained by this method is 1.06 ± 0.22 cpm.

From these results it is clear that at this level of U^{235} content, which is already about two maximum permissible lung burdens, we cannot calibrate our equipment accurately. If the sensitivity of the detector was increased sufficiently, however, the method might be of value. Since the U^{235} content in the subject we have studied was equivalent to about 55 mμc of Pu^{239}, this may be regarded as a fairly realistic estimate of our minimum detectable activity for a counting time of 100 min. This is about $3\frac{1}{2}$ times the maximum permissible lung burden of Pu^{239}.

A second possible method of calibration is by the inhalation by volunteer subjects of mock plutonium, emitting x rays of energy similar to those of the uranium L x rays in the appropriate intensity ratio. The mixture we envisage consists of three isotopes:

    Sr^{85} (half life 65 days) emitting 13.4 kev
  Rb K x-rays and 0.51 Mev gamma rays,
    Mo^{93} (half life >2 years) which decays by
  electron capture, emitting 16.6 kev Nb K x
  rays,

and

    Cd^{109} (half life 470 days) which decays by
  electron capture, emitting 22.0 kev Ag K x rays.

The proportions of the three isotopes having been adjusted to produce the required relative x ray intensities, the lung content after inhalation can be estimated from measurements of the 0.51 Mev quanta from the Sr^{85}. The isotopes will need to be incorporated into insoluble particles of suitable size. An advantage of this method is that much higher x ray intensities may be achieved, while avoiding large radiation doses to the lungs, since the energy emissions are quite low and the half lives relatively short. One possible disadvantage is that the energy of the Ag K x ray at 22.0 kev is 1.8 kev higher than the corresponding L x ray of uranium. The difference in the linear absorption coefficients in muscle for these energies is nearly 20 percent and there is a difference by a factor of two in the transmission through about 4 cm. of tissue.

This difficulty might be overcome by the use of 17 day Pd^{103} (which emits Rh K x rays of energy 20.2 kev), but the short half life would introduce some complications. Another disadvantage of this method is that the distribution of the mock plutonium in the lung may be quite different from that of plutonium because of the different densities. A similar criticism may be leveled at the U^{235} method because of differences in particle sizes of U_3O_8 and PuO_2.

CONCLUSIONS

Although we are still some way from a system capable of routine measurements at levels around or below the maximum permissible lung burden, we believe that a full exploitation of the method may prove of great value. Extensive further studies of the uniquely difficult problems of calibration are essential before much reliance can be placed on estimated lung burdens.

REFERENCES

1. Mehl, J., and Rundo, J.: Paper presented at Health Physics Society Meeting, Chicago, June, 1962.
2. Roesch, W. C., and Baum, J. W.: Proc. 2nd U. N. Conf. P.U.A.E., 23:142, 1958.
3. Gale, H. J., Peaple, L. H. J., and Richards, J. E.: Atomic Energy Establishment Report AERE-M 595, 1960.

4. De Voe, J. R.: Radioactive contamination of materials used in scientific research. Publication 895, U. S. National Academy of Sciences, National Research Council, 1961.

5. Roesch, W. C., and Palmer, H. E.: Paper presented at Symposium on Biology of the Transuranic Elements, Hanford, Washington, May, 1962.

DISCUSSION

Chairman: CHARLES E. MILLER

Argonne National Laboratory

Argonne, Illinois

ALAIN LANSIART: Did you use a point source in measuring the spectra from the standard source of plutonium, and if so, have you looked at possible variations in pulse height as you moved the source across the window?

JOHN RUNDO: We did use a point source. We have moved the source across the window. There was not much falling off either in pulse height or in counting rate until we came fairly close to the sides. Counting rate, of course, fell off more than pulse height did, which was only perhaps 5 per cent down when we were almost at the edge.

ALAIN LANSIART: When you use xenon, is the background higher than with argon?

JOHN RUNDO: We haven't yet used argon. I think this is going to be our next step. We anticipate that commercially available xenon would give a higher background because of the content of about 1 per cent crypton, but we are proposing to have our xenon purified by gas chromatography to reduce the crypton about, we hope, 100 times.

HAROLD MAY: In view of the somewhat unrealistic attitude of the Surgeon General about any radioactivity detectable being too much, I can understand why Mr. Weiland could finally include the activity in the cans as well as in the meat. I wonder if he will identify the activities he tabulated in his slide as to which were in the meat and which were in the cans?

GEORGE R. MENEELY: Before Mr. Weiland comments, it is not the attitude of the Surgeon General. The mission of the Surgeon General in this case is to determine the wholesomeness of the food, and wholesomeness of food is defined as food which will meet the requirements of the Food and Drug Administration.

RAYMOND L. WEILAND: We did remove several samples of food

from the cans, then put it in cans and counted it again. Certain photo-peaks disappeared, showing that some of the radioactivity was in the cans and other radioactivity was in the food. I can't say which isotopes appeared where.

CHAIRMAN CHARLES E. MILLER: Did you ever count the same sample before and after irradiation?

RAYMOND L. WEILAND: No, we did not. We had one ton of each food prepared before this investigation started, and we used the food at random. We mixed the cans thoroughly, and we felt each sample repre-sented the entire batch.

ROBLEY EVANS: Did I understand Mr. Weiland to say that some of his results he reported as radium equivalent?

RAYMOND L. WEILAND: Yes.

ROBLEY EVANS: May I make a suggestion, then, that you call these instead radium gamma-ray equivalent. There are several reasons for this. You will save yourself some pain at the hands of administrators or scientists who are not reading carefully. You really are measuring only gamma rays. You do not wish to imply that the toxicity of the induced radioactivity is comparable with that of radium. You have not measured any beta ray-induced activities, only gamma rays.

RAYMOND L. WEILAND: Thank you. We will add that to the manu-script before it is published.

O. M. MEREDITH: Mr. Weiland, what percentage of the radio-activity was removed when you removed the food from the can and counted it separately?

RAYMOND L. WEILAND: A factor of about 2 or 3. About half of the activity was on the can and about half in the food.

JOSEF BROZEK: Dr. Sevelius, would you care to enlarge on your studies on the experimentally induced changes in the blood distribution?

GUNNAR SEVELIUS: We eventually plan to do detailed studies on the effect of tilting on the blood volume. You have to tilt the person side-ways, because the counter needs to follow the table. We used just what we had in the laboratory, without going into other expenses, to see if it would be feasible to use this technique to study blood volume distribution.

It is a good, simple technique, is fast and atraumatic, and you can re-peat it for studying tilting or shock-induced redistribution of the blood volume. The accuracy may be improved by having a pulse height analyzer and getting the load background. We had a background of about .003, and the whole body counts were about 8,000 with 200 μc. We used $7\frac{1}{2}$ ft. as the distance to the counter so the geometry factor for different portions of the body would even out. The person needed to bend his body a little bit so that the central portion of the body did not have too much emphasis.

We found that the best way is to have the back to the counter. The person can bend his body easier, and the belly will not stick up so much. One of the most significant things is how to place the body along an isodosic line. If you do not have an even distribution in the whole body count and you place the person in a chair, I think you may have false conclusions. It is better to place him on his side along an isodosic line.

ALEXANDER REMENCHICK: Dr. Sevelius, I object to the term "blood volume." The only thing you have done in your experiments is to show how accurately you can measure the volume of a beaker. You haven't presented any data which indicates how accurately you can measure the volume of a mammal. I think this would involve at least doing your experimental study and sacrificing the animal and draining the animal of its blood volume.

Further, I do not think you are justified in comparing the numbers that you get with the numbers that you get with dye studies. There are numerous theoretical and practical objections to the use of dyes.

GUNNAR SEVELIUS: I agree. We cannot draw any direct conclusion on blood volume studies from this little experiment.

However, I think the dye dilution technique is an accurate technique to measure volume. We got figures, the means of which agree with those with dye dilution techniques. The mean would indicate that the technique should be feasible for further evaluation in dog or human experiments.

ALEXANDER REMENCHIK: I hope you come to our presentation tomorrow about the problems of interpretation of numbers that come out of whole body counters.

WILHELM VON DÖBELN: Concerning the figures you gave on the distribution of the blood with thorax 41 percent, and head 10 percent and the rest 43 percent, how do you define separating lines between thorax and abdomen, and do you refer that to the respiratory phase when there is a shift?

GUNNAR SEVELIUS: You couldn't do as sensitive an examination as defining the blood volume directly to the dye value. That is impossible with this technique. But you can get a general distribution. Re-examination would show the rearrangement in the blood volume. You do not have much radiation coming in from other media because you cover close to the monitored region.

WILHELM VON DÖBELN: I wonder where you put your screen. That must be referred to some defined point on the body.

GUNNAR SEVELIUS: We kept out the thorax by radio-percussion and outlined it with a line of ink, then with lead breaks along that line. It is amazing how close we got.

CHAIRMAN CHARLES E. MILLER: What was the size of the crystal?

GUNNAR SEVELIUS: It was 5 by 5 in.

CHAIRMAN CHARLES E. MILLER: You were just looking at the total spectrum?

GUNNAR SEVELIUS: Yes.

CHAIRMAN CHARLES E. MILLER: So you did have rays for other parts of the body scattering down and scattering out the parts?

GUNNAR SEVELIUS: Yes.

CHAIRMAN CHARLES E. MILLER: If you worked strictly with the counting rates in the photopeaks, then you improved the results.

GUNNAR SEVELIUS: Yes.

CHAIRMAN CHARLES E. MILLER: The plastic phosphor made a very poor arrangement.

GUNNAR SEVELIUS: It was not photopeak you worked on.

CHAIRMAN CHARLES E. MILLER: I think that technique can be improved.

ROBERT J. EPSTEIN: Dr. Rundo, would you make a few remarks about the improvement in background counting rate provided by the anticoincidence ring around your proportional counter in the energy spectrum, where you would expect counts from plutonium. Isn't it true that most of the 175 counts per minute would have produced a pulse in the counter far larger than those from the plutonium?

JOHN RUNDO: The spectrum of the background without any anti-coincidence showed a pronounced peak at 13 kev. This is fairly close to what one calculates for a minimal analyzing particle passing through 15 cm. of argon at atmospheric pressure, and so the spectrum looks much like the Compton distribution from the plastic phosphor and gamma ray. You have fairly flat continuing energies rising to a little peak at about 13 kev and then trailing off sharply at 13 kev. This is just the place where one is interested in getting background. It is not like sodium iodide, where the peak pulses are much bigger than the x-ray energies one is looking for.

SESSION III, SEPTEMBER 5

INSTRUMENTATION, TECHNIQUE and CALIBRATION, Continued

Chairman: ROBLEY D. EVANS

8
EVALUATION OF A WATER SHIELD WHOLE BODY COUNTER[1]

Richard E. Peterson, Eugene V. Weiner and William S. Cook, Jr.

State University of Iowa College of Medicine, and
Veterans Administration Hospital
Iowa City, Iowa

WE WANTED a whole body counter in order to measure body potassium rapidly and to study the metabolism of tracer doses of radionuclides. In 1960, after considering many materials, we decided to use a water shield.

Sievert, in 1951, used water from the River Thames for shielding his ionization chamber apparatus because its radioactivity was several times lower than that of tap water in Stockholm (1). Later the Finsen Laboratory scientists in Copenhagen used water for shielding their human ionization chamber apparatus (2). More recently, they have built a shielded gamma spectrometer enclosure using processed water. In 1957, workers from the Radioactivity Center at Massachusetts Institute of Technology reported their studies of a different enclosure for measuring radioactivity in humans (3). In their efforts, they included studies in a swimming pool and found that the background did not change appreciably with water thickness greater than 4 ft. They noted that the background obtained in water, even though its contamination is 10 to 100 times lower, was not a great deal less than in steel. They felt that water tanks could be fabricated for roughly the same price as steel enclosures. They concluded that until the inherent activity in crystals and phototubes is greatly reduced, one could not gain much benefit from the reduced contamination of the water. They built a steel room. In 1961 a

[1] Supported by the Veterans Administration Medical Research Program and U. S. Public Health Service.

water-shielded low background laboratory built at the Atomic
Weapons Research Establishment, Aldermaston, England, was
described (4). This laboratory is a cylindrical room 18 ft. in
diameter with 6 ft. of water around the sides, 7 ft. of water over
the ceiling (total 60,000 gallons) and 3 to 12 in. of steel as floor.
The evaluation was that this shield is better than 12 in. of steel
shielding for gas proportional counters and equal to this amount
of steel for scintillation counters. Additional water shields for
low background facilities were reported on by Mehl and Rundo
(5).

DESCRIPTION

For our final shield design (Fig. 1) we chose a minimum

Figure 1. Shield under construction. Two workmen are standing on maze
passage and inner room.

thickness of 5 ft. of water to assure the maximum absorption of
external gamma activity, and because this thickness plus the tank
wall would be equivalent in mass to 8 in. of steel. The counting
enclosure is 7 ft. in diameter and 8 ft. high in order to facilitate

a wide number of detector configurations. The inner room and passage is made of selected uncontaminated ¼ in. steel joined together by arc welding in an inert gas atmosphere to avoid the contamination of welding flux. The entrance passage is a spiral maze to avoid the expense of a shielded door and claustrophobia problems. This also permits two-way visual communication via full-length mirrors in lieu of closed circuit television monitors. These requirements dictated that the water tank should be 22½ ft. in diameter and 19 ft. deep. It was decided, because of space requirements and construction costs, that the tank top should be 2 ft. underground with an entrance into the Veterans Administration Hospital basement. The outer wall of the water tank is made of corrugated steel, ¼ in. thick with exterior coating of coal tar-epoxy 0.014 in. thick and cathodic grounds at four points. The interior of the water tank is protected from the high corrosive action of pure water by five coats (total 9 to 10 mils) of a vinyl chloride polymer lacquer containing titanium dioxide pigment, on top of two coats of modified vinyl copolymer resin priming lacquer.

After hydrostatic testing of the tank with tap water, it was filled with once-distilled water obtained by taking condensate from the hospital boilers and cooling it to room temperature by passage through 100 ft. of ½ in. diameter copper tubing out-of-doors during a typical Iowa winter "cold snap." When the tank was two-thirds full of distilled water, circulation through an ion exchanger was begun. Thereafter the water was circulated at the rate of 500 gal. per hour in order to purify the water to the maximum extent. The full tank contains 60,000 gal. or 228,000 liters of distilled water (specific resistance greater than 5 megohms per centimeter).

A steel shield used in part of our evaluation is included in the facilities. This laminated shield is constructed of 1 in. thick steel plates (Blanchard ground to a tolerance of 0.001 in.) stacked and bolted to tie bolts anchored in the floor (Fig. 2). This provided 10 in. of steel in all directions around a cylindrical chamber 15 in. in diameter and 15 in. high.

A thallium-activated NaI crystal 5 in. thick and 9 in. in diameter was our primary detector. It was encased in a 32 mil thick

Figure 2. Laminated steel shield.

copper can with a 20 mil aluminum back cap window. The crystal is observed by four debased Dumont 6363 photomultipliers. The detector spectrum (Fig. 3) was taken within the steel shield previously described with ⅛ in. low background lead surrounding the crystal. This spectrum is the basis for stating both that the crystal is relatively free of radioactivity and that there is clearly a thorium contaminant in the detector assembly and probably in the crystal itself. There is a broad peak from 3.2 to 3.8 Mev, probably due to alpha and gamma interactions being

DETECTOR

NaI crystal 9 diameter x 5" thick

with 32 mil Cu can

& 20 mil Al back cap window

observed by 4 Dumont 6363   debased photomultipliers

sensitive volume 5200 cm^3

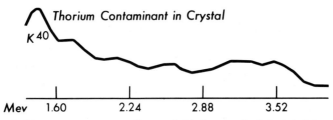

Figure 3. Detector spectrum. Integral background, 0.1–2.0 Mev due to detector assembly, is <585 cpm. By using quartz photomultipliers this should be reduced to <485 cpm.

SHIELD ACTIVITY AS SHOWN BY ADDING 1/8" LEAD

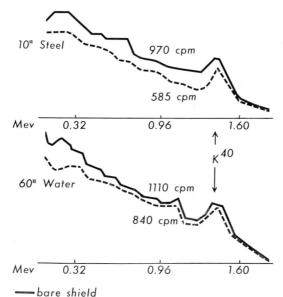

—— bare shield
- - - 1/8" lead added

Figure 4. Background spectra in steel and water shields.

DETECTOR SUPPORT

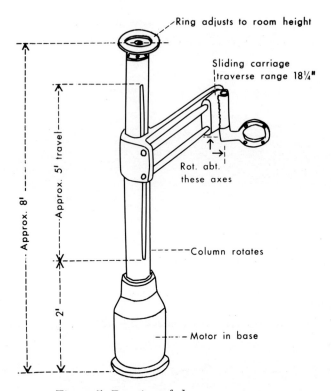

Figure 5. Drawing of detector support.

summed. The 2.62 and subsidiary thorium peaks are also detectable. Figure 4 shows the spectrum from 0.1 to 2.0 Mev both with and without the $\frac{1}{8}$ in. lead surrounding the crystal in our steel shield and in the water shield. These spectra provided the first evidence that the water shield had detectably less K^{40} than the steel shield by the relative effects of the same shield mass on this photopeak.

Our detector support (Fig. 5) has considerable flexibility in that we can move our detector up and down over a distance of 5 ft. and rotate the crystal to all angles within the 18 in. radius of the carriage arm. The support is fixed in position by turning a nut which raises the ring until it is wedged to the ceiling, so that shifting the support is easily accomplished.

While the water shield was filled with tap water, short lived gamma emitters were introduced to observe the efficiency with which shield radioactivity was detected (Table I). After the tank was filled with once-distilled water, the background was

TABLE I
ACTIVITY ADDED TO WATER SHIELD MASS

	I^{131}		Na^{24}	
Activity added	272 µc	272 µc	8.13 µc	8.13 µc
Dilution, pc/Liter	1193	1193	36	36
Peak width	160 Kv	240 Kv	140 Kv	180 Kv
Energy observed, Mev	0.36	0.64	1.4	2.8
Fraction of decay scheme	85%	15%	100%	100%
Thickness of water, added to ¼″ steel to reduce to 10% cts.	7.5″	10″	15″	21″
Approx. distance to crystal	48″	48″	48″	48″
% of total volume contributing majority of counts	2.3	3.3*	5.4	8.5+
Total cts./minute	4890	473	200	145
Cts./min./µc	782	53	4555	2098
Total net counts	14,233 cpm		2353 cpm	
Total counts /µc above background	*1585 cpm/µc		+34,050 cpm/µc	

measured at intervals as the water circulated through the ion exchanger. Figure 6 illustrates the changes seen in the specific resistance of the tank water. After the first regeneration and the second cycle was started, a definite decrease in background was noted. A sample of the resin was removed from the ion exchanger and counted in the steel shield with the result that the spectrum of Rh^{102} was observed. No further decline in background was noted with further circulation through the ion exchanger, nor does background increase when the ion exchanger is not used. However, when the ion exchanger is excluded, the specific resistance does decrease. In observing the water through the manhole, there is a slight turbidity, but no significant defects in the lacquer surface. Culture of the tank water has revealed a mixed flora of water bacteria even with the ion exchanger maintaining a specific

TANK WATER SPECIFIC RESISTANCE

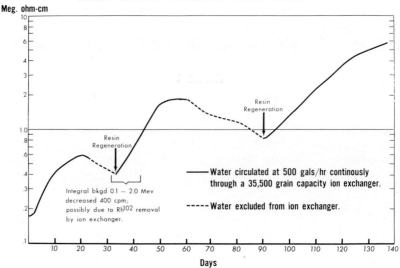

Figure 6. Tank water specific resistance.

resistance in excess of 3 meg ohm-cm. It is not yet known whether there is any significant movement of ions through the vinyl chloride polymer lacquer film.

COMPARISON

Most of our evaluation is based on integral count rates between 0.1 and 2.0 Mev and between 4.0 and 5.0 Mev. The first energy range was chosen because it encompasses the range of medical interest, and the 4.0 to 5.0 Mev range was chosen as an index of cosmic ray contributions. Figure 7 shows how these two different parts of the spectrum are influenced by different shielding. Spectrum A in this figure was taken 30 in. on top of the earth over the tank. It is of interest to note that the background within the water shield is less than 1 percent of that in the hospital basement. The changes in the 4.0 to 5.0 Mev region make it clear that the water walls provide 25 percent of the shielding in this part of the spectrum, and that only three fourths of the cosmic ray contribution comes through the ceiling.

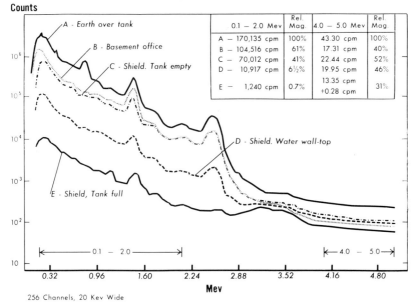

BACKGROUND
200 min. intervals

Figure 7. Water shield backgrounds.

TABLE II

Comparison of Shielding Effectiveness
(Using 9″ x 5″ NaI Crystal)

	10″ Steel		60″ Water and Tank (Equivalent Mass to 8″ Steel)	
Chamber Volume	1.5 cu. ft.		308 cu. ft.	
Chamber Surface Area	7.3 sq. ft.		252 cu. ft.	
Incident				
	0.1-2.0 Mev	*4.0-5.0 Mev*	*0.1-2.0 Mev*	*4.0-5.0 Mev*
Radiation	104,500 cpm	17.8 cpm	70,000*cpm	22.4 cpm
Bkgd. Bare	970 cpm	10.6 cpm	1,110 cpm	13.3 cpm
Bkgd. ⅛″ Pb	585 cpm	9.0 cpm	840 cpm	12.0 cpm
Minimum Bkgd. as % of				
Incident Radiation	<0.6%	55%	1.2%	53%

* This is after shielding by ½″ steel in empty shield, assuming 50% reduction by this steel, the true incident radiation would be at least 105,000 cpm and the minimum 0.1-2.0 Mev bkgd. in the water shield also <0.6%.

The first comparison between water and other shielding masses was using our two shields (Table II). This was not entirely satisfactory because of the striking differences in the chamber volumes and the greater mass thickness of the steel shield. However, despite these features apparently favoring steel, it was evident that the water shield reduced the count in the 4.0 to 5.0 Mev range more than the steel shield, and the 0.1 to 2.0 Mev background count in the water shield was better than previous ones reported for a crystal of this volume in a whole body counter facility (5). The steel shield appeared to have more K^{40}.

A second comparison without these ambiguities was done by Harold May of Argonne National Laboratory. A 7 by 3½ in. sodium iodide crystal was used to get a background count in ANL Steel Room No. 2 and in our water shield (Fig. 8). In this com-

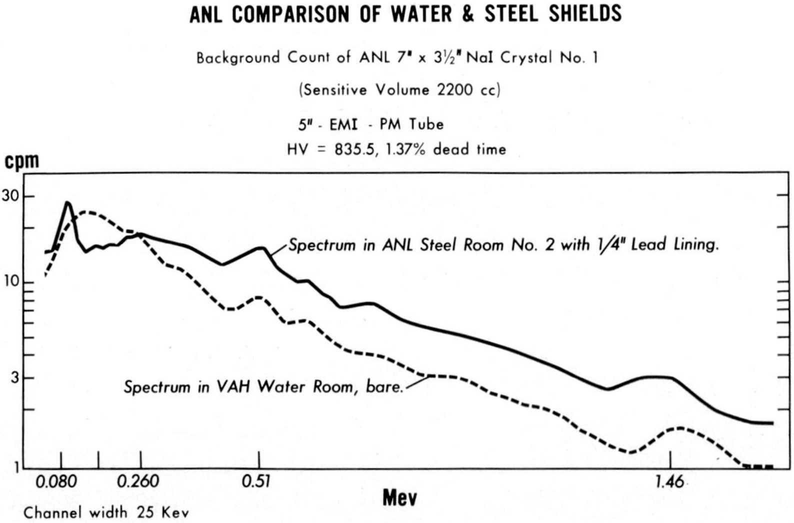

ANL COMPARISON OF WATER & STEEL SHIELDS

Background Count of ANL 7" x 3½" NaI Crystal No. 1

(Sensitive Volume 2200 cc)

5" - EMI - PM Tube

HV = 835.5, 1.37% dead time

Figure 8. ANL Comparison of water and steel shields.

parison the chamber volumes were identical, and the only difference in shielding mass thickness was that the ANL Steel Room had ¼ in. lead lining added to the 8 in. steel, and the water shield was bare and equivalent to 8 in. steel alone. The clear difference in backgrounds is broken down for comparison in Table III. The water shield had a background 20 percent lower than the steel shield over the range of 0.1 to 2.0 Mev. In the region of the photopeak for K^{40}, the reduction was 30 per cent. The spectrum was not collected over the 4.0 to 5.0 Mev region, but the 0.51 Mev annihilation peak is less prominent in the water shield spectrum,

TABLE III

ANL COMPARISON OF WATER AND STEEL SHIELDS

Chamber			0.51 Mev	1.46 Mev
Room	Surf. Area	0.1-2.0 Mev	[80 Kev]	[140 Kev]
Steel	252 ft²	530.5 cpm	46.1 cpm or 8.7%	15.0 cpm or 2.8%
Water	252 ft²	425.1 cpm	25.3 cpm or 6%	10.3 cpm or 2.4%
Net Bkgd. Reduction		105.4 cpm or 20%	20.8 cpm or 45%	4.7 cpm or 31%

and the count rate in that region shows a 45 percent reduction. Clearly there are significantly less K^{40} and cosmic ray contributions to the water shield background than to the background of the steel shield. Adding a ⅛ in. lead lining to the water shield room might further reduce background.

DISCUSSION

The cosmic ray contributions to the gamma background spectrum have been estimated at approximately one third of the total. The intensity at sea level approaches one particle/cm²/min. of this, about 30 percent is the soft component due chiefly to electrons and, to a lessor extent, neutrons. The most important of the penetrating cosmic radiation consists of the μ-mesons (+,−,O) produced by the decay of π-mesons high in the air. We have used the integral count 4.0 to 5.0 Mev as a measure of the cosmic ray contributions to background.

We became impressed with the reality of a cosmic ray "shadow effect" as we checked backgrounds in the vicinity of our shields. In the northern hemisphere, the predominance of charged cosmic particles come into the earth's atmosphere from the southwest. Even though the east-west asymmetry in the vicinity of 40°N does not exceed 4 percent on a plane (6), in the close proximity of a 10 story building, the effect is some multiple of that seen on a plane. Figure 9 illustrates the relative locations of three background counts in the 4.0 to 5.0 Mev range.

COSMIC RAY 'SHADOW' EFFECT

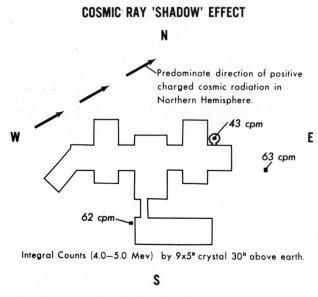

Figure 9. Cosmic ray shadow effect.

It is seen that the water shield is fortuitously located on the optimum northeast side of a tall building. The background count was one-third less (4.0 to 5.0 Mev) over the water shield than in areas out of the "cosmic ray shadow" of the building. This has also been shown by comparable differences in the meson peak count rates measured by the 9 in. by 5 in. sodium iodide crystal. It would seem desirable to utilize this phenomenon by placing low background enclosures in the optimum building shadow. Undoubtedly this "cosmic ray shadow" is part of the reason for lower background in the water shield. However, there remains good reason for crediting the water mass for major reduction in cosmic ray contribution (Table II). The 10 in. thick steel shield has incident radiation in the 4.0 to 5.0 Mev range, which is 4.6 cpm less than that in the empty water shield because of its location in the basement of a ten story building. The same incident radiation spectrum in the water shield is through ½ in. steel walls, so that filling the shield with water is mass equivalent to only 1½ in. of steel. This shield of only 75 percent comparable mass is none the less equal in attenuation of the 4.0 to 5.0 Mev count rate.

We have received several suggestions that a water shield should have unique opportunities to lower neutron background contributions by dissolving high neutron capture cross-section materials such as boron (720 barns), gadolinium (30,000 barns) and cadmium (2900 barns). We have delayed making any observations of this nature until sufficient experience is accumulated regarding the durability of the vinyl chloride lacquer surfaces in the tank and the rate and type of ions moving through these films into the water.

Neutrons are not part of the primary cosmic radiation entering the atmosphere. However, at sea level the neutron intensity is a measure of the intensity of the low energy portion of the primary radiation (7). Such atmospheric neutrons, if not already at thermal energy levels, would be reduced to these levels in traversing the earth overlying the shield and the tank wall. Some neutrons might arise from the uranium and radium in the surrounding earth. However, the most significant neutrons in terms of background contribution are probably those arising within the shield itself due to meson and nucleonic component intractions. In this regard, a shield of low atomic number material should produce fewer of these meson interactions than high atomic number material.

Since the mean free path for thermal neutron collision in water is 0.7 cm., and mean free path for thermal neutron capture is 54 cm. in water, a water shield alone is a highly effective neutron eliminator. The minimum thickness of 152 cm. water in our shield should readily reduce to negligible levels any thermal neutrons introduced through the exterior of the tank. However, neutrons produced within the shielding material may be numerous enough to warrant dissolving some high cross-section neutron "scavenging" material within the shield. The magnitude of such contributions to gamma background would be best judged from direct trial. The same attitude should apply to the optimum concentration of high cross-section material, although it can readily be calculated that a 0.02 molar solution of borax should very significantly reduce the neutrons available for N, γ reactions.

Although the magnitude of neutron contributions to our gamma background cannot now be described,* we have accumulated evidence suggesting the presence of neutrons within our shielding counting enclosures. As previously stated, we have used the integral counts between 4.0 and 5.0 Mev as a measure of cosmic ray contribution. Under similar conditions with counting intervals exceeding 200 minutes, twenty studies of this counting rate showed a standard deviation of 2 percent. We compared the effect of 5 in. thickness of borax (10 gms. boron/sq. cm.) shielding with that of various thicknesses of lead upon the 4.0 to 5.0 Mev counting rate of our NaI crystals. The mass of 5 cu. in. of borox is approximately that of a ½ in. thickness of lead/sq. in. Comparisons were made with a 4 in. by 4 in. crystal in a 10 in. thick steel shield and the 9 in. by 5 in. crystal in the water shield. Adding the 5 in. shield of borax reduced the 4.0 to 5.0 Mev contribution by 25 percent in the steel shield and 13 percent in the water shield relative to counts in the bare enclosures. Adding ⅛ in. lead to the shields reduced these count rates relative to those in the bare shields 17 percent in the steel shield and 8 percent in the water shield. Adding further thickness of lead up to ½ in. thickness, which equaled the mass of the borax shield, did not appreciably alter the count rate over that with ⅛ in. lead. Thus, the neutron contribution to gamma spectrum background appears to approximate one-half that shielded by ⅛ in. lead. Although no gamma photopeak was seen in this region, it is presumed that neutron reactions were occurring in the crystal assembly and were reduced by the borax shield. Presumably, the ⅛

---

* Neutron background counts have been made with BF₃ tube serial No. 52 loaned from Argonne National Laboratory. Its tube and electronic noise background was 0.16 cpm. The net thermal neutron count was 0.008 cpm in the water shield, 0.015 cpm in the 10 in. steel and 0.14 cpm in the adjoining hospital basement. The net fast neutron count was 0.04 cpm in the water shield, 0.05 cpm in the adjoining basement, 0.25 cpm on the earth over the water shield and 0.38 cpm on the earth at the southwest side of the hospital.

in. lead attenuated gammas in this region arising from the shield, but adding further thickness of lead brought no further decrease. This may be due to the high atomic number of lead, which could be associated with increased meson interactions equaling the added shielding. The greater prominence of these effects in the steel shield could be due to its atomic number predisposing to more meson interactions within that shield than within the water shield. No valid extrapolation from these studies can be made to the magnitude of potential benefits from adding borax, etc., to the water mass.

Leo Marinelli pointed out to us that the possibilities of observing Cerenkov radiation in the water mass should be explored (8). If Cerenkov radiation is observable, then + and − mesons traversing the water shield should be countable and anticoincidence circuits could be introduced to exclude contributions from such individual meson interactions (9). In 1956, Porter made a Cerenkov counter using vinyl chloride with titanium oxide pigment as wall covering and 1 meter thickness of water (10). Within the past year, Giamati and Reines have described a 2.0 meter high by 2.4 meter diameter Cerenkov detector using water for an anticoincidence counter of cosmic rays (11). This Cerenkov detector observed 3.6 by 10^5 cosmic ray events per hour. The water tank used for our shield is much larger than previous Cerenkov detectors. Approximately 25 percent of the 4.0 to 5.0 Mev events come through the walls rather than through the ceiling of the inner room. In addition to the difficulties in monitoring interactions coming into the shield at a low angle, the large volume should mean a tremendous number of cosmic ray events monitored. It is not now possible to predict the magnitude of this effect on the system deadtime. It has not yet been possible to adequately attempt observing Cerenkov radiation in our shield. There is no theoretical reason to anticipate that a Cerenkov anticoincidence system should preclude simultaneous use of dissolved high neutron capture materials.

We gratefully acknowledge the help in design, evaluation, planning and construction provided by Harold May and Leo Marinelli of Argonne National Laboratory, Prof. J. Merle Trummel and Prof C. J. Posey, State University of Iowa, Robert Buss of Hall Engineering Co., G. F. Fisher of Stanley Engineering Co. and David Molloy of Martin Building Service Co.

REFERENCES

1. Sievert, R. M., and Hultquist, B.: Some Swedish investigations of the radioactivity of the human body. *Brit. J. Radiol.*, Suppl. No. 7, The Measurement of Body Radioactivity, 1957.
2. Rundo, J.: The use of the Copenhagen ionization chamber apparatus in the study of thorium dioxide poisoning. *Brit. J. Radiol.*, Suppl. No. 7, The Measurement of Body Radioactivity, 1957.
3. Radium and mesothorium poisoning and dosimetry and instrumentation techniques in applied radioactivity, Progress Report May 1957. Contract AT (30-1)-952, Radioactivity Center, Massachusetts Institute of Technology.
4. Wilson, H. W., Watt, D.E., and Ramsden, D.: A low background laboratory. *Int. J. Appl. Radiat.*, 10:156, 1961.
5. Mehl, J., and Rundo, J.: Preliminary results of a world survey of whole body monitors. *Int. Atomic Energy Agency*, Vienna, 1962.
6. *Rev. Modern Phys.*, 10:193, 1938 as quoted by Marshak in *Meson Physics*.
7. Hooper, J. E., and Scharff, M.: *The Cosmic Radiation* Methven & Co. Ltd., 1958.
8. Jelley, J. V.: *Cerenkov Radiation*. Pergamon Press, 1958.
9. May, H. A.: Supplement to the use of low level gamma scintillation spectrometry in the measurements of activity in human beings. In *Radioactivity in Man, First Symposium*. Thomas, pp. 84-96, 1961.
10. Porter, N., and Sherwood, A. C.: The Oxford Conference on Extensive Air Showers. AERE, Harwell, p. 71, 1956.
11. Giamati, C. C., and Reines, F.: Experimental test of the conservation of nucleons. *Phys. Rev.* June 15, 1962.

9

SOLID VS. LAMINATED LARGE STEEL SHIELDS

S. REGAS, E. C. ANDERSON AND V. W. WALTER

Metrix, Inc.
Deerfield, Illinois
and
Los Alamos Scientific Laboratory
Los Alamos, New Mexico

INTRODUCTION

WITH THE CONSTANT rise in the number of applications for low level gamma counting, the problem of selection of the proper shielding materials and construction techniques becomes increasingly important.

One of the controversial design considerations has been laminated versus solid plate construction of shields. Steel is one of the commonest and least expensive of the shielding materials used, but, of course, is not the only one. Particular needs, situations and local conditions will often dictate the most desirable shielding material. This discussion will apply equally well to any steel shield with wall thickness of approximately 4 in. or more.

DISCUSSION

The choice between the alternate methods of constructing steel rooms and low level counting facilities must be made on the basis of several parameters, the relative importance of which may vary. A monolithic construction using single pieces of thick steel for the walls, roof and floor may be used or a laminated system in which many small thin plates are overlapped to produce the desired total thickness.

COSTS

The first consideration is the cost of the material itself. There is only a small difference in the total cost of materials if the steel is purchased in thin, let us say $\frac{1}{4}$ in. thick plates or in solid 5 or more in. thick plates. An 8 ft. by 8 ft. steel plate 6 in. thick costs $1.50 per cwt. over the thinner material. Plates up to about 1.5 in. thick can be provided in the desired sizes by shearing at $1.45 per cwt., while thicker plates are usually flame cut at a cost of around $0.50 per cwt. Additional costs of 25¢ per sq. ft. for shot blasting makes a much higher cost factor in laminated than in solid shields. Nevertheless, the difference is small in proportion to total costs.

Another source of satisfactory steel is the use of massive naval armor plates or old gun barrels, which are sometimes available at "no cost" for the material. Several steel shields have been built with this armor plate because of valid radiological consideration. This steel was made before man-made isotopes in large quantities were in use. But it is equally, if not more, expensive to install this "free" steel than to buy new, freshly rolled material. Part of the reason is that the costs of cutting and machining are high due to the extreme hardness of armor steel. Noncommercial suppliers tend to be a little more independent and cannot always be depended on to meet delivery schedules.

The greatest portion of the total cost is the fabrication of the steel plates. There is a tendency when studying fabrication costs to compare finished thick plates with machined edges and tight tolerances with flame cut or sheared thin plates completely unfinished and held together with "C" clamps. This latter technique produces uneven and ragged edges and large voids. A cover is often used to hide these voids which can be as much as $\frac{1}{4}$ in. wide. The covered voids then become excellent dust and contamination traps. In this comparison, the end product and the expected appearance, tolerance and finishing is assumed to be of equal quality, whether of solid or laminated construction.

In a laminated construction, there is usually a need for more bolts, and therefore, more holes to maintain structural strength than is required of solid construction. Since the holes through several plates must be all lined up, the location tolerances must be tighter. This takes more time and makes this portion of the fabrication more expensive for laminated shields. If instead of bolts, a welded construction is used, there are fewer linear feet of welding necessary in solid construction and the cost is again much less for solid shields. Radiological precautions are the same for solid or laminated construction, but when solid plates are used, the welds can be kept on the outside only. Laminated shields, for structural purposes, require welds inside as well as outside. This requires more careful selection of the welding materials and techniques with increase in costs. On this point it is more economical to have a solid construction.

One local condition which might strongly influence the selection of the method for the steel fabrication is the availability of equipment. Small steel fabricators often do not possess the necessary machinery and services to handle and machine heavy steel pieces. When a small machine shop is the only one available, the laminated construction must be selected. Several objective comparisons on the cost of fabricating thin or thick plates have shown that it is more expensive to fabricate with thin plates, assuming that the final product is of comparable quality.

Shipping costs are independent of the thickness of the material and vary purely on the basis of weight. But it is possible that the final destination will be a remote location away from large cities where unloading equipment and personnel are not readily available. By unloading materials with light unit weight with available local labor, considerable savings are obtained, and the unloading costs are definitely in favor of laminated construction. The cost might be 10 to 50 percent less than that for unloading large pieces. The limiting factor is the availability of handling equipment. A large crane, although it costs about $25.00 per hr., is economical to use and with expert labor results in a cost of 1.5 to 2¢ per lb. for moving material on site. If a crane or expert labor has to be brought from far away, the traveling expenses multiply the total unloading cost quickly. Most towns have riggers capable of handling heavy loads; therefore, handling of the steel is not a deciding factor in most cases.

The theory often has been advanced that existing laboratory

personnel can easily handle laminated construction, while outside workers must be hired for the erection of steel in heavy pieces. Professional, scientific and technical people can and have provided this type of labor for the erection of laminated shields and their labor has not been considered in the total cost analysis, but it is discouraging to many to see competent scientists doing such jobs when there is so much emphasis recently on our shortage of technical personnel.

When an organization considers building a shield, it should not overlook labor conditions. If a steelworkers' union local finds that a steel shield is being erected by non-union members, it can legally obtain full payment for the time that it would have taken union workers to erect the shield.

RADIOLOGICAL CONSIDERATIONS

Although the costs are strongly in favor of solid construction, radiological considerations are of much more importance. Here again we find many advantages in solid construction.

All materials, thick or thin, must be tested, and most steel is not without detectable radioactivity. Prewar material, such as scrap naval armor plate, has the least chance of being contaminated since it predates the large production of artificial radioactivity. Many samples of contemporary steel production have been studied, and many cases of serious gamma contamination have been found.

Cobalt sources are often used for inspection of the lining of the furnace walls, and when this lining deteriorates, the source falls into the melt. Special precautions are taken to encapsulate this source in high temperature materials and to recover it afterwards. Despite these efforts, often the source disintegrates and diffuses into the rest of the metal, contaminating it slightly, but enough to be objectionable in shielding material for low level counting. Two or three steel mills had been using this method, but after the Vanderbilt University Symposium on Radiation in Man, where the problem first became public, most or all of the mills in the United States discontinued this method.

The contamination problem in steel imported from other

countries still remains and, through reprocessing, some of this contaminated scrap finds its way into steel used for shields. However, this is the same for either type construction. Pretesting of the steel before construction for significant internal contamination should be required for steel used in either type of construction.

Contamination is almost universally observed on all steel samples, whether prewar or current production. Sand or shot blasting or flame cleaning to remove mill scale and radioactive surface contamination is necessary. Here the large number of surfaces associated with laminar construction is a definite disadvantage since more work is required for decontamination and there is greater chance of recontamination. In solid slab construction only two surfaces are involved and, except for the lower floor surface and the joints, all faces remain accessible after construction. Airborne radioactivity from fallout products, radium in natural dust, active deposits from natural and ubiquitous radon gas, laboratory contamination, etc. can seep into laminations and reach positions from which gamma rays can penetrate into the low level enclosure. It is nearly impossible to remove them without complete disassembly of the shield. Hermetic sealing of the edges of the laminate is indicated, but it is expensive.

Since thin plates, let us say $1/4$ in. thick, of large area would not be perfectly flat, stacking several of those plates together would result in an accumulation of tolerances and voids between the plates, further increasing the contamination potential. In addition, when laminated construction exists, the structural rigidity of the room is reduced to a point where solid anchorage is not provided for the door hinges. Additional strength is provided by inside bracing which again increases the surfaces and pockets where contamination can accumulate. Solid construction, then, provides the least probability that contamination will occur and allows easier decontamination if it does occur.

ENVIRONMENTAL CONSIDERATIONS

It is difficult to visualize that it can be impossible to erect a solid steel shield where a laminated shield can be erected. If the design is handled by professionals, difficulties can be over-come.

Another factor often considered is the portability of the shields. Even a small box 20 by 20 by 24 in. inside, weighing 4,000 to 8,000 lbs., is by no stretch of the imagination "portable." If this shield has to be moved to a new location, it can be moved as a unit if the passages are large enough and the floor support is adequate or it will have to be disassembled and moved piece by piece. If the whole shield is to be moved, then the method of construction is important. If the moving is to be done by disassembling, the problems are exactly the same as those of erection. The difference in cost of moving a solid versus a laminated shield using specialized labor is minor. If the shield is not going to be moved often, the other advantages of solid con-struction far outweigh the extra expense, if any, of a few dollars for the moving.

Another point of consideration is the appearance of the equipment. It is always gratifying to show visitors scientific apparatus which not only functions perfectly but also looks pro-fessional. The psychological effect of a pleasing appearance upon a disturbed and suspicious human subject may make the differ-ence between obtaining valid data from him and not. There is no question that monolithic construction lends itself better to a finished look without need of covers, leads and other make-up.

An intermediate method which has been satisfactorily tried is the use of laminated shields with plates 2 or 3 in. thick. This method overcomes some of the disadvantages of thin lam-inars, especially radiological ones, and still maintains ease of fab-rication by small shops and possibility of erection and moving by nonspecialized personnel.

CONCLUSIONS

There are economical considerations in constructing large steel shields with single thick plates, but the most important con-siderations are the radiological advantages due to the danger as-sociated with thin laminations. Thick plated shields have to be fabricated and installed by professionals, but they provide a cost advantage and a handsome appearance to the finished product. There are special situations, especially when erection costs can be absorbed, where laminated construction could be selected.

There are no radiological advantages to the laminated construction, while there are definite disadvantages. So-called "portability" has been considered as a factor, but the cost for moving a shield in relation to the initial cost of the equipment and the general installation costs is so small that it should not be a factor in the construction of a shield which probably will not be moved for at least several years. A compromise is the use of laminated shields with plates 2 or 3 in. thick. This method partially overcomes the radiological disadvantages of the laminars, but maintains the advantages of ease of fabrication by small shops and moving and installation by nonspecialized personnel.

Country stores as well as metropolitan banking giants for many years have been buying and moving their steel safes and vaults with no difficulty. There is no reason why these methods cannot be used by scientists also. Nor is there any difficulty in finding properly qualified persons to do the installing and moving of heavy shields, especially since a better and more economical product results.

10

EXPERIMENTAL TECHNIQUE FOR HIGH PRECISION CALIBRATION OF WHOLE BODY COUNTERS: APPLICATION TO A 4π LIQUID SCINTILLATOR AND A LARGE NaI (Tl) CRYSTAL SPECTROMETER[1]

Phillip N. Dean

Los Alamos Scientific Laboratory
University of California
Los Alamos, New Mexico

INTRODUCTION

THE ACCURACY of measurements of radioactive isotopes in the body is limited by the precision of calibration of the detector. Consequently, the calibration of a whole body counter should be carefully accomplished. Several factors must be taken into account. One is the change in counting efficiency with weight of the subject. This is due to the self absorption of radiation emitted within the body by the mass of the body itself and to geometry effects of shape of body and counter positioning. This effect can be determined by using calibration subjects with weights varying over the range of interest. Since the ultimate aim is to measure radioactivity in human subjects, the calibration would best be performed using them. This is preferred to phantoms, because with the great variety of human shapes, geometry effects may be encountered. The precision of a measurement of a random individual must take this into account. The location of the isotope within an individual must also be considered, which is rather difficult to duplicate with phantoms.

[1] Work performed under the auspices of the U. S. Atomic Energy Commission.

Isotopes for calibration can be administered to humans orally or intravenously. In either case the translocation time or time required for the isotope to reach its normal position in the body must be determined. The intravenous method is to be preferred, since the isotope will go immediately into the blood stream. The translocation time will then be limited to the time required for the isotope to leave the blood. With the oral method, the isotope has to go from the stomach to the blood, somewhat increasing the translocation time.

The first step in the calibration procedure is to administer the isotope intravenously and to measure the counting efficiency as a function of time after administration. All successive measurements on other calibration subjects are then made after a time interval in which the counting efficiency has stabilized. This time interval must be determined for each isotope to be used and preferably on more than one subject to determine the range of variation.

Another important factor in determining the precision of the calibration is the stability of the detector itself. The variation of counting efficiency and background with time must be determined. This can be done rather accurately with the 4π liquid scintillator with its short counting time. With a shield which is essentially sealed off from external air circulation, variations in background of the 4π counter are usually due to changes in gain of the photomultipliers and amplifiers. This detector uses fixed wide energy intervals that include the multiple Compton peaks of the different isotopes. Consequently, gain shifts can cause changes in the counting efficiency of the various isotopes in the different channels. For precise calibration, the effects of gain shifts must be determined.

The shield for the crystal spectrometer must be opened to allow entry of a subject. To prevent background fluctuations from radioactive gases entering the room and having time to decay there, the shield must be force-ventilated with air that has been filtered to remove radioactive fallout contaminants. The importance of electronic gain shifts with this counter depends on the type of data analysis. Gain shifts might distort the shape of the photopeak, but the number of counts under the total peak will be the same.

EQUIPMENT

The 4π whole body counter calibrated utilizing the technique described was Humco II (Human Counter II) of the Biomedical Research Group, Los Alamos Scientific Laboratory and which has been described elsewhere (1-3). All data are punched directly into IBM cards for computer processing. A 400 channel analyzer is used to monitor photomultiplier gain and energy resolution. Six channels are routinely used (Table I), allowing for simultaneous measurement of as many as six isotopes. Twelve single channel analyzers are used to allow duplication of any channel as a safeguard against either analyzer or scaler failure. Since the primary energy deposition mechanism in this counter is by two Compton scatters, energies are specified as double Compton. The half energy resolution for Cs^{137} is 25 percent, and for K^{40} it is 18 percent. The counter is capable of fully automatic recycling operation. This allows an accurate determination of counter stability by observing the magnitude of short and long term variations in background and counting efficiency.

The crystal spectrometer used at this laboratory for whole body counting is a $9\frac{3}{8}$ in. diameter by 6 in. thickness NaI (Tl) crystal. The crystal is mounted so that it has $5°$ of freedom for positioning. A standard chair of the $90°$ geometry was constructed to minimize geometry effects. In the counting position, the back of the chair is at $45°$ to the vertical, the angle between the back and seat is $90°$ and the angle between the seat and foot of the chair is $90°$. The standard counting position of the crystal is with the center of the face of the crystal 16 in. from the back and seat of the chair. The crystal and chair are enclosed in a shield made of 7 in. thick steel armor plating. The inner walls of the room have a $\frac{1}{8}$ in. thick layer of lead to reduce backscatter and to remove low energy gammas originating in the steel. The energy resolution for this detector is 10 percent for Cs^{137}. The instrumentation consists of a preamplifier, an amplifier and a 400 channel pulse height analyzer with magnetic tape, punched paper tape and printed paper tape outputs. An IBM computor is used for data reduction.

TABLE I
ENERGY BANDS AND COUNTING EFFICIENCIES FOR HUMCO II

	1	2	3	4	5	6	7	Total Efficiency (Per Cent)
Nuclide	Bremss.	I^{131}	Cs^{137}	Zn^{65}	K^{40}	Co^{60}	Na^{24}	
Energy Range (Mev)	0.10-0.17	0.17-0.42	0.42-0.67	0.67-1.15	1.15-1.68	1.68-2.68	2.68-4.60	
Background Rate (c/s)	260	620	285	390	380	200	60	
Cesium^{137}	5.2	22	56	8.4	0	0	0	92
Zinc^{65}	2.8	10	10	52	9.5	0	0	85
Potassium^{40}	4.9	13	7.2	14	36	1.3	0.1	77
Cobalt^{60}*	(0.3 ?)	2.1	3.6	14	24	38	1.7	83
Radium^{226} (equilibrium)*	6.8	22	5.2	9.2	14	11	0.3	69
Thorium^{228} (RdTh)*	12.3	16	5.2	5.5	3.7	6.2	14	50

*Efficiencies entered in table are per cent of gamma rays emitted from a point source that are counted. Cascade gamma rays (as in Co^{60}, Ra^{226}, Th^{228} are considered as only 1 because of high coincidence efficiency. It is assumed that there are emitted 1.6 gammas per Ra^{226} disintegration and 1.4 gammas per Th^{228} disintegration (all daughters in equilibrium). A natural potassium specific activity of 3 gammas per second per gram is assumed.

RESULTS

Both detectors have been calibrated for potassium by the use of K^{42}. The first step was to determine the translocation time. Four subjects were used in two different experiments. They were given an intravenous solution of approximately 0.6 μc of K^{42}, produced by activating KOH in a reactor. The precision of intravenous delivery of the isotope was $\pm$ 0.05 percent for repeated delivery from a single syringe and $\pm$ 0.3 percent for different syringes. The four subjects were counted at intervals from the time of injection to 25 hrs. afterward. The count rate of the 4π counter stabilized within 10 to 15 min. after injection after the isotope had become thoroughly mixed in the blood. With its greater sensitivity to location of the isotope in the body, the crystal spectrometer required a much longer time to achieve stability of counting rate. Figure 1 shows the count rate as a function of time after administration of K^{42} for one of the four subjects. The count rate essentially stabilized in 4½ to 5 hrs. after injection.

To obtain absolute calibration of the K^{42}, 2.2 kg. of KCl was

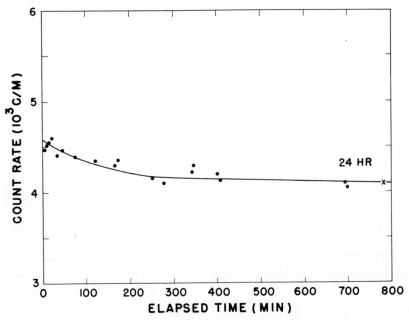

Figure 1. Count rate versus time after intravenous administration of K^{42}.

added to a polyethylene bottle containing 20 kg. of distilled water, and the counting efficiency in c/s kg. potassium was determined. The same amount of K^{42} used with the human subjects was then delivered to the phantom, and the phantom recounted. From the ratio of the K^{40} efficiency and the net count rate of the K^{42} in identical geometry, one can calculate the equivalent amount of normal potassium represented by the K^{42} solution. The ratio should be independent of the mass and geometry of the phantom because of the nearly identical energies of the gamma rays. This was verified by using four phantoms of different shapes and weights from 15 to 32 kg. The K^{40}/K^{42} ratios agreed to within ± 0.7 percent.

The 4π counter was calibrated once with ten people and four phantoms, and once with eleven people and two phantoms. The subjects were injected with K^{42} and then counted after 20 min. and after $4\frac{1}{2}$ to 5 hr. Results are shown in Figure 2. The data were fitted with a least-squares fit of a polynomial function of sixth order. Counting efficiencies for random subjects were deter-

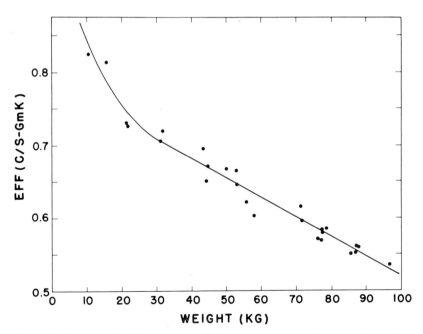

Figure 2. Humco II K^{40} counting efficiency versus weight of subject (potassium channel).

mined from the resulting equation. The standard deviation of all points to the computed curve was ± 2.1 percent. The statistical accuracy of a given point was ± 0.5 percent. To determine whether or not geometry effects were present due to differences in body stature, subjects of the same weight but different height and waist measurements were selected. No dependence on body shape was observed with the 4π counter for this isotope.

Since the measurement of Cs^{137} in humans is of interest, the counting efficiency of potassium in the cesium channel (channel 3) was determined (Fig. 3). The variation with weight was less,

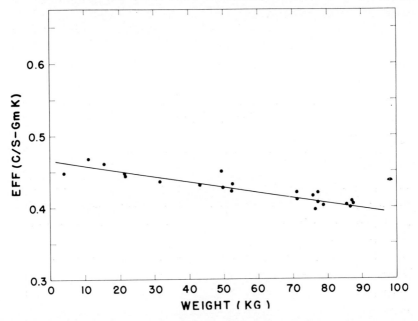

Figure 3. Humco II K^{40} counting efficiency versus weight of subject (cesium channel).

since multiple scatter was more likely in the heavier subjects and the gamma rays would have less than 360 kv energy when they enter the scintillator.

The 4π counter was also calibrated for Cs^{137} by the use of phantoms in the range of 4 to 85 kg. (Fig. 4). Phantoms were

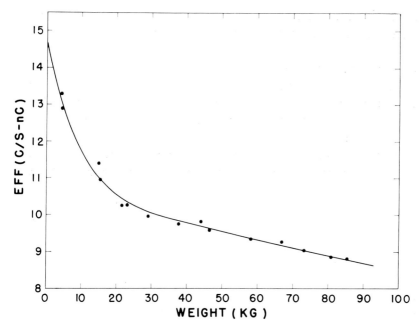

Figure 4. Humco II Cs^{137} counting efficiency versus weight of subject (cesium channel).

used because of the present unavailability of short lived Cs^{132}. The standard deviation of all points to the computed curve was ± 1.4 percent. With the particular energy band in which cesium is measured and because of its low energy, the weight effect was not as strong as with potassium, amounting to only 10 percent over the range of 30 to 80 kg. as contrasted to 25 percent for potassium. Considering counting statistics and precision of calibration, the cesium level can be determined to ± 0.18 nc or ± 3.0 percent in a normal 70 kg. man.

A calibration of the crystal spectrometer was performed using thirteen people (Fig. 5). The standard deviation of the individual points from the computed curve was ± 2.7 percent. The statistical accuracy of a single point was 0.2 percent. These subjects were the same ones used in the calibration of the 4π counter. There was an apparent dependence on body geometry, as shown by the two low points at 82 and 86.5 kg. These two subjects had

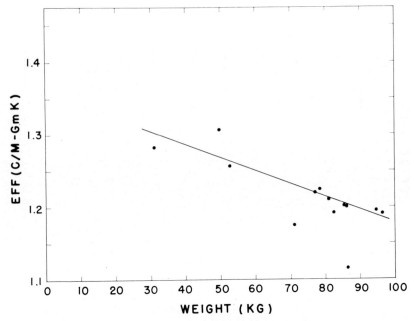

Figure 5. Sodium iodide (T1) crystal K⁴⁰ counting efficiency versus weight of subject (photopeak).

counting efficiencies within 1 percent of the computed curve with the 4π counter. Here they differ by as much as 8 percent from the computed curve. They differed from the average person used in the calibration in being tall and slim. No attempt has been made as yet to calibrate this counter for cesium.

SUMMARY

With the 4π liquid scintillator, potassium determinations can be made on random subjects to a precision of ± 2.1 percent based on the calibration alone. Including statistics, the precision is ± 3.0 percent for a counting time of 200 sec.

With the crystal spectrometer, potassium determinations can be made on random subjects to a precision of ± 2.7 percent based on the calibration alone. Including statistics, the precision is ± 3.5 percent for a counting time of 50 min.

REFERENCES

1. Van Dilla, M. A., and Anderson, E. C.: Human counters using liquid
     scintillators in *Whole Body Counting*, Vienna, IAEA, 1962.
2. Anderson, E. C., Schuch, R. L., Kerr, V. N., and Van Dilla, M. A.:
     Humco II: A new four pi liquid scintillation counter. *Radioactivity
     In Man.* Springfield, Thomas, 1961.
3. Hiebert, R. D., and Gallagher, J. D.: Electronics for whole body liquid
     scintillation counters. *IRE Trans. Biomed. Electronics,* BME-9(1)
     (January) 1962, pp. 54-61.

11

A SCINTILLATION SPECTROMETER STABILIZATION SYSTEM[1]

ROBERT A. DUDLEY AND REMIGIUS SCARPATETTI

International Atomic Energy Agency
Vienna, Austria

INTRODUCTION

A FEEDBACK SYSTEM has been developed for stabilizing a scintillation spectrometer against drifts of virtually any common origin. The spectrometer consists of an 8 by 4 in. NaI(Tl) crystal coupled to a 400 channel pulse height analyzer. Preliminary results give promise that stability adequate for almost any purpose can be maintained over a day or longer without significant penalty.

The two predominant types of instability in scintillation spectrometers are drifts in amplification and zero. Drifts in amplification may originate in the analog to digital converter (ADC), in the amplifier or preamplifier, or most commonly in the photomultiplier. The photomultiplier gain depends critically on the dynode chain high voltage (e.g., 1 percent gain change for 0.1 percent high voltage change). It may also depend on counting rate or past history of counting rate, on the magnitude of local magnetic fields and on temperature. Drifts in zero can originate only after the last stage of AC coupling, which in general means only within the ADC. These zero drifts may depend on aging of components, temperature and counting rate. Other instabilities, such as changes in resolution or degree of linearity of the system, normally occur over intervals longer than one day.

The degree of stability required depends on the application. However, in order that system instability not be the limiting feature in the performance of the spectrometer itself, the pulse

---

[1] This work was supported in part by the U. S. Atomic Energy Commission.

energy vs. channel number correlation should remain fixed within
a rather small fraction of one channel. For example, a zero stability within 0.1 channel and a gain stability within 0.1 percent
(0.2 channel shift at channel 200) may be required in certain
applications, especially when a gamma peak of low counting rate
is under study on the steep side of a gamma peak having a much
higher counting rate.

We had two reasons for developing a stabilization system.
First, we feared gain changes resulting from movement of our
crystal through variable magnetic fields in our steel room, as we
expected to rely primarily on a scanning technique for assay of
patients. Second, we expected to use extensively a magnetic tape
spectrum stripper for data processing. The usefulness of such a
system is severely curtailed if not all tapes in the library have
the same energy vs. channel number correlation, since no possibility exists for adjusting this correlation in playing back the
tapes.

At least three methods exist for achieving high stability. The
electronic equipment, especially the photomultiplier high voltage supply, should be inherently stable. The apparatus should be
calibrated with standard gamma ray sources as frequently as
necessary. Finally, gain and zero may be positively controlled
through continuous feedback stabilization (1-6). Most of these
feedback systems provide somehow for maintaining a certain
gamma peak of the spectrum or an artificial peak produced by a
light pulser in a predetermined channel. We have developed
such a system with certain distinctive characteristics which may
make it especially suitable for our needs. Its feedback loop encompasses virtually the entire system; its operation is independent of the gamma spectrum under investigation and it puts no additional pulses into any part of the spectrum. The system is at
present designed only for gain stabilization, not for zero stabilization. It can, however, be simply expanded to include zero
stabilization if this proves to be necessary.

PRINCIPLES OF STABILIZATION SYSTEM

Our gain stabilization is accomplished by reference light
flashes introduced into the 8 by 4 in. NaI(Tl) crystal through a

special window. These flashes occur at about 65 per sec., and the moment of occurrence is known. (This ability to distinguish calibration flashes from gamma scintillations is fundamental to the operation of our system.) The calibration pulses are processed by the preamplifier, amplifier and ADC just as gamma pulses. When the channel number of the calibration pulse is established on the address scaler in the analyzer, the scaler is examined (it being known that this is a calibration pulse) to determine whether the channel number is higher or lower than a predetermined value. If higher, a small decrease is made in gain; if lower, an increase is made in gain. Finally, the analyzer storage program is interrupted to prevent this calibration pulse from being transferred from address scaler to memory; hence, it contributes no background. (For testing purposes, the calibration pulses can be allowed into the memory.)

Instrumental Design

The reference light flashes are produced by Pu[239] alpha scintillations in an auxiliary NaI(Tl) crystal. This crystal, ½ by ½ in., has a glass window at each end. The plutonium is deposited as a thin layer under one window. Part of the light passes through the front window into the 8 by 4 in. crystal, and part through the rear window into a monitor photomultiplier which informs the stabilization system when calibration pulses occur.

The ½ in. diameter window in the large crystal, through which the calibration flashes are introduced, is located at the geometrical center of the back of the crystal between the three windows for the three photomultipliers. On smaller crystals provision of this extra window would be less convenient.

The electronic circuitry of the stabilization system is made apparent by Figure 1. The circuitry consists primarily of standard gates and switches whose operation is not critical. Coupling to our analyzer (RIDL Model 34-12) has been simple. The pulse from the monitor photomultiplier is first passed through an amplifier and integral discriminator, then through two gates (if open) to set bistable No. 1. Gate 1 is open only when the analyzer is in the pulse height analysis mode, not during print-out.

STABILIZATION SYSTEM BLOCK DIAGRAM

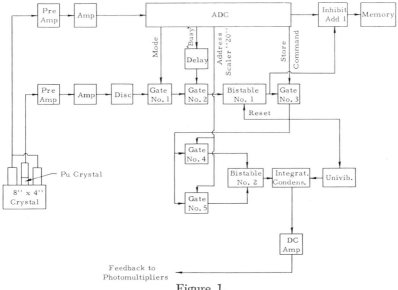

Figure 1.

Gate 2 is open only while the analyzer is not processing a previous pulse. The delay allows the monitor pulse to get through the gate before the gate is closed by the associated calibration pulse which is simultaneously entering the analyzer. The setting of bistable No. 1 inhibits the "add 1" stage of the store program, so that the calibration pulse is not added into the memory. It also opens gate 3, allowing the analyzer's "store command" pulse into the stabilization circuitry to accomplish three things. It triggers a univibrator, sets bistable No. 2 through either gate 4 or gate 5, and later resets bistable No. 1 with its trailing edge. Gates 4 and 5 are coupled to the channel 20 bistable in the address scaler of the analyzer, gate 4 being open only when the channel 20 bistable is off, gate 5 only when it is on. Hence the store command sets bistable No. 2 to one or the other of its states depending on the setting of the channel 20 bistable. The combined action of bistable No. 2 and the univibrator is to feed one unit of either positive or negative charge onto the integrating condenser, depending on whether the calibration pulse fell into channel 20 or higher, or into channel 19 or lower. The integrating condenser is simply a counting rate meter which integrates many increments of positive or negative charge. The voltage built up on the condenser, after DC amplification, adjusts the photocathode voltages of all the photomultipliers to alter gain in that direction which divides the calibration pulses more equally above and below channel 19.5. Feedback to the photocathodes has been a convenient method of gain adjustment, since they are near ground potential and draw negligible current. If large gain adjustments are required, resolution may be affected by variations in voltage difference between photocathode and first dynode. To reduce this effect, it might be preferable to connect the photocathodes to the negative end of the dynode resistor chain and to vary the potential of this point above or below ground. This would be the same as varying photomultiplier high voltage, but at a more accessible DC potential of approximately ground. The spectrometer amplification constantly hunts, but the magnitude of hunting can be kept inconsequential. Oscillation is impossible.

Theory of Stabilization

The theory of the stabilization process must be concerned with the average behavior of the system and the statistical fluctuations associated with the hunting.

Under certain approximations which introduce only inconsequential errors, a simple description of the average behavior of the stabilization system may be derived. Suppose a sudden change of amplification is introduced anywhere in the spectrometer, such that in the absence of stabilization a gamma ray peak position (and simultaneously the calibration peak) would be shifted by E per cent of its original channel number. If the same change were to occur while stabilization was in operation, the residual error ϵ, as a function of time t after the gain change, would be:

$$\epsilon = \frac{E}{S} + E\left(1-\frac{1}{S}\right)e^{-t/\tau}$$

S is the stabilization factor, the ratio E/ϵ at large t. τ is the time constant for stabilization and is equal to τ_c/S, where τ_c is the RC of the integrating condenser. If S is large, ϵ quickly becomes much smaller than E. The magnitude of S can be derived in terms of the parameters of the system. It is proportional to the frequency of the calibration pulses, to the sharpness of the calibration pulse peak, to τ_c and to the magnitude of the gain correction made following each pulse.

The magnitude of the statistical fluctuations introduced into the gain *by the stabilization system itself* (i.e., beyond those otherwise inherent in gamma spectroscopy) can be simply calculated using generating functions (7) and the theory of statistical fluctuations in counting rate meters. Again under approximations which introduce only inconsequential errors, the following expressions result:

$$(1)\ \frac{\sigma_N}{N} = \frac{1}{K}\ \frac{1}{\sqrt{2a\tau}}$$

$$(2)\ \frac{\sigma_N(T)}{N} = \frac{1}{K}\ \frac{1}{\sqrt{aT}}$$

where:

$N \equiv$ channel number of peak in spectrum,

$\dfrac{\sigma_N}{N} \equiv$ standard deviation of channel number of peak for single observation,

$\dfrac{\sigma_N(T)}{N} \equiv$ standard deviation of channel number of peak, for spectrum recorded over time T,

$K \equiv \dfrac{\text{percent change in count rate of calibration pulses whose channel number is too high}}{\text{percent change in gain}}$

(For example, at the correct value of gain the calibration pulses fall in equal numbers above and below the preassigned mean peak height, let us say 32 cps above channel 19.5 and 32 cps below channel 19.5. If a gain increase of 1 percent not corrected by stabilization causes $32 + 4$ cps to fall above channel 19.5 and $32 - 4$ to fall below,

$$K = \frac{4/32 \text{ x } 100 \text{ percent}}{0.01 \text{ x } 100 \text{ percent}} = 12.5.)$$

$a \equiv$ average rate of occurrence of all calibration pulses,

$\tau \equiv$ time constant of stabilization $(= \tau_c/S)$,

$T \equiv$ total time of measurement $(>> \tau)$.

The first equation gives the fractional standard deviation in the channel number of a gamma ray peak for single observations (That is, suppose bursts of gamma rays occurred in 50 successive intervals, each short compared with τ but separated from each other by times greater than τ. One would observe a set of fifty peaks, whose fifty mean channel numbers would scatter with standard deviation σ_N about N.) The second equation gives the fractional standard deviation in the channel number of the cumulative gamma ray peak recorded during the counting time T.

Since in our system τ is only a few seconds, all measurements extend over times $T >> \tau$. Therefore the second equation gives the standard deviation of the recorded peak position. $\sigma_N(T)$ should be less than the tolerable gain drift in order that the stabilization system not defeat its own purpose. This condition is not difficult to meet. The first expression, applying to short term variations in gain, characterizes the contribution of hunting to the width of the gamma ray peak, i.e., the effect of hunting on resolution. σ_N/N should be much less than the inherent peak width (with which it adds in quadrature) in order that its effect on resolution be negligible. This stipulation also is not difficult to meet.

RESULTS WITH STABILIZATION SYSTEM

Our system has been in operation long enough to give only preliminary results. These are promising, and certain modifications are in progress which should lead to even better performance.

Calibration Light Source

The amount of light produced by the 5 Mev plutonium alpha ray in the small crystal is equal to that which would be produced by total absorption of a 3.5 Mev gamma photon in this crystal. However, the amount of light at present reaching the 8 by 4 in. crystal is equivalent to that produced by total absorption in the 8 by 4 in. crystal of only a 0.25 Mev photon. The transfer of light from the small to the large crystal is thus very inefficient.

The small size of the calibration pulse has two disadvantages. First, the peak falls into a low channel number, setting a severe demand on zero stability. If a small shift in the calibration pulse height is caused by a zero shift but is corrected by a gain adjustment, a large error is introduced into the energy vs. channel number correlation at high channel numbers. Second, a small calibration pulse inevitably has poor resolution and gives a smaller stabilization factor. We believe that a considerable increase in light transfer efficiency can be achieved with a small crystal of improved design, and we expect that zero stabilization, if necessary, can be rather simply provided.

The calibration pulse peak is fairly symmetrical with a low energy tail containing only a few percent of the pulses. Resolution is 14 percent, and the factor $K = 13$. The inherent spread of pulse height in the source itself is approximately half this value; most of the 14 percent spread is attributable to the usual scintillation statistical considerations.

The activity of the plutonium source, 130 dps., or 65 calibration pulses per sec., was selected as a reasonable compromise between rapid stabilization and low hunting on the one hand and excessive dead time loss and possible deterioration of the crystal under α bombardment on the other hand. Its value is not critical.

The most important attribute of the light source is the degree of its pulse height uniformity over times long compared with τ; i.e., hours or days. The promise of good stability in an alpha ray light source was the reason for its selection in our system. The equivalent gamma ray energy of the calibration pulses in the 8 by 4 in. crystal was examined over a period by recording simultaneously on the analyzer two gamma peaks in addition to the calibration peak. The two gamma peaks, Co^{57} at 0.12 Mev and Cs^{137} at 0.66 Mev, bracketed the calibration peak and provided by linear interpolation the equivalent gamma energy of the calibration peak. One set of results is shown in Figure 2, where percent shift in equivalent gamma energy is plotted against time. Six consecutive 200 min. runs were recorded the first day, and four consecutive 200 min. runs the fourth day. During the 15 to 20 hr. measurements, the average calibration pulse height stayed constant to within about 0.1 percent, but a drop of about 0.5 per-

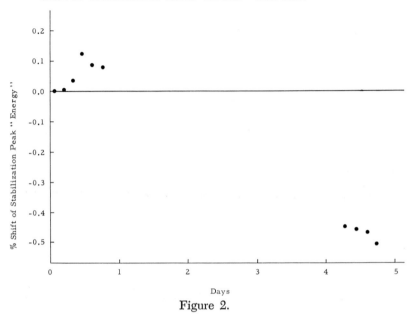

SHIFT OF STABILIZATION PULSE "ENERGY" WITH TIME

Figure 2.

cent occurred over the four days. The error in the measurement of each point probably amounted to a few hundredths percent. It is likely that the drift in pulse height is attributable to changes in the coupling of the two crystals, rather than to an actual decrease in light available.

Stabilization Circuitry

The value observed for the stabilization factor S has been about 12. This is much less than the ratio τ_c/τ, which exceeds 100, as a result of the fact that the increments of plus or minus charge fed to the integrating condenser are slightly dependent on the amount of charge already on the condenser. A larger S could be achieved in a variety of ways, but preferably by eliminating this dependence. Simple circuits exist for accomplishing this modification.

The stabilization circuit has itself been very stable (Fig. 3). The percent shift in channel number of calibration peak is plotted against time for the same set of measurements as in Figure 2. At

SHIFT OF STABILIZATION WITH TIME

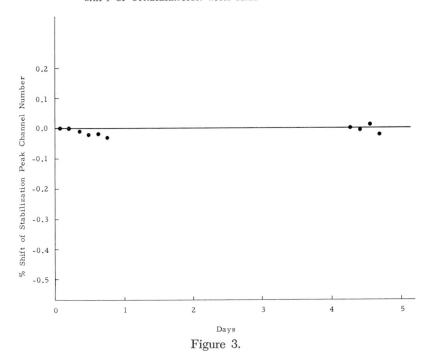

Figure 3.

the start of the last four measurements, on day 4, amplifier gain
was adjusted until the stabilization feedback voltage was zero. By
this means drifts in the analyzer itself were eliminated to allow
more critical observation of the stability of the stabilization circuit alone. Gain drifts introduced by the stabilization circuit
alone, as distinct from those in the analyzer or in the calibration
light source, are negligible.

The stabilization factor τ has been adjusted to about 4 sec.
Using $K = 13$, one finds

$$\frac{\sigma_N}{N} = \frac{1}{13} \frac{1}{\sqrt{2 \times 65 \times 4}} = 0.0033 = 0.33\%$$

This contribution to the width of the spectral peaks is negligible.
For example, a possible resolution at high gamma ray energies in
the absence of gain stabilization might be 6 percent. With stabilization it would become $\sqrt{6^2 + (2.3 \times 0.33)^2}\ \% = 6.05\%$. No deterioration in resolution was observable under stabilization.

For a comparatively short measurement time of 2 min. the parameter

$$\frac{\sigma_{N}(T)}{N} = \frac{1}{13}\frac{1}{\sqrt{65 \times 2 \times 60}} = 9 \times 10^{-4} = 0.09\%$$

Hence, gain shifts caused by the statistics of stabilization are negligible and become even less important for the longer counting times for which the stabilization system was intended.

DESIRABLE IMPROVEMENTS

A new plutonium alpha light source has been designed to focus the stimulated light more efficiently into the 8 by 4 in. crystal. Insufficiency of light in the calibration pulse is not, however, a fundamental defect of the system. It would be possible to mount the alpha source within the main 8 by 4 in. crystal immediately below the present special window. The light coupling problem would thereby be largely eliminated, while recognition of the calibration events would still be possible by a monitor photomultiplier immediately outside the window. The disadvantage of internal incorporation of the plutonium is that adjustment of the calibration peak to a particular equivalent gamma ray energy is not possible, and removal of the alpha peak from background is not possible if the "inhibit add 1" circuitry is out of order.

It is hoped that a more constant light coupling system can be provided, such that even the present small drift in calibration peak energy can be reduced.

In case constancy of calibration light pulse magnitude remains inadequate, we have under active development a rather basic modification to this system. Instead of providing calibration signals by introducing a light flash into the 8 by 4 in. crystal from an external source, we will irradiate the crystal by calibration gamma rays from an external source. This external gamma ray source will be a phosphor containing, for example, an isotope which emits a beta ray and a gamma ray in coincidence. The beta ray will be absorbed in the phosphor, producing a monitor scintillation and thereby an electronic signal which functions analogously to our present monitor signal. The gamma ray, interacting within the 8 by 4 in. crystal, will produce a calibration scintillation free of all light coupling problems. The electronics for such a system is only slightly different from our present circuitry.

If necessary, zero stabilization will be accomplished by feeding small electronic pulses directly into the ADC and using their channel number to adjust zero, just as the channel number of the present calibration pulses adjusts gain. Since zero drift cannot originate outside the ADC, nothing but the ADC need be contained in the feedback loop.

The stabilization factor S will be increased by electronic alterations which make the charge fed onto the integrating condenser independent of the amount already there.

SUMMARY

A gain stabilization system has been developed for a scintillation spectrometer which is based on an essentially all-inclusive feedback loop. The input is a reference light flash to the photomultiplier tubes, and the output for adjustment of the gain is taken from the digitalized resultant pulse amplitude within the analyzer. The system operates independent of the particular gamma spectrum under investigation, yet contributes no background of its own. Preliminary results suggest that stability of about 0.1 percent can be expected over one day, and it is hoped that this time can be considerably extended.

REFERENCES

1. von Dardel, G. F.: A portable 24 channel kicksorter, *J. Sci. Instr.*, 32:302, 1955.
2. Haun, S. and Kamke, D.: A universal method of stabilizing scintillation spectrometry apparatus. *Nucl. Instr. Methods*, 8:331, 1960.
3. Marlow, K. W.: A system for stabilizing the gain of a scintillation spectrometer. *Nucl. Instr. Methods*, 15:188, 1962.
4. Scherbatskoy, S. A.: Stabilized scintillation counter. *R. S. I.*, 32:599, 1961.

5. Valckx, F. P. G.: Direct current stabilization of scintillation counters used with pulsed accelerators. *Nucl. Instr. Methods, 10*:234, 1961.
6. de Waard, H.: Stabilizing scintillation spectrometers with counting-rate-difference feedback. *Nucleonics, 13 N., 7*:36, 1955.
7. Breitenberger, E.: Scintillation spectrometer statistics. *Progr. Nucl. Phys., 4*:56, 1955.

DISCUSSION

Chairman: ROBLEY D. EVANS

Massachusetts Institute of Technology
Cambridge, Massachusetts

PHILIP SHEVICK: Dr. Dudley, how do you account for the temperature coefficient over the light source? The sodium iodide presumably has a coefficient of about 0.2 percent per degree.

ROBERT A. DUDLEY: We hope, of course, that the response of the sodium iodide being irradiated by the alpha particle drifts in the same way as the sodium iodide being irradiated by the gamma ray. If this were so, there would be no temperature effect. We don't know whether this is so or not. Our correction may be incomplete in this respect.

JOHN RUNDO: Mr. Peterson, what was the cost of your shield?

RICHARD E. PETERSON: The actual construction cost was $34,000; then various things had to be done such as adding lead and extra painting. All of this, including ion exchanger, was $40,000.

JOHN RUNDO: There is a large water shield at Aldermaston in England. It is not used as a low background room for whole body counting, but merely as a large room for installing many low background counters. The water thickness is about 8 ft., and there are elaborate precautions to keep the water at the same temperature. I have no details of the cost.

CHAIRMAN ROBLEY EVANS: Dr. Peterson, why don't you dispense with the ion exchange column and put a gel in and save that operating expense?

RICHARD E. PETERSON: Maybe we will in time. We don't know how this will hold up. If we put in some neutron capture material, we won't have the ion material circulating at that time.

STELIOS REGAS: Just before the meeting a question was brought up about Mr. Walter's paper: Isn't it more probable that solid steel construction will have the ability of being magnetized much more than the thin plates? The answer is that the probability of having magnetism in any size of steel is approximately the same. Even if it is not the same, one

117

should check the steel for magnetism, which is very detrimental to the measurement. If there is magnetism in the steel shield, it is much easier to demagnetize a solid plate than it is to demagnetize the same thickness made of thin plates.

ERNEST C. ANDERSON: Dr. Dudley, in your equation for the precision of the standard deviation of the channel number of the peak, an important parameter which occurs is K, which is the percent change in gain. Could you give the value for this factor?

ROBERT A. DUDLEY: In our case this is 13. One could probably expect to get something like 20 if he had a light of amplitude equal to about 1 Mev. Our peak is not very sharp because it is low energy in the normal fluctuations coming up.

HAROLD MAY: Concerning these equations, you had sigma sub N, the standard deviation of a single determination. Over what time interval is this? Is this a single pulse?

ROBERT A. DUDLEY: This is a single observation. If you could have a needle on a meter which is reading different gains, and if you took an instantaneous reading of what this needle shows and then waited for a time long compared with tau so your readings are not correlated with each other, and if you then took another reading in half a minute, you would get a set of numbers, and the standard deviation of this set of numbers is sigma sub N.

It is a function of the counting rate of the alpha source, the magniture of the corrections made after each pulse, the sharpness of the peak and one or two other things that are more or less evident as one looks at it.

HAROLD MAY: Is the value of S experimentally determined or can this be related to the parameters of the system?

ROBERT A. DUDLEY: You can compute it directly in terms of the parameters of the system.

HAROLD MAY: What value do you come up with?

ROBERT A. DUDLEY: In our case, S equals 12. In theory it should be equal to the ratio of tau sub C, the integrating condenser time constant, divided by tau, the observed stabilization time constant. In our case the ratio of tau sub C to tau is equal to 100 or so, whereas S is equal only to 12. This means I haven't given you the full story.

The problem is that the magnitude of plus and minus charges that we put on the integrating condenser are not quite constant, and it depends somewhat on the magnitude of the charge already on the condenser. We have circuits that will get rid of this, but we could not get the transistors to do this conveniently, so we have done this temporarily. We had no trouble getting an S of 100 or so.

ROBERT W. WOOD: Do you think this stabilization system is readily incorporated into an existing apparatus that is now in operation?

ROBERT A. DUDLEY: Not in its present form. It involves putting in an extra window through which the signal can be introduced. The best system to use would be an isotope which emitted a gamma ray of 1 Mev in coincidence with an alpha ray. This does not exist, but one could get an approximation. If one had this, one would use the same thing I have here, except that instead of feeding the light from the alpha scintillation in the small auxiliary crystal into the big crystal, one would feed the gamma ray in coincidence with the alpha ray into the main crystal, and then one would get away with the light coupling problem and could also adapt it to a system that is already built without needing an extra glass window. Such an auxiliary source could be made.

CHAIRMAN ROBLEY EVANS: How would you handle the Compton continuum?

ROBERT A. DUDLEY: That would be no problem. If one did nothing about it, it would reduce S. However, let's say the calibration peak should go normally into channel 120. With the analyzer, you could exclude from the memory any pulse in coincidence with the alpha ray, but use for stabilization purposes only those which exceed channel 100. That would handle it electronically in a simple way.

WILLIAM B. RIVKIN: Why not introduce a low energy gamma source that would not add any additional Compton to the spectrum and use that as a stabilizer without the additional alpha source? Why wouldn't this monoenergetic or essentially low energy gamma source or low energy of the spectrum do as well?

ROBERT A. DUDLEY: We would hope to have a signal greater than 0.25 Mev when we get into business. We would like to have a calibration signal which contributes nothing to any part of the background of the spectrum we are interested in which in our case extends from bremsstrahlung energies of 50 Kv on up. The gamma ray you describe would not occur at a known moment, so one could not prevent this calibration signal from getting into the memory, and it would be a useful system only if the gamma ray were lower than what anyone was studying.

This would give rise to other problems, as does ours now, in that zero stability must be very good unless one stabilizes zero. A small shift in zero if corrected by a gain alteration to bring the calibration peak to the right channel will introduce a large error into the energy versus channel number correlation at high energies. So, low energy gamma is not desirable from that point of view. Also, gamma, unless one uses it in some special system, coincident with an alpha for example, gives troubles in background.

WILLIAM A. McCARTHY: Dr. Dudley, you mentioned that you felt there was no zero shift in the analyzer itself. Where you are talking of low counting rates, this is true; but have you excluded pulse pile-up? How would you classify a constant shift of channels all the way across the spectrum?

Apparently you feel this is a better way to go about it than to get at the source of the errors. What do you feel are the sources of gain shift in the system? Why not stabilize better the high voltage supply to the multiplier, and why not temperature-regulate the photomultiplier? Or are there other things you are looking to stabilize here, too?

ROBERT A. DUDLEY: I did not say there are no zero drifts in the analyzer. What I said was that any zero drifts that occur must occur within the ADC. They cannot occur in the photomultiplier or amplifier which are AC-coupled to the analog digital converter. There are drifts in zero in the ADC. Pulse pile-up, zero shift with counting rate we have observed; zero stabilization by feeding an electronic pulse to the ADC would correct for this.

In answer to your second question, one does of course try to stabilize all the components. One is never altogether successful in this; even if one were, this still would not get away from one of our main original worries, namely, the shift in gain with motion of the crystal through a nonuniform magnetic field.

I like the philosophy of the system. It is a complete feedback loop. You start with light and end up with a digitalized pulse, and it corrects for everything.

VOICE: Dr. Dean, I think it is a little unfair against the sodium iodide crystal to compare 4 pi liquid scintillator with chair geometry. It is well known that we get much better stability of the calibration factor with a scanning geometry.

SESSION IV, SEPTEMBER 5

INSTRUMENTATION, TECHNIQUE and CALIBRATION,

Continued

Chairman: ROBERT A. DUDLEY

12

QUANTITATIVE MEASUREMENT OF MIXED RADIOISOTOPES IN HUMANS BY GAMMA RAY SPECTROSCOPY: THE MIXED FISSION PRODUCTS Ba^{140}-La^{140}, Zr^{95}-Nb^{95} and Ru^{103}-Rr^{103m} [1]

Werner Mehlhorn,[2] Raymond L. Weiland,
Robert T. Lagemann and George R. Meneely[3]

Vanderbilt University
Nashville, Tennessee

INTRODUCTION

A s long as human beings are using radioactive material in science and technology, the problem will exist of determining the total amount of radioactive isotopes in case of an incorporation of fission products.

To start solving this complex problem, we considered a case in which at time t = 0 a human body took up a mixture of radioactive isotopes. We assume that we know the isotopes forming the mixture, so that no identification is necessary. The following questions need to be answered:

How can the initial amounts of the radioactive isotopes be determined?

What is the probable error in the final results?

Our method is suitable for any mixture of isotopes; however, the accuracy depends on several factors, such as the energy of

[1] This work was supported in part by U. S. Public Health Service, U. S. Atomic Energy Commission and U. S. Army Medical Research and Development Command.

[2] On leave from Technische Hochschule, Karlsruhe, Germany. Now at University of Münster, Münster Germany.

[3] Now at University of Texas, Houston, Texas.

the γ-transitions and the number of transitions. Take as an example the six fission products Ba^{140}, La^{140}, Zr^{95}, Nb^{95}, Ru^{103} and Rh^{103m}. For the development of the method we do not have to assume that the parent-daughter isotopes Ba-La, Zr-Nb are in equilibrium. Because of the short half life of Rh^{103m} (57 min.), the isotopes Ru and Rh are in equilibrium several hours after the incorporation. Later, proving the method by experiment, we will use the isotopes in equilibrium; this is only a small simplification of the more complex case.

METHOD

The most direct way should be to measure a single spectrum of each of the six isotopes which are given to human beings. Knowing the amount of radioactivity each spectrum represents, a standard spectrum for one isotope and for a certain size and shape of the human body (height, thickness) can be established. Each complex spectrum produced by a mixture of the six isotopes is then only a superposition of the single spectra and can be separated in single spectra by a computer.

In this case we will not use the human body for the calibration because some isotopes may have too small a permissible body burden.

There is a possibility of calibration by using other isotopes with approximately the same energy of γ-transition.

Energy and intensity of a radioactive isotope are given by the maximum and the area of the photopeak, respectively, in the pulse height spectrum of a scintillation crystal spectrometer recorded from the isotope. The total photopeak area $A(E)$ in units of counts per minute of a γ-transition with energy E is given by the following equation:

$$A(E) = R \cdot I(E) \cdot F_A(E) \cdot F_G \cdot E(E) \qquad (1)$$

where R is the total amount of the isotope in μC,

$I(E)$ is the number of quanta of energy E per one disintegration,

$F_A(E)$ stands for the absorption in the source itself,

F_G is a geometrical factor and stands for the solid angle subtended by the crystal,

$E(E)$ is the efficiency of the crystal; that is the fraction of the γ-quanta reaching the crystal and contributing to the photopeak area.

Because the human body is an extended source with considerable change in size, we have to consider carefully several points.

The position of the body relative to the crystal (given by factor F_G) is important. It was shown experimentally that the factor F_G deviates from a mean value by as much as ± 50 percent for the different parts of a human body with body weight 75 kg. and a mean thickness of 20 cm. in the tilting chair position. Furthermore, the location of the isotopes can be time dependent. This will give a time dependent factor F_G which complicates the problem.

In the arc position, where the human body is laid along an arc at whose center the crystal is located, one can get approximately the same factor F_G for each part of the body. Assuming a radius of the arc of 2 meters and the same size of body as before, the maximum deviation in F_G is ± 10 percent; that means the mean value of F_G for different body sizes is independent of time and shape of human body with an error of about 15 percent.

Because of the scattering effect in the human body it is impossible to calculate the attenuation F_A of a γ radiation with the tabulated total mass attenuation coefficient. So one has to determine the self absorption F_A of the human body in an experiment. There is also the fact that with time dependent location of the radioactivity, the absorption may become time dependent. To decide whether this should be taken into consideration, one has to know the biological pathway of the radioactive isotope. We will neglect as a first aproximation this effect in our method.

If $R(0)$ is the amount of radioactive isotope incorporated into the body at time $t = 0$, the photopeak area $A(E,t)$ at any time t of the γ radiation with energy E is given by

$$A(E,t) = R(t) \cdot I(E) \cdot F_A(E) \cdot F_G \cdot E(E), \qquad (2)$$

where $R(t)$ is for a parent isotope:

$$R(t) = R_P(0) \cdot G_P(t) = R_P(0) \cdot \exp(-\lambda_P t), \qquad (3)$$

and for a daughter isotope:

$$R_D(t) = R_D(0) \cdot G_D(t) + R_P(0) \cdot H_{DP}(t) \qquad (4)$$

$$= R_D(0) \cdot \exp(-\lambda_D t) + R_P(0) \frac{\lambda_D}{\lambda_D - \lambda_P}$$

$$[\exp(-\lambda_P t) - \exp(-\lambda_D t)]$$

λ is connected with the physical and biological half lives $T_{phys.}$ and $T_{biol.}$ by

$$\lambda = \frac{\ln 2}{T_{phys.}} + \frac{\ln 2}{T_{biol.}} \qquad (5)$$

In order to get the initial amounts $R(0)$ of radioactive isotopes by means of a measurement at time t, one has to know the biological half lives, $T_{biol.}$.

Equation (2) should be rewritten in the following form of a parent isotope:

$$A(E,t) = R(0) \cdot G_P(t) \cdot CF(E), \qquad (6)$$

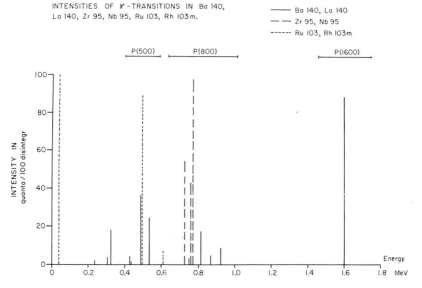

Figure 1. Intensities of γ transitions in quanta per 100 disintegrations of Ba^{140}, La^{140}, Zr^{95}, Nb^{95}, Ru^{103}, Rh^{103m}. (Transitions with energies <0.2 Mev are not listed, except the 0.040 Mev transition of Rh^{103m}.)

and for a daughter isotope:

$$A(E,t) = [R_D(0)(G_D(t) + R_P(0) \cdot H_{DP}(t)] \cdot CF(E) \qquad (7)$$

Here CF(E) is a calibration factor in units of

$$\frac{\text{counts (of total photopeak area)}}{1 \text{ min} \cdot 1\mu C \text{ (of the isotope making the photopeak)}}.$$

The calibration factor must be determined by experiment.

In our case we have to deal with the isotopes La^{140}, Ba^{140}, Zr^{95}, Nb^{95}, Ru^{103} and Rh^{103m}. Figure 1 gives the intensities of the γ transitions of these isotopes in quanta per 100 disintegrations. Intensities less than 1 quantum per 100 disintegrations are neglected. Figure 1 shows that there are three groups of γ transitions, a single transition at 1600 kev and two groups around 800 kev and 500 kev. Because the crystal spectrometer cannot resolve the components of the groups, the pulse height spectrum of the six isotopes together shows three photopeaks (Fig. 2), a single photopeak P(1600) and two complex photopeaks P(800) and P(500). The single spectra and the mixed spectrum were obtained by the isotopes Ba^{140}-La^{140} in equilibrium, Zr^{95}-Nb^{95} in equilibrium and Ru^{103}-Rh^{103m} in equilibrium.

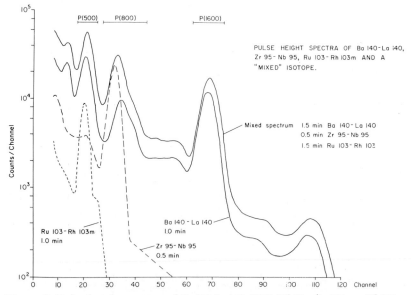

Figure 2. Pulse height spectra of Ba^{140}-La^{140}, Zr^{95}-Nb^{95}, Ru^{103} - Rh^{103m}, each in equilibrium, and of a "mixed" isotope.

The areas of the three photopeaks are given by the following three equations:

$$A(1600,t) = A_{La}(1600,t)$$
$$A(800,t) = A_{La}(923,t) + A_{La}(868,t) + A_{La}(815,t) + A_{La}(748,t)$$
$$+ A_{Zr}(760,t) + A_{Zr}(726,t)$$
$$+ A_{Nb}(768,t) \qquad\qquad (8)$$
$$A(500,t) = A_{Ba}(535,t)$$
$$+ A_{La}(491,t)$$
$$+ A_{Ru}(496,t)$$

where each single area is given by an equation (6 or 7).

Because we cannot obtain the single calibration factors of, for example, the La components of the complex photopeak P(800), we shall use the more comprehensive calibration factor $CF_{La}(800)$. So system 8 can be written in the final form

$$A(1600,t) = R_{Ba}(0) \cdot H_{LaBa}(t) \cdot CF_{La}(1600)$$
$$+ R_{La}(0) \cdot G_{La}(t) \cdot CF_{La}(1600)$$
$$A(800,t) = R_{La}(0) \cdot G_{La}(t) \cdot CF_{La}(800) \qquad\qquad (9)$$
$$+ R_{Zr}(0) \cdot [G_{Zr}(t) \cdot CF_{Zr}(800) + H_{NbZr}(t)\, CF_{Nb}(800)]$$
$$+ R_{Nb}(0) \cdot G_{Nb}(t) \cdot CF_{Nb}(800)$$
$$A(500,t) = R_{Ba}(0)\, [G_{Ba}(t) \cdot CF_{Ba}(500) + H_{LaBa}(t) \cdot CF_{La}(500)]$$
$$+ R_{La}(0) \cdot G_{La}(t) \cdot CF_{La}(500)$$
$$+ R_{Ru}(0) \cdot G_{Ru}(t) \cdot CF_{Ru}(500).$$

Here the functions $G(t)$ and $H(t)$ are defined by equations 3 and 4 and are known when the biological half lives, $T_{biol.}$, are available. The calibration factors CF are also known. So we have a system of three linear equations with the five unknowns $R_{Ba}(0)$, $R_{La}(0)$, $R_{Nb}(0)$, $R_{Zr}(0)$, $R_{Ru}(0)$.

In general there exists no definite solution. Therefore we have to take a second spectrum at a different time t. Because the physical half life T of La is only 40 hr., the functions $G_{La}(t)$ and $H_{LaBa}(t)$ change rapidly with time. So the second spectrum can be recorded about 40 hr. after the first one. Unfortunately, the change in $G(t)$ and $H(t)$ of Zr and Nb is too small within 40 hr., so with these two spectra it is possible to determine only $R_{Ba}(0)$, $R_{La}(0)$, $R_{Ru}(0)$ and $R_{Zr+Nb}(0)$. In order to get $R_{Zr}(0)$ and $R_{Nb}(0)$ separately, one has to record a third spectrum about twenty to thirty days after the first one.

If we assume — opposite to our previous assumption — some

relations between the isotopes at the time $t = 0$ of the incorporation, then the problem becomes simpler.

The isotopes La-Ba, Zr-Nb are in equilibrium at $t = 0$ (Ru-Rh are always in equilibrium). This gives us two more pieces of information in addition to the three equations 9.

$$R_{La}(0) = \frac{\lambda_{La}}{\lambda_{La} - \lambda_{Ba}} R_{Ba}(0) \qquad (10)$$

$$R_{Nb}(0) = \frac{\lambda_{Nb}}{\lambda_{Nb} - \lambda_{Zr}} R_{Zr}(0)$$

In this case we need to record only one spectrum.

There are not only relations between parent and daughter isotopes, but the composition of the mixed isotope is known. The composition of the radioactive isotopes at any time after a slow neutron fission is well known (1). In this case one has to determine only the absolute amount of one isotope at $t = 0$; all other isotopes can then be evaluated by the relationships. In our practical case the determination of $R_{La}(0)$ by means of the photopeak $P(1600)$ would be the most direct way.

EXPERIMENT

The following experiments have been made to test the method and to determine which errors can be expected by application of the method to human bodies. The radioactive isotopes were Ba^{140}-La^{140} in equilibrium, Zr^{95}-Nb^{95} in equilibrium and Ru^{103}-Rh^{103m} in equilibrium. About 20 μc of each of these three mixed isotopes were filled in 20 ml. containers. These sources were used as standard sources. Each mixed spectrum was recorded by counting each of the sources for a different time and adding the single spectra to a mixed spectrum (Fig. 2). This can be done very easily by the electronic memory of our crystal spectrometer. Figure 3 shows the experimental arrangement. In this experiment we carried out the following steps:

Determination of the calibration factors CF of the three standard sources in counts per minute of photopeak area for three absorber thicknesses (0 cm., 9 cm., 15 cm.H_2O),

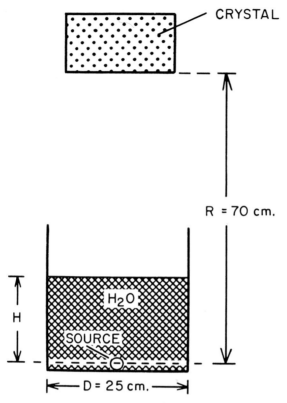

Figure 3. Experimental arrangement.

TABLE I

CALIBRATION FACTORS IN COUNTS OF PHOTOPEAK AREA PER MIN. OF THE
STANDARD SOURCES FOR DIFFERENT ABSORBER THICKNESSES

		CF(1600)		CF(800)		CF(500)	
		By Hand	Computer	By Hand	Computer	By Hand	Computer
no	Ba - La	82850	82857		54137		116442
absorber	Zr - Nb			223634	229523		
	Ru - Rh					31424	32383
9 cm	Ba - La	56827	56793		38566		67503
H_2O	Zr - Nb			139777	143572		
	Ru - Rh					18607	18917
15 cm	Ba - La	45019	45020		27797		45790
H_2O	Zr - Nb			101885	104288		
	Ru - Rh					13097	13110

Calculation of the three photopeak areas A(1600), A(800) and A(500) of the mixed spectra,

Calculation of the counting times t for each standard source contributing to the mixed spectrum.

Table I gives the calibration factors CF in units of counts of photopeak area per minute for different absorber thicknesses. $CF_{9,La}(1600)$ means the calibration factor $CF_{La}(1600)$ with an absorber thickness of 9 cm. H_2O. The calibration factors $CF_{Ba-La}(1600)$, $CF_{Zr-Nb}(800)$, $CF_{Ru-Rh}(500)$ were calculated manually as well as by the computer; $CF_{Ba-La}(800)$ and $CF_{Ba-La}(500)$ were calculated only by the computer.

The calculation of the three photopeak areas A(1600), A(800) and A(500) was done by the computer (IBM 650) by the following steps. A constant Compton background due to the 2.5 Mev radiation of La^{140} is subtracted. The photopeak area A(1600) is calculated by totalling the counts of channels 62 to 74. Multiplying by a factor 1.0 instead of the correct factor 1.0073 to get the total area involves an error of 0.7 percent. According to the photopeak area A(1600), the Compton background given by the 1.6 Mev radiation is subtracted. For this purpose a reference spectrum of K^{42} with only one γ-transition of 1.52 Mev and the Compton background due to this radiation is given to the computer. The K^{42} spectrum was recorded with a slightly higher photomultiplier voltage, so that the photopeak of the 1.52 Mev radiation of K^{42} falls on top of the 1.6 Mev transition of La with an error <1 channel. The photopeak area A(800) is calculated by integrating over channels 27 to 43 and multiplying by a factor 1.0. This involves an error <1 percent. According to the photopeak area A(800) the Compton background given by the γ radiations which form the complex photopeak P(800) is subtracted from the mixed spectrum. A reference spectrum of Zr^{95}-Nb^{95} with a complex photopeak P(800) and the Compton background due to these transitions is fed to the computer. The photopeak area A(500) is calculated by integrating over channels 17 to 25 and multiplying by a factor 1.0, thus involving an error <1.0 percent.

We recorded one mixed spectrum without absorber, three mixed spectra with 9 cm. H_2O absorber and four mixed spectra with 15 cm. H_2O absorber. These absorber thicknesses were chosen because the average thickness of human bodies is 20 to 28 cm. Assuming an extended source through the whole body, the average absorber thickness is roughly 10 to 14 cm.

Table II gives the results of the mixed spectrum without absorber. In column 1 the single isotopes are listed, in column 2 the recorded time of each isotope, in column 3 the time calculated by the computer, and in column 4 the deviation of the calculated value from the true value in per cent.

Tables III and IV give the results of the mixed spectra for 9 cm. and 15 cm. H_2O absorber, respectively. In order to study the influence of different body sizes on the determination of the total amounts of isotopes with not exactly known Compton backgrounds (C) and calibration factors (CF), we made four calculations of each mixed spectrum by changing the Compton background and the calibration factors.

TABLE II
MIXED SPECTRUM WITHOUT ABSORBER

Stand. Source	Recorded Time in Min.	Computed Time in Min. with C_0, CF_0	Deviation in %
Ba^{140}-La^{140}	1.5	1.45	− 3.4
Zr^{95}-Nb^{95}	0.5	0.49	− 2.0
Ru^{103}-Rh^{103m}	1.5	1.43	− 1.4

TABLE III
MIXED SPECTRA WITH 9 CM. H_2O ABSORBER

Standard Source	Rec. Time in Min.	C_9 Min.	CF_9 %	C_{15} Min.	CF_9 %	C_9 Min.	CF_{15} %	C_{15} Min.	CF_{15} %
Ba^{140}-La^{140}	0.4	0.381	−4.8	0.381	− 4.8	0.481	+20.2	0.481	+20.2
Zr^{95}-Nb^{95}	0.4	0.425	+5.3	0.377	− 5.8	0.598	+49.5	0.531	+32.8
Ru^{103}-Rh^{103m}	3.4	3.30	−2.9	2.90	−14.7	5.04	+48.3	4.46	+31.2
Ba^{140}-La^{140}	0.3	0.286	−4.7	0.286	− 4.7	0.361	+20.3	0.361	+20.3
Zr^{95}-Nb^{95}	0.5	0.502	+0.4	0.479	− 4.2	0.699	+39.8	0.678	+35.6
Ru^{103}-Rh^{103m}	2.5	2.36	−5.6	1.88	−24.8	3.62	+44.9	2.92	+16.8
Ba^{140}-La^{140}	0.2	0.190	−5.0	0.190	− 5.0	0.239	+19.5	0.239	+19.5
Zr^{95}-Nb^{95}	0.6	0.602	+0.3	0.591	− 1.5	0.835	+39.2	0.821	+36.9
Ru^{103}-Rh^{103m}	1.6	1.48	−7.5	0.92	−42.5	2.27	+41.9	1.47	− 8.1

TABLE IV
Mixed Spectra with 15 cm. H_2O Absorber

Standard Source	Rec. Time in Min.	Computed Time in Min. and Deviation in %							
		C_{15} Min.	CF_{15} %	C_9 Min.	CF_{15} %	C_{15} Min.	CF_9 %	C_9 Min.	CF_9 %
Ba^{140}-La^{140}	0.6	0.587	− 2.2	0.587	− 2.2	0.467	−22.2	0.467	−22.2
Zr^{95}-Nb^{95}	0.2	0.223	+11.5	0.258	+29.0	0.150	−25.0	0.176	−12.0
Ru^{103}-Rh^{103m}	2.6	2.48	− 4.6	2.79	+ 7.3	0.941	−64.0	1.69	−35.0
Ba^{140}-La^{140}	0.4	0.391	− 2.3	0.391	− 2.3	0.310	−22.5	0.310	−22.5
Zr^{95}-Nb^{95}	0.4	0.421	+ 5.3	0.444	+11.0	0.298	−28.0	0.315	−21.2
Ru^{103}-Rh^{130m}	3.4	3.24	− 4.7	3.70	+ 8.8	2.09	−38.6	2.40	−29.4
Ba^{140}-La^{140}	0.3	0.293	− 2.3	0.293	− 2.3	0.232	−22.7	0.232	−22.6
Zr^{95}-Nb^{95}	0.5	0.514	+ 2.8	0.532	+ 6.4	0.368	−26.4	0.381	−23.8
Ru^{103}-Rh^{103m}	2.5	2.36	− 5.6	2.89	+15.6	1.52	−39.2	1.89	−24.4
Ba^{140}-La^{140}	0.2	0.197	− 1.5	0.197	− 1.5	0.156	−22.0	0.156	−22.0
Zr^{95}-Nb^{95}	0.6	0.609	+ 1.5	0.620	+ 3.3	0.438	−27.0	0.447	−25.5
Ru^{103}-Rh-^{103m}	1.6	1.43	−10.6	2.03	+27.0	0.911	−43.0	1.33	−16.9

As already mentioned, the computer was fed with two reference spectra of K^{42} and Zr^{95}-Nb^{95} to subtract a Compton background according to the photopeak areas A(1600) and A(800). We recorded Compton backgrounds of K^{42} (for the normal voltage of the photomultiplier as well as for a slightly increased voltage to match the photopeaks of K^{42} and P(1600) of La^{140}) and Zr^{95}-Nb^{95}, each without absorber, with 9 cm. and 15 cm. H_2O absorber. A comparison of these K^{42} Compton backgrounds with the K^{42} Compton backgrounds of human bodies in the tilting chair position, which were investigated extensively in the past, shows the following facts (Fig. 4). The Compton background of a point source with an extended absorber of 9 cm. thickness falls within the limits of human body Compton backgrounds. These two limits were established by extreme body shapes: a child and a tall, obese man weighing 133 kg. The Compton background for 15 cm. absorber thickness lies in the P(800) region a little above (2), in the P(500) region between (1) and (2), but lies in general about 10 to 15 percent above the Compton background for 9 cm. absorber. The photopeak areas of the mixed spectra in Tables III and IV were calculated with both Compton backgrounds C_9 and C_{15}.

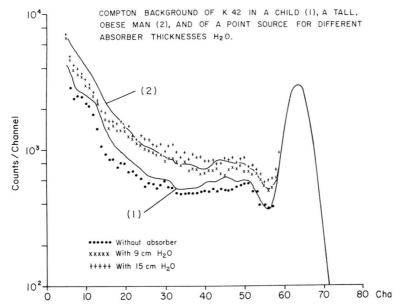

Figure 4. Compton background of the 1.52 Mev transition of K⁴² in a child, a tall obese man and a point source for different absorber thicknesses H_2O.

The determination of the total amounts of radioactive isotopes in the human body depends strongly on the knowledge of the calibration factors CF. It is, therefore, important to study the influence on the calculated absolute amounts of isotopes by changing the calibration factors. Using the calibration factors CF_{15} for 15 cm. H_2O absorber for the computation of the photopeak areas of the mixed spectrum recorded with 9 cm. H_2O absorber and vice versa is almost equivalent to changing the body thickness from 18 cm. to 30 cm. and using either the calibration factor of the 18 cm. body or the 30 cm. body. The calibration factors actually used are indicated by CF_9 and CF_{15}.

RESULTS AND CONCLUSIONS

Tables III and IV show that the changes of the Compton background do not give a great error in the results except for

Ru^{103}. There is an increase in the error of the calculated time with the decrease of the recorded time. This indicates in general that isotopes giving only a small contribution to the mixed spectrum are determined with a greater error than the others.

On the other hand, the change in the calibration factor is more severe than the change in Compton background.

From these results we draw the following conclusions.

The Compton background is an important factor for computing the photopeak areas of the unknown spectrum. Change of this background with body thickness is not so strong that it must be corrected for different body thicknesses. We therefore believe that a "standard" Compton background of a "standard" human body in the arc position will give satisfactory results. Because the Compton effect is less sensitive to the shape of the body, the standard Compton background can be measured by using a plexiglass phantom in the arc position.

It was found that the calibration factor depends strongly on the absorber thickness and with this on the thickness of human body. To keep the error in the final results with confidence smaller than 50 percent, we believe that different calibration factors should be used for different thicknesses of the human body. If it is impossible to measure directly the calibration factors by giving the isotopes in question to human beings, then it is almost always possible to get the calibration factors of isotopes which have a γ radiation close to the γ radiation of the isotope to be calibrated and can be incorporated in the human body in well measurable quantities (2). In indirect calibration, care must be take to insure that the γ radiation of the replacing isotope has about the same attenuation in the body as the γ radiation of the replaced isotope.

REFERENCES

1. Hunter, H. F., and Ballou, N. E.: *Nucleonics*, 9:Nr. 11, C-2, 1951.
2. Malamos, B., Belcher, E. H., Binopoulos, D., and Constantinides, C.: Whole body counting, 435. International Atomic Energy Agency, Vienna, 1962.

13

GEOMETRICAL AND ATTENUATION CORRECTIONS FOR A TWO CRYSTAL WHOLE BODY COUNTER; BODY SCANNING WITH AN 8 BY 4 IN. NaI CRYSTAL

GERALD J. HINE, SEBASTIAN GENNA AND BELTON A. BURROWS

Boston University School of Medicine
Veterans Administration Hospital
Boston, Mass.

INTRODUCTION

CRITERIA FOR THE design of a whole body counter for studying the metabolism of administered radioisotopes in humans have been well stated by many investigators. Miller (1) says: "If reliable and reproductive total body measurements are to be made, a counter should be designed to satisfy the following specifications, listed in the order of importance.

The sensitivity of the counter should not depend upon the subject's body build or upon the distribution of the material within the body.

It should be possible to calibrate the counter with reasonable accuracy by using an appropriate phantom.

The position of the subject and of each crystal should be the same for all total body measurements, regardless of the subject's body build."

Numerous whole body counters using one or several sodium iodide crystals of various sizes have been described (1). Though for some installations additional factors such as available space or economical conditions were of importance, the stated criteria were of concern to most authors. However, the gamma ray absorption for each patient has not been evaluated to obtain re-

TABLE I

FRACTION OF EMITTED GAMMA RAYS OF VARIOUS ENERGY THAT HAS INTERACTED
WITHIN TISSUE OF GIVEN THICKNESS

Gamma Ray Energy (Mev.)	Per Cent Absorption in Tissue of Thickness*			
	5 cm.	10 cm.	20 cm.	30 cm.
0.279	46	70	92	98
0.364	44	68	90	97
0.511	37	61	85	94
0.662	35	57	82	92
1.25	27	47	72	85
1.46	26	45	70	83
2.0	22	40	55	78

* Since gamma rays are absorbed in tissue mainly by Compton interaction, a
scattered gamma ray is produced each time. Even in cases where the scattered
gamma ray has nearly the same energy and direction as the primary gamma ray,
the latter is regarded absorbed in tissue.

sults which do not depend on the subject's body build and also
upon the distribution of the radioisotope within the body.

In Table I the gamma rays of various energies are listed
which cover the spectrum of radioisotopes most commonly used
in medical research. Assuming an original intensity of 100 percent at a given body site, that fraction of the gamma rays that is
lost by their interaction with tissue of a given thickness is stated.
For example, the 364 kev gamma rays of I^{131} diminish to about
one half (46 percent) of their initial abundance when penetrating 5 cm. of soft tissue. Therefore, from any I^{131} labeled compound distributed evenly within the body or concentrated mainly
in one organ, only a small fraction of the I^{131} gamma rays will
escape from the body without an interaction.

The present paper describes a method which allows a determination of the average gamma ray absorption for each individual
body count. No assumption has to be made concerning the radioisotope distribution within the body. The actual distribution
can remain unknown.

In addition to body counts it is frequently desirable to ex-
plore the radioisotope distribution by body scan. In our installation we employ one of our 8 by 4 in. sodium iodide crystals from
the body counter for body scanning within the iron room. Such
a focussing collimator has not been reported previously.

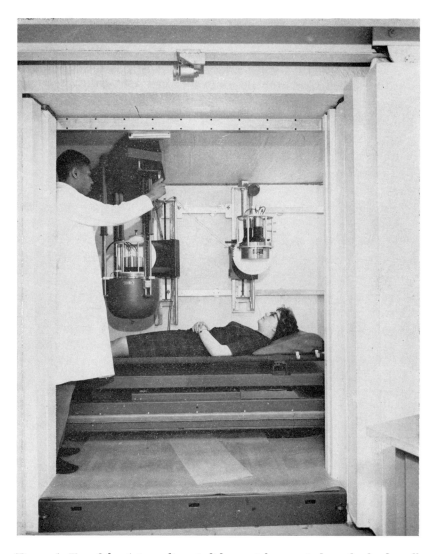

Figure 1. Two 8 by 4 in. sodium iodide crystals mounted on the back wall inside the iron room. Each crystal can be raised, lowered and tilted and moved along the center line of the iron room. One of the crystals has been placed inside a 3 in. thick lead shield with a multi-hole focussing collimator. The subject rests on a scanning bed.

WHOLE BODY COUNTER

Iron Room and Crystal Mounting

The iron room, located in the basement of the Boston University Medical Research Building was built of 9 in. thick armor plates fabricated during World War II. In order to provide maximum access to the room, two sliding doors, each 3 ft. wide, close one of the 12 ft. walls of the room (Fig. 1). The doors can be operated independently, either manually or by motor drive.

The two 8 by 4 in. sodium iodine crystals[1] are mounted on tracks along the back wall of the iron room. Each crystal can be raised, lowered and tilted with respect to the horizontal plane. Furthermore, they travel the length of the steel room along its center line, since the crystals are mounted at a fixed distance from the back wall of the steel room. This keeps the two crystals

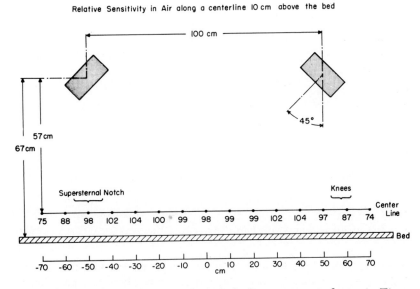

Figure 2. Schematic of two crystal whole body counters as shown in Figure 1. The numbers along a line corresponding to the center line of the patient represent the relative count rate of a point source in air.

[1] Harshaw Chemical Company, Cleveland, Ohio.

permanently aligned along the long axis of the patient positioned on a plane surface.

With a two crystal array moderate sensitivity was obtained without undue sacrifice of uniformity in counting efficiency. Figure 2 shows the results for a 100 cm. separation of the centers of the two crystals. The best results were obtained by placing the crystals at a 45° angle at 57 cm. above a line corresponding to the long axis of a human subject. For sources along this center line in air, reasonably uniform counting efficiency is obtained over a 100 cm. long center section. The suprasternal notch of each subject is positioned beneath the center of the left crystal. The knee of a subject of average height comes then at a point somewhat beyond the center of the right crystal. The support on which the subject lies is 67 cm. from the crystal center place.

Additional variations in counting efficiency will occur for points displaced above, below or lateral to the center line. For a 13 cm. lateral displacement the mean efficiency falls by 3 percent. Considerable variations for positions above and below the center line can occur, particularly for points located directly below one of the crystals. If, however, the subject is measured in both the supine and prone position, these variations are markedly reduced. The mean value of the supine plus prone determinations can be demonstrated to vary by less than ± 7 percent over a region 10 cm. above or below the center line.

Correction for Gamma Ray Attenuation Within the Human Body

The counting efficiency for a given amount of radioactivity will vary not only with changes in geometrical location relative to the two crystals, but also with differences in tissue thickness between the source and the body surface. One way to minimize variations in gamma ray absorption is to have all measurements done in pairs by adding the count rates in the supine and prone position. Then a source of radioactivity close to the skin would have in one position a minimum of tissue as absorber and a maximum in the other position. Furthermore, a source which is in one position closer to the crystals than the center line will be further away in the other position.

The pair measurement in the supine and prone position corrects for geometrical and attenuation variations only approximately. Gamma ray absorption is exponential, and the geometrical sensitivity varies with the square of the distances between the source and the two crystals. Supine plus prone measurements apply a linear correction to these variations.

Further corrections for gamma ray absorption and geometrical variations can be obtained from analysis of appropriate phantom measurements. Figure 2 shows the spectrum of I^{131} gamma rays for a point source placed 1, 4 and 7 in. below the surface of an 8 in. Masonite phantom. The counts in the photopeak (P) decrease exponentially. Adjacent to the photopeak, at lower energies, a region has been marked Compton (C). The count rate in this region does not decrease exponentially, since some of the primary gamma rays which have been absorbed by small angle scattering appeared as secondary gamma rays in this region. It may, therefore, be assumed that the Compton region can be

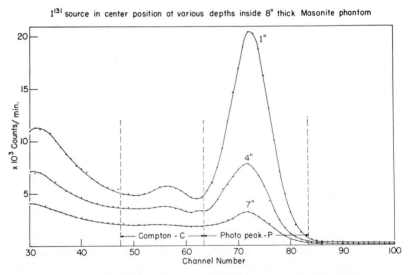

Figure 3. Photopeak and adjacent Compton region of I^{131} pulse energy spectra. Data taken with I^{131} source under 1, 4 and 7 in. of Masonite. The count rate in the photopeak decreases exponentially with increasing absorber thickness, while the count rate in the adjacent Compton region falls off much slower due to accumulation of small angle scattered radiation.

used along with the photopeak to derive the desired correction factor.

A Masonite phantom 8 in. thick, 12 in. wide and 5 ft. long was positioned on a horizontal plane such that its center line was 57 cm. below the center of the crystals. (Fig. 3). Spectral distributions of the count rate for an I^{131} source at various positions throughout the phantom were determined. The data were analyzed by adding the P and C values for points equidistant above and below the center line. The addition of these conjugate points produces data corresponding to the supine plus prone measurement of the source at any position within the phantom.

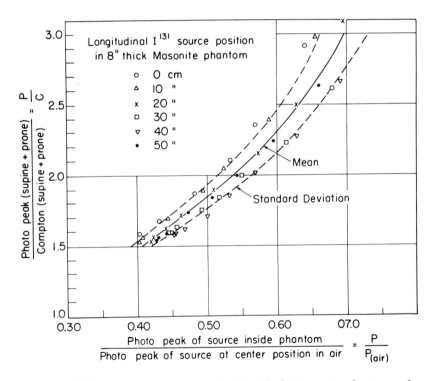

Figure 4. I^{131} source measurements in 8 in. thick Masonite phantom relative to source in air at the center position (Fig. 2). For each measurement the count rates for the supine and prone position of the source in the phantom relative to the counters are added. Most values fall within one standard deviation from a mean curve.

In addition, the photopeak for the source at any position in the phantom was compared with the photopeak of the same source in air at the center position between the two crystals. Then the ratio of count rate in the photopeak area (P) from the source in the phantom to the count rate of the photopeak area of the source in air, $P_{(air)}$, is a measure of the effective gamma ray absorption in the phantom.

In Figure 4, the ratio P/C for each pair of measurements is plotted as a function of $P/P_{(air)}$. The experimental points scatter around a mean curve (solid line), and most of them fall within one standard deviation from the mean (dotted lines). The latter corresponds to about a ± 5 percent difference from the mean.

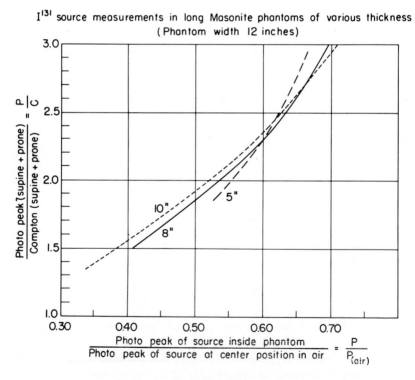

Figure 5. Mean curves of experimental data (Fig. 4) for I[131] source in 5, 8 and 10 in. thick Masonite phantom.

Therefore, for any observed P/C value, the absorption correction $P/P_{(air)}$ might have a 5 percent inaccuracy by using a mean correction curve.

Actually, the mean curve itself depends somewhat on the phantom thickness. The same measurements were repeated with a 5 in. and a 10 in. thick phantom (Fig. 5). The mean values for the 5 in. and 10 in. phantom fall within a few per cent from the mean values for the 8 in. phantom. Though some of the experimental points for the thinner and thicker phantoms fall outside the 5 percent range of the 8 in. phantom mean curve, it still appears to be a good approximation for the correction factor for all three phantoms.

Though the human body does not conform to any one of these phantoms, a combination of the three phantoms represents a fair approximation for various body weights and shapes. Only by giving patients of different body build known amounts of radioactivity, can the adequacy of the average correction factor determined with the 8 in. phantom be tested. Tables II and III show some examples of *in vivo* measurements. Applying the correction factor yields data which account for 100 percent of the dose at all times with an accuracy of $\pm$ 5 percent.

TABLE II

I^{131} IN VIVO MEASUREMENTS
SUBJECT'S WEIGHT: 165 LBS.
SUBJECT'S HEIGHT: 5 FT., 11IN.

Maximum I^{131} Concentration	Time after Oral Dose (Hrs.)	Uncorrected %	Corrected %
Stomach	0.0	45	100*
	0.3	49	96
Blood and Thyroid			
	0.7	50	96
	1.0	51	96
	2.3	52	96
	70% excretion		
Thyroid	20.0	56	99

* Normalized after oral dose of iodide.

TABLE III

I[131] In Vivo Measurements

Maximum I[131] Concentration	I. V. Doses	Subject I Wt. 108 lbs. Ht. 5 ft., 7 in.		Subject II Wt. 195 lbs. Ht. 6 ft., 1 in.	
		Uncor-rected %	Cor-rected %	Uncor-rected %	Cor-rected %
Blood	RISA	54	100*	46	100*
Blood	Rose bengal	53	100	45	100
Blood & Liver	"	51	96	45	101
	"	52	98	44	104
Liver	"	50	96	44	101
Kidney	Hippuran	57	100	46	100
Bladder	"	50	95	43	103

* Normalized after I. V. dose of RISA.

FOCUSSING COLLIMATOR FOR 8 IN. DIAMETER CRYSTAL

For radioisotope distribution studies, scanners with 3 in. diameter sodium iodine crystals are commonly used. The multi-hole focussing collimator attached to the crystal has its maximum sensitivity at about 2.5 in. below the front face of the collimator. This distance may be adequate for thyroid scanning, since the thyroid extends to only a few centimeters in depth inside the neck. Most organs, however, lie several inches below the body surface and extend frequently to or beyond the body midline.

In increasing the dimensions of crystal and focussing head, the weight of the required shielding becomes a major factor. However, a crystal mounted inside a steel room requires only additional shielding on the sides facing the subject. Therefore, it was decided to use one of the 8 by 4 in. sodium iodide crystals for body radioactivity distribution studies. Figure 1 shows one of the crystals inside the 3 in. thick lead shield which also contains the focussing head. The whole assembly can be raised and lowered and moved to any position along the midline of the steel room. Twelve springs[2] which counterbalance the weight of the shield of about 500 lbs. enable an effortless manual vertical movement of the whole shield crystal assembly.

For the scanning operation it is much simpler to move the patient back and fourth and keep the focussing collimator stationary instead of moving the collimator. Therefore a scanning bed was built[2] which allows selecting the scanning speed and line width. The movement from side to side is so smooth that it is not objectionable to the patient.

The focussing collimator is constructed so that it can be lifted out of the lead shield after the crystal has been removed (Fig. 6). This allows one to have a set of collimators available which differ in the number of holes and the septa thickness between them. The collimator design has to be different depending on the gamma ray energy and required resolution. In all cases the sensitivity should be as great as possible. Only the outside dimensions of the focussing collimator are fixed by the size of the hole in the lead shield. The height of the collimator, the distance between the front face of the crystal and the outside of the lead shield, is 5 in. (Fig. 7). The diameter of the collimator at the crystal face is 8 in., and at the opposite end it is 4 in.

Any one collimator cannot yield optimum results in all respects. Therefore, a collimator was designed for high sensitivity,

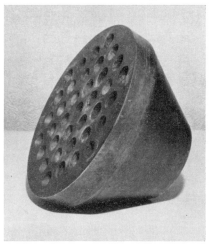

Figure 6. The 37 hole collimator has been removed from lower section of lead shield (Fig. 1). It can be replaced by a collimator of different design.

[2] Hunter Spring Company, Lansdale, Penna.
[3] Laboratory Associates, Inc., Belmont, Mass.

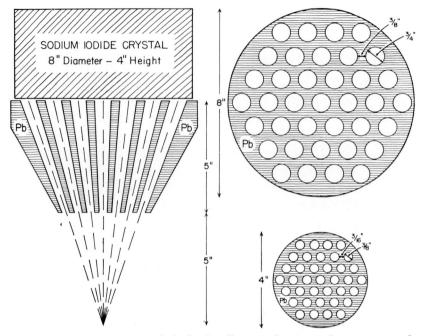

Figure 7. Schematic of 37 hole lead collimator for 8 in. diameter crystal.

medium resolution for I^{131} gamma rays and limited usefulness for high energy gamma rays (Co^{60}, Fe^{59}). Figure 7 shows the dimensions of the 37 hole collimator chosen. It was cast out of lead, though tungsten would be superior for high energy gamma rays.

The isocount curves in air for a small I^{131} source are shown in Figure 8. Only the counts from the photopeak area of the main gamma ray line were registered. For comparison the isocount lines of a standard 19 hole collimator (Picker) for a 3 in. diameter crystal are shown. Its focussing point is at 2.5 in. from the collimator surface, while the 37 hole collimator has the focal point at 4.5 in. The lines of 80, 50, 30 and 10 percent sensitivity relative to that at the focal point penetrate to correspondingly deeper depths for the large collimator. The isocount lines obtained with the 37 hole collimator using only the outer ring of holes is also shown. The depth penetration is slightly reduced, and adjacent to the collimator, where the center sets of holes are closed, there is now an area of low sensitivity.

ISOCOUNT CONTOURS IN AXIAL PLANE
FOR I¹³¹ POINT SOURCE IN AIR

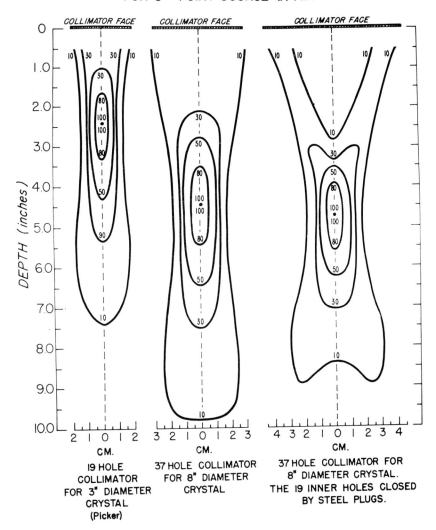

Figure 8. Comparison of isocount curves for I^{131} in air with two types of collimators. On the left side, the 19 hole collimator (Picker) for a 3 in. diameter crystal with a focal depth of 2.5 in. In the center 37 hole collimator for 8 in. diameter crystal with a focal depth of 4.5 in. On the right same 37 hole collimator, but all holes closed by steel plugs except the 18 outer holes of the collimator.

Though the present 37 hole collimator was not constructed for high energy gamma rays, its isocount lines were determined for Co[60] (Fig. 9). The volumes encompassed by the surfaces of different relative sensitivity are considerably enlarged compared with those for I[131]. A rather large fraction of the Co[60] gamma rays penetrates the collimator septa. If the collimator were made of tungsten instead of lead, the difference between the I[131] and Co[60] isodose lines would be reduced.

The resolutions of the Picker 19 hole collimator for I[131] and our 37 hole collimator for I[131] and Co[60] in the planes of their focal

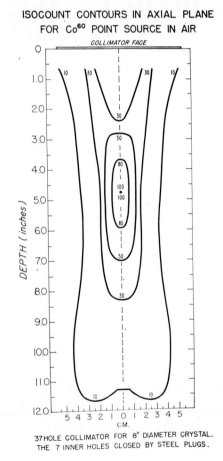

Figure 9. Isocount curves for Co[60] cource in air with 37 hole collimator.

points are shown in Figure 10. The full width of half of the maximum count rate is 1.4 cm. for the Picker collimator and 2.0 cm. for the 37 hole collimator using I^{131}, while for Co^{60} it increases to 2.7 cm. This poorer resolution is further enhanced by the fact that even at rather large distances the count rate does not fall below the 10 percent level for the Co^{60} gamma rays.

By placing I^{131} sources of different spherical volumes at the focal points of the 19 and 37 hole collimators, their absolute and relative sensitivity can be determined. Table IV gives the net counts per minute per microcurie of I^{131} for a 70 kev window at the 364 kev photopeak and the relative sensitivities of the two collimators. Using the 8 in. diameter crystals instead of the 3 in. about doubles the sensitivity. The small increase in sensitivity is due to the increase in collimator length and the increase in focal distance from 2.5 to 4.5 in.

COMPARISON OF 37 HOLE COLLIMATOR FOR 8" CRYSTAL
WITH 19 HOLE COLLIMATOR FOR 3" CRYSTAL

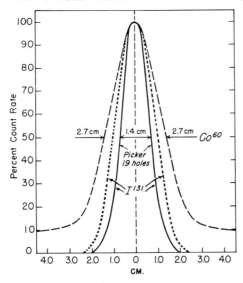

Figure 10. Comparison of resolution of two collimators within their focal plane for I^{131} and Co^{60} sources (Fig. 9 and 10). The two inner curves are for an I^{131} point source with the 19 and 37 hole collimators; the outer curve is for Co^{60} with the 37 hole collimator.

TABLE IV

COMPARISON OF COLLIMATOR SENSITIVITY FOR SPHERICAL I^{131} SOURCES AT THE FOCAL SPOT

(70 KEV WINDOW AT 364 KEV LINE)

I^{131} source (ml.)	Counts Per Minute-microcurie		Relative Sensitivity 37 and 19 Hole Collimators
	19 Hole Collimator 2.5 In. Focal Distance	37 Hole Collimator 4.5 In. Focal Distance	
0.25	4800	8300	1.7
1.0	4300	7800	1.8
10	2000	4600	2.3
25	1500	3900	2.6
50	900	2900	3.2

Figure 11 shows an example of two kidney scans with Hg^{203} neohydrin of the same patient with the 19 and 37 hole collimator. A 20 percent cut-off level for background erase was used with the 19 hole collimator, while no background erase is used with the 37 hole collimator. Only from a larger group of patients scanned with the two collimators will it be possible to decide if the increase in focal depths results in any improvement of the scans.

SUMMARY

A whole body counter has been described which uses two 8 by 4 in. sodium iodide crystals inside a steel room. It allows the estimation of radioactivity *in vivo* independent of its distribution within the human body. This is accomplished by applying a geometrical and gamma ray absorption correction to each measurement. The exact value of the correction factor is derived from an analysis of the measured energy distribution of the gamma rays incident on the two sodium iodide crystals.

One of the two crystals can be placed inside a 3 in. thick lead shield with a focussing head at the side of the crystal face. By placing a patient on a scanning bed, scans can be obtained with I^{131} comparable to those by moving a smaller crystal over stationary patients. The advantages of using the larger crystals are increased focal distance, higher sensitivity and adaptability to high energy gamma ray emitters.

REFERENCES

1. Miller, C. E.: Whole Body Counting. Proceedings of a Symposium, International Atomic Energy Agency, Vienna, 1962.

DISCUSSION

Chairman: ROBERT A. DUDLEY

International Atomic Energy Agency
Vienna, Austria

ERNEST C. ANDERSON: In the early days at Los Alamos we had difficulties with our liquid scintillators. We found it difficult to establish the magnitude of the background depression with the sugar phantom rings and eventually determined that low level surface contamination was causing the difficulties. You need careful repeats over long periods and with extra counting statistics, because the background depression is rather small to begin with and, if you aren't careful, the depression will get lost. It doesn't take much additional difficulty with a little contamination to cover it up.

It appears that the new Humco 2 does not show this background depression. We ascribe this to the fact that the scintillator thickness is 12 in. rather than 6 in., and therefore the transmission of gamma rays through the scintillator through the subject and into the other side is smaller.

As far as I can tell, if you take statistical averages of many people, the 4π liquid and the Argonne chair geometry with the sodium iodide crystal are giving very close to the same total numbers of potassium in the average. We are particularly uncertain about small children, for whom we don't have any *in vivo* calibrations; and we have questions about massive persons, for whom our calibrations are scarce. But if you talk about the average value for everybody, or if you talk about individual values for an average person, I think we can say that the two methods agree quite well.

CHARLES E. MILLER: The average value agrees quite well, but when you are working with a specific individual you don't want an average value on an average man; you want to know how much that man has.

ERNEST C. ANDERSON: My last statement wasn't clear. What I was saying was that with individual values on one man, — if the man is of average stature — the agreement is at the 2 to 3 percent level.

E. H. BELCHER: Dr. Hine, I was interested in your excellent whole body counting measurements with two detectors, because we have been using a three detector system, weighing the individual count rates to achieve a flat response along the axis of the subject. In your whole body counting measurements were the counting rates the means of the counting rates with the patients prone and supine?

GERALD J. HINE: Yes. We always take the average to the two.

E. H. BELCHER: In the corrections for self absorption, your diagram showed the phantom at the center point of the couch. It seems to me that the correction factor will vary somewhat, falling off slightly as you approach either detector. Have you looked into this question?

GERALD J. HINE: We move the source to various positions along the central line, and we always vary it within different depths in the phantom, also in supine or prone positions. There is some variation crosswise in the phantom, and the phantom does not represent any body shapes, therefore the phantom measurements are done just to study what such an absorption correction would look like. The final curve will be obtained by giving doses with different distribution in the body to patients of different body builds. We will redevise this curve from actual points in measurements, and the phantom measurements will not be used in the final analysis.

GUNNAR SEVELIUS: On the small study we did with blood volume distribution, we tried the chair arrangement and did not get any sense in our values. I believe if you don't have an even distribution of the isotopes, it does not make any sense in having a chair, and counting should be along an isodosic line like Dr. Hine uses.

GERALD J. HINE: Potassium distributes very uniformly throughout the body wherever the muscles are and is a high gamma ray emitter; therefore, this scheme works well on potassium, but not necessarily for other isotopes which are lower.

C. J. MALETSKOS: What effect would the K^{42} beta ray have on the calibration factors in the two different devices in handling this discrepancy?

CHARLES E. MILLER: On the sodium iodide crystals we have lucite beta shields, which we use for all measurements. Back in the early days when we were concerned about K^{42}, beta measurements and beta effect, we put them on and have never taken them off. I can't say what effect this would have on the liquid counter.

What is the thickness of the inside metal?

ERNEST C. ANDERSON: Thirty-seconds.

CHARLES E. MILLER: If you stretch a man out and place multiple crystals over him and look at the gamma rays coming out, and if you put a phantom somewhere, you will get a certain counting rate. If you move it down 24.5 cm., it is going to go down to one-quarter.

We counted people in seven crystal positions and added them up, and we found the difference with potassium. Then we did the same thing with people with radium in their body thirty to thirty-five years, and we found a marked difference from one individual to the other. One lady had a high percentage in the long bones; another, in the skull.

When we did this work with the tilting chair and found the average value per microcurie, it turned out that we had an uncertainty of $\pm$ 10 percent with a calibration factor of the tilting chair for radium in the scalp, one person having it in the long bones and another in the skull, others having it more uniformly distributed.

When we went to the multicrystal array, which for all practical purposes is nothing less than a blanket of scintillator wrapped around the man, we found just as high a variation from one person to another. You have to have a counter quite a bit longer than the individual. When you do that, you pick up background from all of the sensitive volume. The S^2 over B goes out when you start making the thing longer. So unless you have some data to talk about, some assumptions can be wild.

Our bodies are not cylinders. A bone-seeker is not uniformly labeled in the body. Even though you have it for thirty years and you got it by multiple injections, you still get a wild distribution.

I didn't find more migration with the chair than I did with the crystal arrays. A lot of the material will be in the liver or spleen or in the torso. We mainly use the chair for skeleton bone-seekers and soft tissue bone-seekers, not specific organs.

GERALD J. HINE: I think this geometry is quite different from the type I was talking about. If you have a type of arrangement with the study, you have a uniform sensitivity in the bed where the activity is. This approximately corresponds to the metered heart which Professor Evans introduced many years ago, except that it is difficult to put patients in an arc. By placing them in multiple crystal arrangements, the metered arc will stretch out the geometry.

JOHN RUNDO: Dr. Mehlhorn, have you considered the use of light squares fitting in the analysis of these mixed spectra, because, particularly at low levels of activity, this has the advantage of using all the information in the spectrum and not just that confined to photopeaks?

WERNER MEHLHORN: In this experiment we had fairly large activities, and so we had only to consider photopeaks, which were fairly distinct. The ratio between photopeak and background was large. We started with the consideration that in an actual case a man would have a large amount of activity in his body. When he has only a small amount, then probably it is useful to measure him; but maybe there is no necessity for any treatment.

DAVID C. PRICE: Dr. Hine, people working with multiple crystals have noticed considerable variation in count rate with very minor shifts in the patient's position on the table. Have you made any observations on patient position changes?

GERALD J. HINE: We have not made this investigation. A 1 meter area that we cover is probably not sufficient in some cases, but this we have to see. The reason we choose two crystals and not a multiple array is because it is easier to line up two crystals. It is hard to cover with single crystals as large a source as a human body.

JOHN RUNDO: We have been using multicrystal array for some years now, and our experience has been that there are not very large changes in the total counting rates with position.

One thing we have noticed in some recent work with Sr^{85}, where we have been recording the four counters individually, was that when we plotted these as a function of time after correcting for decay, there were some rather odd effects. One counter would go down from one day or one week to the next, whereas another counter would go up. This was because of variations in the subject's position of about 2 cm. When you took the four sums and plotted the points, these made a smooth curve. In subjects with the Sr^{85} only recently deposited, we had essentially the same patterns of deposition in all five we have done. If you had one counter pushed up, another one went down on the curve somewhere else, and the two effects just about cancel out.

CHAIRMAN ROBERT A. DUDLEY: I am glad to see this concentration of discussion on the question of degree of uniformity of sensitivity for different detector-body arrangements. It seems to me that there is often an unnecessary degree of confusion introduced into this subject by failure to recognize two distinct situations.

There is one in which the activity is distributed fairly uniformly throughout the body and is rather similar from person to person, such as K^{40}. The other extreme is an isotope which localizes, such as I^{131}.

I am sure Dr. Miller would say that his chair is for conditions where the isotope is rather generally distributed throughout the body, and he would not propose to use it for an isotope which localizes, as does I^{131}.

If there is a large change in distribution or special localization of the isotope within the body, it seems to me one must use a detector-body geometry that is not particularly sensitive to localization within the body. There are various procedures which have been described for this, and many of them must be good because they are rediscovery of principles which were set out clearly by Dr. R. D. Evans in 1937 in the American Journal of Roentgenology.

A DISCUSSION OF THE ACCURACY AND PRECISION OF THE MEASUREMENT OF Cs^{137} BURDENS BY WHOLE BODY COUNTING METHODS

Chairman: S. ALLAN LOUGH

(EDITOR'S NOTE: This discussion was not formally a part of the symposium program, but was called at the time to consider the question of possible interlaboratory calibration because many of those interested were in attendance. Formal presentations rarely reveal the trials and tribulations of working scientists in their pursuit of precision and accuracy. In this discussion, the participants rather frankly stated some of the difficulties they had experienced or which they suspected in the work of others, thereby reflecting with greater truth the roughness of the road to scientific progress. The fact of the matter is that every time different laboratories in any field of endeavor have cross-checked their results, it has invariably become evident that *Truth* is an objective more honored in the search for it than in its achievement. We asked for permission to publish these comments, and the participants graciously granted it. It seemed to us to have the flavor of a fine scientific bull session. These are often engaged in, but seldom published.)

CHAIRMAN S. ALLAN LOUGH: The discussion this evening was suggested by problems which have arisen in an effort to evaluate the level of Cs^{137} in people in various parts of the United States since atmospheric weapon testing was resumed. One approach was to measure the same subjects in the same locality at frequent intervals to see what happens to the individual cesium level with time. The primary objective this evening is to discuss the question of the feasibility of intercomparison of whole body counting Cs^{137} measurements from laboratory to laboratory. When we examine results from various parts of the country, we would have more confidence in our conclusions if we had evidence from intercomparison that the results really were comparable.

WILLIAM F. MARLOW: Many laboratories have felt a need for interlaboratory calibration. Two or three separate proposals have been made as to how this could be done. There is an apparent lack of agreement among the reports from different laboratory groups. Some workers have experienced difficulties in calibration at their own laboratories. An adequate method for interlaboratory calibration should help all those who are trying to measure cesium and potassium.

In an Atomic Energy Commission program a number of different laboratories have counted the same three to fifteen subjects as carefully as possible at weekly intervals. With people on vacation or away for other reasons, not everybody is counted every week.

There are three groups of levels reported. M.I.T., U.C.L.A. and Hanford report values between 30 and 60 pc of Cs^{137} per kilogram whole body weight. Los Alamos, Vanderbilt and Rochester report values from 80 to 110 pc per kilogram whole body weight. In recent weeks Vanderbilt's average has gone up as high as 200 pc of cesium per kilogram of whole body weight. The Health and Safety Laboratory of New York has tended to run over 100 pc per kilogram. There are great fluctuations from week to week. In addition, individuals have varied. Weekly observations on one individual fluctuated several hundred per cent up and down. On a recent trip I visited three laboratories within a two week period. On the 19th of July the U.C.L.A. Medical Center was observing a level of 113 pc of Cs^{137} per kilogram of whole body weight. On July 31st Hanford had 98 and on August 7th, Idaho Falls was finding 75.

Some believe we should express Cs^{137} in terms of grams of potassium. Reducing the data from these three laboratories on this basis, we have 53.6 pc of cesium per gram of potassium at U.C.L.A.; at Hanford it was 50.1; at Idaho Falls, 53.5.

CHAIRMAN LOUGH: When I see the marked fluctuations from week to week, I immediately wonder, is this fluctuation real? If it is, is the dietary intake so variable? Are the measurements varying in the same laboratory from week to week to such an extent? By factors of 2, 3 in many cases?

Is the reporting meaningful on the basis of units of cesium per gram of potassium or kilogram of body weight? Should it be on the basis of lean body weight? If so, is the index to lean body weight the body potassium content? In that event we have just as much need for intercomparison of potassium measurement as we do for cesium. Both potassium intercalibration and cesium intercalibration may be the real need.

MERRIL EISENBUD: Why did absolute cesium determination in these three laboratories vary so much, when the potassium-cesium ratios seem reasonably consistent, the total spread being 50 to 53?

CHAIRMAN LOUGH: The arithmetic must mean that the potassium estimations in the various laboratories were also different.

ERNEST C. ANDERSON: Yes. This would suggest to me that there is a consistent error relating to the gamma sensitivity of the detectors, the geometry factor or the efficiency factor, which is in the same direction for both the cesium and the potassium determinations.

Our experience at Los Alamos with one detector used under presumably reproducible conditions showed that the actual day to day physiological variation of potassium in an individual is small. While it depends on the individual and on his state of exercise and nutrition, it is usually very constant.

We have observed that the total body potassium (expressed either as total grams or as grams per kilogram of body weight) shows a standard deviation of the order of $\pm$ 3 gm., about 2 or 3 percent in particularly reproducible individuals over periods up to five years. Such consistency has been observed in many individuals.

When we look at large numbers of people, we discover a coefficient of variation among individuals of a given sex and age group of about 9 to 14 percent in total body potassium. The cesium burden variation is much larger, about 35 percent.

If you examine total cesium independent of potassium, you see a pattern in which the variations and the correlations are about the same. However, the cesium to potassium ratios tend to be more reproducible for a large population group than cesium per kilogram. We think this is not because of any chemical similarity of potassium to cesium, but because the potassium and the cesium calibration factors are influenced in the same way by body build and superficial fat. The net effect is to make the cesium to potassium ratio more constant.

But none of these effects is the sort of thing that would account for the type of variation reported among three laboratories. I think one could eliminate the possibility that dietary change is responsible for the short term fluctuations on the basis of the rather well established biological half life of cesium. This has been measured in a number of laboratories; and while there is the expected degree of biological variability, generally the numbers that people come up with are about 100 to 150 days. This means that if you were suddenly to expose the person to an instantaneous doubling of the cesium level in his diet, it would be 150 days before his body level rose by 50 percent.

This inherent sluggishness of the biological system, this inherent integration time of the human body for its cesium content, would rule out the possibility that these abrupt fluctuations are dietary, and practically rules out the possibility that the fluctuations are real.

Another source of entry could be inhalation, but computations suggest that this is completely negligible. You need significant ecological concentrations to build up the cesium.

This leaves you with the explanation that the observed variability is in the counter system or that other contaminating agents are being included as cesium in some of the data. This latter was definitely true of the early Los Alamos data. We know that the data which we took back in 1956 and 1957 included sizable amounts of I^{131}, probably also barium and Th^{140} coming from the Nevada test site.

It is perhaps also worth reviewing the actual measuring conditions at different laboratories?

NORMAN S. MACDONALD: I think the absolute values for cesium must vary in different parts of the country for the obvious reason that each food supply has a different content of cesium.

I would like to hear somebody quote a figure for reproducibility of cesium measurement, whether by liquid counting or single crystal or multiple crystal counting.

MERRIL EISENBUD: Our figures are fairly consistent. In our laboratory we get reliable counts that are reproducible from one week to the next and one month to the next. In fact, the peculiar thing to us is that we haven't seen any shift in the cesium load of the people we have been measuring since we started, some for almost a year now. Our problem is that we don't know how to convert our counts into body burden. We are unsophisticated when it comes to absolute standardization of our cesium measurements.

Another problem is that it is rather difficult to get permission to conduct a human experiment. Secondly, there are restrictions on the source of volunteers, and it makes it almost impossible to administer isotopes to people for purposes of standardization.

We hoped we would not have to go through the K^{42} standardization of our potassium calibration because it involves human subjects. We would rather have somebody else standardize, and then we will accept their standardization. But nobody has been able to develop a secondary standard. Primary standardization takes a great deal of time.

RAYMOND L. WEILAND: We can talk all we want about how we calibrate our whole body counts, but everything has to go back to what we use for a primary standard, the cesium microcurie. There are not many places in the United States where you can procure a microcurie of cesium and know it really is a microcurie.

At Vanderbilt we based our calibration for cesium on the primary calibration for potassium and the difference in the energy of the cesium gamma rays. While the theory of this procedure is valid, it all depends upon a valid cesium standard, which raises the question of what is the correct standard for cesium. We bought one cesium standard, and right after we bought it we found a 10 percent error in the shipment. Somehow we have got to get the people who supply cesium standards straightened out with each other, because at present they don't agree.

ERNEST C. ANDERSON: Cesium is rather tricky for absolute calibration because of the peculiar decay scheme. A 4 pi beta calibration method will give you a result that is 10 percent high unless you are aware of the fact that there are more beta electrons than disintegrations.

However, perhaps the problem of reproducibility is more important than the problem of absolute accuracy. If a particular laboratory is producing consistent numbers over a period of time you can reliably compare the average numbers that come from this laboratory at one time with the averages that come at other times. The problem of an absolute calibration now becomes a separate one.

You can evaluate consistency by arbitrary normalization. You can then see the quantitative difference rather precisely. Until you have a consistent set of numbers, you are rather at a loss to get on to an absolute study. The minimum variation which one observes among cooperating laboratories will set an upper limit upon the true physiological variation for individuals. Those laboratories that are reporting a greater variation presumably have another source of variability added to the basic physiologic variability. [Editor: This assumes there *is* no real difference in variability in different geographic locations.]

One must qualify this of course, by pointing out that in a certain region the diet may vary more drastically than in another. A person's dietary habits may change; but here again the 150 day biological half time is going to set an upper limit on the time scale upon which this variation can occur.

C. E. MILLER: I hope no one is measuring anybody in street clothes. This obviously could change the figures.

GEORGE R. MENEELY: Have any laboratories measured subjects in street clothes? Is everybody actually washing off all their subjects?

ERNEST C. ANDERSON: It isn't necessary. We have measurements with and without showers.

C. E. MILLER: When you measure a girl with long hair and then shower her, you remove radon daughter products from her hair.

ERNEST C. ANDERSON: I question if some of this cesium measurement is due to radon daughter products. Just walking from the shower room to the counting facility, you can pick up a lot of daughter products. Radium C emits a line of 670 kv. I wonder if this is part of the trouble.

C. E. MILLER: We have a difficult situation at Argonne. Our backgrounds fluctuate quite widely. If we have a south wind from the reactors, we have Ar^{41}. We have a cyclotron, and we see 10 minute nitrogen from it. We have a Van de Graaff 100 feet in one direction and 200 feet in another direction. We are in the world's worst situation for low level gamma counting.

There is also the problem of radon in the atmosphere itself; 1 pc of radon in the atmosphere of our room increased our background 100 counts a minute. The ordinary concentration ranges about 0.6, and it may vary from 0.01 to 2.5 pc under an inversion; so the radon counting rate can go from 0 to 250 counts in a 8 by 8 ft. steel room.

Barney Fisher has been measured in several laboratories. His potassium varied from 224 down to 163 among the various laboratories. There were five laboratories reporting between 167 and 163, one at 224, one at 204 and one at 187 gm. of potassium. These are obviously outside the possible range of physiological variation.

We have given K^{42} to many people so we have K^{42} spectra on a large variety of heights and weights. With the 8 by 4 in. crystal over the tilting chair, I can plot out the net K^{42} spectrum for a person of 100 pounds and a person of 200 pounds and not find any difference in shape. They agree all the way across the energy band, even down at the low end where other people are reporting that this is a very sensitive region for differences due to body size and shape. I have been amazed with the reproducibility if we put a second 8 by 4 in. crystal over our tilting chair. We use a ring arrangement to line it up in the same position. The spectrum from the second 8 by 4 in. crystal matches the first one within 1 percent. (Editor: Not everyone agrees that subjects of different stature and habits have exactly the same shaped spectrum.)

In all our K^{42} subjects there is a constant ratio of counts in the cesium photopeak region. If people would calibrate with some K^{42}, they would know how much to peel off for potassium to obtain the net counts due to Cs^{137}.

Norman S. MacDonald: About 37 percent of the counts in the net K^{40} photopeak appear in the region of the cesium photopeak.

Raymond L. Weiland: We found 20 percent to 37 percent of the K^{40} photopeak counts appear under the cesium photopeak.

Chairman Lough: The comments you have contributed so far, for the most part, have dealt with techniques of measurement and pitfalls in measurement techniques. It is evident there should be a general procedure which would be applicable to all kinds of equipment which would get away from some sources of variation. If you don't get away from procedural differences such as showering, and so on, you won't have any basis for deciding whether an intercalibration method is worthwhile or not. There is a real need to develop a procedure to which all workers could subscribe.

Raymond L. Weiland: It is the old problem of precision versus accuracy. There may be laboratories in which day-to-day results are reproducible within 1 percent, but the absolute values are way off, precise but inaccurate. Other laboratories, because of their inherent procedure, may have wide fluctuations from measurement to measurement, but on the average may come closer to the true mark. A manikin could be used, but I would much rather see a person go around and be measured. A human could make notes on how it is being done.

George R. Meneely: I can't help but be reminded of the parallel to the thorough I^{131} uptake studies some years ago when Marshall Brucer set up a program of interlaboratory thyroid I^{131} calibration.

You will recall there were fantastic variations in estimated thyroid iodine uptake. The "uptake" of one of the manikins was measured as low as 30 or 40 percent in certain laboratories and as high as 130 percent in other laboratories when it should have been 60 percent. There were important technical variations among the laboratories such as whether there was or was not a filter, the shape of the collimator field, etc.

The striking thing about that study was that practically everybody found the correct value for microcuries of the standards which were provided despite their poor performance on the manikin. Therefore, it seems to me a place to start is a point source or a reasonable approximation of one. We should first find out how well various laboratories agree on point source microcuries. If agreement cannot be obtained on point sources, it is axiomatic it cannot be obtained on volume sources.

Raymond L. Weiland: What we have done at Vanderbilt is what we consider the best, and I am sure everybody else has done their calibrating in what they considered the best way. I would hate to see a program built around a manikin because it is not like a human, and it would serve no real purpose. The whole problem is that *humans* vary.

CHAIRMAN LOUGH: We will only find out by trying. On the assumption that the effective half life of Cs^{137} is about 100 to 150 days and that this is the only rate of elimination, I can see how one day or one week from now my Cs^{137} total body content could go up precipitously, but I don't see how it can go down so fast the next week. Is there a short term excretion superimposed along with the long term?

THORNTON SARGENT: Yes.

NORMAN S. MACDONALD: What you don't absorb, the cesium in the gut, gets counted.

FRANK SWANBERG: There really is quite a lot of agreement among the discussants. I personally think there is something in favor of all of the things that have been suggested: a standardized procedure, the circulation of some standard sources, both point sources and volume sources and the participation of volunteers including some with a known added body burden of Cs^{137}. Such an intercalibration plan would provide us with data by which we could evaluate and improve our own performance, and by which the observations of different laboratories could be compared.

CHAIRMAN LOUGH: I think the dietary intake should be fixed every day in such traveling human "standards." For example, one could use Metrecal which came from one production lot, purchased directly from the factory.

FRANK SWANBERG: There is another possibility here we may be overlooking. Perhaps the dose of Cs^{137} could be so large that the contributions from fluctuation in the diet from day to day would be nil with the "standard" human, yet very important to "normal" humans with low burdens.

CHAIRMAN LOUGH: When you administer Cs^{137} to a human subject, it is different from administering K^{42}. For such a program I think one would have to have a specific license. Would you be willing to administer 1 μc of Cs^{137} to a normal human volunteer subject?

H. E. PALMER: That is too much.

ERNEST C. ANDERSON: Even 0.1 μc is high. It isn't necessary, is it, that a person making this tour go from one laboratory to another consecutively around the entire sequence? If he were centrally based, he could return at weekly intervals to his home base laboratory for another check. If his base laboratory were one that had demonstrated consistency on control subjects in the past, then the question of any actual change in the human "standard" burden during visits to the other laboratories would be eliminated by the constant value recorded at the base laboratory.

CHAIRMAN LOUGH: That is fine, if we can believe the base laboratory.

ERNEST C. ANDERSON: It is merely a matter of believing the precision of the base laboratory, and this is simple to prove. Are the fluctuations which we see percentage fluctuations so that they would remain this large as you increase the dose, or are they fluctuations in the absolute level?

RAYMOND L. WEILAND: We probably have more observations on fluctuations than any of the other laboratories. We count a sodium standard several times each day and record the counts from this standard. It is always less than 1 percent away from the standard mean.

ERNEST C. ANDERSON: This is encouraging because it suggests that the reported variation may not be percentage variation. It does not have to be in the people, but could be a variation of a constant number of plus or minus nanocuries at a very low level.

On a hot sample such as your sodium sample, the same nanocurie variation would look like a small percentage. If this is true, then measurements at your laboratory on a person loaded with cesium to a high level so you have high counts, no statistical wobble and no trouble with background and radon variation should level out.

C. E. MILLER: How many people are using tilting chair techniques for these measurements? When we use the tilting chair, we have our subjects put their knees out against the arms of the chair. This is essentially putting the knees and thighs out about the same distance from the crystal as the rest of the body. For a person with a radium burden, if they put their knees together in the tilting chair, the radium counting rate will change 10 percent. If people are using our tilting chair technique and are not paying attention to where the hands and knees are, and if at one time the person has his hands and knees together and the next time they are apart, I can see appreciable variations.

RAYMOND L. WEILAND: We make sure the knees are against the arms of the chair every time.

C. E. MILLER: The subjects' own garments are easily eliminated, but pajamas, scrub suits or coveralls can be a source of variation. A long time ago we gave up sending our coveralls out to a laundry because they were getting contaminated, so we have our own washer and dryer in the steel room laboratory; our technicians wash and dry the clothes, and we count them to make sure they are clean.

Even though our laundry went out under a special contract, it would still go to the same contract laundry that all the Argonne wash goes to. We would probably still get cross-contamination.

CHAIRMAN LOUGH: Do you ever use a batch of clean laundry without monitoring it before you use it?

C. E. MILLER: After we wash it, we don't measure each one, but we do occasionally measure these, and as long as we wash them ourselves, they are always clean. We ordinarily don't let people wear their coveralls to the cafeteria. If they do, they take a piece of plastic and cover the chair.

ERNEST C. ANDERSON: We have used a commercial laundry, and for the past three years we have seen no contamination on scrub suits returned from the laundry. However, within the last three months comparative large quantities, enough to produce a 30 percent error in the cesium level of an activity which has been identified as primarily Zr^{95}, have shown up in the scrub suits coming back from a commercial laundry divorced from the laboratory and where there is no possibility of cross-contamination. We believe this is a case of airborne contamination because they blow large quantities of air through the dryer.

This contamination is not always uniformly distributed throughout a batch of scrub suits. In one case we found about 80 percent of the activity in a batch of forty scrub suits was concentrated on one suit. A great deal of care these days is necessary to guarantee that the scrub suits do not get contaminated.

WILLIAM F. MARLOW: Do you think it is worthwhile going to paper suits?

ALAN R. HARBERTSON: It is much cheaper. It costs us as much to have one suit laundered as it does to buy a new gown at 35 cents. There is never a question of having one person wear another's clothing. There are several individuals at the N.R.T.X. who have body burdens of Cs^{137} ranging from 0.1 μc up.

CHAIRMAN LOUGH: Would the contractor who is the employer be willing to let them participate in an intercalibration study?

ALAN R. HARBERTSON: There are several AEC people who have body burdens of Cs^{137}, Cs^{134}, Zn^{65} and other isotopes as well. I am sure some would be willing and able to help in worthwhile studies.

J. RUNDO: At the Health Physics Society meeting in June, 1962, Dr. Mehl from the International Atomic Energy Agency in Vienna gave a paper based on a world survey of whole body counters. He collected all the calibration data for potassium and cesium from institutions using an 8 by 4 in. crystal and a tilting chair. There is also information on the energy band used for calibration.

If you plot cpm per gram of potassium against the width, delta E of the channel, there is an isodotic value of about 0.8 cpm per gram. One laboratory using a channel width of 30 kv. had around 0.1; another laboratory with a channel width of about 150 kv. quoted 1.6 cpm per gram potassium.

It looks as though there is room for improvement for at least one laboratory. Perhaps some of the scatter may turn out to be a consequence of this difference, and perhaps the added 10 percent variation from position of the knees.

With cesium, the situation is worse. We plotted counts per minute per nanocurie of Cs^{137} against delta E. We formed a curve, plateauing at about 9 cpm per nanocurie, again with a lot of scatter and differences in counts. Some of this is obviously due to the same effects as are causing scatter with potassium, but the scatter was worse with cesium, and I think some of that is due to inaccuracies in the reference standards.

I would hesitate to give anyone a lesson in radiochemistry, but I know of an eminent physicist in the whole body counter field who once calibrated his equipment for cesium by taking the cesium standard out of the bottle and diluting it up to 70 liters in a phantom and getting figures which indicated cesium contents differing from average levels by a factor of 5. Then he measured the empty glass bottle and found that 80 percent of his cesium standard was still in the original bottle.

Maybe this sort of thing is contributing to some of the scatter and to the high points. There are some difficulties in standardizing cesium absolutely, which also may be contributing. We have started looking at this on a very small scale in England with our four counters in the Atomic Energy Authority, and we are seeing variations in cesium calibration of 20 to 30 percent.

C. E. MILLER: Back in 1955, we calibrated seven Marshallese natives flown to us. A couple of them had cesium burdens between 0.5 and 0.7 μc. We counted them in the tilting chair and on the 1 meter arc. We broke their spectra apart using Dr. Evans' phantom.

In 1959 my wife and I were counted by Dr. Rundo and by Dr. Anderson, from Stockholm. There was a 2 gm. difference in potassium. One had calibrated his counter using a metal phantom with potassium and then with cesium. One had calibrated his counter using the same technique of loading up these tanks, but was using a different geometry. Dr. Rundo was using four crystals stretched out, and Dr. Anderson was using a 4 by 4 crystal and a version of our tilting chair. We agreed this well back in 1959.

James Watson, from Savannah, counted himself. He was measuring himself at 124 gm. of potassium. We found 142 gm. of potassium for him. He had calibrated with one of the Alderson phantoms, where they had filled the different volumes with water and with potassium in uniform concentration in water.

Dr. Watson stretched out several normal people and measured the counting rates at five positions along the body. He then reloaded his Alderson phantom with potassium in the various compartments until he got the same relative counting rates from the different positions. He then used this as a calibration source for his crystal and tilting chair. He then brought himself up to 138 gm. using that phantom.

On the basis of the way we agree here and what Watson did with his phantom loading, I think we can come out with something as to phantoms. If you have some people who are up to 0.1 or 0.5 μc, they could be counted in different places. If some are using a crystal, they could be counted on the one meter arc, and then by the crystal standard method.

ERNEST C. ANDERSON: Another check on this interlaboratory comparison could be made from a different approach. Instead of looking at individuals, look at population averages over a period. Over one period the Argonne National Laboratory results for cesium in the midwest population, averaged over a population sample, was 31 pc per gram of potassium. Dr. Rundo at Harwell, on the English population during the same time, had 32. For 1957, the numbers were 37 and 38. For 1958, the numbers were 49 and 48. For 1959, they were 59 and 58. For the first half of 1960, they were 50 and 55.

Here are two laboratories measuring different population samples with different types of instruments, but the averages for these population samples are extraordinarily close. The Harwell observations were made with sodium iodide crystals. Los Alamos used a liquid scintillator. Our samples are computed for the midwest population and are based primarily on our averages for a large New Mexico sample corrected by the ratio of New Mexico to the midwest as averaged over the whole period.

Agreement is not perfect, but there are no factors of 2. This is the sort of precision and accuracy that one should expect from different laboratories.

What about the precision with which one can redetermine the cesium values on an individual? At Los Alamos from November 1961 through May 1962 we made twenty repeat determinations on the cesium content of an individual. These measurements were made with shower and without. The average of ten determinations with shower was 45.8 with a standard deviation of 5.7. With no shower, the average for the same period was 44.3 ± 6.7. If you assume that these 10 determinations are subject to a random error of 5.7, then the standard error of the mean should be smaller than the standard error of the individual determinations by the square root of the number of determinations; therefore, the mean value should be ± 2 in each case.

The difference between them is 1.5, and this will be ± 2 times the square root of 2, or essentially ± 3. It is on the basis of these data that I argued that a shower is not always necessary, at least in the case of short haired men.

During this period the cesium levels in people were leveling out after the abrupt drop which occurred during the several years following the cessation of weapons tests and were just getting ready to turn around and go back up again. So the reproducibility of the average values is quite good.

The precision of an individual value, however, is not extremely large; I wonder, Dr. Marlow, if in your analysis of this data, you have made an attempt to see how well successive averages compare in terms of the standard error of the mean that you would estimate from the standard error of the individual values.

WILLIAM F. MARLOW: No, we haven't.

ERNEST C. ANDERSON: We have something like a 10 percent total error in the individual determination. We have not felt it profitable to increase the counting time to decrease the error on the individual one, because we are primarily interested in population averages, and the standard deviation of a random sample of most populations which you look at for cesium is about ± 35 to 36 percent. So, an error of 10 percent on individual determination is small compared to the error in variants of population that you are sampling at this time.

RAYMOND L. WEILAND: But the three laboratories should have the same answer.

ERNEST C. ANDERSON: If you look at the meterological patterns, it is not at all unreasonable that midwestern Illinois should be like England.

J. RUNDO: Only on a fallout rate, not on diet. We don't eat the same things you do nor in the same ratio.

RAYMOND L. WEILAND: We have higher cesium in white people

than in colored people [Nashville]. In this part of the world [Chicago] you should get a different answer. If you get the same answer, then you are wrong.

ERNEST C. ANDERSON: Not necessarily. But the chance that random factors will cancel out to give you the same answer is rather improbable. One would expect to find different answers among populations that have strikingly different eating habits.

NORMAN S. MACDONALD: We are not after averages of the whole population. We are after a method which will bring out sudden increases in certain sections of the country; so, we want to have in different laboratories enough individual precision, so for the little group we study we can say, "This is a significant increase over the population average."

ERNEST C. ANDERSON: Yes. The individual precision you require in your laboratory will be chosen on the basis of the precision needed for the diagnosis at hand. On the other hand, it is hard to see how you can get the precision on the individual basis until you have consistency on the average basis.

Average agreement is a lot easier to get. If we are having trouble with disagreements, let's try for the easy thing first. Let's compare population averages and watch how population averages vary with time.

J. RUNDO: Our data has never been suggested as being a population average. These are mean values of about a dozen people, and there are big variations even within a country as small as England. If you look at individuals, the individual cesium content varies by a factor of 3 to 1 from the highest to the lowest.

ERNEST C. ANDERSON: I said that right here: Standard deviation, 36 percent.

J. RUNDO: At any one time.

GEORGE R. MENEELY: No, I believe it is much larger than that.

MERRIL EISENBUD: We may be beginning to worry about the wrong thing. The thing that surprises me is that after nine years the procedure isn't sufficiently well standardized and sufficiently well understood so that the less sophisticated people like me, who don't have the resources or the willingness to spend this much time on standardization, can get together.

I don't think it is necessary that we all adopt the same procedure. However, the procedure should be comparable. Dr. Rundo has good basic information on what various people are doing around the world in the making of cesium and potassium measurements, and certainly this is the place to start.

I would favor development of some sort of interlaboratory standardization, whether it is a human "standard" who travels around, or a point source, or a manikin, or all three. There ought at least to be something we can ship around in a box to see whether we get the same answers.

GEORGE R. MENEELY: I couldn't agree more with what Dr. Eisenbud has just said. You have accuracy and precision, but you have some other things besides. It is silly to compare three year old colored girls with middle aged white men. You have to get things separated by age, by sex, and by race. The race element is grossly underestimated by many people. For example, in the Nashville population, the potassium content of Negroes is much higher than that of whites, but the cesium content is much lower.

People commonly assume that cesium behaves like potassium, and it doesn't at all. If you take some people of the same age, race and sex, and then look at the cesium data within that presumably "homogeneous" group, there is variation by a factor sometimes as large as 6 among the individuals in that group.

That is only one part of the trouble. The other part is that we still have got to get back to first principles. If laboratories can't agree about a point source, they can't agree about anything. It is imperative that we all get to work on a point source or a good approximation of one.

NORMAN S. MACDONALD: Would it be possible to get one standard sample of a known number of microcuries? I think that would set us off on the right foot. It doesn't mean we all have to agree in our present setup, but if we were handed something and were told this is so many microcuries, we would work our own factors. Start with the point source.

WILLIAM F. MARLOW: I think we can easily persuade the National Bureau of Standards to provide us with a suitable point source.

C. E. MILLER: In Stockholm in 1959, Dr. Anderson counted people with and without showers and he found a 30 percent difference in his counting rate. I measured a lady recently who had 0.7 μc of radium, and all I saw was zirconium-neodymium. There was fallout on the lady's sunporch. I am sure we are going to see huge variations, probably in the hair.

RAYMOND L. WEILAND: This discussion only proves that three of the biggest laboratories in the world probably know what a microcurie is. By averaging data, you have washed out completely all the fluctuations you are talking about. We could take our data and average it and get a good number, and then apply the right factor to it, and we will get 32, just as you have.

ERNEST C. ANDERSON: That figure of 5.7 pc per gram is our computed standard deviation for individual determinations, and it is pretty large.

RAYMOND L. WEILAND: We are talking about fluctuation within one individual.

ERNEST C. ANDERSON: That is what those data are. That is, one individual's figures on twenty occasions. Perhaps some of this data from other laboratories isn't quite as bad as it looks. If you will analyze the standard deviation, if you can show that it is a normal distribution about its own mean value, then you have some confidence at least that the errors are random errors and can be treated by the methods of statistics. If, on the other hand, they show an abnormal distribution, then you have a different problem.

The important thing to do is to begin with a point source. There are a lot of subtleties and refinements we can get into in a calibration program, but it is necessary that everybody get the same answer on a standard point source.

RAYMOND L. WEILAND: I suggest a very low cesium standard that each person can keep. We have been counting a relatively hot sodium standard. I wish now we had also been counting a low cesium standard with each patient counted. If it stayed constant, then the subject should have a good reading, too.

ERNEST C. ANDERSON: If someone will prepare fifteen identical standards and measure them at the Bureau of Standards and verify that they are indeed the same, they could be distributed to the various laboratories and retained as a reference standard.

CHAIRMAN LOUGH: I think you are more likely to get fifteen samples of approximately the same activity with stated activity within a range of precision, but I doubt if you will get fifteen rated at 0.1 $\mu c \pm 2$ percent or anything like that.

ERNEST C. ANDERSON: Then circulate these standards among the national laboratories, who have some obligation to perform such a service. Let this work be performed at Argonne or the National Bureau of Standards; then send the standards back to a central location where they can be relabeled and redistributed.

VOICE: And have them checked for radiocontamination.

RAYMOND L. WEILAND: A single human would not do, because it would be a human of a particular shape. You wouldn't do a routine laboratory radioisotope experiment without making sure the sample always has the same geometry. People have different thicknesses and different shapes. They have a different solid angle relation to the crystal.

Everything we think about when we count nonhuman samples we forget about when we start calibrating humans.

ERNEST C. ANDERSON: The point source comes first; the individual comes next, and population averages comes third.

WILLIAM F. MARLOW: It has been suggested with regard to humans traveling around that a minimum of three people of different sizes be employed.

J. RUNDO: I would like to make the point that a subcommittee of the I.C.R.U. is considering the preparation of low level standards for circulation. They haven't been considered specifically with human counting in mind, but they have considered such things as measurement of cesium and Sr^{90} in dried milk. I wonder whether it would be possible to put this suggestion to them.

ROBLEY D. EVANS: Both with respect to point sources for circulation and exchange and persons to go around from one laboratory to another, I think it is essential to have a wide variety of activities — low, medium and high.

If you have a person with 0.5 μc, everybody can get 0.5 μc on him. There should be a minimum of three; perhaps a minimum of eight, of different body shapes and different activity levels for each shape and at least four point sources.

C. J. MALETSKOS: We used the sodium iodide efficiency by Miller and Snow and checked it against other known isotopes and saw it worked for them. Making little corrections for backscatter, you can get the standardization down to at least 5 percent, which is good enough for what we are talking about.

Along with sending a person around, depending on how fast he is going to go around, or how fast this group of people can go around, there will be a discrepancy in terms of retention of cesium. This might make a significant difference in the final answer, because the burden of a man traveling around may not be decreasing with the same retention function.

WILLIAM F. MARLOW: After they make the rounds, it was suggested that they be followed in their home laboratories for several weeks, to determine the individual decay rate. You wouldn't take any average, but you would take the average data found on that subject.

C. J. MALETSKOS: Would you use Cs^{137} or Cs^{132}?

WILLIAM F. MARLOW: Cs^{137}.

ERNEST C. ANDERSON: Each subject should return to his home base frequently during the course of the studies.

Our method of intercalibration was to compare several methods. We obtained standards from the National Bureau of Standards and from a commercial firm. One set of standards was calibrated locally by 4 pi beta counting. A series of about seven standards was intercompared between our sodium iodide crystal and scintillation counter and the sodium iodide scintillation counter at Walter Reed.

HENRY WELLMAN: Has anyone worked with infants in doing calibrations for cesium? I have cesium balance data on some twenty-four children for nine months on each child. I have six children at this time whom I am studying in connection with a strontium balance study. We count ashed samples on planchets for the cesium on a monthly basis. We could do it on a weekly basis. I wonder if anybody would like to work with me on it. I don't have a whole body counter available.

The Division of Radiological Health has set up a quality control group and has been intercomparing National Bureau of Standards standards among all the laboratories that are doing gamma spectra on milk. Some of the laboratories have had a great deal of difficulty. The sealed standard is sent around to the various laboratories. They have had a great deal of difficulty coming to agreement.

C. J. MALETSKOS: Has there been any comparison between a calibration with a living person and a phantom by the same laboratory?

RAYMOND L. WEILAND: We used the Alderson phantom, and we have also used fifteen subjects, several of whom have the same size and weight as the phantom. We got entirely different calibration factors from the phantom and from the humans. The phantom had a much lower factor.

C. J. MALETSKOS: Did you standardize the activity and then dilute it to fill the phantom?

RAYMOND L. WEILAND: Yes.

GEORGE R. MENEELY: There is another problem with the phantom, it is very difficult to get a phantom to sit itself comfortably in the chair in a position comparable to the human.

H. E. PALMER: We have tried this both ways at Hanford, and we also found differences from 15 to 24 percent for potassium and 24 percent for cesium. We found the phantom had a large difference from the humans.

C. E. MILLER: Has anybody done what James Watson did, where he studied the local distribution of potassium in a number of people and loaded his phantom accordingly? The muscle volume and distribution in the phantom does not match the muscle volume and distribution in the human. You don't get as many counts from potassium and cesium in the legs. Most of the high potassium local concentrations are up in the torso.

ERNEST C. ANDERSON: In calibrating the 4 pi liquid scintillator for potassium, we compared crude phantoms, simple polyethylene jugs of 10, 20 or 30 gal. capacity, loaded with K^{40} and K^{42} with mixed potassium chloride-sugar phantoms, and also with K^{42} injected into people. At the 3 percent level, we found no difference between phantoms and people. The two curves mesh beautifully. The points interlock. That is with the 4 pi liquid scintillator.

J. RUNDO: Isn't this what you would expect with the 4 pi counter? With the crystal counters, if you fit one of these solid phantoms into a chair, it does not sit in the chair like a human. The phantom doesn't fit the chair properly. This must be a large part of the explanation.

CHAIRMAN LOUGH: Gentlemen, let me thank you for your participation in the discussion tonight and for the ideas you have contributed. We may go on to some positive action, form an *ad hoc* committee or otherwise try to bring your suggestions to effective positive action, but before we proceed to that, I would like to pull together the points we have generally agreed on.

Various laboratories about the country are reporting Cs^{137} levels in humans which do not appear to be comparable. Some laboratories report fluctuations in Cs^{137} in the same individual from week to week which are improbably large. When mean values for Cs^{137} from different laboratories are recomputed, not on the basis of micro microcuries per kilogram of body weight but rather per gram of potassium, some highly inconsistent values become quite consistent. This suggests that body potassium measurements using K^{40} gamma rays also are not comparable, but that they err in the same direction so the Cs^{137}/potassium ratios are therefore artificially made more consistent.

Differences of the sort observed could be accounted for by errors in calibration factors, either in the instrumental efficiency component, the account taken of subject stature and habitus or the compensation made for self absorption. Contamination of the subject, of the instrument, of the atmosphere in the chamber or of the garments provided for the subject do occur and would contribute to error if undetected. It does not appear to be necessary to bathe subjects except under unusual circumstances. Care must be taken to place the subject in a standard position. It is perfectly possible to sit in a "standard" chair in a variable way.

"Standard" point sources currently available are not necessarily standard. One can transfer a "standard" activity from one container to another with large losses unless adequate technique is used. Manikins and phantoms leave much to be desired. A uniform solution poured into a hollow human shape does not have the same distribution of isotope as occurs in the human subject. The situation can be improved by re-distributing activity to match observed human differences, e.g., in leg *versus* trunk activity, but such a manikin still does not have the self ab-sorption properties of the human. It does not sit naturally in a standard chair.

In order to improve calibration, better standards are needed. Point sources come first. It should certainly be possible to make up some point sources which are reliable as to Cs^{137} content. If laboratories cannot agree on point source calibrations, it is axiomatic they cannot agree on anything else. The value of volume sources, whether "bottles," other "standard phantoms" or "standard manikins" is debatable. Sources for reference should include both weak activities and strong ones. Errors in low level work could be concealed by high activity standards. It would be highly desirable if some human volunteers of different stature and habits and with a wide range of Cs^{137} burdens were available to travel from laboratory to laboratory. If such were done, it would be important to return the subjects to their home base laboratory frequently to see that their burdens were not fluctuating. For this purpose, the precision of the home laboratory should be high, but this is easy to confirm. For evaluation of population burdens, measurements on groups of people are superior to measurements on individuals, because the true and unavoid-able differences are random and group means are therefore more com-parable than individual values.

SESSION V, SEPTEMBER 6

POTASSIUM AND BODY COMPOSITION

Chairman: ALBERT R. BEHNKE

14

RELATIONSHIP OF POTASSIUM CONTENT OF MAN WITH AGE AND SEX

Results of 10,000 Measurements of Normal Persons; Factors Influencing Potassium Content

Erich Oberhausen and Charles O. Onstead

Universität des Saarlandes
Hamburg, Germany
and
U. S. Army Medical Research Unit
Landstuhl/Phalz, Germany

THE MEASUREMENTS reported here were made in Landstuhl/ Phalz from June 1959 through December 1961 with the aid of a 2π liquid scintillation whole body counter designed by Anderson and co-workers (1) at Los Alamos. Calibrations with plastic phantoms filled with solutions of KCl were made to eliminate the influence of height and weight of the measured person upon the determination of the potassium content of the subject.

In calculating the results of the total potassium content and the potassium content per kilogram body weight, a standard deviation of about 12 percent was found for a single determination. The value of the standard deviation is also the same for the different groups of age and sex; therefore, it may be concluded that one should presume the same biological variation for all the different groups. As an example, Figure 1 shows the results of the measurements of males, aged sixteen to twenty-one. The distribution curve calculated with the values of the measured pattern gives a standard deviation of 12 percent.

Figure 2 shows the total potassium content of males in relation to age and the mean body weight in relation to age.

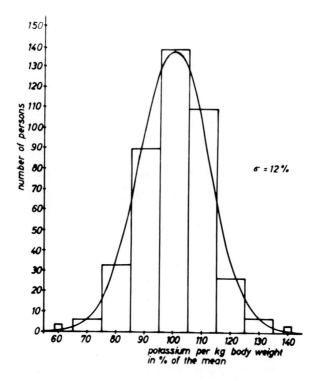

Distribution pattern of potassium per kg body weight
in young males (16-21 years of age)

Figure 1.

Up to about age twenty-two, the potassium content and
body weight both increase; the body weight then remains constant with increasing age, and in contrast the potassium content
decreases from 150 gm. at age twenty-two to 116 gm. at age
seventy. These results alone do not allow any conclusion about
changes of body composition during the lifespan. These conclusions are only possible if in addition the potassium concentration in different tissues is known. Talso and co-workers (2)
measured a potassium concentration of 153 mEq./liter intracellular water in skeletal muscle of adults. Considering that the total
cation concentration in serum is 152 mM./liter serum water, it
may be assumed that because of the osmotic equilibrium this
value of 153 mEq./liter intracellular water is the upper limit of
the intracellular potassium concentration in tissues. Talso and co-

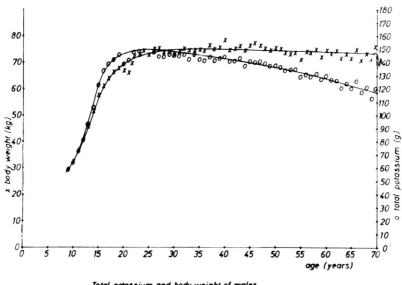

Total potassium and body weight of males

Figure 2.

workers also have shown by measurements of total water in muscle that the potassium concentration of muscle related to total water is 120 mEq./liter total water. In considering the total organism a concentration of 85 mEq./liter is found, assuming a total potassium content of 140 gm. or 3580 mEq. and a total water content of 42 liter. Since the total water content is related to the lean body mass, the comparison of both these concentrations of 120 mEq./liter and 85 mEq./liter reveals that the skeletal muscle as part of the lean body mass takes a special position with regard to its potassium content. If it is further assumed that the skeletal muscle is 53 percent of the total lean body mass, it follows that the potassium concentration is 120 mEq./liter total water in muscle and 50 mEq./liter total water in the other part of the lean body mass. This difference of the concentrations shows that the potassium content cannot be used as an index of lean body mass without further assumption. It would not be expected that the relationship between muscle and other lean body mass is the same in all persons. However, this relationship can be calculated if both the total body water and the potassium content are measured. From the measurement of total body water, the lean body mass can be calculated. From the measurement of the potassium content, its composition can be found.

When the measurements of a large number of persons are compared, the ratio of muscle and the other lean body mass or the ratio of total body water and potassium content is nearly constant in the mean. This will be shown by the comparison of the mean potassium content measured by us to the mean values of the total body water measured by Edelman and co-workers (3). These authors found in males a relationship of the mean body weight to age which is in good correspondence with our measurements. Their values of total body water may be compared with the mean potassium values obtained by us to calculate the ratio of total potassium content/total body water for different ages. These values (Table I) show that the quotient is constant for adults up to age fifty; therefore, it may be assumed that the composition of the lean body mass is the same. At age fifteen the quotient has a maximal value which may be caused by the relatively rapid muscular development in this period.

Though the quotients for children aged ten and for adults are nearly the same, it cannot be concluded that the composition of the lean body mass for these two groups is the same, because there are two age dependent variations which compensate. In

TABLE I

POTASSIUM CONTENT AND TOTAL BODY WATER AT DIFFERENT AGES

Age (Years)	TBW (l)	Total Potassium (g)	g K / l TBW	mEq. K / l TBW
10	20	65	3,3	83
15	33	123	3,8	95
20	41	147	3,6	92
25	45	148	3,3	84
30	45	146	3,3	83
35	44	144	3,3	84
40	43	142	3,3	84
45	42	140	3,3	85
50	41	136	3,3	85
55	41	131	3,2	82
60	40	127	3,2	81
65	40	123	3,1	79
70	37	116	3,1	80

children the intracellular potassium concentration is very high. From the values of exchangeable potassium, total body water and extracellular water published in the literature (4-7), an intracellular potassium concentration of 138 mEq./liter for age ten can be calculated. Thus at this age the intracellular potassium concentration of the total lean body mass is nearly as high as that of muscle. But the ratio of extracellular water to total water is also much higher than in adults, therefore the quotient, potassium content/total body water, remains constant. Therefore, it may be assumed only for adults that the same quotient means the same composition of the lean body mass.

These considerations reveal that the measured decrease of the potassium concentration from twenty-two to fifty years is caused by a uniform reduction of the lean body mass. Because the quotient, total potassium/total body water, is constant, the reduction of muscle and other lean body mass is the same. It is only after age fifty-five that the quotient becomes smaller and that muscle reduction may be greater. As the mean body weight after age twenty-two is nearly constant, it follows that the reduc-

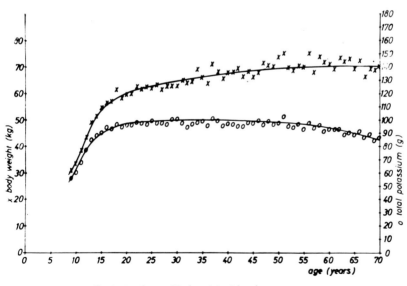

Total potassium and body weight of females

Figure 3.

tion of the lean body mass is accompanied by an increase of fat content.

Figure 3 shows the relationship of total potassium content and of body weight to age for females. In contrast to males, body weight increases throughout life. Also in contrast to males, the potassium content remains constant up to age fifty, later decreasing. In males the maximum potassium content is 150 gm.; in females it is 100 gm. This difference is caused not only by higher fat content, but also because the ratio of muscle to lean body mass in females is much lower. Since potassium content is constant from age twenty-two to fifty, it may be assumed that the reduction of the lean body mass in females begins at age fifty.

Figure 4 shows the potassium content/kilogram body weight for both sexes in relation to age. These curves are the result of the several interrelating factors. In females a continuous decrease of the potassium concentration with age is obtained. The decrease in childhood is caused by the decrease of the intracellular potassium concentration in the lean body mass. In adults the lean

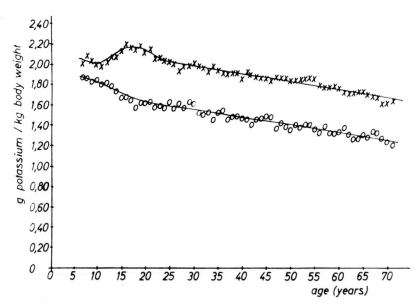

Potassium concentration in general population

Figure 4.

body mass and its potassium content is constant; the diminution of the potassium concentration is caused by an increase of fat.

In males it is not exactly the same. In childhood a decrease is obtained initially because of the decrease of intracellular potassium concentration. At puberty a maximal value is obtained caused by the rapid muscular development at this age which overcompensates the further decrease of intracellular potassium content. The decrease in adult males is caused by reduction of the lean body mass, which is replaced by fat.

REFERENCES

1. Anderson, E. C., Hayes, F. N., and Hiebert, R. D.: *Nucleonics*, *16*:Nr. 8, 106-107, 1958.
2. Talso, D. J., Spafford, N., and Blaw, H.: *J. Lab. Clin. Med.*, *41*:281-286, 1953.
3. Edelman, I. S., Haley, H. B., Schloerb, P. R., Sheldon, D. B., Friies-Hansen, B. J., Stoll, G., and Moore, F. D.: *Surg. Gynec. Obstet.*, *95*:1-12, 1952.
4. Corsa, L. Jr., Gribetz, D., Cook, Ch. D., and Talbot, N. B.: *Pediatrics*, *17*:184-190, 1956.
5. James, I. A., and Robertson, I. S.: *Amer. J. Dis. Child*, *93*:217, 1957.
6. Friies-Hansen, B. J., Holiday, H., Stapleton, Th., and Wallace, W. M.: *Pediatrics*, *7*:321-327, 1951.
7. Fellers, F. X., Barnett, H. L., Have, K., and McNamara, H.: *Pediatrics*, *3*:622, 1949.
8. Ely, R. S., and Sutor, W. W.: *Pediatrics*, *10*:115-125, 1952.

15

INTERPRETATION PROBLEMS OF WHOLE BODY POTASSIUM MEASUREMENTS STUDIED ON VARIOUS COMPONENTS OF DISSECTED PIGS

ALEXANDER PFAU

Max-Planck-Institut
Mariensee, Germany

THE TECHNICAL performance of large volume detectors has come to a point where natural K^{40} gamma activity of humans or large domestic animals can be measured routinely. However, it is less certain whether these data will be of any practical value, since the knowledge of whole body potassium as related to gross body composition is still insufficient.

It is true that a lot of valuable information has accumulated during the last years relating total potassium to gross body weight (1, 2) or to fat-free dry body mass minus bone mineral (3) or to lean body weight (4, 5). But all the results are obtained by indirect methods. Little has been done to confirm the data by direct analysis. There also seems to be some evidence that total K^{40} should not be used for estimating lean body mass (6).

The K^{40} content of large meat cuts, especially from pigs, less from lambs or cattle, was found to be highly correlated to separable lean or to chemical components like protein, fat or water (7-11). Therefore, external counting of K^{40} gamma activity appeared to be a useful technique for estimating the lean content or the chemical gross composition of meat cuts. However, the potassium content of meat cuts weighing less than 15 kg. is too small to get statistically significant results within short counting times (8). Furthermore, the chemical analysis of gross meat composition was found to be more accurate in some cases than the results obtained by nondestructive K^{40} measurements (10). Therefore, the K^{40} technique should be of no value for all potential applications where time is a limiting factor or high accuracy is required.

The first limitation could be overcome by increasing the sample weight using whole bodies of large mammals instead of small meat cuts. But the concept might be invalid for whole bodies, because additional gamma activity not detectable in small biological material could interfere with whole body K^{40} counting. Furthermore, the body components and the distribution pattern of potassium might be different.

There will be no interference with the K^{40} measurements by other radionuclides as long as the gamma activity is below the detection sensitivity of whole body counters (about10^{-10}c). When higher gamma activities are present, K^{40} counting will lead to reliable results if gamma quanta are not equal or higher in energy than the K^{40} channel settings of the counter. This appears to be valid for the natural gamma activity of radium and thorium either being incorporated or passing the gastrointestinal tract of humans (12, 13), but not for people contaminated by radium or formerly treated by thorotrast (14, 15). Even though the natural specific gamma activity of radium or thorium is very low in biological material, with large domestic animals of high weight and feed intake, some difficulties might arise in determining the true K^{40} content of the body.

A more serious problem to whole body K^{40} counting is radioactivity from nuclear weapon tests and from increasing peaceful use of atomic energy. But in normal persons no gamma-quanta-emitting fission products interfering with the K^{40} measurements could be found by external counting if thorough cleansing of the bodies was done. Similar results were obtained by measuring hams of pigs (8). However, the premise must not hold true when people handling radioactive material or being treated by radionuclides are counted (16, 17).

There might be some difficulties with large domestic animals, too. The gamma activity of fission products was estimated to be about 0.5 μc in the rumen of gazing cattle during springtime 1962 in northern Germany (18). In 2 or 4 π liquid scintillation detectors especially designed for counting large mammals, gamma quanta due to energy and activity interfere with the K^{40} measurements (19). These detectors, appreciated for their good geometry, will always have problems in accurate determination of K^{40} if gamma emitting radionuclides are present producing sum peaks higher than the K^{40} gamma ray energy of 1.46 Mev (20). These and some other difficulties could be avoided or reduced by the use of NaI crystal assemblies, but then other problems arise.

However, in most cases well designed counting facilities and properly calibrated detectors will lead to reliable total body K^{40} measurements.

All conversions of K^{40} whole body activity to total body potassium are based on the fact that K^{40} has been shown to be present in a constant ratio in naturally occurring potassium (21). Therefore, potassium can be determined first, and then the K^{40} gamma activity can be calculated (22).

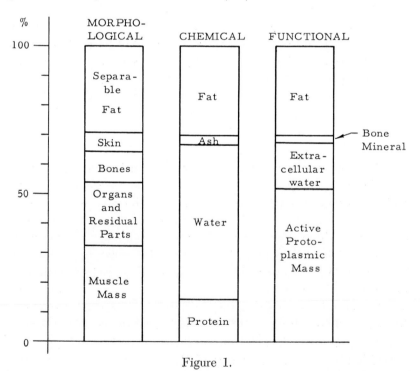

Figure 1.

Generally speaking there are three types of body models (Fig. 1). The morphological way divides the body according to separable depot or separable fat, muscle mass, organs, bones, skin and residual mass. The chemical way speaks of fat (ether extract), protein (nitrogen x 6.25), water (weight loss after careful dehydration) and ash (residual mass after burning a cadaver). The functional type divides the body into active protoplasmic mass and metabolic inactive mass consisting of extracellular water, fat and bone mineral. From all these models the chemical one offers the most reliable basis for the calculation of body components in animals (23).

Whole body analysis of pigs, both morphological and chemical, have been done for over 100 years (24). Recently some data about the functional body composition have been reported (26). Figure 1 presents an illustration of the mean body composition of 110 kg. pigs for all types of body models. Pigs with different feeding and management may have the same chronological age, but not the same gross body composition (24).

At first, we studied the morphological and chemical body model only and examined whether the potassium content of muscle from pigs of the same management and slaughter weight depends on type of muscle, sex or breed.

METHODS

For the study, sixty-one male castrates and female pigs were used. During the summer and winter of 1961-62 pigs of the German improved Landrace and Belgian Piétrain breeds were reared at the experimental field station of Mariensee. At the same time pigs of the Dutch improved Landrace breed were reared at the progeny station of Rohrsen. The relative composition of the diet was the same at both stations. The amount of feed given per day was a little higher at Mariensee. Therefore, only the German and Belgian breeds had the same feeding and environmental conditions and could be compared as different breeds.

The pigs were slaughtered when they weighed 110 kg. Two selected muscles from sixty pigs of different sex and breed were analyzed and compared to each other. All the muscles from one pig were analyzed and compared to the results of selected muscles from sixty pigs.

For the analysis of selected muscles from different pigs, the carcasses of the slaughtered animals were hung 26 to 28 hr. in a cool storage house at 4° C. Then the musculus longissimus dorsi and the musculus semimembranaceus were separated from the left half. External fat was removed from the muscle, and a slice of meat, 1.5 cm. thick, was taken between the 10th and 11th rib. Another slice the same thickness was taken from the semimembranaceus 2.5 cm. from the edge of the muscle. Each slice was ground and mixed thoroughly. Aliquot samples were taken for analysis. Up to then, about 32 hr. were gone since the animal was killed.

For the investigation of whole body composition, a pig was killed and depleted, and aliquot blood samples were taken for analysis. The carcass was scalded by hot water. The bristles were rubbed off and collected. The internal organs were taken out. The carcass was divided in half. The halves hung for 24 hr. at 4° C., then were dissected into main muscles, separable fat, organs, skin and bones. All the components were weighed, and, except bones, were thoroughly ground and mixed. Aliquot samples were taken for analysis. Until then, about 32 hr. were gone since an animal was killed. The bones were only cleaned.

The analysis of tissues for dry matter, fat and nitrogen was done by conventional methods (27). Protein was determined by calculation (N x 6.25). For potassium analysis, the samples were ashed at 500° C. in a muffle furnace. The ash was dissolved by concentrated hydrochloric acid. The solution was evaporated, and the residual mass was dissolved by dilute hydrochloric acid. After filtration, the solution was diluted by bidistilled water. The potassium content of the solution was determined by a flame photometer working with a filter at 768 mμ and using propane gas. The interference with other elements was found to be 1/100 to 1/1000 of the potassium values related to 100 percent (28). The flame photometer was calibrated by potassium chloride pro analysis from Merck AG., Darmstadt, Germany.

In analysis of selected muscles from sixty pigs, all the data on chemical meat components and on potassium content were classified according to sex (male castrates and female pigs), to different type of muscles and to the breed. Evaluation of the data was done by an analysis of variance (29).

In whole body analysis, the data on chemical components and potassium content of the single muscles were tabulated in series of their anatomical location. Correlation coefficients and regression equations were calculated between muscle potassium and various muscle components, and comparisons on mean specific potassium values obtained from selected muscles of sixty pigs and all the muscles of pig were made.

Some of the terms are abbreviated as follows:

DvL	= Deutsches veredeltes Landschwein (German improved Landrace)
Piétrain	= Belgian Piétrain pigs
HvL	= Holländisches veredeltes Landschwein (Dutch improved Landrace)
l.d.	= Musculus longissimus dorsi
s.m.	= Musculus semi-membranaceus
M	= Original muscle sample
FM	= Fat-free muscle sample
FDM	= Fat-free dry matter
AFDM	= Fat-free dry matter minus the ash
GI	= Gastrointestinal
C.V.	= Coefficient of variation
F_v	= Variance ratio from analysis of variance
F_p	= Value of F distribution at point p for degrees of freedom from the analysis of variance according to tables in (30).

RESULTS

Table I presents the mean values of gross meat composition in percentage of the original weight of the muscle samples from l.d. and s.m. of pigs for different sexes and breeds. From all the components analyzed, fat shows the greatest and water the lowest

TABLE I

Summary of Data on Means and Coefficients of Variation of Chemical Composition of the Analyzed Muscle Samples Obtained from 110 kg. Pigs Belonging to Different Sex and Breed

Item	10 Observations	Muscle	DvL Male l.d.	DvL Male s.m.	DvL Female l.d.	DvL Female s.m.	Piétrain Male l.d.	Piétrain Male s.m.	Piétrain Female l.d.	Piétrain Female s.m.	HvL Male l.d.	HvL Male s.m.	HvL Female l.d.	HvL Female s.m.
Fat	Mean	%	2.67	2.74	2.33	4.07	1.96	2.89	0.91	1.53	1.43	2.47	1.15	2.11
	C.V.	%	±58	±49	±47	±61	±68	±60	±35	±49	±36	±41	±43	±36
H₂O	Mean	%	74.23	74.59	74.49	73.53	74.15	74.16	74.84	75.11	75.02	74.87	75.30	74.89
	C.V.	%	±1.4	±1.9	±1.1	±2.6	±1.2	±1.5	±0.3	±0.8	±0.6	±1.3	±0.5	±1.1
N	Mean	%	3.58	3.50	3.57	3.49	3.69	3.55	3.70	3.54	3.62	3.46	3.57	3.48
	C.V.	%	±4.6	±4.1	±3.2	±4.3	±4.3	±5.2	±3.2	±3.1	±3.4	±2.5	±3.3	±3.7
AsH	Mean	%	1.10	1.09	1.10	1.07	1.13	1.12	1.12	1.13	1.13	1.12	1.15	1.12
	C.V.	%	±3.2	±4.1	±4.1	±3.2	±4.3	±4.6	±2.0	±5.8	±2.6	±2.8	±3.8	±3.7
FDM	Mean	%	23.13	22.67	23.18	22.51	23.89	22.93	24.25	23.36	23.56	22.57	23.56	23.09
	C.V.	%	±2.5	±3.5	±2.5	±3.9	±2.9	±4.5	±1.6	±3.2	±2.4	±2.7	±1.9	±1.8
Protein	Mean	%	22.36	21.87	22.29	21.79	23.02	22.18	23.15	22.15	22.63	21.72	22.31	21.75
	C.V.	%	±4.6	±4.1	±3.1	±4.3	±4.3	±5.2	±3.2	±3.1	±3.4	±2.5	±3.3	±3.7
AFDM	Mean	%	22.02	21.58	22.09	21.44	22.73	21.77	23.13	22.34	22.42	22.46	22.41	21.97
	C.V.	%	±2.5	±3.6	±2.5	±4.0	±2.8	±4.8	±1.6	±3.3	±2.5	±2.5	±2.0	±1.9

TABLE II

Summary of Data on Means and Coefficients of Variation of Potassium Content as Related to Intact Meat and to Components of Muscle Samples Obtained from 110 kg. Pigs Belonging to Different Sex and Breed

Item	10 Observations	Muscle	DvL Male l.d.	DvL Male s.m.	DvL Female l.d.	DvL Female s.m.	Piétrain Male l.d.	Piétrain Male s.m.	Piétrain Female l.d.	Piétrain Female s.m.	HvL Male l.d.	HvL Male s.m.	HvL Female l.d.	HvL Female s.m.
K/M	Mean	mg/g	3.55	3.43	3.59	3.42	3.80	3.60	3.72	3.67	3.69	3.50	3.73	3.56
	C. V.	%	±5.1	±4.6	±4.1	±5.5	±3.0	±5.0	±3.4	±3.8	±4.1	±6.1	±5.5	±6.0
K/FM	Mean	mg/g	3.65	3.52	3.67	3.56	3.88	3.71	3.76	3.72	3.74	3.59	3.77	3.63
	C. V.	%	±4.9	±4.6	±3.3	±4.0	±2.5	±3.7	±3.5	±3.8	±3.9	±5.9	±5.3	±5.5
K/Ash	Mean	mg/g	323	316	327	321	336	323	333	325	326	313	326	316
	C. V.	%	±2.9	±2.6	±2.4	±3.3	±2.8	±4.0	±2.1	±3.6	±5.2	±4.5	±4.1	±3.9
K/N	Mean	mg/g	99.6	98.1	100.7	98.1	103.3	101.7	100.6	103.4	102.1	101.2	104.5	102.3
	C. V.	%	±6.9	±5.4	±3.9	±3.8	±4.8	±4.4	±4.5	±3.8	±5.7	±7.1	±5.3	±6.5
K/FDM	Mean	mg/g	15.4	15.1	15.7	15.3	16.7	15.7	15.4	15.7	15.7	15.4	15.8	15.4
	C. V.	%	±4.6	±3.7	±4.3	±3.2	±3.4	±3.5	±3.0	±3.2	±3.4	±6.2	±5.0	±7.1
K/Protein	Mean	mg/g	15.9	15.7	16.1	15.7	15.9	16.2	16.1	16.6	16.4	16.2	16.7	16.4
	C. V.	%	±6.9	±5.4	±3.9	±3.8	±4.8	±4.4	±4.5	±3.8	±5.7	±7.1	±5.3	±6.5
K/AFDM	Mean	mg/g	16.1	15.8	16.3	16.0	15.5	16.5	16.1	16.5	16.5	16.4	16.6	16.2
	C. V.	%	±5.2	±4.0	±3.5	±4.1	±4.8	±3.5	±3.0	±3.4	±3.3	±6.5	±5.2	±6.9

coefficient of variation. On an average there is not too much variation between the mean values or the coefficients of variations of fat-free dry matter, protein and fat-free dry matter minus the ash. Nitrogen will be represented by protein due to the calculation N x 6.25.

Table II summarizes the data on mean potassium content as related to the original muscle sample, to the fat-free muscle sample and to various other meat components for the different groups of pigs. Besides the mean specific potassium ratios, the coefficients of variation have been calculated. The literature is rather poor on new reports of potassium content in muscles of pigs (review up to 1960 in 31). Therefore, no comparison with other values were made.

In Tables III and IV the final results of analysis of variance are given for various meat components and potassium ratios. Comparing the variance ratios with the F values, the following statistical conclusions can be drawn.

The assumption cannot be refuted at a p = 0.001 level that there are differences between the mean content of fat or fat-free dry matter in meat samples due to the variability of muscles and breeds. There could be differences between the mean values of the water and ash content for the different breeds (p = 0.01). But no differences appeared to exist between the sexes for all the meat components (p = 0.05).

TABLE III

FINAL RESULTS OF ANALYSIS OF VARIANCE FOR THE CHEMICAL COMPONENTS OF THE MEAT SAMPLES OBTAINED FROM M. LONGISSIMUS DORSI AND M. SEMIMEM-BRANACEUS OF 110 KG. PIGS OF TWO DIFFERENT SEX AND BREED

Source of Variation	Variance Ratio F_v for				F_p Value for p		
	Fat	H_2O	Ash	FDM	0.001	0.01	0.05
Sex	2.24	1.18	0.00	2.88	11.38	6.85	3.92
Muscle	14.90	0.69	4.21	38.23	11.38	6.85	3.92
Breed	10.84	7.06	11.95	12.69	7.32	4.79	3.07
Muscle x Sex	0.88	1.59	0.06	0.27	11.38	6.85	3.92
Breed x Sex	4.51	4.04	0.50	1.24	7.32	4.79	3.07
Breed x Muscle ...	0.08	0.66	0.50	0.77	7.32	4.79	3.07
Breed x Muscle x Sex	1.82	1.75	0.54	0.82	7.32	4.79	3.07

TABLE IV

FINAL RESULTS OF ANALYSIS OF VARIANCE FOR POTASSIUM CONTENT AS RE-
LATED TO INTACT MEAT AND TO COMPONENTS OF MUSCLE SAMPLES OBTAINED
FROM M. LONGISSIMUS DORSI AND M. SEMIMEMBRANACEUS OF 110 KG. PIGS OF
DIFFERENT SEX AND BREED.

Source of Variation	Variance Ratio F_v for				F_p Value for p		
	K/M	K/FM	K/Ash	K/FDM	0.001	0.01	0.05
Sex	0.29	0.02	0.03	0.00	11.38	6.85	3.92
Muscle	23.45	17.60	15.86	2.96	11.38	6.85	3.92
Breed	13.26	10.30	6.20	1.88	7.32	4.79	3.07
Muscle x Sex	0.31	0.81	0.08	0.46	11.38	6.85	3.92
Breed x Sex	0.28	1.06	0.90	1.68	7.32	4.79	3.07
Breed x Muscle ..	0.16	0.13	0.31	1.03	7.32	4.79	3.07
Breed x Muscle x Sex	0.74	0.46	0.52	0.74	7.32	4.79	3.07

The assumption cannot be refuted at a p = 0.001 level that there are differences between the mean values of the potassium content as related to the original muscle sample, to the fat-free muscle sample or to the ash for the variability of muscle and breed. But there seems to be no statistical evidence that there are differences between the mean values of the potassium content as related to the fat-free dry matter for all the different sources of variation, such as sex, type of muscle and breed. No differences between the mean values of the different potassium ratios from the various groups could be found for sex.

From all potassium ratios investigated, only potassium as related to fat-free dry matter appeared to be independent from sex, type of muscle and breed of 110 kg. pigs being reared under the same feeding and environmental conditions. The premise must also hold true when feeding is slightly changed and different environments are given, because this happened to be the case for the third group of pigs in the study presented. Independency of sex, type of muscle and breed must also exist for the potassium content as related to nitrogen or protein, as well as to fat-free dry matter minus the ash. There seems to be no statistical evidence that water content of muscle samples should be a reliable reference quantity in studies on muscle potassium.

Data on potassium ratios found to be independent of sex,

TABLE V

SUMMARY AND COMPARISON OF DATA ON MEAN POTASSIUM CONTENT OF
MUSCLES AS RELATED TO MUSCLE COMPONENTS FOUND TO BE INDEPENDENT OF
SEX, TYPE OF MUSCLE AND BREED OF 110 KG. PIGS.

Potassium Content of Muscle Samples as Related to		Means and Standard Deviations Calculated from Data of	
		2 Muscles (l.d.&s.m.) of 60 Pigs (120 Observations)	All the Analyzed Muscles of 1 Pig (117 Observations)
FDM	mg/g	15.54±0.68	14.38±1.21
Protein	mg/g	16.21±0.87	15.28±1.29
AFDM	mg/g	16.30±0.75	15.11±1.39
Nitrogen	mg/g	101.30±5.47	95.41±8.05

type of muscle and breed of 110 kg. pigs obtained from analysis
of single muscles of sixty pigs is shown in Table V with the mean
values from all the muscles of one pig. The means from one pig
appear to be slightly lower than the means from different pigs,
but the standard deviation is higher in the one pig, so no differences between measurements can be assumed. Therefore, the
statements made for selected single muscle samples should also
be valid for total muscle mass of 110 kg. pigs.

The statistical analysis of all dissected muscles of two halves
of a 110 kg. pig is summarized in Table VI. The correlation between muscle potassium and weight or fat-free dry matter of intact muscles appears ideal, but only fat-free dry matter or other

TABLE VI

CORRELATION COEFFICIENTS AND REGRESSION EQUATIONS BETWEEN G. POTASSIUM AND
WEIGHT OR CHEMICAL COMPONENTS OF INTACT MUSCLES. DATA OBTAINED FROM
CADAVER ANALYSIS OF TWO HALVES OF 110 KG. PIG

Independent Variable X	Dependent Variable Y		Correlation Coefficient r^1	Regression Equation	Standard Deviation S_{YX}
Muscle	Muscle	(g)	0.993	Y=329.05 X + 12.86	± 47.11
potassium	FDM	(g)	0.997	Y= 71.29 X + 2.35	± 6.65
(g)	Water	(g)	0.739	Y=229.22 X + 8.30	± 251.34
	Fat	(g)	0.735	Y= 28.52 X + 7.72	± 31.69

[1] 0.32 at p = 0.001.

related items are found to be the reference quantities for potassium being constant on an average from pig to pig at 110 kg. The correlation coefficient between muscle potassium and muscle water or muscle fat has appeared highly significant. However, the correlation coefficients are considerably lower as compared to that obtained for fat-free dry matter. This seems to be another hint that total body potassium should not be used for estimating total body water respecting lean body weight.

TABLE VII

SUMMARY OF PRELIMINARY DATA ON MEAN POTASSIUM CONTENT OF VARIOUS MORPHOLOGICAL BODY COMPONENTS AS RELATED TO THOSE CHEMICAL COMPONENTS APPEARED TO BE INDEPENDENT OF SEX, TYPE OF MUSCLE AND BREED IN MUSCLE ANAYLSIS OF 110 KG. PIGS

Potassium Content of Analyzed Body Components as Related to		Body Components (Means Calculated from Data of Cadaver Analysis of a Female 110 kg. DvL Pig.)					
		Organs[1]	Blood	Separate Fat	Bones[2]	Bristles	Skin
FDM	mg/g	15.20	9.35	10.34	2.09	5.20	1.41
Protein[3]	mg/g	16.12	9.82	11.57	4.93	5.34	1.45
Nitrogen	mg/g	100.10	61.40	72.33	30.80	33.40	9.10

[1] Represent 72 percent of all internal and external organs.
[2] Includes the teeth.
[3] N × 6.25.

Table VII summarizes data on mean potassium content related to fat-free dry matter, protein and nitrogen content of various morphological components of a 110 kg. pig. The mean specific potassium values of the organs are in good agreement with those obtained for the muscles in Table V. Blood, separable fat, bones, bristles and skin show partly considerable differences. But the specific potassium values of blood, separable fat, bones and bristles appear to be close to each other. The specific potassium values of the skin do not fit in either range.

The potassium protein ratio is shown in Table VIII with the potassium distribution pattern due to the morphological body model tabulated.

The relative values of the morphological body composition are in good agreement with those averages presented in Figure 1. As expected, most of the total potassium has been found to be

TABLE VIII

MORPHOLOGICAL BODY COMPOSITION AND POTASSIUM CONTENT OF BODY COMPONENTS OBTAINED FROM CADAVER ANALYSIS OF A FEMALE GERMAN IMPROVED LANDRACE PIG

Body Components	% of Total Weight (100 % ≙ 115.57 kg)	% of Total K (100 % ≙ 192.66 g-K)	Body Components with K/Protein≈ const	% of Total K (100% ≙ 192.66 g)
Skin Bristles Claws	4.09	1.31	Skin	0.92
Bones	10.58	5.69	Bristles Claws Bones	6.08
Separable fat	28.75	5.60	Separate fat, Blood	9.95
Blood Organs	13.20	15.06	Organs Muscles	80.14
Muscles	40.32	69.43		
Content of GI-tract	3.06	2.91	Content of GI-tract (K/total)	2.91

Figure 1. Relative mean morphological, chemical and functional body composition of pigs at 110 kg. (25, 26).

concentrated in the muscles (about 70 percent). But 3 percent must be attributed to the content of the gastrointestinal tract. About 80 percent of total potassium of a 110 kg. pig represents a mass of protein of nitrogen or of fat-free dry matter, distinguished by a potassium ratio which on an average has been found to be independent from sex and bred in muscle analysis of 110 kg. pigs.

DISCUSSION AND SUMMARY

This study was designed primarily to examine whether the potassium content of muscles from pigs of the same management and slaughter weight depends on sex, type of muscle or breed. Single muscles from sixty pigs and all the muscles of one pig were analyzed.

The procedure of sample taking and preparing was standarized for a reliable comparison of data. Values reported might change independently from biological variations to some extent if other techniques are used. However, this change should not hold true for the conclusions drawn from statistical analysis as long as the premise of such an analysis is correct.

An objection can be made against the relative small numbers of repetitions used in each classification for the analysis of variance. But it could be shown by the Duncan test (32) that the mean content of fat-free dry matter and the potassium content of the intact muscle samples were significantly different in various muscles from pigs belonging to different breeds, whereas no differences could be noticed for the mean potassium content as related to fat-free dry matter.

The restriction on the analysis of muscle slices instead of total muscles in single muscle studies from different pigs had no influence on the true evaluation of the data, because the independent potassium ratios of partial and total analysis were in good agreement within experimental errors. This was also the case for values obtained from single muscle studies of many pigs, as well as from total analysis of all the muscles of one pig. Therefore, the results found in analysis of variance for two types of muscles can be extended to all the muscles of a pig. This means that fat-free dry matter, protein, nitrogen or fat-free dry matter minus the ash appeared to be the only reference quantities for potassium being independent from all body muscles of different sex and breed of healthy 110 kg. pigs reared under the same or slightly different conditions.

This does not necessarily mean that there are no differences. Even in whole body muscle analysis with long dissection time that might introduce experimental errors, the coefficient of variation of the mean potassium content as related to independent reference quantities does not exceed a value of $\pm$ 8%. Therefore, if no experimental errors would be present the biological variation cannot be greater than $\pm$8%. However, this value is based on an unfavorable assumption. In actual cases the biological variation from muscles of different pigs should be lower than the variation coefficients obtained for single muscle analysis of $\pm$ 4%. It can even be assumed that there are no differences at all between various muscles from healthy pigs at 110 kg. It is not surprising that most of the bigger organs show potassium ratios in good agreement with those obtained for the muscles. On the other hand it could hardly be expected that the concept of a constant potassium ratio holds true for all the residual morphological body components. So the values of blood, separable fat, bones, bristles and skin are lower than the corresponding data of muscles or organs.

No potassium should be found in neutral fat. But during slaughtering and dissection, it can hardly be avoided that intermuscular fat will be contaminated by blood. Furthermore, connective tissue will always be attached to separable fat. Less than 1 kg. blood remains in the cadaver of a 110 kg. pig after depletion. This amount will not contribute much in body components rich in potassium, such as muscles. But it cannot be neglected in those body components poor in potassium. All these arguments could be used to explain the presence of potassium in separable fat and the rather close agreement between values of blood and separable fat. The rather good agreement between the mean potassium:protein ratios of bones and bristles might be incidental.

It is too early to further speculate on the interpretation of whole body potassium measurements. But it can be concluded from this study that total body potassium measurements cannot be related morphologically or chemically to one reference quantity only. If one is not concerned with uncertainties of a few per cent, total potassium as related to one reference quantity such as gross body weight, lean body weight, etc., should be of good use in large numbers. There is some hope that total body potassium can be described by three or more body compartments, each of them with constant specific potassium content, by a linear equation. However, for the solution of such a linear equation, the knowledge of more than one unknown is necessary. Up to now it is doubtful whether there are enough substitutions for the unknowns, that by measurements of total potassium only the body component in question can be derived.

REFERENCES

1. Anderson, E. C., and Langham, W. H.: *Science, 130*:713, 1959.
2. Onstead, C. D., Oberhausen, E., and Keary, F. V.: *Atompraxis, 6*:337, 1960.
3. Allen, T. H., Anderson, E. C., Langham, W. H.: *J. Geront., 15*:350, 1960.
4. Woodward, K. T., Trujillo, T. T., Schuch, R. L., and Anderson, E. C.: *Nature, 178*:97, 1956.
5. Anderson, E. C.: *Brit. J. Radiol.,* Supplement No. 7:27, 1957.
6. Von Döbeln, W.: In *Whole Body Counting.* Vienna, I.A.E.A., Sti/Pub/ 47, 1962, p. 351.
7. Kulwich, R., Feinstein, L., and Anderson, E. C.: *Science, 127*:338, 1958.
8. Pfau, A., Kallistratos, G., and Schröder, J.: *Atompraxis, 7*:279, 1961.
9. Kulwich, R., Feinstein, L., Golumbic, C., Hiner, R. L., Seymour, W. R., and Kauffman, W. R.: *J. Animal Sci., 20*:497, 1961.
10. Kirton, A. H., Pearson, A. M., Porter, R. W., and Nelson, R. H.: *J. Food Sci., 26*:475, 1961.
11. Kulwich, R., Feinstein, L., Golumbic, C., Seymour, W. R., Kauffman, W. R., and Hiner, R. L.: *Food Technology, 15*:411, 1961.
12. Muth, H., Schraub, A., Aurand, K., and Hantke, H. J.: *Brit. J. Radiol.,* Supplement 7:54, 1957.
13. Hursh, J. B.: *Brit. J. Radiol.,* Supplement 7:45, 1957.
14. Oberhausen, E.: in Organic Scintillation Detectors. G. H. Daub, F. N. Hayes and E. Sullivan (Editors). T.I.D.-7612 *Instruments,* 1960.

15. Suguri, S.: in *Whole Body Counting*. Vienna, I.A.E.A., Sti/Pub/47, 1962.
16. Boulenger, R. R., Colard, J. F., and Henry, J.: in *Whole Body Counting*, Vienna, I.A.E.A., Sti/Pub/47, 1962.
17. Heinrich, H. C., and Pfau, A.: *Atomkernenergie*. 6:463, 1961.
18. Pfau, A., and Hoeck, H.: *Milchwissenchaften*. 17:673, 1962.
19. Pfau, A., and Kallistratos, G.: in Organic Scintillation Detectors. G. H. Daub, F. N. Hayes and E. Sullivan (Editors), T.I.D.-7612, *Instruments*, 1960.
20. Van Dilla, M. A., and Anderson, E. C.: in Whole Body Counting, Vienna, I.A.E.A., Sti/Pub/47, 1962.
21. Vinogradow, A. P.: *Bhiokimia*, 22:14, 1957.
22. Wetherill, G. W.: *Science*, 126:545, 1957.
23. Hörnicke, H.: Z. *Tierphysiol.*, *Tierernährung Futtermittelkunde*, 16:237, 1961.
24. Hörnicke, H.: Z. *Tierphysiol. Tierernährung Futtermittelkunde*, 16:344, 1961.
25. Schröder, J.: Max-Planck-Institut, Mariensee. (Unpublished results.)
26. Hörnicke, H.: Z. *Tierphysiol. Tierernährung Futtermittelkunde*, 17:28, 1962.
27. Grau, R.: Fleisch Und Fleischwaren, Verlag, Berlin, A. W. Hayn's Erben, 50:36, 1960.
28. Netheler, & Hinz GmbH, Hamburg: *Handbuch Flammenphotometer*, Eppendorf, 1956.
29. Koller, S.: Statistische Auswertungsmethoden: in Rauen, H. M., (Editor). *Biochemisches Taschenbuch*. Berlin, Göttingen, Heidelberg, Springer-Verlag, 1956.
30. Fischer, A. R., and Yates, F.: *Statistical Tables*, 5th Edition. London, Oliver & Boyd, 1957.
31. Simonnet, H.: in *Potassium In The Animal Organism*. International Potash Institute (Editor), Berne, 1960, pp. 67-208.
32. Duncan, D. B.: *Biometrics*, 11:Nr. 1, 1955.

16

CORRELATION OF TOTAL BODY POTASSIUM AND TISSUE POTASSIUM MEASUREMENTS[1]

ALEXANDER P. REMENCHIK, PETER J. TALSO
AND CHARLES E. MILLER
Veterans Administration Hospital
Hines, Illinois
Loyola University
Stritch School of Medicine
Chicago, Illinois
Argonne National Laboratory
Lemont, Illinois

THE USE OF TOTAL body potassium measurements for the estimation of body solids (1), muscle mass (2) and total body fat (3) has been suggested by several investigators. The development of low level counting techniques has provided an opportunity for the rapid measurement of total body potassium. However, a number of assumptions have been made by the investigators using this technique. We have made measurements designed to evaluate these assumptions. Our studies suggest that the medical application of potassium measurements made by whole body counters is premature.

We designed our experiments to answer the following questions.

How accurate are the potassium measurements made by whole body counters?

What effect does body composition have on the accuracy of the measurement?

Do measurements of total body potassium reflect muscle content of potassium?

[1] This investigation was supported in part by the Psychiatric and Research Fund of the Illinois Department of Mental Health.

The subjects measured were patients hospitalized in the Veterans Administration Hospital, Hines, Illinois. The methods used for measuring total body potassium calculated from K^{40} gamma ray activity ($K_B{}^{40}$), total body potassium calculated from K^{42} ($K_B{}^{42}$) and total body water have been reported elsewhere (4, 5). Extracellular fluid volume was determined by radiosulfate. Chemical analysis of muscle was done by methods to be reported (6).

To assess the accuracy of $K_B{}^{40}$ determinations we measured $K_B{}^{42}$ at the same time the $K_B{}^{40}$ measurements were made and calculated the $K_B{}^{42}/K_B{}^{40}$ ratio for each subject. The lean body mass (LBM) of these subjects was calculated from their total body water measurements, and each subject's lean body mass content of potassium calculated from these data. Figure 1 de-

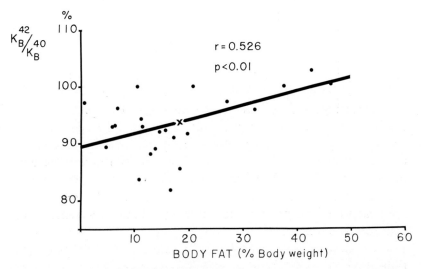

Figure 1. The effect of body fat on the assay of K^{40} in a whole body counter.

picts the $K_B{}^{42}/K_B{}^{40}$ ratio plotted as ordinate against the relative amount of fat in the body. There is a significant correlation ($p < 0.01$) between this ratio and per cent of body fat. Figure 2 depicts graphically the relationship between the lean body mass content of potassium from $K_B{}^{40}$ ($K_B{}^{40}/LBM$) and the relative amount of fat in the body. It is evident that a significant nega-

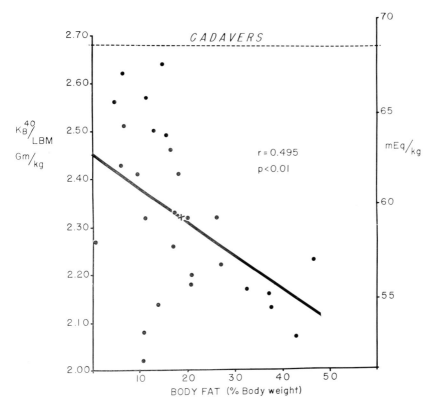

Figure 2. The effect of body fat on the lean tissue content of potassium calculated from the measurement of potassium in a whole body counter.

tive correlation ($p<0.01$) exists between K_B^{40}/LBM and body fat. Extrapolation of the regression line for $K/_B^{40}LBM$ vs per cent of body fat to a fat content of 0 percent gives 2.45 gm./kg. as the potassium content of the fat-free body. Tritiated water probably overestimates total body water because of exchange of tritium for hydrogen in other compounds. This overestimate may be as high as 5 percent. A 5 percent overestimate will increase our value for the fat-free body content of potassium to 2.57 gm./kg., which is 4.3 percent below the average value of 2.68 gm./kg. obtained by the analysis of cadavers.

In contrast to the relationship that has been demonstrated between K_B^{40}/LBM and per cent of body fat, Figure 3 shows that

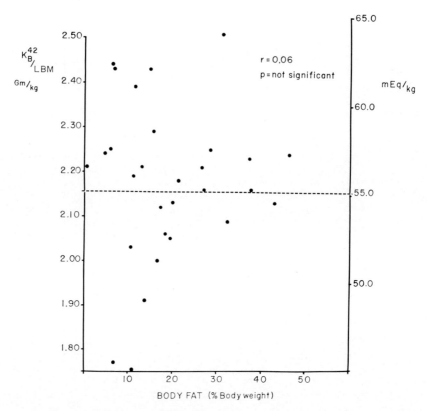

Figure 3. The effect of body fat on the lean tissue content of total body potassium calculated from K⁴².

there is no significant correlation between K_B^{42}/LBM and per cent of body fat. The possibility exists that the size of the lean body mass compartment may influence the concentration of potassium in this compartment. However, no significant relationship was found between K_B^{42}/LBM and LBM.

These data suggest to us that the accuracy of the measurement of the K^{40} content of man in whole body counters is affected by the composition of the subject measured. Therefore, this measurement should not be used to calculate body fat, body solids or muscle mass at present.

What is the extent to which K_B^{42} measurements of total body potassium reflect tissue levels of potassium? Since skeletal

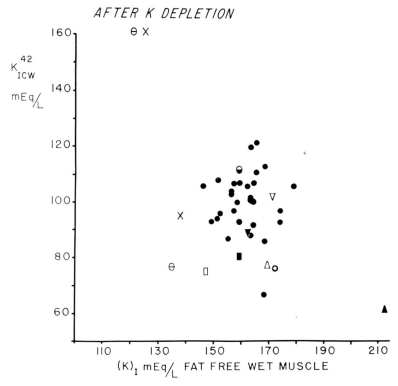

Figure 4. Relationship between the intracellular potassium concentration calculated from isotopic dilution data and the intracellular potassium concentration calculated from data obtained by direct analysis of muscle.

muscle contains most of the potassium in the body, we only analyzed skeletal muscle. Samples of gastrocnemius muscle were obtained one to two days after isotopic dilution studies were done. Figure 4 compares the intracellular potassium concentration, expressed as mEq./liter of intracellular water, obtained by the isotopic dilution technique to the intracellular potassium concentration, determined by direct analysis of muscle. There is no significant correlation between the two measurements. However, two patients who were depleted of potassium by antihypertensive therapy did show a low intracellular potassium concentration by the isotopic dilution method and by direct analysis of muscle. There was no significant correlation of intracellular con-

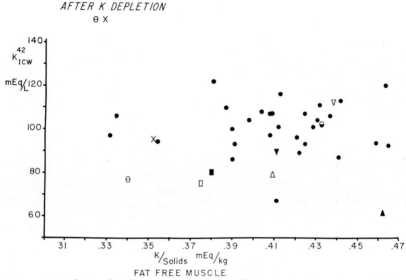

Figure 5. Relationship between the intracellular potassium concentration calculated from isotopic dilution data and the muscle potassium/nitrogen ratio obtained by direct analysis of muscle.

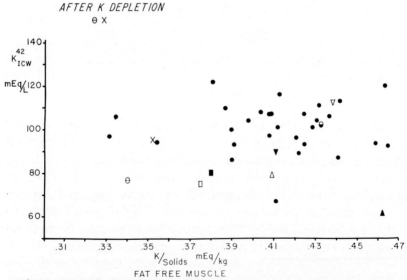

Figure 6. Relationship between the intracellular potassium concentration calculated from isotopic dilution data and the muscle potassium/solids ratio obtained by direct analysis of muscle.

tent of potassium from isotopic dilution measurements to the potassium content of muscle when the latter was expressed as a potassium/nitrogen ratio (Fig. 5) or as a potassium/muscle-solids ratio (Fig. 6). However, subjects who had been experimentally depleted of potassium did show a decrease in intracellular potassium, potassium/nitrogen ratio and potassium/muscle-solid ratio.

These data suggest to us that a single study of a patient by the isotopic dilution technique does not allow prediction of muscle content of potassium, but serial studies of patients during the course of an illness may indicate whether a potassium deficit did or did not exist.

REFERENCES

1. Talso, P. J., Miller, C. E., Carballo, A. J., and Vazquez, I.: Exchange-able potassium as a parameter of body composition. *Metabolism,* 9:456-471, 1960.
2. Von Döbeln, W.: Estimation of muscle mass of the human body from K^{40} determination. *Medd. Flyg. Navalmed. Namnd.,* 11:1-4, 1962.
3. Anderson, E. C., and Langham, W. H.: Estimation of total body fat from K^{40} content. *Science,* 133:1917 1961.
4. Remenchik, A. P., and Miller, C. E.: The measurement of total body potassium in man and its relation to gross body composition. Proc. Symp. Whole Body Counting, Vienna, June 12-16, 1961, 427-432, 1962.
5. Miller, C. E.: An experimental evaluation of multiple crystal arrays and simple crystal techniques, Proc. Symp. Whole Body Counting, Vienna, June 16, 81-120, 1962.
6. Remenchik, A. P., and Talso, P. J.: In preparation.

17

DETERMINATION OF BODY POTASSIUM BY 4π GAMMA COUNTING[1]

ERNEST C. ANDERSON

University of California
Los Alamos, New Mexico

INTRODUCTION

THE FIRST MEASUREMENTS of body potassium by means of its natural radioactivity were made using high pressure ionization chambers as detectors. The studies were directed at quite a different problem — the determination of the natural radium contentrations in the human body which were in considerable doubt at the time. The first successful apparatus of this kind to reach the natural potassium level was described by Sievert in 1951 (1). He observed gamma radioactivity in twelve normal subjects equivalent to 10 nc radium, the nuclide for which his counter was calibrated. In a later paper (2), while still reporting values in units of 10^{-9} gm. radium gamma equivalent, he clearly ascribed the normal activity to potassium, reported the body potassium for 99 subjects as a function of age, sex and body weight and outlined the major features which we are now rediscovering.

The development of a similar apparatus was proceeding at the University of Leeds (3), and in 1953 Burch and Spiers (4) reported that thirteen subjects were measured using an ion chamber, and their potassium content was $0.21 \pm 0.01\%$ by weight. In 1954 (5) they reported potassium determinations on fifteen additional subjects.

[1] Work performed under the auspices of the U. S. Atomic Energy Commission.

The ion chamber method was further extended by Rundo and Sagild (6), who first compared total potassium with exchangeable potassium measured on the same subjects.

The ion chamber method suffered from the difficulty of requiring an excessively long measurement time; Sievert used 8 hr. Then in 1953 the Los Alamos group reported the measurement of seven normal and two contaminated subjects using a 4π liquid scintillation counter with a counting time of only a few minutes (7). No quantitative potassium concentrations were calculated, but a phantom calibration showed that potassium would account for most, if not all, the counts observed from the normal subjects. A study of the sex and weight effects (8) and of the correlation of potassium with body water (9) using the liquid scintillator appeared in 1956.

In the same year, Miller and Marinelli reported the quantitative measurement of body potassium using the crystal spectrometer (10) on twelve men and three women.

Also in 1956, the first conference on human radioactivity was held at Leeds (11). The conferences at Vanderbilt University (12) and Vienna (13) contain reports of subsequent progress.

The present paper summarizes the results of continuing studies at Los Alamos using the original 4π liquid scintillator, Humco I (14, 15) and its successor, Humco II (16). The studies have been primarily concerned with establishing the precision or reproducibility and the absolute accuracy of the method, the accurate determination of the variation of potassium content of the body with age and sex and the investigation of the correlation of potassium content with body composition.

PRECISION OF THE DETERMINATION

Statistical Methods

As a quantitative measure of reproducibility of results, we used the usual statistical parameter, the standard deviation σ. For a normal distribution, this is the deviation from the mean ($\pm$), which includes 68 percent of the total number of observations. For a series of repeated measurements of the same quantity (which has been shown to be normally distributed), the standard deviation can be calculated from the equation,

$$\sigma_i = \sqrt{\frac{\sum_i \Delta_i^2}{n-1}} \qquad (\text{Eq. 1})$$

where Δ_i is the deviation of the ith determination from the mean, and n is the total number of determinations. This standard deviation applies to a single determination.

Again assuming a normal population, the standard deviation σ_m of the mean computed by averaging n determinations with standard deviations σ_i is given by,

$$\sigma_m = \frac{\sigma_i}{\sqrt{n}} = \sqrt{\frac{\sum_i \Delta_i^2}{(n)(n-1)}} \qquad (\text{Eq. 2})$$

If a large number of groups of size n have been measured, one can compute σ_m in two ways. The first method applies Eq. 1 to the n members of each group to give σ_i and then computes σ_m from Eq. 2. The second method regards the averages for the several groups as the primary data and uses Eq. 1 to give directly the standard deviation applicable to a single average. If there are secular drifts or non-normal variations, then the first method will predict a much lower standard deviation than that determined more directly by the second method. We have written an iterative computer code which uses this principle applied to a long series of repeated determinations to assess the maximum time over which it is profitable to make a single extended measurement.

Another parameter of interest in this connection is the limit on precision of the method set by counting statistics. This sets a lower bound to the random error which can exceed this value if there are additional sources of variation but which can never be less. For the simple case of a single observation of N total counts, the statistical standard deviation σ_s is given by,

$$\sigma_s = \sqrt{N} \qquad (\text{Eq. 3})$$

For determinations involving additions or subtractions, the error propagates by the unusual square-root-of-the-sum-of-the-squares law (17). A comparison of the standard deviation as derived by Eq. 1 from the actual scatter of the data about its own mean with the limiting statistical error as deduced from Eq. 3 provides valuable evidence on the inherent stability of the counting apparatus. A standard deviation greatly exceeding the statistical error is a sign that effects are occurring such as electronic instability, background changes, sample contamination or true changes in the radioactivity of the sample. When the standard deviation of a measurement drops below a few per cent or less of the background rate, it becomes very difficult to attain the limiting statistical error, and great care must be taken that enough measurements are made to permit proof of the precision by statistical analysis.

In proving the precision of measurement of the potassium content of a human subject as opposed to that of an inert phantom or inert reference sample, one faces the problem of distinguishing between variations resulting from errors in the apparatus and true biological changes. However, biological changes must always be less than the total variation observed.

Counting Method

Subjects or samples to be measured are placed in a cylindrical cavity 18 in. in diameter and 72 in. long, which is completely surrounded by the liquid scintillation solution. Geometrical efficiency is nearly 100 percent, and counting efficiency varies little with position of the nuclide in the sample. Humco I operates with two energy channels set for Cs^{137} and K^{40}, and the amounts of these two nuclides are calculated on the assumption that no other gamma activity is present. Humco II operates in six energy channels, and the computer program can be adjusted to the nuclides thought to be present, usually only Cs^{137} and K^{40}. Both machines operate with a basic counting period of 100 sec. Two measurements of each sample are made routinely. Backgrounds are normally determined at approximately 1 hr. intervals.

Normal subjects are not required to shower before a measurement, but do change into surgeons' scrub suits which have been laundered and monitored.

Counter calibration is based on a series of phantoms containing KCl and on control subjects using K^{42}. Gross weight appeared to be the only parameter affecting the counting efficiency (Fig. 1). The fifth degree equation given on the graph was used by the computer in analyzing the data. Daily calibrations with

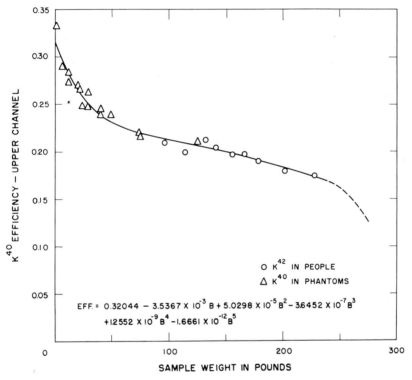

Figure 1. Potassium calibration of Humco I; K^{40} efficiency versus weight of sample.

a standard 66 kg. phantom proved a normalization point; it was assumed that all efficiencies changed in the same proportion as the standard. Electronic adjustments were made to hold the standard efficiency within ± 3 percent of the reference value.

Precision of the Apparatus

In order to provide a running check on the counter, frequent measurements were made on a 50 lb. sample of nonfat dry milk solids. This sample contained about three times as much potassium as the average adult man and so provided a higher statistical precision in the same counting time. It is also invariant in time. Table I summarizes the results of 155 determinations made over six years. There is no significant change in the average of 413

TABLE I

PRECISION OF REPEATED MEASUREMENTS OF POTASSIUM CONTENT OF
CONTROL MILK SAMPLE

Year	Number of Determinations	Average Potassium (gm.)	Observed σ_i (gm.)
1957	11	410	3.4
1958	57	411	5.1
1959	28	413	4.3
1960	26	415	6.8
1961	18	411	6.4
1962	15	413	4.3
Average	155	413	5.0= 1.3 %
Statistical			3.0= 0.7 %

gm. potassium over the period, indicating that the calibration of the system changed by less than 1 percent. The standard deviation of the six averages from their own mean is 2 gm. potassium, or 0.5 percent. The last column of the table gives the values of σ_i, the standard deviation of a single determination from the yearly mean calculated by Eq. 1. The average value of σ_i over the six years is 5 gm. potassium, or 1.3 percent. The value calculated on the basis of counting statistics is 3 gm., or 0.7 percent. At this level of precision, therefore; there is an error of about 1 percent in addition to counting statistics. The source of this error has not been positively identified, but it may be slight instabilities in the electronics or small variations in background. The precision attained appears adequate for the studies made.

Precision of Human Potassium Measurements

During the same period as the milk control measurements, repeated determination of the potassium content of a series of control subjects was made. Results of 174 measurements of a typical subject are shown in Table II. This subject was studied

TABLE II

YEARLY AVERAGE RESULTS OF POTASSIUM DETERMINATIONS ON A CONTROL SUBJECT

Year	Number of Determinations	Average Weight (kg.)	Potassium (gm.)	Observed σ_i (gm. K)
1956	71	65.7	135.7	11.7
1957	26	65.2	133.3	9.8
1958	24	65.3	134.9	5.3
1959	11	66.4	133.0	5.6
1960	8	65.4	130.3	3.5
1961	14	69.0	140.7	4.6
1962	20	70.4	139.7	6.3

for the longest period and shows the main features of stability and instability occurring in other runs. The subject's weight was apparently constant to 1 percent over the first five years, then rose abruptly by about 4 kg. There is a similar discontinuity in the measured potassium, which rose from an average of 133.4 gm. to 140.2 gm. There seems little doubt that this change is real and due to a true increase in body potassium of 5 percent (compared with a weight increase of 6 percent). During the first five years, there is no evidence of a secular trend. The average σ_m calculated from the yearly σ_i by Eq. 2 is 1.4 gm.; calculated from the scatter of the yearly averages by Eq. 1, it is 2.1 gm. A stability of better than 2 percent is indicated.

The standard deviation σ_i of the individual values show a higher value during the first two years. This is believed to be associated with nuclear weapon testing in Nevada. Ba^{140} and La^{140} were observed in a number of milk samples during 1957 (18) and may well have introduced small errors into the human potassium determinations. Variable low level surface contamination could also have been present. Since 1958, σ_i has been constant with an

TABLE III

Subject	Sex	Number of Determinations	Potassium (gm.)	Observed Standard Deviation Potassium (gm.)	(Per Cent)
SXG	F	33	93.3	3.3	3.5
PAH	F	30	107.1	3.3	3.1
AEH	F	37	112.5	4.4	4.0
MAVD	M	31	147.1	5.1	3.5
MWR	M	33	175.6	7.5	4.3
		Average	127.1	4.7	3.7
		Statistical		2.6	2.0

* Routine 200 sec. counts over seven months, November 1961 through May 1962.

average value of 5 gm. potassium, the same value observed for the milk samples, but corresponding in this case to a 3.7 percent error. The calculated statistical error is 2.6 gm., or 2 percent.

Table III summarizes similar studies on five subjects over seven months. The average σ_i is again equal to about 5 gm. potassium.

The measurements were made using the routine procedure in which counter backgrounds are determined at irregular intervals, usually hourly. There is evidence that slight changes in background over this long a period may be contributing a few percent to the error. Table IV summarizes the results of two series of special measurements in which backgrounds were measured just before or after the subject was counted. The standard deviation σ_i is now nearly identical with that expected from counting statistics. There was no change in the calibration procedure for these measurements. (Counter calibration was performed once a

TABLE IV
PRECISION OF HUMAN POTASSIUM DETERMINATIONS ON HUMCO I*

Series	Number of Determinations	Potassium (gm.)	Observed Standard Deviation Potassium (gm.)	(Per Cent)
A	10	144.2	2.38	1.7
B	9	139.3	2.73	2.0
		Statistical	2.60	1.8

* Routine 200 sec. counts over seven months, November 1961 through May 1962.

day, first thing in the morning. The counts were generally taken late in the afternoon.) Similar results have been obtained on other special runs under these conditions. Since the standard deviation obtained with hourly backgrounds (4 percent) is small compared with the biological variation of potassium in a population group of given age and sex (10 to 12 percent), the routine method for potassium and cesium determinations has not been changed.

Effects of a Shower Bath

The two series of Table IV are actually measurements on the same subject. In series A the subject took a shower bath immediately before the measurement, but did not do so in series B. The results seem to indicate that contamination results from bathing. However, measurements of the water, soap and hair shampoo used showed no significant radioactivity. The series was repeated using Humco II, a liquid scintillation counter of greatly improved energy resolution (Table V). In both sets of measurements, counts in the two series were alternated on an approximately weekly basis so that there is no possibility of a physiological change.

The standard deviations entered in this table are the σ_m, the standard deviations of the means as calculated by Eq. 2. Also entered are the differences between the "shower" and "no shower" series. It is clear that with Humco II, the apparent difference of 1.2 percent is less than 1σ and cannot be considered significant. For the earlier Humco I series, the difference of 3.5 percent is 4σ and apparently real. The average of the Humco II results, 137.8,

TABLE V

EFFECT OF SHOWER BATH BEFORE MEASUREMENT ON RESULTS OF
HUMAN POTASSIUM DETERMINATION

| Detector | Dates | Measured Potassium (gm.) | | Difference |
		Shower	No Shower	
Humco I	November 1961- May 1962	144.2±0.8	139.3±0.9	4.9±1.2
Humco II	June-August 1962	138.6±1.2	136.9±1.5	1.7±2.0

is in excellent agreement with the Humco I "no shower" measurement.

Cs^{137} measurements under the two conditions showed no significant differences, the values for the Humco I series being 9.04 ± 0.37 (σ_m) nc with shower and 8.86 ± 0.42 nc without shower. The explanation of this puzzling effect is not known. It would appear either that the "contamination" present during the November-May period of the Humco I study was absent during the June-August Humco II series, or that the poorer energy resolution of Humco I rendered it sensitive to a continuing interference which does not affect the other counter. The amount of contamination is so small (about 0.5 nc) that it would be extremely difficult to identify in the presence of some 15 nc of K^{40} and 9 nc of Cs^{137}. Measurements of the subject's spectrum with our 9 by 6 in. NaI crystal spectrometer have failed to solve the problem. It is suggested that when high precision measurements are desired a careful study of the effects of shower baths be made. The LASL routine procedure has never required showers except for persons known to have been subject to external contamination, since previous studies of this type showed no effect from showering.

Possibility of Increased Precision

An attempt is being made with Humco II to determine how much the precision can be improved by increasing the counting time and to determine the level at which biological variations occur in healthy subjects.

By extending the counting time from 3 to 30 min., the counting statistical error should decrease by about a factor of 3. Table VI shows the results of two sets of measurements taken six days apart on the same subject. In each set, four 30 min. determinations were made, the group being preceded and followed by background determinations. The expected statistical precision is 1 gm. potassium or 0.7 percent. Each set shows a standard deviation about its own mean which is close to this value. The statistical standard deviation of each mean is expected to be 0.5 gm.

TABLE VI

PRECISION OF HUMAN POTASSIUM DETERMINATIONS ON HUMCO II*

Date	Potassium (gm.)	Observed Standard Deviation σ_i Potassium (gm.)	(Per Cent)
July 6, 1962	155.3		
	156.5		
	155.4		
	155.0		
Average	155.5	0.70	0.45
July 12, 1962	156.7		
	157.8		
	156.8		
	154.8		
Average	156.8	1.44	0.90
		Statistical 1.04	0.67

* 30 Min. counts (PND).

potassium, or 0.33 percent. The difference between the two means is 1.3 gm., or 2.6 σ_m, which is not significant.

As the counting time is made longer, one can expect to encounter more difficulties due to drift in the electronics and to secular changes in the background. Since the net count on an adult man is about one fourth of the background rate, a precision of 1 percent in the potassium determination will require background to remain constant to 0.25 percent, a rather extreme requirement.

Slow monotonic changes in the background rate can be compensated by alternating sample and background counts on a suitable time scale so that the average measured background is the same as average background during sample measurements. If the trend in background is oscillatory, this method will not work unless the time interval between successive background determinations is short compared with the frequency of the oscillation.

In order to estimate the effective average period of background instabilities and hence the proper spacing of background counts for maximum precision, the following experiment was performed.

The counter was operated in the fully automatic mode in which each measurement is recorded on an IBM punched card, the scalers and timer are reset, and a new count is begun. Background measurements in this mode were taken for two periods of 13 hr. each and for one period of sixteen days. During the latter sequence, the run was interrupted once a day for recalibration. The results were analyzed by a computer code which first averaged the measurements in groups of four and calculated the statistical parameters for each group. A second similar computation was then made using the averages resulting from the first round as input data. The process was repeated until the last cycle provided fewer than four averages. Each computing cycle gives an analysis corresponding to a counting period four times longer with a statistical error two times smaller than that of the preceding cycle (Table VII).

The first experiments of sixteen days used a basic counting time of 500 sec. (about 8 min.) and gave 2,836 determinations for input to the first cycle. This would correspond to 1 per cent precision on an adult potassium determination. The last cycle used forty-four averages, corresponding to 8.8 hr. counting times, and gave averages for eleven groups of four. The significant feature of the data is that the observed standard deviation follows the expected statistical error down to 0.15 percent (33 min.), but fails to decrease when the counting time is increased further. This implies that longer counting times are spanning periods over which there are secular, nonstatistical changes and that no increase in precision is obtained. Similar results are obtained for

TABLE VII

LIMITATION OF POTASSIUM PRECISION BY BACKGROUND INSTABILITY ON HUMCO II

Serial No.	Number of Determinations	Duration of Test	Number of Averages	Standard Deviation (Per Cent) of Background σ_i			Adult K
				Time	Statistical	Observed	(Per Cent)
509–	2,836	16 days	709	8 min.	0.26	0.24	1.0
526			177	33 min.	0.13	0.15	0.63
			44	2.2 hr.	0.065	0.21	0.90
			11	8.8 hr.	0.032	0.25	1.0
1185	480	13 hr.	120	1.7 min.	0.52	0.49	2.1
			30	7 min.	0.26	0.25	1.1
			7	27 min.	0.13	0.16	0.7
1234	484	13 hr.	121	1.7 min.	0.53	0.49	2.1
			30	7 min.	0.27	0.27	1.1
			7	27 min.	0.13	0.27	1.0

the two 13 hr. experiments. In these cases, the initial data were 200 sec. counts, and the point of diminishing return was reached when $\sigma_1 = 0.16$ and 0.27 percent, respectively.

The limitation to 30 min. counting times, while not unexpected, is unfortunate since the counter is well adapted to extremely long counts. Subjects find it easy to sleep in the foam-rubber-lined trough, and one spent the night comfortably. It has been hoped that high precision measurements could be made using an overnight 8 hr. count, which would give a statistical error of 0.1 percent on adult potassium. The necessity of breaking the count into 30 min. periods with interspersed backgrounds destroys the simplicity of the procedure (as well as the subject's rest). Further studies to identify the source of the instability will be carried out, and the possibility of a gain stabilization system such as described by Dudley is under consideration. Concurrently, further measurements using 30 min. cycles will be undertaken to investigate the possibility of other limiting factors such as variable surface contamination with radon daughter or fission products.

It should be emphasized that while one can contemplate a measurement of body potassium to a precision of better than 1 per cent, such measurements are unlikely to be routine. Each subject will have to be carefully treated as a separate experiment with extremely close statistical control. An individual error analysis similar to the type shown in Table VII will be necessary to prove the stability of the system and the reliability of the measurement. One would probably be justly skeptical of a result at the 0.1 percent level unless several repeated measurements could be shown to agree this well. A total time of several days would, therefore, be required to establish the measurement. In addition, surface contamination is almost certain to be troublesome level. The presence of radon daughters in easily detectable amount (the potentially interfering lines are those of RaC, 6.3 percent at 1238 kev and 25.8 percent at 1761 kev) can be demonstrated in almost any air sample. This indicates the probable necessity of special air decontamination, but one can still worry about excess radon (above equilibrium with body radium) dissolved in the subject's blood. This quantity is likely to be highly variable and to require appreciable time to equilibrate to a new level. Normal radium in the body is less likely to be a problem (assuming a reproducible rate of radon elimination), since it is unlikely to change over short periods. It could introduce a constant absolute error, but it is assumed that one is interested in high precision potassium determinations only from the point of view of relative secular variations in a single subject and not in absolute comparisons of different individuals. Absolute calibration problems limit the latter type of measurements to errors of a few per cent at present.

ACCURACY OF THE METHOD

Comparison with K^{42} Isotope Dilution

In order to establish the absolute accuracy of the method, as opposed to its precision or reproducibility, it is necessary to compare the results obtained with those derived from an independent method. The determination of body potassium by K^{42} isotope dilution (19) is well known. While the fraction of total potassium which will not exchange in a given period is not accurately known, this fraction appears to be only a few percent when mixing times of a day or two are allowed. A total potassium measurement less than the exchangeable potassium would clearly indicate difficulties; a converse result may be real, but interpretation is

TABLE VIII

COMPARISON OF TOTAL BODY POTASSIUM MEASURED BY GAMMA COUNTING (LASL) AND BY POTASSIUM^{42} DILUTION (NRDL)

Subject	Weight (kg.) LASL	Weight (kg.) NRDL	Potassium (gm.) LASL	Potassium (gm.) NRDL	Ratio of Potassium Values K^{42}/K^{40}
ARB	95.0	93.6	170	166	0.977
TC	80.0	79.3	182	180	0.987
KJ	90.0	94.6	205	203	0.990
EH	93.1	83.4	203	194	0.954
JJH	80.5	78.6	196	181	0.917
				Average of 5	0.964
				(Average of 3	0.985)

difficult because of the problem of resolving experimental errors from a true biochemical effect.

We have compared (Table VIII) total body potassium as measured with Humco I on five subjects with exchangeable potassium as determined by K^{42} dilution on five subjects at the U. S. Naval Radiological Defense Laboratory (20). Captain Behnke and his group used a 40 hr. equilibrium time following intravenous injection of K^{42} and made correction for excretion. The subjects were all healthy adult males with a narrow range of weights. The average ratio of exchangeable to total potassium is 96.4 percent with a range of 91.7 to 99.0. The two lowest values were in subjects who probably had a true change in body potassium in the several months between the two measurements. Subject EH gained 10 kg. in weight during the interval, and subject JJH was engaged in strenuous training for Olympic wrestling competition. If these two were omitted from the average, the ratio of exchangeable to total potassium would be 98.5 percent.

The uncertainties prevent drawing firm conclusions regarding the fraction of exchangeable potassium and counter efficiency from such a limited experiment, but the results do suggest that the absolute accuracy of the counting method is better than 4 percent.

Interlaboratory Comparisons on Individuals

A second method of estimating absolute accuracy is to com-

TABLE IX

INTERLABORATORY COMPARISON OF POTASSIUM DETERMINATIONS
ON INDIVIDUALS*

Laboratory	Type of Counter	Subject MAVD	JR	ECA
Landstuhl	2π liquid	0.97	—	1.11
Leeds	Plastic blocks	0.90	1.00	—
Harwell	NaI crystal	0.98	0.98	1.03
Argonne	NaI crystal	—	0.96	0.96
Sutton	NaI crystal	0.98	—	—

*Expressed relative to LASL values.

pare the results on individual subjects obtained in different laboratories using independently calibrated detectors of different types. Results (Table IX) are presented for three subjects and five other counters of three different types: 2π liquid scintillator (21), plastic blocks (22) and three NaI spectrometers. The data are reported as ratios to the value as determined with the LASL 4π liquid scintillator. The average of the 10 ratios is 0.987, indicating excellent average agreement among the methods. Individual discrepancies at large as plus 11 percent and minus 10 percent occur in two cases, but these show no obvious pattern. The standard deviation calculated, including these two extreme values, is 5.7 percent; omitting them, it is 3 percent.

Interlaboratory Comparisons of Population Averages

An alternative method of interlaboratory comparisons is based on the observed constancy of the average potassium concentration in persons of a given age and sex. This quantity was first studied by Sievert (23). Later at Los Alamos (24) 1,590 subjects ranging from less than one year old to seventy-nine were measured. They were persons who responded to a request for volunteers and were drawn from the local population, professional and social visitors to Los Alamos and groups of children touring the laboratory.

The first set of measurements extended over 1956-1958. A second independent set of 802 determinations was obtained during 1959-1960 (25). A comparison of the two sets is shown in Figure 2, the curves taken from the first set and the points from the second set. The curves have been displaced downward by 2 percent to optimize the fit, a displacement that is within the uncertainties of both experiments. The basic similarity of the two population samples is evidenced by Figure 3, which shows the variation of weight with age. Note the aberrant point for the thirteen year old girls who are significantly overweight in the 1959-1960 group. This same group shows an unusually low potassium concentration in Figure 2. The fourteen to eighteen year boys in the two groups showed a definite maximum in the first ex-

TABLE X

COMPARISON OF AVERAGE POTASSIUM CONCENTRATIONS IN AGE GROUPS FROM OTHER POPULATIONS WITH LASL RESULTS

Method	Population (Ref.)	Sex	Age	Number of Subjects	Potassium (gm. per kg.) Comparison Group	LASL Group (24,25,30)	Number of Subjects	Potassium Ratio
NaI Spect.	Canadian (26)	M	19	30	2.12	2.125 / 2.150	19 / 21	1.006
K⁴² Diln.	Scots (27)	F	25—49	32	1.60	1.632 / 1.606	180 / 72	1.012
Liq. Scin.	German (21)	M	22—50	1000	2.07	1.975 / 1.995	271 / 602	0.959
		F	22—50		1.64	1.606 / 1.632	72 / 188	0.987
NaI Spect.	Norwegian (28)	M	17—48	15	1.75	2.017 / 2.051	323 / 650	1.161
NaI Spect.	Illinois (29)	M	28—52	17	2.11	1.947 / 1.949	203 / 457	0.923
NaI Spect.	Illinois (31)	M	23—34	10	1.84	2.076 / 2.031	185 / 68	1.116

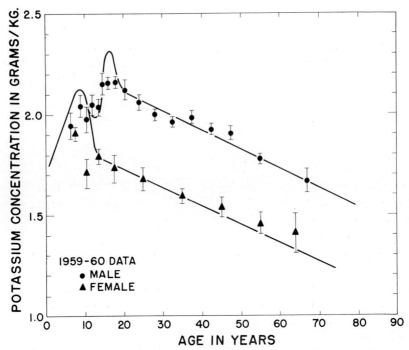

Figure 2. Average potassium concentration in the human body as a function of age.

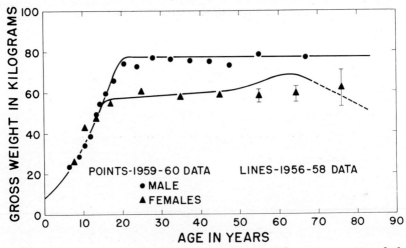

Figure 3. Average weight of human subjects (who were measured for potassium) as a function of age.

periment, but not in the second. These discrepancies indicate the necessity of careful sampling techniques for younger subjects.

The constancy of potassium concentration for adults (age and sex specified) observed in these experiments suggested the possibility of interlaboratory comparisons on this basis. One faces the difficulty of not knowing to what extent agreement is to be expected. However, on the basis of the law of combination of uncorrelated errors, one can expect that observed discrepancies will set an upper limit on both measurement errors and true population variations. A further limitation of this method of intercomparison is that the quantity being compared is an average value for subjects of a variety of body weights. No evidence regarding possible systematic errors on individuals of unusual size or shape is, therefore, obtained.

Six groups of five different nationalities measured by three different methods are compared with the results of two LASL studies (Table X). The ratio of the average LASL value to that determined at the other laboratory for a similar age-sex group is 1.023 with a range of 0.923 to 1.161. Since the observed standard

TABLE XI

PRECISION AND ACCURACY OF HUMAN POTASSIUM DETERMINATIONS BY 4π LIQUID SCINTILLATION GAMMA COUNTING*

I. PRECISION

    A. Long term precision of the system (based on yearly averages of control milk sample): $\sigma = 0.5\%$.

    B. Precision of single determination on control milk sample: $\sigma = 5$ gm. or 1.3%.

    C. Biological stability of individual potassium (based on yearly averages): $\sigma = 2.1$ gm. $= 1.6\%$.

    D. Precision of individual potassium determinations (200 sec. count):

        1. Backgrounds hourly: $\sigma = \pm 5$ gm. K.

        2. Backgrounds with each sample: $\sigma = \pm 3$ gm. K.

II. ACCURACY

    A. Based on comparison with K^{42} dilution: better than 3%.

    B. Based on interlaboratory comparison of individuals: LASL $= +1.3\%$ of average.

    C. Based on interlaboratory comparison of age groups: LASL $= +2.3\%$ of average.

* Based on a seven year study with Humco I.

deviation σ_i for individuals in a given age-sex group is 10 to 12 percent, the standard deviation of the mean σ_m for a group of ten subjects should be about 3.5 percent, and for a group of sixteen subjects about 2.8 percent. Most of the variation in the ratio is with $3 \sigma_m$, but some values exceed this limit.

SUMMARY

The conclusions regarding the precisions and accuracy of the determination of human potassium with a 4π liquid scintillation counter are summarized in Table XI. Using a 200 sec. counting time per subject and determining backgrounds hourly, the standard deviation of a single determination is 5 gm. potassium of 3.5 percent on an average adult man. By measuring backgrounds more frequently, this can be reduced to the statistical error of 3 gm. potassium. The absolute accuracy appears to be at least this good.

Attention is called to the possibility of errors of this magniture resulting from contamination, and example being apparent contamination associated with shower baths.

The possibility of reducing the error to less than 1 percent appears feasible, but more research is required to prove this and to determine the extent of the precautions required.

REFERENCES

1. Sievert, R. M.: *Arkiv. Fysik,* 3:337, 1951.
2. Sievert, R. M.: *Strahlentherapie,* 99:185, 1956.
3. Burch, P. R. J.: Thesis, University of Leeds, 1952.
4. Burch, P. R. J., and Spiers, F. W.: *Nature,* 172:519, 1952.
5. Burch, P. R. J., and Spiers, F. W.: *Science,* 120:719, 1954.
6. Rundo, J., and Sagild, U.: *Nature,* 175:774, 1955.
7. Reines, F., Schuch, R. L., Cowan, C. L., Harrison, F. B., Anderson, E. C., and Hayes, F. N.: *Nature,* 172:521, 1953.
8. Anderson, E. C., Schuch, R. L., Perrings, J. D., and Langham, W. H.: *Nucleonics,* 14(1):26, 1956.
9. Woodward, K. T., Trujillo, T. T., Schuch, R. L., and Anderson, E. C.: *Nature,* 178:97, 1956.

10. Miller, C. E., and Marinelli, L. D.: *Science, 124*:122, 1956.
11. Alsopp, C. B. (Editor): *Brit. J. Radiol,* Suppl. 7, 1956.
12. Meneely, G. R. (Editor): Radioactivity in Man. Springfield, Thomas, 1961.
13. International Atomic Energy Authority (Editor): *Whole Body Counting.* Vienna, I.A.E.A., 1962.
14. Anderson, E. C.: *Liquid Scintillation Counting.* Bell, G. C. and Hayes, F. N. (editors). New York, Pergamon Press, 1958, p. 211.
15. Anderson, E. C.: *Brit. J. Radiol.,* Suppl. 7:27, 1956.
16. Van Dilla, M. A., and Anderson, E. C.: *Whole Body Counting.* Vienna, I.A.E.A., 1962, p. 41.
17. Evans, R. D.: *The Atomic Nucleus.* New York, McGraw-Hill Book Co., 1955, p. 766.
18. Anderson, E. C., Schuch, R. L., Fisher, W. R., and Van Dilla, M. A.: *Science, 127*:283, 1958.
19. Corsa, L., Olney, J. M., Steenburg, R. W., Ball, M. R., and Moore, F. D.: *J. Clin. Invest., 29*:1280, 1950.
20. Boling, E. A., Taylor, W. L., Entenman, C., and Behnke, A. R.: Research and Development Technical Report, USNRDL-TR-313, 1959.
21. Onstead, C. O., Oberhausen, E., and Keary, F. V.: *Atompraxis, 6*:337, 1960.
22. Burch, P. R. J., Hughes, D., Iinuma, T. R., Overton, T. R., and Appleby, D. B.: *Whole Body Counting.* Vienna, *I.A.E.A.,* 1962, p. 57.
23. Sievert, R. M.: *Strahlentherapie, 99*:185, 1956.
24. Anderson, E. C., and Langham, W. H.: *Science, 130*:713, 1959.
25. Anderson, E. C., and Clinton, B. E.: *Los Alamos Sci. Lab. Rep.,* LAMS-2526, 1961, p. 121.
26. McNeill, K. G., and Green, R. M.: *Canad. J. Phys., 37*:683, 1959.
27. MacGillivray, I., Buchanan, T. J., and Billewicz, W. Z.: *Clin. Sci., 19*:17, 1960.
28. Baarli, J., Madshus, K., Liden, K., and McCall, R. C.: *Nature, 191*:436, 1961.
29. Remenchik, A. P., and Miller, C. E.: *Whole Body Counting.* Vienna, I.A.E.A., 1962, p. 331.
30. Allen, T. H., Anderson, E. C., and Langham, W. H.: *J. Geront., 15*:348, 1960.
31. Talso, P. J., Miller, C. E., Carballo, A. J., and Vasquez, I.: *Metabolism, 9*:456, 1960.

DISCUSSION

Chairman: ALBERT R. BEHNKE

San Francisco, California

CHAIRMAN ALBERT R. BEHNKE: It would be inappropriate if I did not hold 15 sec. of silence for those physicists who are responsible for developing a magnificent tool to get into cells themselves, to detect energy that is practically buried by nature itself and buried by man himself under a blanket of fat.

In the development of these counters we have something that may be as important as the electrocardiogram. We are picking up a little energy from a substance within the cell itself.

One application is to aging, where there is a loss of lean body substance. If there is one measure of age that is direct and apparent, it is the loss of lean tissue; and the ability to measure this tissue — which is almost an accomplishment despite a few wrinkles that remain to be ironed out — is truly a great achievement.

Expressing potassium in terms of kilograms of body weight may not have too much meaning except for mean values. Perhaps it is the only standard one can refer to, unless one does body water or estimates some of the other parameters, and certainly there are other parameters that can be estimated. Dr. Von Döbeln, would you discuss a few calculations that may be helpful as tentative mean values of potassium referred to several parameters including muscle.

WILHELM VON DÖBELN: It is generally agreed that the concept of lean body mass has been useful in the study of body composition, but it is also agreed that the total potassium determination has enabled further study and a split-up of the lean body mass into different components.

Dr. Behnke and I yesterday made a compilation of some data in the literature which might illustrate how one can look at the problem. An average value for muscle mass is 50 percent of the lean body mass, and 67 percent of the potassium in the body is located in muscle.

Twenty percent of a lean body mass is skeleton and 10 percent of the

232

potassium is contained in the skeleton. The remaining 30 percent of the lean body mass contains 23 percent of the potassium.

If we look at the figures compiled from the literature, which seem to be representative for the body composition of the sexes, potassium of the female is 100 gm. and the male is 150 gm., making a quotient between the sexes in potassium of two-thirds. Looking at other parameters of lean body mass and total water, the quotient is higher than two-thirds. This means that we can no longer hold the concept of a lean body mass of uniform composition within the sexes.

The total body water determination has been used very much, and this has been of big advantage; but in many cases it has created a lot of confusion. What we are really interested in is the composition of the body, not in terms of total body water or space of different electrolytes, but in composition with respect to the tissues. We want to know how much fat, muscle and other tissues a certain individual is composed of. A further step in the study of body composition which has been possible through potassium determinations is that we can estimate the relationship in an individual between muscle and the other parts of the lean body mass.

Dr. Oberhausen showed that women have a constant potassium up to age fifty and an increase in weight. This conclusion was a constant lean body mass. That means that the added tissue would not contain any potassium. Dr. Oberhausen, is your opinion that with increasing weight the added tissue does not contain potassium?

ERICH OBERHAUSEN: Of course, it cannot be only added fat, as we know that adipose tissue has all the components of fat. This question arises as to what we mean by the term lean body mass. A better expression would have been that the cellular mass remains the same, and the gain in weight is the addition of fat.

SESSION VI, SEPTEMBER 6

POTASSIUM AND BODY COMPOSITION,
Continued

Chairman: JOSEF BROZEK

18

DECREASE AND INCREASE OF POTASSIUM AT DEPLETION OF POTASSIUM; GAMMA SPECTROMETRIC DETERMINATIONS OF THE DISTRIBUTION AND EXCRETION OF THORIUM DAUGHTERS IN THOROTRAST PATIENTS

ALEXANDER KAUL AND BORIS RAJEWSKY

Max-Planck-Institut for Biophysics
Frankfort, Federal Republic of Germany

AT *in vivo* measurements of incorporated radionuclides it is necessary to distinguish between two kinds of distribution patterns. Consequently at the calibration of devices for the determination of the total body content of radionuclides, the kind of distribution of the incorporated radioactive material has to be taken into account. Potassium and cesium are practically uniformly distributed in the body, but iodine, radium and thorium dioxide accumulate at specific spots. This report is on the excretion and intake of potassium at a depletion of potassium, as well as on the distribution and excretion of thorium and daughters in thorotrast patients.

The measurements were carried out at the Frankfort total body gamma ray spectrometer that is similar to the total body counter developed by Marinelli and co-workers (1) at the A.N.L. It consists of a noncollimated 8 by 4 in. NaI(Tl) crystal and three multipliers Dumont 6363. The energy resolution for Cs^{137} is about 12 percent, for K^{40} about 9 percent. The three multipliers were connected in a parallel arrangement: no loss of the energy resolution caused by a shift of any of the multipliers had been observed over almost one year. During the testing period the slope of the energy calibration was constant within a limit of instrument error of $\pm$ 3 percent. At a slope of 10 kev per channel, the 3 percent is equal to a maximal shift of $\pm$ 4 channels related to the channel with the maximum energy of K^{40} (1460 kev). This corresponds to a variation of the pulse rate less than $\pm$ 3 percent. This stability was achieved by an extremely constant temperature within the steel chamber and high stabilized voltage applied to the cathode and the first dynode (2). It was possible to trim each multiplier for an optimal resolution of the energy by variation of the voltage at the focusing electrode.

Calibration of the total body counter was carried out with a phantom matching as perfectly as possible the *in vivo* conditions. In a case of a quasi uniform distribution of the incorporated radionuclide, K^{40} or Cs^{137}, plastic bottles were used which contained solutions of known activity. The calibration of the K^{40} was carried out by a KCl solution of known potassium content. The arrangement of the phantom or the patient under test below the crystal was similar to that of Marinelli.

Testing the problem whether the phantom equals the human conditions, the crystal was moved at different heights above the floor of the steel chamber, and the measured counting rates were determined to the position of the crystal in respect to the phantom or the person under test. In a horizontal range corresponding to the upper part of the body of the phantom and the person under test and in a vertical range of about 60 to 80 cm. above the floor, the counting rate is practically constant and independent of the position of the crystal along the axis of the subject. This means that the horizontal positioning of the crystal is not important for geometrical efficiency. The counting rate versus the vertical position shows the same characteristic slope for both the phantom and the person under test. An uncertainty in the vertical positioning of the crystal of $\pm$ 1 cm. results in a maximum deviation of the efficiency of $\pm$ 2.5 percent. These results show that the phantom is satisfactory for the desired requirements.

The total body content of potassium of about 200 persons has been measured. The average specific content of potassium is 1.8 gm./kg. total body weight for men and 1.6 gm./kg. for women. The variation width is about 15 percent. The values are identical to those published by other authors. These investigations were carried out using a running control of the employees of a laboratory (3).

In cooperation with the M.P.I. für Arbeitsphysiologie at Dortmund the problem was investigated in five cases of how the total body content of potassium is varied during artificial depletion of potassium.

Over about fifty days the persons ate a diet consisting mainly of rice and milk, the potassium content of which was almost completely absorbed by means of an ion-exchanger. Prior to and during this diet the variation of the total body potassium content was determined (Fig. 1). After about six weeks with the same food, the average normal daily potassium content was given. In two of the five persons tested, the total body content of potassium during the depletion was reduced about 11 percent, and in a third case about 6 percent.

Assuming an exponential decrease of the total body potassium content of 11 percent or 6 percent, the biological half life is calculated to be 200 or 400 days, respectively. The increase of the potassium content corresponds to a half life of 160 or fifty days, respectively.

The results reveal that in the case of slower excretion of

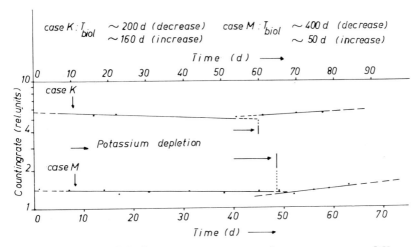

Figure 1. The total body potassium content of two persons at different times of potassium depletion.

potassium, the increase takes place more rapidly, as in the case of quicker excretion. It will be necessary to study more cases of potassium depletion to give final conclusions.

The second problem deals with the excretion and distribution of thorium and its daughters in thorotrast patients. This problem is important since statements on the internal radiation of the thorium daughters are known. It is important to know ex-dose are only possible if the activity and the location of the depot act data of the excretion of the thorium daughters.

In these cases one has to distinguish between two kinds of

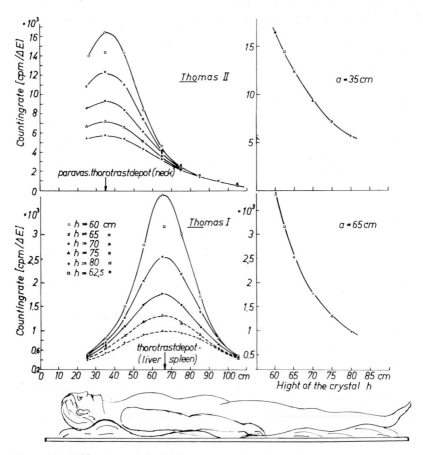

Figure 2. Calibration of the body counter for Th[228] for the different distribution patterns observed *in vivo*.

distribution patterns. The contrast medium is almost exclusively located in the liver, spleen and bone marrow. The thorotrast is simultaneously deposited paravasally at the location of the injection.

The depots were localized in such a way that the noncollimated NaI (Tl) crystal was moved in steps along the axis of the patient in a well defined height above the patient. To show the amount of deposits of the *in vivo* measured distribution pattern, similar patterns were imitated in a phantom consisting of a plexiglass cover and a real skeleton. After the desired distribution has been simulated, say a liver-spleen depot with a calibrated Th^{228} solution, the phantom was filled with a tissue equivalent substance of plexiglass beads, and the appropriate distribution curves were picked up for various heights of the crystal over the phantom (Fig. 2). In the case of deposition of contrast medium, mainly in the liver and in spleen, a quantitative determination of the amount of deposits of the *in vivo* distribution is quite easy. Yet, the analysis of curves for simultaneous deposition of contrast medium at the point of injection and within liver and spleen requires a noncomparable higher expense. The results, however, show that the measured distribution agrees with the results found by calibration. This makes it possible by using the noncollimated crystal to give rather exact information of the amount of the various deposits. In some cases it was possible before and after extirpation of an organ to determine the *in vivo* distribution of the thorium daughter products (Fig. 3). In one case, we had an extirpation of a paravasal depot on the arm. During the course of the the operation, the total activity of the paravasal deposit was reduced by 50 percent, as shown *in vivo* and *in vitro*. The 100 percent corrected extirpation results in a distribution that corresponds with the determined distribution of the contrast medium with the phantom with TH^{228} exclusively in liver and spleen.

In another case with exclusive deposition of contrast medium in spleen and liver, a splenectomy was undertaken. There was good agreement between the *in vivo* distribution and the distribution in the phantom (Fig. 4).

In four cases we were able to get an answer to the distribution of the Th^{232} and its daughter products in the liver and spleen

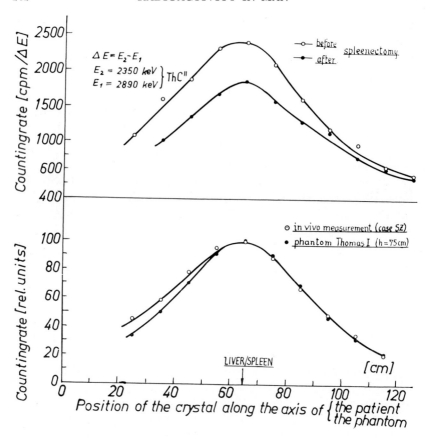

Figure 3. *In vivo* distribution in a thorotrast patient before and after splenectomy.

by making *in vivo* measurements before and after a splenectomy or measuring section samples.

In agreement with Rundo (4, 5), the results showed that about 74 percent of the deposited radionuclides of the thorium series are deposited in the liver and 26 percent in the spleen. The specific Th[228] activity in the spleen was higher by a factor of about 6.5 (Table I).

To determine the steady state activity ratio between the short-lived daughter products of the Th[228], the liver and spleen, as well as samples of paravasal infiltration, were welded in plastic containers immediately after the extirpation and measured by gamma spectrometry without foregoing chemical preparation underneath the 8 by 4 in. crystal in additional shielding. The re-

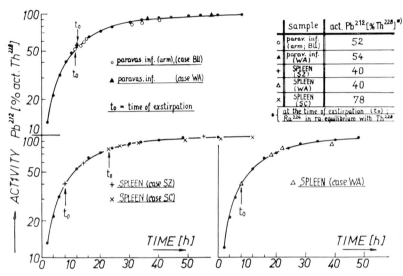

Figure 4. Steady state equilibrium between Th^{228} $(+Ra^{224})$ and Pb^{212} in different extirpated organs and tissues.

TABLE I

Th[232] AND DAUGHTER PRODUCT DISTRIBUTION IN LIVER AND SPLEEN OF THOROTRAST PATIENTS

Method	Case	Total Act. of Liver and Spleen	Activity (% of Total Act.) Liver	Spleen	Spec. Act. (Th[228]) Spleen/Liver
Total body γ-ray-measurement (in vivo)	SZ	100	75	25	5,3
	SC	100	67	33	6,3
γ-ray-measurement of liver and spleen	GI	100	73	27	11,2
	WA	100	80	20	3,3
	Average	100	74±3*	26±3*	6,5±3,5*

* Standard deviation.

sults show that in all cases the radium isotope ThX, together with its parent substance, Th^{228}, was almost in radioactive equilibrium within about 10 percent as opposed to Pb^{212} (ThB) in the spleen which only was up to 40 percent. In paravasal infiltration Pb^{212} was only 52 percent in radioactive equilibrium with its parent substance, Ra^{224}. In one case the washout of the ThB from the spleen was about three times less than in both other cases. The less washout of ThB is attributed to increased shrinkage and less blood circulation.

Similar to Pb^{212}, the long-lived daughter products of Th^{232}, namely Ra^{228} and Th^{228}, were not in radioactive equilibrium. Radiothorium, together with its parent substance, Ra^{228}, in the spleen and liver were in radioactive equilibrium at approximately 89 percent. In paravasal infiltration both radionuclides were in radioactive equilibrium at even 96 percent. The deficiency of the Th^{228} in contrast to Ra^{228} was at about 11 percent in the *in vivo* total body measurements, too, and agrees to one measurement by Miller (6) (12%), related, however, to the activity ratio between Th^{208} and Ac^{228}. Measurements by Rundo (7,8) showed 29 to 35 percent. Muth and Oberhausen (9) found values of 19 percent to 26 percent.

When we were able to determine the total body Th^{228} and Ra^{228} content *in vivo* in respect to both the location and the amount of the deposit down to 5 to 10 percent accuracy, investigations were made to determine the total body content by making excretion measurements.

The feces were welded in plastic containers and measured underneath the 8 by 4 in. crystal without any chemical preparations. That was the only possible way to show exactly the short-lived isotope Pb^{212} (ThB) by quantity and to distinguish the ThB content of feces at the time of the excretion. There have been at least eight and in some cases up to fourteen daily feces of a pa-
the thorium daughter products, which can go up to 50 percent.
tient tested because of the variations noticed in the excretion of
The results clearly show that in all cases within biological variability the lead isotope ThB is excreted by feces contrary to its parent substance Ra^{224} at about 20 percent below the radioactive equilibrium. The excretion of Ra^{224} is above the excretion of Th^{228} at

TABLE II
THE FECAL EXCRETION OF THORIUM DAUGHTERS

Case	Thorotrast depot	Th^{228}-Activity $(10^{-7}\,c)$ before extirpation	after extirpation	*Fecal Excretion* Pb^{212}/Ra^{224} $\mu\,\mu c/g./\mu\,\mu c/g.$ before extirpation	after extirpation	Ra^{224}/Th^{228} $\mu\,\mu c/g./\mu\,\mu c/g.$ before extirpation	after extirpation	Ra^{224}/Th^{228} $\mu\,\mu c/g./\mu\,\mu c/g.$ before extirpation	after extirpation	Ra^{224}/Th^{228} $\mu\,\mu c/g./\mu\,\mu c/g.$ before extirpation	after extirpation
SZ	Liver	6.0									
	spleen		4.5 liver	—	1.05	—	164	—	24.4	—	6.8
SI	liver	1.76		0.98		120		37.7		3.07	
	spleen										
SC	liver	2.93		0.82		66.5		62.5		1.43	
	spleen		1.96 liver		0.87		105		38.3		2.97
	liver	0.6									
	spleen		0.6								
BU	par. inf.	0.109	0.055	0.84	—	87	77	21.6	20.9	3.52	3.67
	(arm)										
WA	liver	0.557									
	spleen		0.449 liver			1961 8.9 1962 71.2		1961 47.8 1962 17.8		1961 0.19 1962 4.1	
	par. inf.	2.05	2.05	—	—	—	—	—	—	—	—
	(neck)										
FE	liver	0.53	—	0.77		426		26.3		15.7	
	par. inf.	1.11	—								
	(neck)										
	AVERAGE			0.89 ± 0.11		99 ± 35		33 ± 15		3.7 ± 1.7	

a factor of over 100 (Table II). The average daily urinary Pb^{212} excretion proved to be 0.8 percent per total body Th^{228} content, which means an excretion of about 8 x 10^{-10} c Pb^{212} with a 24 hour urine and a total body Th^{228} burden of 0.1 μc. None of the long-lived daughters of the Th^{232} could be observed in the urine (Ra^{228}, Th^{228}).

Considering the daily Ra^{224} excretion in relation to the total body Ra^{224} content, you will find within the above given limits in all cases that approximately 2 percent of the total body Ra^{224} activity is excreted with the feces. If one assumes an average daily stool of 100 gm., approximately 2 nc Ra^{224} will be excreted by the feces a day at a total body Ra^{224} content of 1×10^{-7}c. With relatively little expense this can be determined in making excretion measurements with an accuracy of about 50 percent.

In some cases results showed that about 1×10^{-10}c Th^{228}/ gm. stool will be excreted at a total body Th^{228} content of 1×10^{-6}c. This corresponds to an average daily excretion of about 10^{-10}c, or 0.01 percent of the total body Th^{228} content. In the case of Ra^{228} at 11 percent above radioactive equilibrium with Th^{228}, 3.3×10^{-10}c are excreted with the daily feces of 100 gm., which corresponds to 0.03 percent of the Ra^{228} total body content. The same result had been found by Hursh and co-workers, who stated a value of 0.026 percent in one case (10).

If the value of 0.03 percent body content excreted per day is valid for Ra^{228}, the body Ra^{228} content would increase over the years, with an effective half life of about 3 years to a steady state value equal to about 50 percent of the Th^{232} activity. This value could be found, indeed, while measuring the Th^{232} and Ra^{228} content of several samples of liver and spleen (11, 12). In the liver, spleen and paravasal infiltration the Th^{232} content was about two times that of Ra^{228}. Within marrow-free bones the ratio Th^{232}/Th^{228} was about 0.6 on the average, indicating a translocation of Th^{228} to the marrow-free skeleton.

REFERENCES

1. Marinelli, L. D.: *Brit. J. Radiol., Supp.* 7:38, 1956.
2. Kaul, A., and Heigwer, G.: *Kerntechnik,* in press.

3. Kaul, A., Schoeppe, W., Koch, K. M., and Hierholzer, K.: *Biophysik*, in preparation.
4. Rundo, J.: *Brit. J. Radiol.*, 28:615, 1955.
5. Rundo, J.: *Acta Radiol.*, 47:65, 1957.
6. Miller, C. E.: *ANL Report 5829*, July-December 1957, Argonne National Laboratory, Argonne, Illinois, 144, 1958.
7. Rundo., J.: *Phys. Med. Biol.* 1:138, 1956.
8. Rundo, J.: Thesis, London, 1958.
9. Muth, H., and Oberhausen, E.: Whole Body Counting Proceedings of a Symposium, Vienna 13-16 June, 1961, 267, I.A.E.A.
10. Hursh, J. B., Steadman, L. T., Looney, W. B., and Colodzin, M.: *Acta Radiol.*, 46:481, 1956.
11. Staflhofen, W., and Kaul, A.: Radiol. health and safety in mining and milling of nuclear materials, Proceedings of a Symposium, I.A.E.A. Vienna, 1963.
12. Unnewehr, F., Kaul, A., and Stahlhofen, W.: *Atomkernenergie, II*:475, 1964.

19

CLINICAL APPLICATIONS OF WHOLE BODY POTASSIUM DETERMINATION[1]

A. R. LORIMER, B. C. SINCLAIR-SMITH, C. CONSTANTINIDES,
R. L. WEILAND, C. O. T. BALL AND R. M. HEYSSEL

Vanderbilt University School of Medicine
Nashville, Tennessee

WHOLE BODY COUNTING techniques permit determination of total body potassium in humans by measuring body content of the naturally occurring isotope K^{40}. Extensive data exist (1-3) on the normal human content of K^{40} measured by this method. The applications of these techniques to clinical research have been investigated.

COUNTING FACILITY AND CALIBRATION

The Vanderbilt University Medical School low level counting facility consists of a steel room, 71 in. long, 95 in. wide and 95 in. high inside. The walls, floor and ceiling are made of 8 in. thick low radioactivity steel, lined with $\frac{1}{4}$ in. of lead and $\frac{1}{16}$ in. of stainless steel. A metal chair which may be tilted so that the back makes an approximate 45° angle to the floor is fixed in the center of the room. This is comparable to the arrangement described by Miller (4) as the Argonne No. 1 position. The thallium-activated sodium iodide crystal is 8 in. in diameter and 4 in. thick. It is suspended from a movable gantry and locks into a standard position. Three DuMont Type 6363 photomultiplier tubes are attached. These have been carefully selected to give identical gain characteristics (5). Output is fed into 256 channel pulse height analyzer, where it is sorted and stored in a mag-

[1] Supported by grants from U. S. Atomic Energy Commission, U. S. Army Research and Development Command and U. S. Public Health Service.

netic core memory. At the end of each counting period, accumulated counts in each channel are automatically printed on paper tape and punched in IBM cards for electronic data processing.

Calibration of the instrument for total body potassium was done by comparison with the efficiency of accurately known amounts of K^{42} and K^{40} in a 22 liter polyethylene bottle with the efficiency of K^{42} in the human. K^{40} efficiency was then calculated (3, 4). By selecting 15 normal subjects with a wide range of stature and habitus, an expression was derived where

Body K (gm.) = F x subject's K^{40} cpm

where F is a constant for each individual, correcting for body thickness. Since efficiency varies with stature and habitus, the use of a constant factor disregarding this variation is erroneous.

Because K^{40} is present in a fixed proportion in all naturally occurring potassium, the K^{40} cpm/gm. potassium can be related to three factors: the solid angle which is formed by the detector and the sample, the efficiency of the instrument in the detection of 1.46 Mev gamma rays and the absorption of 1.46 Mev gamma rays by the sample.

A formula for factor F has been derived where

$$F = \frac{A \cdot e^{B\sqrt{W/H}}}{\sqrt{W \cdot H}}$$

or

$$F = \frac{27.43 \cdot e^{1.091\sqrt{W/H}}}{\sqrt{W \cdot H}}$$

A and B are empirically derived constants; W is weight in pounds, and H is height in inches.

Attempts to find a simple relationship between size of subject and conversion factor were unsuccessful, although it was obvious that obese subjects had higher F values than lean. Only by plotting log $F\sqrt{W \cdot H}$ against $\sqrt{W/H}$ could a satisfactory relationship between F and body build be obtained.

NORMAL TOTAL BODY POTASSIUM

During 1959-61, 30 min. whole body counts were done on

917 people. Two-thirds of this number constitute a random sub-sample of the population of Nashville, Tennessee, reflecting the percentage of race, social class and geographical distribution of the community (6). This sample is supplemented by determinations made on normal white subjects in the course of laboratory investigation and instrument calibration (Table I).

TABLE I
NUMBER OF ANALYSES

Race and Sex	Survey	Non-Survey	Total
White Females	247	91	338
White Males	195	166	361
Negro Females	121	—	121
Negro Males	97	—	97

Race, sex and age variations in total body potassium concentration are shown in Figure 1. Ages eight to twenty are averaged by three years running average to consider rapid height and weight variations, thereafter they are averaged by decade. Potassium values obtained correspond to those of Anderson and Langham (1) in showing male levels to be higher than female, this difference decreasing from age twenty throughout life. The Negro male has a higher average potassium concentration than the white male, the values becoming similar after middle age. Negro females have a higher average potassium concentration than white females.

Because potassium concentration in lean fat-free mass is a constant (7-10), the present data for potassium concentration reflect an increased lean fat-free mass of Negroes as compared to whites. Height was similar in each race.

WHOLE BODY COUNTING AND METABOLIC TECHNIQUES

Alterations in body potassium content have been reported in congestive cardiac failure (11), hyperaldosteronism (12) and muscular dystrophy (13). Accurate determination of potassium

GRAMS POTASSIUM PER KG. BODY WEIGHT AS A FUNCTION
OF AGE

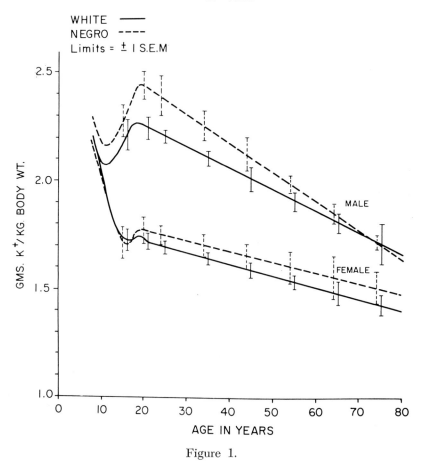

Figure 1.

balance by routine methods is time consuming. In the present
study whole body counting as an alternative method was used
for determination of potassium balance over short and long
periods. Since November 1961, twelve normal persons were
counted at weekly intervals in a study of Cs^{137} body burdens.
Concurrently, computer analysis provided total body potassium
content. The precision of the facility (Fig. 2) is such that 7 percent of eighty-four measurements differ from the mean by ± 2

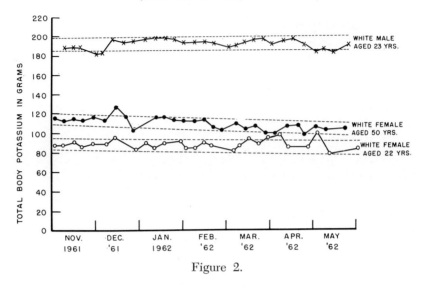

Figure 2.

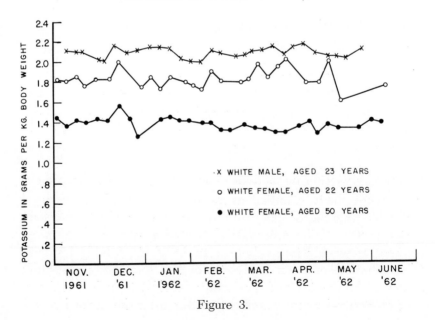

Figure 3.

standard deviations. Of the three people whose potassium content is shown, two maintained a constant weight, while the study period in the fifty year old woman coincided with a diet designed to lose weight. Potassium concentration in grams per kilogram body weight was plotted against time (Fig. 3). The subjects with a constant weight have no change in potassium concentration, while the subject whose weight decreased has a loss of total potassium content and a reduction in potassium concentration. Her weight loss may thus be due to fat plus lean fat-free mass loss.

Conventional metabolic balance technique was compared to whole body counting technique over ten days in two patients suffering from congestive cardiac failure. The first patient was a twenty-seven year old Negro woman with mitral insufficiency and severe untreated congestive cardiac failure with ankle edema, hepatomegaly and basal lung congestion. No ascites was present. On admission, a constant daily 1,500 cal. diet containing 82 mEq. of potassium and 25 mEq. of sodium was begun.

A 10 kg. weight loss occurred. Daily urine and fecal collections were analyzed for potassium, sodium and chloride. On two occasions whole day collections of the constant diet were homogenized, aliquots taken and analyzed for potassium, sodium and chloride. Frequent serum electrolyte estimations were done. The Metabolic Unit was air-conditioned, and potassium losses by sweat have been considered as 4 percent of the total daily loss in urine and feces (14). Whole body counts of 30 min. were done daily at noon. The bladder was routinely emptied immediately preceding the whole body count. Values were expressed as milliequivalents of potassium, and a three day running average calculated for each day.

Over the ten days of study, cumulative retention of dietary potassium was 117 mEq. by balance (Fig. 4). Although the metabolic balance shows retention of potassium throughout the study, apart from a twenty-four hour loss occasioned by a mercurial diuretic, whole body counting does not indicate retention until the dry weight of the patient was achieved. After ten days the retention of potassium by whole body counting was 15 mEq.

Average total body potassium was 2,000 ± 130 mEq. or

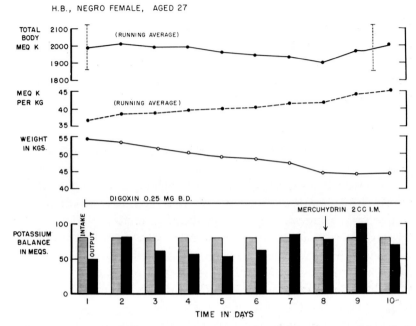

Figure 4. Potassium balance in congestive cardiac failure measured by whole body counting and by standard metabolic technique, patient H. B.

2,000 $\pm$ 6.5 percent. By metabolic balance total body potassium increased by 5.8 percent, and by whole body counting the increase was 0.75 percent. Neither value is significant. During the study, potassium concentration in milliequivalents per kilogram body weight increased from 36.7 to 46.4, indicating that proportionally more fluid was lost than potassium and that possibly tissue concentration of potassium increased. The normal potassium concentration of Negro females in the third decade is 45 $\pm$ 1.55 mEq./kg., suggesting that the patient, initially deficient in potassium, returned to normal.

The second patient was a forty-eight year old Negro woman in gross refractory congestive cardiac failure of unknown etiology, with anasarca, gross acites and hepatomegaly. A constant diet of 1,200 cal., 76 mEq. of potassium, and 30 mEq. of sodium was given. Initially digoxin 0.25 mg. twice daily was administered, but possible digitalis toxicity developed on the fourth day, and supplemental oral potassium to a total of 150 mEq. was given over the next three days. A satisfactory weight loss of 13.75 kg. was achieved by mercuhydrin, ammonium chloride and subsequent reintroduction of digoxin. Urine, feces and diet were collected and analyzed as before. Sweat loss was estimated at 4 per cent of total daily loss in urine and feces.

The whole body counting technique was similar to before.

During the first six days of metabolic balance, a retention of potassium occurred; intensive diuretic therapy, however, resulted in a loss of 111 mEq. Total body potassium in milliequivalents also showed an initial retention, but the values were not comparable to those obtained by metabolic balance (Fig. 5). Utilizing whole

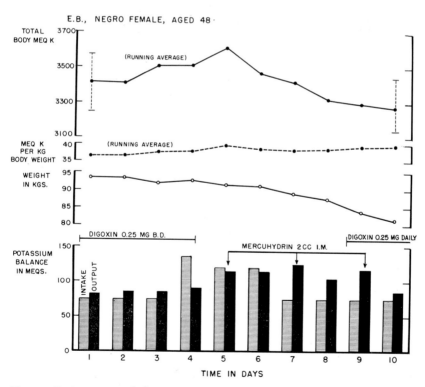

Figure 5. Potassium balance in congestive cardiac failure measured by whole body counting and standard metabolic technique, patient E. B.

body counting the final loss over 10 days was 137 mEq. potassium. Average total body potassium was 3,300 mEq. ± 5 percent. The reduction in total body potassium by balance was 3.4 percent, and by whole body counting was 4.1 percent. Neither value is significant. Potassium concentration rose from 36.5 to 39.5 mEq./kg., possibly indicating an increase in tissue concentration of potassium. The normal value for a Negro woman in the fifth decade is 39.4 mEq./kg. with a standard error of the mean of ± 1.17. Both patients were thus initially deficient in potassium.

There are difficulties in interpretation of these data. First, a metabolic balance study may itself have an error of ± 10 percent, so that it is not a reliable standard against which to evaluate a new technique. Second, there are difficulties in the use of K^{40}. The counting rate is only one to three times above background in our single crystal type counter and a coefficient of variation of about 5 percent per observation means that changes of more than 100 mEq. may be required before significance can be established. In both patients potassium values were calculated using the factor derived from height and weight. Therefore as the weight of the patient became less, the factor also decreased. The first patient manifested her congestive failure largely as edema of the legs. Since the contribution of the legs to the total count is small (about 6 percent), it might be considered more useful to use a constant factor, that of the patient's dry weight. Using this factor a retention of 59 mEq. of potassium is given by whole body counting as compared to 15 mEq. using the varying factor and 117 mEq. by metabolic balance. The tendency in all methods is towards retention. Gross ascites, hepatomegaly and edema of the legs were present in the second patient. Loss of weight brought about a reduction in ascites, in liver size and in edema of the legs. Using the factor for lowest weight attained as a constant, this patient retained 25 mEq. of potassium as compared to a loss of 137 mEq. by using the varying factor, and a loss of 111 mEq. by metabolic balance. In this case the varying factor and balance results were in agreement as before, but use of a constant factor showed the opposite trend. From these admittedly scanty data we consider that trends of potassium balance are more realistically appraised by using a factor which changes as the habitus of the patient alters. Further, the whole body counter provides a check on balance studies and may show concentration or dilution of tissue potassium levels not shown by balance. It does not provide a valid indication of day-to-day potassium kinetics.

HYPOKALEMIC STATES

When potassium deficiency is suspected, the variation in normal makes it difficult to state the degree of deficiency in a given individual. It is, however, possible to measure retention of administered potassium to subjects deficient in the element. Typically, there is poor correlation between serum potassium levels and total body potassium. Figure 6 shows a patient with primary

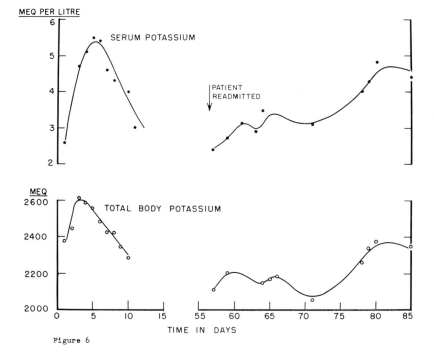

Figure 6

hyperaldosteronism secondary to an adenoma of the adrenal cor-
tex. Oral potassium was administered, then withheld. A corresponding rise and fall in serum and total body potassium occurred. At this time, it was felt that diuretic therapy prior to admission was a possible contributory factor in her hypokalemia, and
she was discharged. On readmission two months later, oral potassium was administered. An imprecise balance study showed a retention of 456 mEq. of potassium. This was an over estimate since
it included neither measurement of fecal potassium nor estimates of loss in sweat. Simultaneously, a retention of 256 mEq. of
potassium was measured by whole body counting.

A further study was made on a twenty year old white female
with hypokalemic alkalosis of undetermined origin. An admission

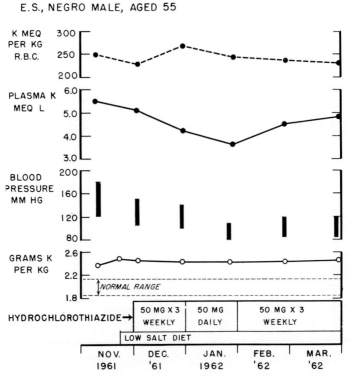

Figure 7. Whole body potassium, serum potassium and erythocyte potassium in treated essential hypertension, patient E. S.

serum potassium of 3.6 mEq./liter remained constant during the administration of supplemental oral potassium. Whole body potassium increased during four weeks from 1,400 to 2,300 mEq. with an increase in tissue concentration of potassium from 30 to 45 mEq./kg. body weight (normal 44.6 ± 0.7 mEq./kg.). In this case serum potassium levels gave no indication of potassium retention.

ESSENTIAL HYPERTENSION

A long term study was made of total body potassium changes in the course of essential hypertension. Five Negro females and one male were followed. They had well documented, uncomplicated essential hypertension, untreated for at least one year.

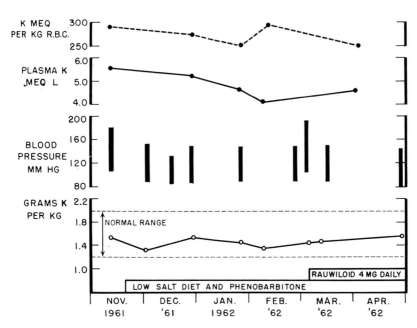

Figure 8. Whole body potassium, serum potassium and erythrocyte potassium in treated essential hypertension, patient W. L. O.

Duplicate initial measurements were normal for all females, but a significantly high value was obtained in the male, possibly because of muscular build. All patients were placed on a low salt diet of 30 mEq. sodium daily. If this regimen did not produce an adequate lowering in diastolic blood pressure, 50 mg. of hydrochlorothiazide was administered three times weekly, increased to 50 mg. daily if required. A satisfactory response in blood pressure readings was obtained in four of the six patients, diastolic blood pressure being reduced to 90 mm. mercury or less. Data for three patients are shown in Figures 7, 8 and 9. A moderate fall in serum potassium concentration occurred with the administration of hydrochlorothiazide, but this was not paralleled by a reduction in total body potassium. In these patients low serum potassium levels are not an indication of total body potassium depletion. Concomitant estimations of erythrocyte potassium also

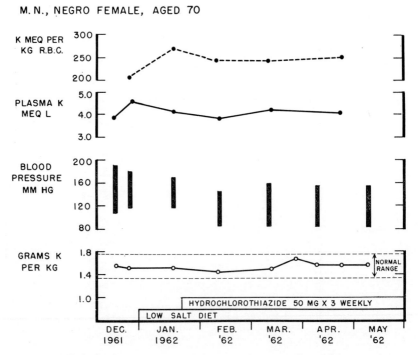

Figure 9. Whole body potassium, serum potassium and erythrocyte potassium in treated essential hypertension, patient M. N.

remained within the control values and within normal limits. These findings are in agreement with those of Hollander *et al.* (15) using K^{42}, who found that exchangeable potassium was not altered in uncomplicated essential hypertension.

SUMMARY

Normal values for total body potassium have been established for race, sex and age. The Negro has a higher total body potassium than the white race. The precision of the facility is such that, in repetitive measurements of a normal individual over a long time, less than one in ten of potassium estimations will differ significantly from the mean. The contribution of physiological variation in potassium balance is not known.

The whole body counter is not satisfactory as a day-to-day indicator of metabolic balance of potassium. It confirms trends in the over-all balance of the element.

Preliminary work would indicate no alteration in total body potassium in essential hypertension in Negroes.

REFERENCES

1. Miller, C. E., and Marinelli, L. D.: Gamma ray activity of contemporary man. *Science, 124*:122, 1956.
2. Anderson, E. C., and Langham, W. H.: Average potassium concentration of the human body as a function of age. *Science, 130*:713 (Sept. 18) 1959.
3. Meneely, G. R., Ball, C. O. T., Ferguson, J. L., Payne, D. D., Lorimer, A. R., Weiland, R. L., Rolfe, H. L., and Heysell, R. M.: Use of computers in measuring body electrolytes by gamma spectrometry. *Circulat. Res., 11*:539, (Sept.) 1962.
4. Miller, C. E.: Low intensity spectrometry of the gamma radiation emitted by human beings. *Progr. Nucl. Energ. Med.,* 2:87, New York, Pergamon Press, 1959.
5. Weiland, R. L.: Phototubes, resolution and multi-channel analyzers for whole body counting. *Radioactivity In Man.* G. R. Meneely, editor. Springfield, Thomas, 1961, p. 61.
6. Zeidberg, L. D., Schuenemann, J. J., Humphrey, P. A., and Prindle, R.

A.: Air pollution and health: General description of a study in Nashville, Tennessee, *J. Air Pollution Control Ass.*, *11*:289 (June) 1961.

7. Woodward, K. T., Trujillo, T. T., Schuch, R. L., and Anderson, E. C.: Correlation of total body potassium with body water. *Nature*, *178*:97, 1956.

8. Anderson, E. C., and Langham, W. H.: Estimation of total body fat from K^{40} content. *Science*, *133*:3468, 1961.

9. Forbes, G. H., Gallup, J., and Hursh, J. B.: Estimation of total body fat from K^{40} content. *Science*, *133*:101, 1961.

10. Allen, T. H., Anderson, E. C., and Langham, W. H.: Total body potassium and gross body composition in relation to age. *J. Geront. 15*: 348, 1960.

11. Flear, C. T. G., Cawley, R., Quinton, A., and Cooke, W. T.: The simultaneous determination of total exchangeable sodium and potassium and its significance with particular reference to congestive cardiac failure and the steatorrhoea syndrome, *Clin. Sci.*, *17*:81, 1958.

12. Chobanian, A. V., Burrows, B. A., and Hollander, W.: Body fluid and electrolyte composition in arterial hypertension. II. Studies in mineralocorticoid hypertension. *J. Clin. Invest.*, *40*:416, 1961.

13. Blahd, W. H., Cassen, B., and Lederer, M.: Determination of total body potassium by K^{40} measurements in patients with muscular dystrophy and related diseases. Whole Body Counting. Proceedings of a Symposium, Vienna, June 1961, Vienna, Austria, International Atomic Energy Agency, 1962, p. 427.

14. Black, D. A. K.: Current concepts of potassium metabolism. *J. Pediat.*, *56*:812 (June) 1960.

15. Hollander, W., Chobanian, A. V., and Burrows, B. A.: Body fluid and electrolyte composition in arterial hypertension. I. Studies in essential, renal and malignant hypertension. *J. Clin. Invest.*, *40*:408, 1961.

20

INTERRELATION OF BODY POTASSIUM AND BODY WATER IN PATIENTS WITH PRIMARY MUSCLE DISEASE[1]

WILLIAM H. BLAHD, BENEDICT CASSEN,
JERRY M. KOPLOWITZ AND MARIANNE LEDERER

Veterans Administration Center and School of Medicine
University of California
Los Angeles, California

THE ROLE OF POTASSIUM in muscle metabolism has been the subject of investigation and speculation for many years. Its obvious importance in muscle disease has been indicated by the effect of potassium administration in familial periodic paralysis and by the profound muscle weakness associated with potassium depletion in severe diabetic coma. Although altered serum potassium levels are frequently observed in these conditions, substantial changes in total body potassium have been noted when serum potassium levels were within the normal range. Since 95 per cent of potassium is intracellular, serum values do not adequately reflect derangements of potassium metabolism.

The availability of artificial isotopes of biologically important elements during recent years has made possible the study and measurement of total body potassium concentrations. Studies of this kind in patients with primary muscle disease have been accomplished with radioactive K^{42} by the isotope dilution technique (1,2). Because of the limitations of the short half life of K^{42} and the relatively large doses of radioactive tracer required, determinations in unaffected children and family members of patients with muscle disease could not be undertaken. With the development in recent years of the whole body counter, the need to administer radioactive potassium tracers for the measurement

[1] Aided in part by a grant from Muscular Dystrophy Association of America, Inc.

of body potassium levels in unaffected family members has been eliminated.

A number of reports have appeared in recent years implying a constant relationship between body potassium content and a fundamental component of body composition variously described as "active tissue mass" (Rubner), "lean body mass" (Behnke), and "M_3" — the residual mass of the body after the removal of bone mineral, fat and water from gross body mass (Allen) (3-7). Since this quantity is largely potassium-rich muscle, its measurement or further description is of paramount interest in muscle disease. It has been demonstrated in normal subjects that total body water is a good index of this quantity (5), and we assume that this relationship may be extended to patients with primary muscle disease. Consequently, total body water measurements by tritium dilution were obtained in a series of patients with primary muscle disease including selected family members and control subjects, and the interrelation of body potassium and water were studied.

PROCEDURE AND METHODS

Total body potassium measurements were determined in fifty-six patients with primary muscle disease by K^{40} measurements obtained with a whole body counter. Aged twelve to sixty-five, forty-three patients had muscular dystrophy and thirteen had myotonia atrophica. Body potassium measurements were also obtained in forty-two unaffected family members.

All body potassium measurements were performed in a whole body scintillation counter in accordance with the standard chair technique described by Miller and co-workers (8). Subjects were counted in a specially constructed reclining metal chair placed in a fixed geometrical position to a scintillation probe containing a 4 by 8 in. sodium iodide crystal on which were nested three matched photomultiplier tubes. The signal output from the photomultiplier tubes was fed into a multichannel pulse height analyzer. Early studies were performed on a 50 channel, and later studies on a 400 channel analyzer. Patient and scintillation detector were placed in a rectangular counting room with 5 in. thick steel walls and ⅛ in. inside lead lining. The instrument assembly was calibrated by measurement of laboratory personnel and normal volunteers of a selected age and body size who received known amounts of K^{42}. After calibration, total body potassium concentrations were calculated from the normal abundance of K^{40}.

Total body water concentrations were determined by tritium dilution in twenty-six dystrophic patients, eight control subjects and four unaffected fathers (9).

RESULTS

A distribution regression line of total body potassium concentration in grams/kilogram for each sex in a series of ninety-

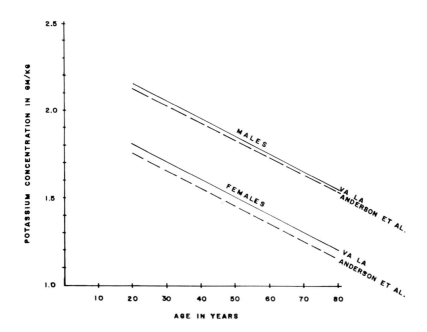

Figure 1. Mean regression curves of total body potassium concentrations in normal subjects compared with data from Anderson and Langham.

five normal subjects, aged twelve to seventy four, was estimated and plotted according to age. The age-sex distribution relationship previously described by Anderson and Langham was observed (10). The mean curves were superimposed on those obtained by them in a much larger group of normal individuals (Fig. 1). It can be seen that there is excellent correlation between these data despite a slight but constant difference in the plotted curves.

Patients with muscular dystrophy had severe depression of body potassium concentration (Fig. 2). In general, the level of body potassium was correlated with the severity of muscular

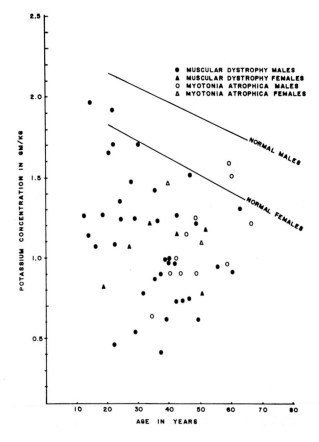

Figure 2. Distribution of total body potassium concentrations in patients with muscular dystrophy and myotonia atrophica.

disease. Decreased body potassium concentrations were also observed in myotonia atrophica patients, but often to a lesser degree and with less obvious correlation with their state of disability.

Body potassium concentration was also measured in a group of family members of dystrophic patients including siblings, parents and first generation progeny (Figs. 3 and 4). Remarkably decreased body potassium concentrations were observed in four of fifteen healthy fathers who had dystrophic progeny, and in two apparently healthy first generation sons of dystrophic fathers. In addition, three seemingly healthy sisters of muscular dystrophy patients also manifested significantly diminished concentrations of body potassium.

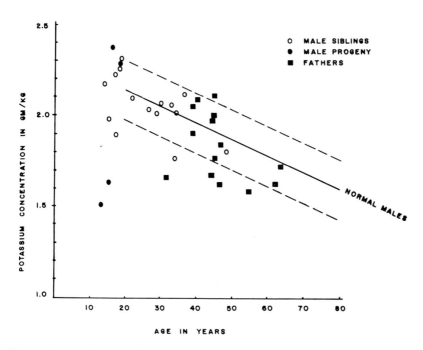

Figure 3. Distribution of potassium concentrations in apparently healthy male family members of muscular dystrophy patients (broken line represents one standard deviation). Triplicate determinations were made on each father whose body potassium concentration fell outside of one standard deviation, and the values obtained are plotted as averages.

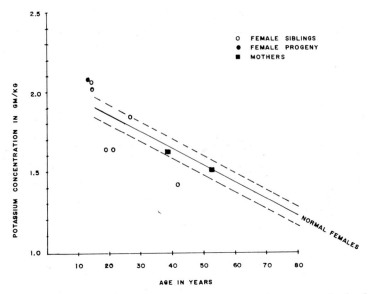

Figure 4. Distribution of potassium concentrations in apparently healthy female family members of muscular dystrophy patients (broken line represents one standard deviation).

Total body water and total body potassium values in twenty-six patients (Fig. 5) were plotted as the ratio of body potassium to body water (K/W) according to age and were compared with the data of Allen and collaborators (5) replotted in this manner. According to this method of data plotting, all individuals previously shown to have reduced body potassium concentrations fall below the normal range.

DISCUSSION

The correlation between total body potassium concentration obtained in our series of normal subjects with those of Anderson and Langham in a much larger normal series appears to confirm the validity of the methodology used (10).

The data obtained in patients with primary muscular disease also confirmed previous exchange studies with K^{42} as well as earlier studies using the whole body counting technique in which

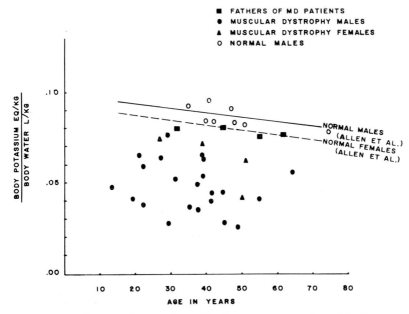

Figure 5. Distribution of ratio of total body potassium and total body water according to age in patients with muscular dystrophy and myotonia atrophica, selected male parents and normal subjects, compared to normal mean curves of Allen *et al.*, replotted as K/W ratio.

the presence of marked diminutions in body potassium concentration in such patients was demonstrated (1, 2, 11).

The abnormal relationship between body potassium concentration and total body water observed in the present studies would seem to support the thesis that absolute intracellular potassium deficiency is a primary factor in the dystrophic process and would tend to refute the notion that the decreased body potassium concentrations of dystrophic patients are solely the result of muscle wasting or atrophy. These findings are also in agreement with earlier muscle biopsy perfusion studies performed by Horvath and collaborators, which also suggested an absolute intracellular potassium diminution in muscular dystrophy (12).

The remarkably low body potassium concentration observed in four healthy fathers, two healthy male progeny of dystrophic fathers and three male and three female siblings of dystrophic subjects suggests a benign biochemical trait which would appear to have serious hereditary portent. It is significant that in the cases of three of the four fathers in whom total body water determination were obtained, the relationship between potassium and body water was similar, though to a lesser degree, to that observed in patients with clinical muscular dystrophy.

Because of their importance in possibly elucidating the hereditary transmission of muscular dystrophy, additional correlative studies with other clinical and biochemical data are required. This problem is now under active and continuing investigation in this laboratory.

SUMMARY

Total body potassium was determined in fifty-six patients with primary muscle disease (muscular dystrophy and myotonia atrophica) and in forty-two unaffected family members by means of K^{40} measurements in a whole body counter.

Muscular dystrophy patients had severe depressions in body potassium concentration. Decreased body potassium levels were also observed in myotonia atrophica, but often to a lesser degree.

Unusually depressed body potassium levels were noted in some healthy fathers who had dystrophic progeny and in several apparently healthy family members of dystrophic patients. These findings suggest a benign biochemical trait.

Total body water, determined by the tritum dilution method, expressed in relation to total body potassium and plotted according to age, revealed discrepant values in dystrophic patients. These data support the thesis that intracellular potassium deficiency may be a primary factor in the dystrophic process.

ACKNOWLEDGMENTS

The authors wish to express their appreciation to Martha McGeein of the Muscular Dystrophy Foundation of California and the staff of the Southern California Chapter of the Muscular

Dystrophy Associations of America for their assistance in locating cases and family members and to J. Johnson for technical assistance.

REFERENCES

1. Blahd, W. H., Bauer, F. K., Libby, R. L., and Rose, A. E.: Studies in neuromuscular diseases with radioactive potassium. *Neurology, 3*: 604-608, 1953.
2. Blahd, W. H., Bauer, F. K., Libby, R. L., and Rose, A. S.: Radioisotope studies in neuromuscular disease, Studies in muscular dystrophy and myotonia dystrophica with sodium[22] and potassium[42]. *Neurology, 5*:201-207, 1955.
3. Rubner, M.: *Die Gesetze des Energieverbrauchs bei der Ernahrung* Leipzig and Vienna, Deuticke, 1962.
4. Behnke, A. R.: Physiologic studies pertaining to deep sea diving and aviation, especially in relation to the fat content and composition of the body, *Harvey Lect.* 37:198-226, 1941-42.
5. Allen, T. H., Anderson, E. C., and Langham, W. H.: Total body potassium and gross body composition in relation to age. *J. Gerontol., 15*:348-357, 1960.
6. Remenchik, A. P., and Miller, C. E.: The measurement of total body potassium in man and its relation to gross body composition. Proceedings of the Symposium on Whole Body Counting, I.A.E.A., Vienna, 1962.
7. Forbes, G. B., Gallup, J., and Hursh, J. B.: Estimation of total body fat from potassium[40] content; *Science, 133*:101-102, 1961.
8. Miller, C. E.: Low intensity spectrometry of the gamma radiation emitted by human beings. *Proc. 2nd U. N. Int. Conf. P.U.A.E., 23*: 113-122, 1958.
9. Vaughan, B. E., and Boling, E. A.: Rapid assay procedures for tritium-labelled water in body fluids. *J. Lab. Clin. Med., 57*:159-164, 1961.
10. Anderson, E. C., and Langham, W. H.: Average potassium concentration of the human body as a function of age. *Science, 130*:713-714, 1959.
11. Blahd, W. H., Cassen, B., and Lederer, M.: Determination of total body potassium by potassium[40] measurements in patients with muscular dystrophy and related diseases. Proceedings of the Symposium on Whole Body Counting, I.A.E.A., Vienna, 1962.
12. Horvath, B., Berg, L., Cummings, D. J., and Shy, G. M.: Muscular dystrophy; cation concentrations in residual muscle. *J. Appl. Physiol., 8*:22-30, 1955-56.

DISCUSSION

Chairman: Josef Brozek

Lehigh University

Bethlehem, Pennsylvania

Chairman Josef Brozek: Francis D. Moore and his collaborators (1) have pointed out that availability of artificial isotopes of physiologically important elements made it possible to determine the amount of these constituents in the living human body by the principle of dilution. On a previous reading an important sentence in this paper had escaped me: "Development of methods for such *chemical anthropometry* is providing valuable new devices for investigation of physiologic and pathologic changes in man." Elsewhere (2) I had credited Macy and Kelly (3) and R. J. Williams (4) with being the originators of the term *chemical anthropology*. However, the priority for the closely related concept and term of chemical anthropometry goes to Moore and his colleagues.

In the proceedings of a symposium *Whole Body Counting* (5), several papers deal with the measurements of total body potassium by whole body counters in the study of gross body composition.

In another publication *Techniques for Measuring Body Composition* (6), I. S. Edelman summarized the available data on body potassium measured *in vivo* by dilution of K^{42}. When expressed in reference to body weight, the total exchangeable potassium shows distinct age trends toward lower values at higher ages and distinct sex differences at comparable ages with lower values in females. These trends and differences are interpretable in terms of differences in the fat content of the body. Edelman wrote: "Acute and chronic illness is almost invariably accompanied by losses of body potassium, and it is significant that no disease process is known which induces accumulation of abnormally high quantities of potassium."

The development of whole body counters for determining total body potassium has been greeted with justification as opening a whole new era in research on body composition. However, few investigators are so sanguine as to believe that the millenium has already arrived.

272

I would like to bring out some of the problems existing in three areas: terminology, methodology and interpretation.

Research on body composition, or somatolysis, is of relatively recent origin. Consequently, one can expect some inaccuracies and vacillations in terminology. But such a state should not become a chronic ailment.

One of the basic terms which has been used carelessly is that of "lean body mass" (L.B.M.). The concept and the term was given currency, and perhaps birth, by A. R. Behnke.

In principle it is a perfectly usable concept, defined as the limit approached by the very lean, yet normally hydrated individuals: L.B.M. = Fat Free Mass + Essential Fat, the latter being an unknown factor. It was unfortunate that L.B.M. became confused with the fat-free body mass (F.F.M.), a concept derived from chemical studies and defined by subtracting the chemically defined fat (petroleum ether extract) from the gross body weight.

When A. P. Remenchik and C. E. Miller (7) divide total body water by the factor 0.73, having assumed that water constitutes 73 percent of the fat-free mass, they obtain fat-free body weight, not lean body mass. Then the total body fat (F) = Body weight − F.F.M. (not Body weight − L.B.M.).

Remenchik and Miller confirmed that the amount of exchangeable potassium, determined from K^{42}, tends to be about 10 per cent smaller than the total body potassium estimated from K^{40} measurements. This finding is interpreted by the authors as suggesting that not all of the body potassium is exchangeable up to 34 hr. after the administration of K^{42}.

On the contrary, P. A. Delwaide et al. (8) concluded that "at the twenty-fourth hour, K^{42} has, for a few hours, had a spatial distribution sufficiently similar to that of K^{40} to permit it to serve as a standard."

What are the implications of these findings and discrepancies for the calibration and use of whole body counters?

In terms of absolute amounts, even the K^{40} data appears to be substantially below the potassium content of man obtained by the direct analysis of cadavers. Remenchik and Miller's average value from K^{40} measurements was 1.86 gm. potassium/kg. of body weight, at the estimated fat content of 19 percent of body weight. The value was 2.32 gm. potassium/kg. of fat-free weight. Except for one case, the cadaver data range from 2.0 to 2.84 gm. potassium/kg. of fat-free weight.

The authors conclude, appropriately, that the clarification of the relationship between the true, directly (chemically) determined amount of potassium in the body and the amount estimated from K^{40} measurements requires that the K^{40} measurements made on cadavers be followed by direct chemical analysis of cadavers. Delwaide *et al.* obtained an anomalously high potassium content (2.57 gm. potassium/kg. of body weight; their other figures for males varied from 1.77 to 2.19 gm. potassium/kg. of body weight) in a person in whom the spectrum revealed slight contamination from a gamma ray source, Zn^{65}, the photopeak of which overlapped that of K^{40}. The authors point to contamination as a possible source of artifact and error.

Remenchik and Miller brought out that in obese subjects the K^{40} measurement underestimates total body potassium. Normally the ratio of body's potassium estimated from K^{42} and from K^{40} measurements is less than one; in obese individuals the ratio was equal to or greater than one. The total body potassium measured by K^{40} was systematically lower than the value predicted from the fat-free weight of these obese subjects.

Consequently, the idea of using the K^{40} data for the assessment of fatness appears at present to break down precisely in that range of fatness in which we are especially interested to measure the amount of fat and muscle for clinical purposes in obese people.

Several authors have noted (9) that with increasing age the potassium values arrived at on the basis of K^{40} measurements tend to decrease and the regression line for females is displaced systematically down toward lower values. For the age trends, we must separate the two factors which could account for the observed changes in the potassium concentration in the body: increased fat content and decreased muscle mass. Both are taking place with aging (10).

We would like to have independent estimates of body fat and of muscle mass. At present, changes in the two body components can not be readily unscrambled. To make matters still worse, in the various tissues of the body the concentrations of potassium are likely not to remain constant throughout the life cycle or even the adult phase of the life cycle.

On the basis of K^{42} studies, Edelman (11) noted that "distortions of body potassium content with disease occur frequently and are of critical significance in many cases."

Let me cite one other problem of interpretation. N. S. Macdonald (12) reported on a young man who had his total body potassium determined by K^{40} measurement before the removal of a pancreatic tumor and after fifteen days. The potassium value remained essentially unchanged (131.2 to 131.4 gm.), while the body weight declined from 82.5 to 74.3 kg. The author concluded that "the decrease in the patient's gross body weight probably was due to loss of water and fats and not to loss of 'lean' tissue or muscle." Unfortunately, no information was given on the size and composition of the tumor or on the time course of the changes in body weight. The body potassium data alone do not allow us to partition the weight loss into water and fat. I would be most surprised if some nonfat tissues had not been lost as well.

ALEXANDER REMENCHIK: The lipid extracted by petroleum ether solvents is neutral fat. The other lipids are not soluble in this solvent. Therefore when one analyzes tissues, one is only removing neutral fats with petroleum ether solvents and leaving other lipids behind. When we are talking about a fat-free body, we are talking about a body free of neutral fat, and this is exactly what Dr. Behnke implied. Do you agree with that?

ALBERT BEHNKE: Essentially. Lean body mass refers to a living individual rather than a post mortem entity.

ALEXANDER REMENCHIK: I don't think anybody is committed emotionally to a particular model. Let us go back to fundamentals. We construct models to enable us to understand certain phenomena, and if our model enables us to make verifiable predictions, then it is a useful model. We discard the model when the predictions are wrong.

CHAIRMAN JOSEF BROZEK: My point is that the lean body mass has been used in various contexts, and in some of those contexts it is different from the fat-free mass.

WILHELM VON DÖBELN: I would like to make the definition that fat-free body mass is what Dr. Brozek said, and lean body mass is the total body weight minus the adipose tissue. Adipose tissue contains water to a percentage different from the lean body mass. Then the use of total body water as determining the lean body mass must lead to a confusion.

ALBERT BEHNKE: We regard the body as the sum of components of which a small amount of fat long ago was described as essential lipid. This lipid does not disappear during fasting and starvation. Unfortunately, it has never been measured. It is in the bone marrow, in the central nervous system, in cell membranes and throughout the body. I have been fighting to preserve it.

We have thought for a while that a fat-free or lean body mass would be the reference standard for men and women; but now we find that although the total body water referred to fat-free or lean mass is constant in men and women, 72 or 73 percent, the ratio of extracellular fluid space to intracellular space is different.

CHAIRMAN JOSEF BROZEK: I think it might be a productive thing to try to approach the problem in terms of anatomically defined tissue, and consider the body as a three-face system with components of muscle, with approximately 3.2 gm. potassium per kg. tissue; lean muscle-free body mass with 1.6, and adipose tissue with 0.7. This is what can be derived from data in the literature and chemical studies.

When we speak of adipose tissue, this is really an average concept. There are variations in the hydration in the adipose tissue; and, as Dr. Behnke and his collaborators have shown, in the course of weight reduction you do not lose adipose tissue changes. This is a fact of quite far-reaching consequence.

I would like to hear from Dr. Blahd regarding the concept of constant concentration of potassium in different tissues. I have been disturbed by the figures on the siblings and parents of dystrophic children.

WILLIAM H. BLAHD: I have been disturbed too, because it is very hard to explain this finding unless you are willing to make the assumption that there is a specific defect involving potassium metabolism associated with these diseases. I tend to accept this idea.

In normal, healthy individuals who had low levels of body potassium, we checked each one at least three times over a period of weeks or months. They were confirmed in each instance; so I believe them to be real and valid readings.

I do feel, however, that potassium in the body is a constant parameter, and I am surprised at the concept that one can increase the amount of potassium by increasing muscle size. I rather feel that muscle may increase, but the actual amount of potassium may remain relatively constant. It may be just a shift in fluid within the cells. It is my feeling that potassium, in the normal individual at least, is a constant figure.

REFERENCES

1. Corsa, L., Jr., Olney, J. M., Jr., Steinburg, R. W., Ball, Margaret R., and Moore, F. D.: The measurement of exchangeable potassium in man by isotope dilution. *J. Clin. Invest.* 29:1280-1296, 1950.
2. Brozek, J.: Methods for the study of body composition-addenda, comment, recommendations. in Techniques for the Study of Body Composition. *Nat. Acad. Sci. Nat. Res. Council,* pp. 245-296, 1961.
3. Macy, Icie G., and Kelley, Harriett J.: *Chemical Anthropology: A New Approach to Growth in Children.* Chicago, University of Chicago Press, 1957.
4. Williams, R. J.: Chemical anthropology—an open door. *Amer. Sci., 46:* 1-23, 1958.

5. Whole Body Counting. Proceedings of the Symposium on Whole Body Counting Held by the International Atomic Energy Agency at Vienna, June 12-16, 1961; International Atomic Energy, Vienna, 1962, 801 Third Avenue, New York 22, N. Y.

6. Brozek, J., and Henschel, A., Eds.: Techniques for Measuring Body Composition. Proceedings for a conference held at Quartermaster Research and Engineering Center, Natick, Mass., January 22-23, 1963. Reprints obtainable from Office of Technical Services, U. S. Department of Commerce, Washington, D.C. as U. S. Government Research Report A. D. 286-506, 1963.

7. Remenchik, A. P., and Miller, C. E.: The measurement of total body potassium in man and its relation to gross body composition. in *Whole Body Counting*, International Atomic Energy Agency, Vienna, pp. 331-339, 1962.

8. Delwaide, P. A., Verly, G., Colard, J. F., and Boulenger, R. R.: Détermination du potassium total dans l'organisme. in Whole Body Counting, pp. 341-349, 1962.

9. Blahd, W. H., Cassen, B., and Lederer, Marianne: Determination of total body potassium by potassium-40 measurements in patients with muscular dystrophy and related disease. in Whole Body Counting, pp. 426-432, 1962.

10. Brozek, J.: Changes in body composition in man during maturity — their nutritional implications. *Fed. Proc.*, *11*:784-793, 1952.

11. Edelman, I. S.: Body water and electrolytes. in Techniques for Measuring Body Composition, pp. 140-154, 1961.

12. Macdonald, N. S.: Recent uses of a total body counter facility in metabolic research and clinical diagnosis with radionuclides. in Whole Body Counting, pp. 501-514, 1962.

SESSION VII, SEPTEMBER 6

COBALT METABOLISM

Chairman: BELTON A. BURROWS

21

COBALT^{60} OXIDE INHALATION

R. D. Jordan, J. S. Burkle, L. T. Brown,
J. W. Hargus and J. H. Nichols

U. S. Naval Hospital
Bethesda, Maryland

INTRODUCTION

INCREASING INDUSTRIAL, clinical and research applications of radioactive materials have made accidents involving radionuclides more common. In view of the popular lack of knowledge and fear of radioactive materials, even minor incidents creating no real health hazard may have medicolegal implications. The Radiation Exposure Evaluation Laboratory (1) is prepared to evaluate personnel actually or potentially exposed to nuclide contamination in minute amounts. The counting equipment is designed to detect and quantitate radionuclide activities several orders of magnitude below the small (0.2 to 50 μc) amounts used in routine clinical isotope studies. We do not plan to count seriously contaminated individuals in our low background room for several reasons. The possibility of contaminating the room is always present in such cases, and other less sensitive instruments are quite adequate. Dead time and pulse resolution limits of the highly sensitive low background systems are also exceeded when a patient contains more than a few hundred microcuries of activity. It appears that the application of low background counting to radiation exposure evaluation lies in two distinct areas. One is the induced activity produced by exposure to a neutron flux, and the other involves the ingestion or inhalation of relatively small amounts of gamma emitting nuclides. This paper will be concerned with the latter.

THE CASE

W. R. was a thirty year old white man. He was 6 ft. 1 in. tall, weighed 210 lb. and appeared healthy. He operated and maintained a high intensity Co^{60} 4π irradiator. The sources are rabbits that are moved pneumatically. Periodically, the rabbits must be removed and repaired, which usually involves removing the cobalt slugs. During these operations a considerable amount of Co^{60} oxide may be accumulated.

Part of the safety procedure for personnel working with the Co^{60} irradiator is whole body counting after any extensive maintenance operations. With the exception of W. R., none of the men on the unit has ever been contaminated with over 0.01 μc of Co^{60}.

In most cases, his contamination appeared to be primarily external. On April 18, 1962, the day after a particularly extensive maintenance operation, his count in the 1.07 to 1.37 Mev range was over twenty-six times the count expected from a man his size. A pulse height analysis of this count is shown in Figure 1, compared to an uncontaminated individual's spectrum. The Co^{60} masks the normal K^{40} component almost completely. The Co^{60} sum peak is evident at 2.50 Mev.

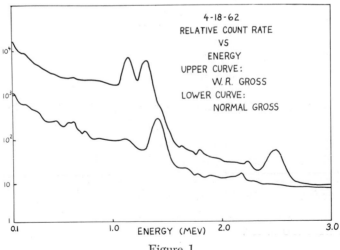

Figure 1

INSTRUMENTATION

Most of the data in this study came from a counting system with a Harshaw electrolytic copper canned 4 by 8 in. thallium-activated NaI matched window detector assembly. The 90° counting chair runs on tracks attached to the deck to insure reproducible geometry. The crystal axis passes through the apex at the bottom of the chair, and the crystal face is 50 cm. from this apex. A Nuclear Data 130 A.T. 512 channel pulse height analyzer is used to sort and store the pulses from the detector. This analyzer is also used to perform most of the mathematical operations required to analyze a count. The multichannel analyzer has Tally B.C.D. tape reader and punch accessories, in addition to oscilloscope, I.B.M. typewriter and Mosley 2D2 X-Y point plotter readout modes. We split the memory of the analyzer in half during the counts, which allows the accumulation of a 255 point spectrum. This number of points is quite adequate and leaves the other half of the memory available for background storage or for a standard source spectrum. The B.C.D. tape reader allows us to insert any spectrum we have on tape. To avoid any possible loss of information, each gross count is punched on tape immediately after the count, which requires only 40 sec. The tape accessories also provide a method for insuring reproducible energy vs. channel calibrations. A standard mixed $Cs^{137} + Co^{60}$ source and its datum tape are used for each calibration. The source is counted and its spectrum stored in one half of the memory. The datum tape is then inserted in the other half of the memory by the tape reader. The two halves of the memory are superimposed on the oscilloscope and compared.

Most data reduction, including point-by-point background stripping and component nuclide stripping, are done in the analyzer. Summations of the contents of channels under a photopeak can be done in less than 1 sec. after upper and lower limits are set. The sum can then be typed out in channel one of the analyzer.

A Nuclear Chicago model 132 B Analyzer computer with

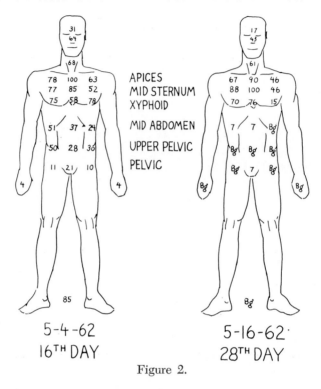

W. R. NORMALIZED DISTRIBUTION OF ACTIVITY

Figure 2.

model DS5R 3 by 3 in. NaI detector and flat field collimator were used to obtain the scans shown in Figure 2.

MEASUREMENTS

The first measurements taken after the initial detection of Co^{60} were scans using a flat field collimated 3 by 3 in. detector. These scans showed the Co^{60} to be primarily situated along the upper respiratory tract and in the right lung. There was also evidence of considerable external contamination of W. R.'s body.

These early scans gave us enough information about the Co^{60} distribution to design phantoms. The first phantoms were constructed of different sized polyethylene bottles filled with a KCl solution which closely approximated K^{40} distribution in a normal man. It was assumed that the Co^{60} burden could be approximated by two extended sources placed at the position of the lungs. Two 2 liter bottles were filled with the KCl solution and 0.92 μc of Co^{60} as $CoCl_2$. This phantom gave a calibration which indicated W. R. had a contamination equivalent to about 0.25 μc of Co^{60} in the lungs.

Another calibration obtained with a Remcal phantom with a total of 1.433 μc of Co^{60} in its lungs yielded an initial lung burden of .32 μc of Co^{60}.

W. R. was counted at the National Institutes of Health by Dr. Howard Andrews thirty-five days after contamination. His Co^{60} burden was estimated to be in the lung area, between 0.10 and 0.12 μc. This would correspond to an initial burden of 0.29 to 0.33 μc.

The values used to determine rate of clearance were obtained as follows. The sum of the gross counts in the channels under the Co^{60} photopeak was obtained from a W. R. gross spectrum. The sum of the counts in the background over the same energy range was determined. The sum of the counts of a normal man's net spectrum in the Co^{60} photopeak range was obtained. The background and normal sums were subtracted from the gross sum to obtain a net Co^{60} count.

This procedure, although somewhat time consuming, gave relatively consistent results. It corrected for contributions due to K^{40} and other naturally occurring body radionuclides, such as RaC.

Unfortunately, we do not know the exact time of exposure. We also do not know if the dose was inhaled during one short exposure or as a result of breathing a small concentration during two days. We therefore let the day after the end of the maintenance operation, time of our first count, be day zero.

RESULTS

The best estimate of the initial Co^{60} burden based on all of the determinations is 0.32 μc. The scans indicate that the material

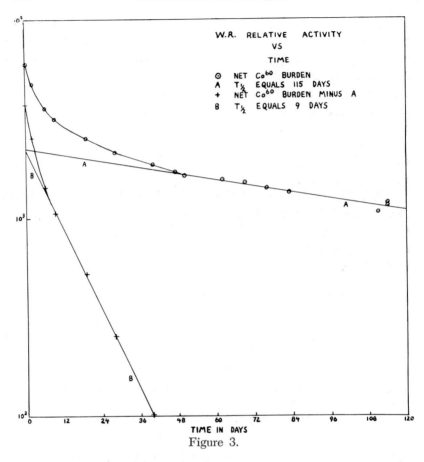

Figure 3.

is distributed along the upper and lower respiratory tract. The greatest concentration appears to be along the right bronchial tree. There is a marked decrease in the relative amount of Co^{60} in the lower torso between the 16th and 28th day. The contamination of the hands and feet on the 16th day is due to recontamination, since earlier counts showed the extremities to be nearly free of activity. To prevent further recontamination, it was necessary to replace a good deal of W. R.'s clothing and to decontaminate his home and automobile.

An analysis of the clearance curve (Fig. 3) yielded two definitely exponential contributions and an initial positive residue which may be exponential. The initial positive residue, if it is exponential, would have a half life of about 1.5 days. The mechanism corresponding to this short half life is important during the first six days. The second mechanism is apparent between the eighth and fortieth days, and has a half life of nine days. The final mechanism takes over at about the fiftieth day and is unchanged to the 114th day. The half life of the final exponential is about 115 days.

Residual activity as a function of time may be expressed by the equation

$$A = .083 \; e \; - \frac{.693t}{1.5} + .117 \; e \; - \frac{.693t}{9} + .120 \; e \; - \frac{.693t}{115} \; ,$$

where t is in days and A in μc.

DEPOSITION AND CLEARANCE

Particle size is the primary factor in determining deposition in the respiratory tract. It is improbable that particles over 10 μ in diameter enter the lung. The fraction deposited in the lower respiratory tract is greatest at about 2 μ with a minimum in the 0.2 to 0.5μ range. Particles over 5μ in diameter have a low probability of reaching the alveolar level. Particles less than 5μ in diameter, however, can be deposited throughout the entire lung and upper respiratory tract. As particle size increases from about 0.4μ where deposition is a minimum to 10 μ, the deposition for the total respiratory tract consistently increases. Particles over 10μ in diameter will not penetrate the passages to the alveoli and are deposited mainly in the upper respiratory tract, where rapid clearance mechanisms are available. Increased particle size moves the site of deposition up the respiratory tract. The filtering action of the nostrils reduces the probability of inhalation of large particles over 10μ.

Removal of particulate material from the respiratory tract is thought to involve at least four mechanisms: ciliary action, transport of soluble material across the alveolar membrane, phagocytosis and physical transport of particulates through the lung parenchyma.

DISCUSSION

An accident (2) involving the inhalation of Co^{60} oxide at Argonne National Laboratory gave results in reasonable agreement to ours. Two men who were decontaminating the ductwork of a hood, in which neutron irradiated cobalt metal had been cleaned with a wire brush, each inhaled approximately 0.5 μc of Co^{60} oxide.

"From the results of whole body counting, the cobalt disappeared from the lung with a biological half life of 1.6 days from the second to the seventh day after the exposure, and with a forty-two day half life from the seventeenth to the fiftieth day. The half life gradually increased to about 110 days, three months after the initial exposure. At that time, the body burden was about .05 μc and the bulk of the cobalt was probably in the liver."

The 1.6 and 110 day half lives are in excellent agreement with the 1.5 and 115 day values obtained by reducing the clearance curve to a sum of exponential functions. The half life for the seventeenth to fiftieth day of forty-two days does not correspond to any of our separate exponential values. However, the slope of our clearance curve would correspond to a forty-five day half life on the twenty-second day which is in good agreement with the forty-second day value from Argonne.

Because of difficulties in obtaining adequate specimens, we were unable to secure any reliable information about the cobalt excretion in urine and feces. The Argonne group obtained good data on both. In their experience, urinary cobalt excretion was greatest in the sample collected a few hours after exposure and decreased by a factor of 5 in one case and 10 in the other, between the first and second day. A total of 10 to 20 percent of the eliminated cobalt was found in the urine. Two thirds of the urinary cobalt was eliminated the first day.

The fecal to urine cobalt ratio was low on the first day but increased to 150 in two to five days after exposure and was 2.5 on the twenty-nineth day.

CONCLUSIONS

It is apparent that our patient and the two cases reported by Argonne followed similar clearance mechanisms. Representation of the disappearance curve by three exponentials supports the hypothesis of multiple mechanisms for the clearance of particle matter from the lungs.

An examination of the area in which W. R. was contaminated revealed a wide distribution of particle sizes, from pieces large enough to pick up to extremely fine dust. These observations were confirmed (in view of the deposition model proposed) by the distribution in the upper and lower respiratory tract as shown by our scans.

It is not possible at this time to associate a specific mechanism of removal with a particular half life component with any certainty. It is, however, possible that the 1.5 day half life mechanism is due to ciliary action. The other longer half lives could well be the result of phagocytosis, solubilization and transport or physical transport through the lung parenchyma. There is also some evidence of translocation to the liver, particularly from the Argonne group.

REFERENCES

1. King, E. R., and Mitchell, T. G.: *Radioactivity In Man, The United States Naval Radiation Exposure Evaluation Center.* Springfield, Thomas, p. 129-144, 1961.
2. Sedlet, J., Robinson, J., and Fairman, W.: A cobalt and tritium incident at Argonne National Laboratory. Proceedings at the 4th Annual Meeting on Bioassay and Analytical Chemistry.

22

METABOLISM OF Co^{60} AND Co^{58}-LABELED VITAMIN B$_{12}$ IN HUMANS AND RATS[1]

H. C. Heinrich

Universität Hamburg
Hamburg, Germany

A LARGE MULTIPURPOSE WHOLE BODY DETECTOR WITH A LIQUID ORGANIC SCINTILLATOR IN MODULES AND A NaI CRYSTAL

OUR EARLIER INVESTIGATIONS on vitamin B$_{12}$ metabolism in man and rats were performed with the GENCO (Geneva Counter), a vertical walk-in 2π detector with a liquid organic scintillator designed by the Los Alamos National Laboratory for the Second Geneva Conference on the Peaceful Uses of Atomic Energy and installed in 1959 at the U. S. Hospital for Europe at Landstuhl/Pfalz.

In 1961 a new modular horizontal large volume 4π detector with liquid organic scintillators combined with a large NaI crystal detector was designed with F. N. Hayes (Los Alamos Scientific Laboratories) and the Packard Instrument Company.

4π Large Volume Detector with Liquid Organic Scintillators
The patient or sample is placed in a plastic sling suspended in a 210 cm. long and 57 cm. wide frame made of old steel, which is pushed into the counting well by a motor. The counting well is 60 cm. in diameter and 200 cm. long and is surrounded by a minimum thickness of 25 cm. liquid organic scintillator. The total of 1360 liters of liquid scintillator is in eight 2π module semirings and is viewed by 16 K 1328 photomultipliers.

[1] Supported by a grant from the Deutsche Forschungsgemeinschaft.

In each 2π module semiring a light shutter is mounted between the two photomultipliers so that the 170 liter scintillator volume can be separated into two 85 liter compartments viewed by a single photomultiplier. Such an adjustment (closed light shutter) is practical for the balancing of the sixteen photomultipliers (one photomultiplier per one scintillator compartment) and for reducing the over-all efficiency if hot samples or persons have to be counted. With open light shutters the two photomultipliers of the 170 liter 2π module semiring can be operated in time coincidence which cuts down photomultiplier noise and permits measurements in a lower energy range, especially interesting for Bremsstrahl counting. The ratio of photocathode area to total wall area is 7.9 per cent for the 85 liter compartment (2π module semiring with closed light shutter) and 8.7 per cent for the 170 liter compartment (2π module semiring with open light shutter).

The pulses from the preamplifiers (gain 10) of the sixteen large photomultipliers are either analyzed in a multichannel analyzer-computer or counted after amplification in a four channel analyzer-scaler.

The module units contain a premixed high flash point (60 to 66°C) liquid organic scintillator of the Arapahoe Chemicals, Inc. It contains 5 gm./liter diphenyloxazole (PPO) as the primary solute and 0.5 gm./liter 1,4-di[2-(4-methyl, 5-phenyl-oxazolyl)] -benzene (= dimethyl-POPOP) as the secondary solute or wave length shifter in a mixture of aromatic hydrocarbons ($C_{10}H_{14}$-$C_{11}H_{16}$ with a density of 0.865 to 0.883).

Optical transparency (410 to 450 nm.) and relative pulse height are approximately identical with that of a comparable solution of the two solutes in reagent grade toluene. The fluorescence spectrum of the secondary solute (dimethyl-POPOP) has its maximum at about 430 nm. and matches the spectral S 11- response maximum (at about 440 nm.) of the large photomultiplier tubes.

NaI(Tl) Crystal Detector

A matched window line assembly made of a 5 by 5 in.

NaI(Tl) crystal and a single selected RCA #8055 5 in. Ø photo-multiplier is used as a crystal detector. The crystal is canned in 0.018 in. stainless steel, and a mu-metal magnetic shield is used for the photomultiplier. The crystal detector is mounted on a semiring type crystal carrier which can be moved on the sling frame over a total distance of about 150 cm. horizontally over the patient or test sample.

The pulses from the crystal preamplifier (gain:25) are either analyzed by a 512 channel analyzer-computer or counted in a two channel analyzer-scaler.

The pulses from the large volume liquid scintillator detector and the 5 by 5 in. NaI crystal are used together with coincidence and/or anticoincidence circuitries so that the liquid scintillation detector has the function of an anti-coincidence external back-ground umbrella or can be used to detect the escape radiation from the large NaI crystal. The detectors together can form a Compton or anti-coincidence spectrometer.

Shielding

The whole liquid scintillation detector unit is shielded by about 55 metric tons of preatomic age steel with 15 cm. thick naval armorplates used to construct a steel room 215 cm. long by 160 cm. broad by 170 cm. high inside. An additional 5 cm. thick blind frame is used to cover the slits. Four hinged doors provide access for installation, servicing and calibration.

The NaI crystal detector gets its shielding from the 15 (+5) cm. of steel plus the 25 cm. minimum thickness of the liquid scintillator. In addition the liquid scintillator can be used as an anti-coincidence umbrella for the large crystal.

Whole Body Counting Conditions

Humans, large animals or samples of 100 to 446 liters were measured with all eight 2π module semirings (200 cm. long 4π detector). For smaller samples with volumes of 10 to 100 liters, only two consecutive 4π module rings (100 cm. long 4π detector) were used by switching off (on the signal distribution unit) the pulses coming from the eight remaining photomultipliers. Small samples with volumes up to about 10 liters were counted in the single 50 cm. long 4π module ring.

Some typical background and Co^{60} over-all efficiency values observed under routine conditions with different counting geometries are summarized in Table I.

TABLE I

Typical Background and Over-all Efficiencies for Co^{60} Integral Counting with Different Counting Geometries of Modular Detector with Liquid Organic Scintillators

Counting Geometry	Sample Size	Over-all Efficiency for Co^{60} (%)	Background (cps)	(Over-all Efficiency)^2/ Background
4π 50 cm.	up to 10 liters	50	250 ± 1	10.0
4π 100 cm.	up to 100 liters	80	1020 ± 3	6.3
4π 200 cm.	up to 200 liters	80	1020 ± 3	6.3
4π 200 cm.	human beings (70 kg.)	55-60-65	1020 ± 3	3.5

In humans and rats studied a few days to several months, about 10 nc of Co^{60} are sufficient; whereas for studies of several months to years 20 nc of Co^{60} are recommended.

Counting periods of three times 100 seconds were used with net count rates of $\geqq 100$ cps; whereas activities of 10 to 100 net cps were counted thrice for 300 seconds. The background showed stability of better than ± 0.5 percent for several hours.

THE RADIO-VITAMIN B_{12} ABSORPTION WHOLE BODY RETENTION TEST

The use of cobalt-labeled vitamin B_{12} within different forms of radio-vitamin B_{12} absorption tests is important for the diagnosis of several hematological, neurological and gastrointestinal diseases and has gained a world wide application during the last ten years (1).

Since in many clinical laboratories only NaI well-type scintillation detectors with a small well-counting volume are available, only low values for the ratio efficiency^2/background can be obtained for urine or blood volumes of 3 to 20 ml. (0.02 to 0.62 $\frac{\text{cpm}}{\text{pc/ml}^2}$)(2). Therefore relatively large amounts of radioactivity (e.g., 500 nc of Co^{60}-labeled vitamin B_{12}) are required for the radio-vitamin B_{12} absorption urinary and fecal excretion test and 1 μc for the blood concentration test. The additional biological radiation burden associated with such test doses of Co^{60} is 2 to 5 mrem per week (3) within the range of the natural radiation burden of the human body from endogenous and exogenous sources (about 5.5 mrem per week), and therefore suggests some restrictions in the diagnostic application of the vitamin B_{12} absorption tests in situations of increased radiation sensitivity (e.g., during pregnancy, childhood, etc.).

In order to reduce the additional radiation burden which is offered to the patient with the diagnostic application of α-emitting radionuclides and to avoid concentration procedures for urine or feces, a combined ring-beaker-well-type NaI scintillation detector was designed and used with an efficiency^2/background ratio of 149.0 for volumes of 1500 ml (2). With this detector it was possible to reduce the test dose of Co^{60} to 50 to 100 nc and the additional radiation burden to 0.2 mrem per week for the Co^{60}-B_{12} absorption urinary excretion test and 0.35 mrem per week for the Co^{60}-B_{12} absorption fecal excretion test.

With large whole body radioactivity detectors and liquid organic scintillators, it became possible to develop a very sensitive and convenient radio vitamin B_{12} absorption whole body retention test, which requires only a test dose of 10 nc Co^{60} vitamin B_{12} corresponding to an additional radiation burden of only 0.05 mrem per week or 1 percent of the natural radiation burden of the human body. Another practical advantage of the whole body retention test for the absorbed vitamin B_{12} is that the often unreliable collection of excreta and unpleasant procedures for preparation of the counting sample are no longer required.

The over-all efficiency within a 200 cm. long and 60 cm. free diameter 4π detector with 1360 liters of a liquid organic scintillator for Co^{60} is very high (80 percent for a point source and a source of several liters and 55 to 65 percent for humans of different weight and size) and the background with about 1000 cps very stable (better than ± 0.3 percent standard error). Therefore only short counting periods of three times 100 seconds are required even if small amounts of Co^{60}-vitamin B_{12} (10 to 20 nc) are administered.

The following procedure was used with the whole body detector with a liquid organic scintillator for radio-vitamin B_{12} absorption whole body retention test (4, 5).

With the *first measurment,* the γ-radioactivity background in the body of the test person is estimated within thrice 100 seconds. This endogenous body α radioactivity results partly from the natural 13 nc K^{40} γ-radioactivity of the body potassium (31.46 dps K^{40} per gm. K) which gives for a 70 kg. standard man with 140 gm. K a total of 4405 dps K^{40}. Since only 11 per cent of K^{40} decays through electron capture with consequent α emission, the 70 kg. standard man emits 140 x 3.46 α ps/gm.K = 484.6α pS. The other considerable source of the γ body background of persons is the world-wide endogenous contamination with Cs^{137} from nuclear weapon fallout which in 1959 and 1962 was 10 to 13 nc. or 310 to 400 α pS Cs^{137}. Depending on the patient's weight and body length, the over-all efficiency for Co^{60}, K^{40} and Cs^{137} shows a variation of about ± 10 percent in the 200 cm. long 4π detector. The body background radioactivity was 150 to 350 cps if a broad channel setting (~100 kev − 3 Mev) was used. Since the amount of the diagnostic Co^{60} α radioactivity is within 10 to 20 nc (370 to 740 dps) in the same range as the sum of the natural K^{40} and contamining Cs^{137} body background radioactivity (800 to 900 dps), it is important to have an accurate measurement for body background radioactivity which remains constant for several weeks and has to be subtracted from the following measurements. The estimation of the patient's body background radioactivity also excludes possible radioactive contamination from earlier diagnostic or therapeutic procedures.

We calibrated 0.10 to 1.0 μg. of labeled CN-DMBC (with 10 to 20 nc of Co^{58} or Co^{60}) in a NaI scintillation well-type detector and used it to check the whole body detector. The radioactive test dose is then administered to the test person, who is afterwards measured (thrice 100 seconds) in the whole body detector

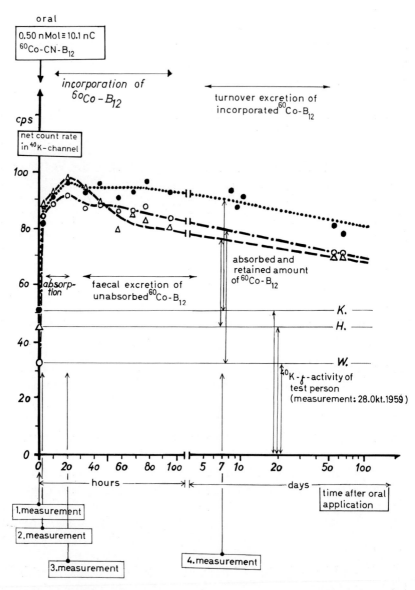

Figure 1. Principal description of the Co[60]-vitamin B_{12} absorption whole body retention test. Net count rate in the K[40] channel of the 2π GENCO at different stages after oral uptake of 0.50 nMol (10.1 nc) Co[60]-CN-DMBC.

to ensure complete oral uptake of the diagnostic test dose (*second measurement*).

About 10 hours after oral uptake a maximum value for the patient's net count rate increase is obtained (Fig. 1) and used as the whole body retention 100 percent value (*third measurement*), since at this moment all the radioactive test dose is still within the patient's body. The unabsorbed radioactive vitamin B_{12} is still within the content of the ileum and colon, whereas the absorbed labeled vitamin B_{12} is already in the storage organs and tissues or in the circulation.

The patient's net count rate increase is then decreasing together with the fecal excretion of the unabsorbed labeled vitamin B_{12}. As soon as the fecal excretion of the unabsorbed radiovitamin B_{12} is completed, the patient's net count rate increase will remain constant for at least several days (before the whole body turnover rate of the absorbed radioactive vitamin B_{12} becomes measurable). At about the seventh day after the oral uptake of the diagnostic vitamin B_{12} test dose, the *fourth and last measurement* (three times 100 seconds) is performed.

The intestinal absorption is then calculated from the ratio:

$$\frac{\text{patient's net count rate increase at 7th day} \times 100}{\substack{\text{patient's net count rate increase maximum}\\\text{10 hours after oral } Co^{60}\text{-}B_{12} \text{ application}}} = \substack{\text{intestinal } Co^{60}\text{-}B_{12} \text{ absorption or } Co^{60}\text{-}B_{12} \text{ whole body retention}\\ (\text{in } \% \text{ of test dose})$$

The absorption values obtained with the whole body retention test are in perfect agreement with the results of the simultaneously performed fecal excretion test (Table II and III). The feces were measured daily within a 50 cm. long 4π module ring of the whole body detector (background 250 cps, Co^{60} over-all efficiency for several liter volumes 50 per cent).

Since the additional radiation burden resulting from a 10 nc Co^{60}-B_{12} test dose is only 1 percent of the natural radiation burden, the whole body retention test can be repeated often. For each new absorption or retention test, the patient's net count rate resulting from the retained Co^{60}-vitamin B_{12} from the earlier test plus the constant K^{40} content and Cs^{137} contamination has to be estimated and used.

TABLE II

RESULTS OF A WHOLE BODY RETENTION TEST AND FECAL EXCRETION TEST FOR Co⁶⁰-VITAMIN B₁₂ ABSORPTION IN A NORMAL HUMAN BEING.

Date	Co^{60}-B_{12} Whole Body Retention Test				Co^{60}-B_{12} Fecal Excretion Test		
	Net Count Rate (cps)	Net Count Rate Increase (cps)	Radioactivity Increase (dps)	W B R (%)	Co^{60}-B_{12} Fecal Excretion (cps)	(dps)	(% of Test Dose)
17.5	189	—	—		5	—	—
20.5	191				4	—	—
21.5 9:26	190 = patients body background radioactivity				2	—	—
21.5 9:35	0.50 nMol Co^{60}-B_{12} = 660 dps oral test dose				—	—	—
21.5 9:45	604	414	641	—	2	—	—
22.5	616	426	660	100	2	—	—
23.5	—	—	—	—	64	127	19.0
24.5	488	298	462	70.0	43	84	12.7
25.5	475	285	442	66.9	13	26	3.9
26.5	—	—	—	—	—	—	—
27.5	476	286	443	67.1	2	—	—
28.5	476	286	443	67.1	0	—	—
29.5	464	274	424	64.3	2	—	—
after 7 days	Intestinal Absorption = W B R = 64.3%				Total fecal excretion = 35.6% Intestinal absorption = 64.4%		

TABLE III

Results of a Whole Body Rentention Test and Fecal Excretion Test for Co⁶⁰-Vitamin B₁₂ Absorption in a Patient with Pernicious Anemia in Remission.
(Test A without and Test B with intrinsic factor)

Date	Co^{60}-B_{12} Whole Body Retention Test — Patient Net Count Rate (cps)	Net Count Rate Increase (cps)	Patient Radioactivity Increase (dps)	WBR (%)	Co^{60}-B_{12} Fecal Excretion Test — Co^{60}-B_{12} Fecal Excretion (cps)	Co^{60}-B_{12} Fecal Excretion (dps)	(% of Test Dose)
26.4 8:42	321 = patient's body background radioactivity						
26.4 8:55	0.50 nMol Co^{60}-B_{12} = 668 dps oral test dose						
A) 26.4 9:07	712	391	670	100	—	—	—
27.4	688	367	629	93.9	—	—	—
28.4	—	—	—	—	42	82	12.7
29.4	634	313	537	80.1	144	280	43.2
30.4	500	179	307	45.8	149	292	45.1
1.5	—	—	—	—	—	—	—
2.5	343	22	38	5.6	10	19	2.9
3.5	327	6	10	1.5	4	—	—
4.5	328	7	12	1.8	1	—	—
5.5	—	—	—	—	—	—	—
6.5	310	0	0	0.0	1	—	—
after 7-10 days	Intestinal Absorption = WBR =	=		0%	Total Fecal Excretion = 103.9%; Intestinal Absorption = 0 %		
7.5 8:51	305 = patients body background radioactivity						
7.5 9:00	0.50 nMol Co^{60}-CN-B_{12} = 670 dps oral test dose + 10 mg Intrinsic Factor—Concentrate						
B) 7.5 9:09	670	365	670	100	—	—	—
8.5	692	387	670	100	5	—	—
9.5	686	381	659	98.4	61	124	18.6
10.5	609	304	526	78.5	44	92	13.8
11.5	592	287	497	74.2	5	—	—
12.5	—	—	—	—	—	—	—
13.5	583	278	481	71.8	4	—	—
14.5	570	265	458	68.4	3	—	—
after 7 days	Intestinal Absorption = WBR =	=		68.4%	Total Fecal Excretion = 32.4%; Intestinal Absorption = 67.6%		

MAXIMUM PERMISSIBLE RADIO-VITAMIN B_{12} INCORPORATION FOR HUMANS AND BIOLOGICAL RADIATION BURDEN FOR THE RADIO-VITAMIN B_{12} ABSORPTION WHOLE BODY RETENTION TEST

The liver cannot be considered the only critical organ for radioactive vitamin B_{12} since microbiological studies have shown that in normal adult men about 1.8 mg. vitamin B_{12} is stored in the liver and about 3 mg. in the skeletal muscles (6). After oral or parenteral application of radioactive vitamin B_{12}, only about 20 to 50 percent of the test dose is incorporated into the liver. Therefore the whole body will be considered as the critical organ.

The maximum permissible incorporation radioactivity for the human body was calculated from

$$q = \frac{2.8 \cdot 10^{-3} \cdot m \cdot R}{f \cdot \varepsilon} \qquad (1)$$

which becomes

$$q = \frac{19.6}{\varepsilon} \qquad (2)$$

if the whole body ($m = 7 \cdot 10^4 g$) is the critical organ and $f = 1$.

q = maximum permissible incorporation radioactivity for the human body (in μc).

m = mass of the critical organ (in gm.); for the standard man, $m = 7 \cdot 10^4$ gm.

R = permissible biological radiation burden (in rem/week); 0.1 rem/week for the whole body.

f = fraction of the incorporation radioactivity in the critical organ in relation to that in the whole body; $f = 1$ if the whole body is the critical organ.

ε = effective absorbed energy per disintegration of a radio-nuclide (in Mev). The values for the cobalt isotopes are given in Table IV.

By conversion of equation (1) and using the whole body values for m and f, the radiation burden of the human body can be calculated from (3)

TABLE IV

EFFECTIVE ABSORBED ENERGY, MAXIMUM PERMISSIBLE INCORPORATION RADIO-
ACTIVITY AND BIOLOGICAL RADIATION BURDEN FOR RADIOCOBALT ISOTOPES

Radio Cobalt Isotopes	Effective Absorbed Energy (Mev)	Maximum Permissible Incorporation Radioactivity (μc/Whole Body)	Biological Radiation Burden from Maximum Permissible Incorporation Radioactivity (rem/week)
56	1.0	10	0.097
57	0.09	200	0.092
58	0.61	30	0.093
60	1.5	10	0.077

$$R(\text{rem/week}) = \frac{1 \cdot \varepsilon \cdot \mu c}{2.8 \cdot 10^{-3} \times 7 \cdot 10^{-4}} = \frac{\varepsilon \cdot \mu c}{196} \quad (3)$$

The calculated effective absorbed energies, maximum permissible incorporation radioactivities and biological radiation burdens are summarized for the four radiocobalt isotopes (4).

The biological radiation burdens from the maximum permissible incorporation radioactivities of the different radiocobalt isotopes are still below the maximum permissible radiation burden for human beings (0.1 rem/week).

For the five different diagnostic radio-vitamin B_{12} absorption tests, data like the minimal Co^{60} test radioactivity, whole body retention in per cent of maximum permissible Co^{60} incorporation radioactivity and resulting biological radiation burden are summarized together with other advantages and disadvantages of the five tests in Table V.

Through the use of whole body radioactivity detectors with organic scintillators it became possible to develop a very sensitive and convenient radio-vitamin B_{12} absorption whole body retention test. With this new test the amount of radioactivity usually required in clinical radio-vitamin B_{12} diagnosis (e.g., 0.2 to 1 μc Co^{60}) can be reduced to 0.01 μc Co^{60}-vitamin B_{12}. Therefore the biological radiation burden from a diagnostic Co^{60}-vitamin B_{12} absorption test can be lowered from 1 to 5 mrem/week down to 50 μrem/week (Table V).

It is thereby possible for the first time to work in the diagnostic application of radioisotopes with test radioactivities which

[+] In parenthesis are given the values for NaI scintillation well-type or end-to-end-type detectors with a poor $\frac{\text{over-all efficiency}^2}{\text{background}}$ value ($<$1-10 $\frac{\text{cpm}}{(\text{pc/ml})^2}$), whereas the values before the brackets are based on measurements with a sensitive ring-beaker scintillation detector and an $\frac{\text{over-all efficiency}^2}{\text{background}}$ ratio of 149 $\frac{\text{cpm}}{(\text{pc/ml})^2}$.

TABLE V

SURVEY ON ADVANTAGES AND DISADVANTAGES OF THE FIVE DIAGNOSTIC Co^{60}-VITAMIN B_{12} ABSORPTION TESTS

Diagnostic Co^{60}-Vitamin B_{12} Absorption Test	Fecal Excretion Test	Urine Excretion Test	Blood Concentration Test	Liver Incorporation Test	Whole Body Retention Test
whole body retention in % of maximum permissible Co^{60}-incorporation radioactivity ($= 10\ \mu c$)+)	0.35(3.5)	0.2(2.0)	7	1.4(4.2)	0.07
Biological radiation burden from retained Co^{60}-B_{12}^+ (in mrem/week) ($10\mu c = 77$ mrem/week)	0.27(2.7)	0.15(1.5)	5.4	1.1(3.3)	0.05
test influences B_{12} metabolism	no	yes	no	no	no
minimum Co^{60}-B_{12} test radioactivity applied (nc) / retained (nc)	50(500) / 35(350)	50(500) / 20(200)	1000 / 700	200(600) / 140(420)	10 / 7
quantitative test for B_{12} absorption	yes	limited	no	no	yes
possible errors	lost feces	lost urine	no	reproducibility of counting geometry	no
invalidation	—	kidney diseases	—	liver diseases	—
counting technique	in vitro	in vitro	in vitro	in vivo	in vivo
counting sample	feces	urine	blood	liver	whole body
required time (in days)	5 - 7	2 - 3	0.5	5 - 7	5 - 7

TABLE VI

COMPARISON OF RADIATION BURDENS FOR HUMANS FROM NATURAL EXOGENEOUS AND ENDOGENEOUS SOURCES, ENDOGENEOUS CONTAMINATION FROM NUCLEAR WEAPON FALLOUT AS WELL AS FROM A DIAGNOSTIC Co^{60}-VITAMIN B_{12} ABSORPTION WHOLE BODY RETENTION TEST

Origin of Radiation	Whole Body Radioactivity Content (nc)	Biological Radiation Burden (mrem/week)
Exogeneous Radiation, natural		$\sim$2.7
cosmic radiation	—	0.67
other environmental radiation		2
Endogeneous Radioactivity, natural		$\sim$2.4
Ra^{226} (222$\bullet$10^{10} dpm/gm. Ra)	0.1	1
Rn^{222} decay products		
140 gm.K $=$ K^{40} (1888 dpm/gm.K)	119 (100%)	$\sim$1
	106 (89% β-)	
	13 (11% EC+γ)	
12600 gm.C $=$ C^{14}(15 dpm/gm.C)	85	0.019
Endogeneous Contamination from Nuclear Weapon Fall Out		
Cs^{137}	1 - 10	0.04 - 0.4
Sr^{90}	10	0.02
Endogeneous Radioactivity from a diagnostic 10 nc Co^{60}-B_{12} Absorption Test	7	0.05

produce an additional radiation burden equal to about 1 percent of the natural radiation burden of the human body from endogenous and exogenous sources (5.5 mrem/week, Table VI). Only about 0.07 percent of the maximum permissible Co^{60}-incorporation radioactivity ($=$ 10μc Co^{60}) are retained in the human body after an oral 10 nc Co^{60}-B_{12} absorption whole body retention test.

No more restrictions in the diagnostic application of γ-emitting radionuclides during pregnancy, childhood and other radiation-sensitive situations are any longer necessary if the sensitive whole body detectors with liquid organic scintillators are available.

METABOLIC TURNOVER OF Co⁶⁰-LABELED 5,6-DIMETHYLBENZIMIDAZOLYL-CYANO-COBAMID (= CN-DMBC) AND Co⁶⁰-LABELED 5, 6-DIMETHYLBENZIMIDAZOLYL-C'₅-DEOXYADENOSYL-COBAMID = DMBC-COENZYME) IN RATS

Recent studies have demonstrated that cyanocobalamin (= CN-DMBC) is not identical with the native form of vitamin B_{12} and does not exist in animal and microbial sources of this vitamin. The C'_5-deoxyadenosyl-DMBC is considered not only the metabolically active vitamin B_{12} form (vitamin B_{12}-coenzyme), but also the only known native storage form of the B_{12} vitamins in animals and man (7,8).

It was therefore of interest to investigate how far the *in vivo* turnover rates of the CN-DMBC and C'_5-deoxyadenosyl-DMBC are primarily different in mammals and become finally identical after a possible conversion of one compound into the other.

In 80 Sprague-Dawley rats, the whole body retention and excretion of the Co⁶⁰-label was measured after intraperitoneal injection and intestinal absorption of Co⁶⁰-DMBC-coenzyme and Co⁶⁰-CN-DMBC over more than 160 days.

For estimation of the Co⁶⁰ radioactivity content in the total body of the surviving rats and in their pooled excreta, a new whole body detector with liquid organic scintillators was used. To get the highest possible value for the ratio efficiency[2]/background, when samples of the size of a rat or their collected excreta are counted, only one fourth of the 200 cm. long 4π detector tank was used. Within this 50 cm. long 4π ring module, point sources and extended sources up to 10 liters gave a Co⁶⁰ over-all efficiency of about 50 percent with a background of 250 cps if the spectrometer was used in the integral position with a low baseline discriminator setting. For each measurement of a single rat, a counting time of thrice 100 seconds was sufficient. The average and standard deviation for each group of ten animals were calculated (Figs. 2 and 5). As soon as the relative total body retention was following the final exponential function (usually after 60 to 80 days), the groups of ten rats were measured together once or twice a week. For this purpose two 4π ring modules, which gave a 100 cm. long 4π detector, were used. With a background of 510 cps an over-all efficiency of 70 percent was obtained.

The whole body vitamin B_{12} pool of rats was calculated from the results of the microbiological assay of the vitamin B_{12} content in the organs and tissues of ten rats. Escherichia coli 113-3 was used as the test organism. A range of 15 to 23 with an average of 20 μg. B_{12} was obtained as the whole body vitamin B_{12} content of the rats which weighed 200 to 250 gm.

Biological Half Life and Turnover Rate of Intraperitoneally Injected DMBC-Coenzyme and CN-DMBC in Rats

Figure 2 shows the curves for the relative whole body retention and fecal excretion of the Co^{60}-label observed over 124 days after intraperitoneal injection of 100 pMol (= 20.0 nc) Co^{60}-CN-DMBC to 10 rats (No. 732-741) and 100 pMol (= 19.9 nc) Co^{60}-DMBC-coenzyme in 10 rats (No. 742-751). The average ($\bar{m}$) and standard deviation ($\pm$ s) are given for each group in the single measuring points.

The exponential functions which describe the curves between the first and the 150th day were estimated from the semilogarithmic presentation of the relative whole body retention curve (Fig. 3) and used for the calculation of the biological half life of the DMBC-coenzyme and CN-DMBC. The initial functions for the CN-DMBC (f_1 with 1.2 days and f_2 with 7.5 days for the biological half life) and DMBC-coenzyme (f_1 with 8.5 days) are of no practical biological interest since the tracer dose of the B_{12} analogue is not yet in equilibrium with the whole body pool of the rat (about 20 μg. B_{12}). The pool size in the compartment which is at the particular moment in equilibrium with the tracer dose is not yet known.

The final functions can be used however for the calculation of the biological half life T $\frac{1}{2}$, since the biological half life remains constant as soon as equilibrium between the Co^{60}-B_{12} tracer dose and the whole body B_{12} pool of the rat is obtained. About 72 percent of the injected Co^{60}-DMBC-coenzyme follows the

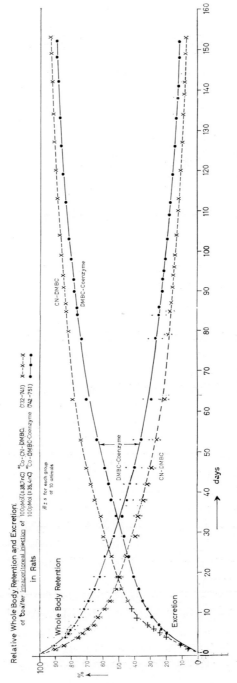

Figure. 2. Relative whole body retention and excretion of Co⁶⁰-label in rats to 150 days after intraperitoneal injection of 100 pMol (38.7 nc) Co⁶⁰-CN-DMBC and 100 pMol (35.4 nc) Co⁶⁰-DMBC-coenzyme.

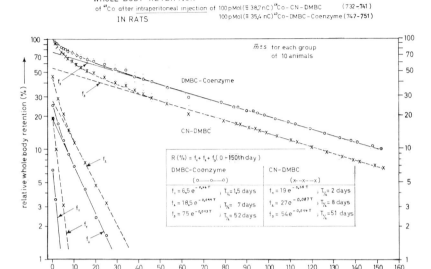

Figure 3. Exponential functions for the relative whole body retention of the Co^{60} label in rats between the 1st and 150th day after intraperitoneal injection of 100 pMol Co^{60}-CN-DMBC and Co^{60}-DMBC-coenzyme.

final function $f_2 = 72 \cdot e^{-0.013 \, T}$ with a final biological half life of fifty-two days, whereas the retention of 57 percent of the injected Co^{60}-CN-DMBC can be described by $f_3 = 57 \cdot e^{-0.014T}$ resulting in a final biological half life of fifty-one days.

Between the 60th and 124th day after intraperitoneal injection, a constant biological half life of fifty-one days for the Co^{60}-CN-DMBC and fifty-two days for the Co^{60}-DMBC-coenzyme was observed (Fig. 4 and Table VII). The corresponding turn-over times (biological half life/ln 2) were 70.6 and seventy-five days.

The whole body vitamin B$_{12}$ content of the rat was estimated with the E. coli 113-3-assay and found to be about 20 μg. B$_{12}$. From this whole body B$_{12}$ pool size and the turnover times for the CN-DMBC and DMBC-coenzyme, the turnover rates were calculated. (Pool = turnover rate $\times$ turnover time.) Between 60 and 100 days after intraperitoneal injection in rats a final turnover rate of 0.28 μg./day or 1.42 per cent of the whole body B_{12} pool per day for the CN-DMBC and 0.27 μg./day or 1.34 percent of the whole body B_{12} pool per day for the DMBC-coenzyme was obtained (Fig. 4, and Tables VII and VIII).

The experiment was repeated with twenty three-month-old rats and with the same results as with the six-month-old rats.

It is evident from the relative whole body retention and biological half life curves, that the CN-DMBC has a significantly

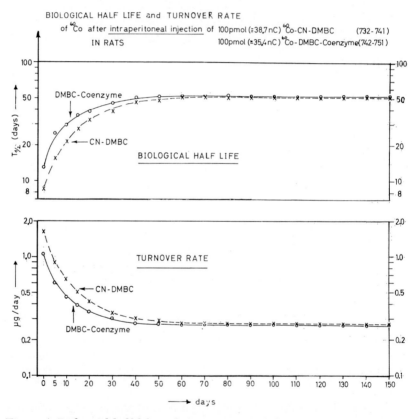

Figure 4. Biological half life and turnover rate of the Co^{60} label in rats between the 1st and 150th day after intraperitoneal injection of 100 pMol Co^{60}-CN-DMBC and Co^{60}-DMBC-coenzyme, respectively. Turnover rate values are only realistic beyond the 50th day; then equilibrium is obtained between the Co^{60}-B_{12} tracer dose and the whole body vitamin B_{12} pool (= 20 μg.).

TABLE VII

Biological Half Life and Turnover Rate of Absorbed and Injected Co^{60}-CN-DMBC and Co^{60}-DMBC-Coenzyme in Rats in Relation to Elapsed Incorporation Time Turnover Rate Values are only Realistic Beyond the 50th to 60th Day, since then Equilibrium is Obtained Between the Co^{60}-B$_{12}$ Tracer Dose and the Whole Body Vitamin B$_{12}$ Pool (= 20 µg.) of the Rat

Days after Intestinal Absorption or Intra-peritoneal Injection	Intraperitoneal Injection				Intestinal Absorption			
	CN-DMBC (Rats No. 732-741)		DMBC-Coenzyme (Rats No. 742-751)		CN-DMBC (Rats No. 752-761)		DMBC-Coenzyme (Rats No. 762-771)	
	Biol. Half Life (Days)	Turnover Rate (µg./day)	Biol. Half Life (Days)	Turnover Rate (µg./day)	Biol. Half Life (Days)	Turnover Rate (µg./day)	Biol. Half Life (Days)	Turnover Rate (µg./day)
0	8.5	1.63	10.5	1.32	—	—	—	—
5	15	0.93	25	0.56	22	0.63	25	0.56
10	24	0.58	30.5	0.46	26	0.53	31.5	0.44
15	28	0.50	35	0.40	29	0.48	34	0.41
20	33	0.42	38	0.37	34	0.41	40	0.35
30	37.5	0.37	45	0.31	41	0.34	45	0.31
40	41	0.34	48	0.29	43	0.32	47	0.30
50	48	0.29	52	0.27	45.5	0.31	49	0.28
60	51	0.27	52	0.27	49	0.28	49	0.28
70	51	0.27	52	0.27	49	0.28	49	0.28
80	51	0.27	52	0.27	49	0.28	49	0.28
90	51	0.27	52	0.27	49	0.28	49	0.28
100	51	0.27	52	0.27	49	0.28	49	0.28
120	51	0.27	52	0.27	49	0.28	49	0.28
140	51	0.27	52	0.27	49	0.28	49	0.28
160	51	0.27	52	0.27	49	0.28	49	0.28

shorter biological half life and therefore higher turnover during the first two months after intraperitoneal injection to rats. After this the biological half lifes and turnover rates for the CN-DMBC and DMBC-coenzyme approach and are finally identical (Fig. 4, Table VII).

One possible explanation for this could be that the injected CN-DMBC is converted after one month into the DMBC-coenzyme and then has nearly the same biological half life and turnover rate in the rat.

Biological Half Life and Turnover Rate of Absorbed DMBC-Coenzyme and CN-DMBC in Rats

After oral application of the labeled B_{12} analogues, it is necessary to wait till all the unabsorbed radio-B_{12} analogues have left the gut of the rats. The fecal excretion of the unabsorbed Co^{60}-B_{12} analogues is complete after about two to four days. Therefore the 7th day after oral administration was used as the 100 percent reference point for the whole body retention (Fig. 5).

Six-month-old Sprague-Dawley rats (10 animals in each group) received a total of 100 pMol Co^{60}-DMBC-coenzyme and Co^{60}-CN-DMBC, respectively, in two separate doses of 50 pMol with 18.3 nc/50 pMol and 19.7 nc/50 pMol, respectively, at an interval of eight hours to be in a more efficient absorption range. The relative whole body retention and fecal excretion curves for the two groups of rats are presented in Figure 5 for about 130 days.

The semilogarithmic presentation of the relative whole body retention was again used for the estimation of the exponential functions which formed the basis for the calculation of the biological half life (Fig. 6). Not taking into consideration the insignificant initial functions f_1 and f_2, it was estimated that about 79 percent of the absorbed amount of Co^{60}-CN-DMBC has a final biological half life of forty-nine days resulting from $f_3 = 79 \cdot e^{-0.014T}$. About 87 percent of the absorbed Co^{60}-DMBC-coenzyme follow $f_3 - 87 \cdot e^{-0.013T}$ and have a final biological half life of forty-nine days.

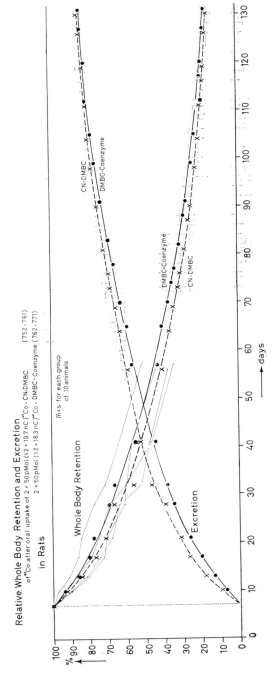

Figure 5. Relative whole body retention and excretion of the Co[60] label in rats to 130 days after oral uptake of 2 x 50 pMol Co[60]-CN-DMBC (2 x 19.7 nc) and 2 x 50 pMol Co[60]-DMBC-Coenzyme (2 x 18.3 nc).

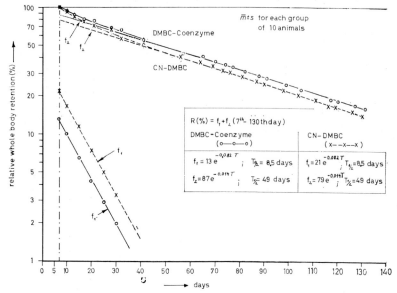

Figure 6. Exponential functions for the relative whole body retention of the Co^{60} label in rats between the 7th and 130th day after intestinal absorption of Co^{60}-CN-DMBC and Co^{60}-DMBC-coenzyme.

TABLE VIII

Summary of Biological Half Life (BHL), Turnover Time (TT) and Turnover Rate (TR) for Absorbed and Injected Co^{60}-CN-DMBC and Co^{60}-C'_5-Deoxyadenosyl-DMBC in Rats.

	Biological Half Life (BHL) in Days	Turnover Time ($TT = \dfrac{BHL}{ln2}$) in Days	Turnover Rate ($TR = \dfrac{Pool^*}{TT}$)	
			in µg./day	in % of pool* per Day
CN-DMBC				
Intestinal Absorption	49	70.6	0.28	1.40
Intraperitoneal Injection	51	73.4	0.27	1.35
DMBC-Coenzyme ($= C'_5$-Deoxyadenosyl-DMBC)				
Intestinal Absorption	49	70.6	0.28	1.40
Intraperitoneal Injection	52	75	0.27	1.35

*A pool size of 20 µg. DMBC was estimated and used for the calculation of TR.

The biological half lifes remain constant from the 70th day to the 130th day after the intestinal absorption of the labeled B_{12} analogues which are then in equilibrium with the whole body B_{12} pool. The calculated turnover times (biological half life/ln 2) for the DMBC-coenzyme and CN-DMBC are 75 and 70.6 days (Table VIII). The turnover rates (Pool/turnover time) were calculated on the basis of a whole body pool of 20 μg. B_{12} in rats (microbiological estimation with E. coli 113-3). Between the 70th and 130th day after intestinal absorption in rats, the DMBC-coenzyme has a final turnover rate of 0.27 μg./day or 1.34 per-

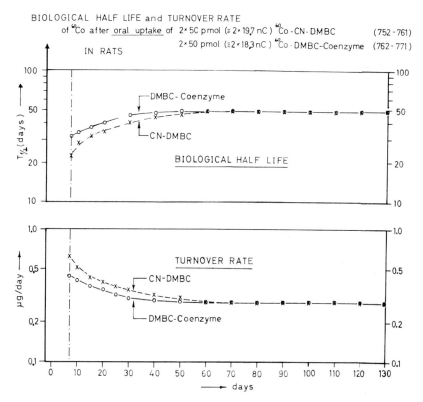

Figure 7. Biological half life and turnover rate of Co^{60} label in rats between the 7th and 130th day after intestinal absorption of Co^{60}-CN-DMBC and Co^{60}-DMBC-coenzyme. Turnover rate values are only realistic beyond the 60th day; then equilibrium is obtained between the Co^{60}-B_{12} tracer dose and whole body vitamin B_{12} pool (20μg.).

cent of the whole body B_{12} pool per day. The corresponding values for the final turnover rate of the CN-DMBC are 0.28 μg./ day or 1.42 percent of the whole body B_{12} pool per day (Table VII, Figure 7).

When the experiment was repeated with twenty three-month-old rats, results were the same. The results show that the final biological half life and turnover rate of the CN-DMBC and DMBC-coenzyme in rats is independent of the route of administration. The biological half lifes and turnover rates after oral administration are identical with the values obtained after intraperitoneal injection (Tables VII and VIII).

As after intraperitoneal injection, a shorter biological half life and higher turnover rate is also typical for the absorbed CN-DMBC during the first six to eight weeks after the intestinal absorption.

The final biological half lifes and turnover rates for the DMBC-coenzyme and CN-DMBC are nearly identical after intestinal absorption of the two B_{12} analogues.

The results obtained after absorption and after intraperitoneal injection of Co^{60}-CN-DMBC and Co^{60}-DMBC-coenzyme in rats clearly demonstrate that both compounds have a different biological half life and turnover rate only during the first six to eight weeks after uptake. Then the metabolic behavior of both compounds becomes more similar and finally identical after sixty to seventy days. This is a strong argument for a conversion of one compound into the other which is completed in the tissues of the rat within the first two months.

Both the kinetics of the biological half life and the dominating occurrence of the DMBC-coenzyme in the livers of mammals (8) are indications that the conversion of the artificial Co^{60}-5.6-dimethylbenzimidazolyl-cyano-cobamid into the Co^{60}-5.6-dimethylbenzimidazolyl-cobamid-coenzyme in the rat was studied in these experiments.

Vitamin B_{12} Turnover Rate and Nutritional
Vitamin B_{12} Requirement in Rats

Whole body retention studies of the Co^{60} label in rats after intestinal absorption or intraperitoneal injection of Co^{60}-CN-DMBC and Co^{60}-C'_5-deoxyadenosyl-DMBC resulted in a final turnover rate of 0.28 μg./day resp. 0.27 μg./day (Table VIII). This value is in excellent agreement with the observation that the rat growth assay for vitamin B_{12} can be used within a range of 0.04 to 0.32 μg. B_{12}/day (9), and that the intestinal absorption in rats reaches a saturation plateau at about 0.1 μg. vitamin B_{12} per dose (10). Earlier lower values for the nutritional vitamin B_{12} requirement in rats (0.025 to 0.1 μg/day (11)) were possibly caused by coprophagy which is sometimes sufficient to cover the vitamin B_{12} requirement in rats (12).

If growing or adult rats have no access to their feces, they should at least absorb 0.27 μg. vitamin B_{12} per day to keep their whole body vitamin B_{12} pool (about 15 to 20 μg.) and vitamin B_{12} metabolism at normal levels.

STRUCTURE SPECIFICITY OF VITAMIN B_{12} METABOLISM IN HUMANS

Large volume whole body radioactivity detectors with liquid organic scintillators also can be used efficiently for studies on the structure specificity of vitamin B_{12} metabolism in humans. Whole body retention can be used as an indicator for the structure specificity of the intestinal absorption after oral application of different Co^{60}-labeled vitamin B_{12} analogues or the structure specificity of *in vivo* retention and excretion after parenteral application of different vitamin B_{12} analogues. In such studies all available modules are used, making a total detector volume of 200 cm. length and 60 cm. diameter (4π geometry). Feces and urine radioactivity are measured with a 50 cm. long 4π ring module without any sample preparation.

The following is a review of the results of our investigations on structure specificity of vitamin B_{12} metabolism.

Structure Specificity of Intestinal Absorption of Vitamin B_{12} Molecule

Incomplete (nucleotide-free) vitamin B_{12} analogues, such as cobinamid (factor B), are not absorbed.

Complete (nucleotide-containing) vitamin B_{12} analogues, which like 3.5.6-trimethylbenzimidazolyl-cyanocobamid (vitamin $B_{12}Nm$), do not contain the intact coordinative linkage between the N_3 of the benzimidazol base and the central Co atom, show the same paper electrophoretic mobility and biological properties as the incomplete vitamin B_{12} analogues and are therefore not absorbed.

The benzimidazol- and the 5. 6-dichlorbenzimidazolcyanocobamids are well absorbed by guinea pigs, rats and humans. Their absorption rates are identical with the absorption rate of the CN-DMBC.

The poor absorption of the 5-hydroxybenzimidazol-cyanocobamid can be considerably improved by the methylation of the free hydroxy group which results in the formation of the 5-methoxy-benzimidazol-cyanocobamid.

Therefore good absorption ability of the vitamin B_{12} molecule requires the existence of the nucleotide-type side chain with the coordinative linkage between the N_3 of the benzimidazol base and the central cobalt atom, and this side chain must contain a benzimidazolyl base which is either unsubstituted or contains a dimethyl- or dichloro- substitution in the 5. 6 position of the benzimidazol ring system (13).

The cyano group at the central cobalt atom of the vitamin B_{12} molecule is not necessary for the intestinal absorption of the vitamin B_{12} molecule since the H_2O-DMBC (= 5. 6-dimethyl-benzimidazol-aquocobamid) and CN-DMBC are well absorbed to the same degree in rats, guinea pigs and humans (14, 15).

Structure Specificity of *in vivo* Retention and Excretion of Vitamin B_{12} Molecule

Studies in rats and humans either with different Co^{60}-labeled vitamin B_{12} analogues or with a radio-vitamin B_{12} competition test have also demonstrated a considerable structure specificity for the *in vivo* retention and excretion of the vitamin B_{12} molecule.

For the full competition of a vitamin B_{12} analogue with the

Co^{60}-labeled CN-DMBC in the metabolic phase of the *in vivo* distribution, retention and excretion, it is necessary that the nucleotide-like side chain with a coordinative linkage between the N_3 of the benzimidazol base and the central cobalt atom exist, the benzimidazol base has a certain substitution at the 5.6-position, a C'_3-phosphoribose linkage exists, the alkanolamin moiety of the vitamin B_{12} molecule has a certain structure and especially no benzyl- or phenyl- substitution at the C_1- or C_2- atom, and all three propionamide side chains on the corrin ring are intact and unsubstituted (16, 17).

Substitution of the CN-group at the central cobalt atom by a H_2O-group resulted in the formation of the physiological vitamin B_{12} depot form H_2O-DMBC (= aquocobalamin) which shows a considerably higher *in vivo* retention after intestinal absorption, especially after intramuscular injection of larger doses (14, 15, 18).

WHOLE BODY RETENTION AND EXCRETION AFTER INTRATHECAL AND INTRAMUSCULAR INJECTION OF PHYSIOLOGICAL VITAMIN B_{12} DEPOT FORM 5.6-DIMETHYLBENZIMIDAZOLYL-AQUO-COBAMID (= H_2O-DMBC)

Studies on the radiation instability of labeled vitamin B_{12} and the structure specificity of vitamin B_{12} metabolism resulted in the discovery of an increased *in vivo* retention of Co^{60} label after intestinal absorption or intramuscular injection of pure Co^{60}-H_2O-DMBC (14, 15, 19).

The whole body retention of injected labeled CN-DMBC and labeled H_2O-DMBC can be increased by 100 and 30 per cent, respectively, if the compounds are applied intrathecally and not by intramuscular injection (Table IX). From an intramuscular dose of 1 mg. CN-DMBC, only about 8.3 $\pm$ 5.3 ($\bar{m} \pm s$)% is retained in the human whole body (Table XII), whereas nearly 45 per cent remains in the body after intralumbal injection of 1 mg. H_2O-DMBC. Using the turnover rate of vitamin B_{12} in the human body (= 2.55 μg./day) as the daily minimum vitamin B_{12}

TABLE IX

Whole Body Retention, Urinary Excretion, Serum and Cerebrospinal
Fluid Concentration of Co^{60}-B_{12} after Intramuscular and Intrathecal
(Intralumbal) Injection of 1000 μg. Co^{60}-CN-DMBC resp. 1000 μg. Co^{60}-
H_2O-DMBC in Patient with Subacute Degeneration of Spinal Cord

Structure	Co^{60}-CN-DMBC		Co^{60}-H_2O-DMBC	
Parenteral Application	Intra-muscular	Intra-thecal	Intra-muscular	Intra-thecal
urinary excretion after 5 days (in % of test dose)	87.3	75.5	66.7	55.5
whole body retention after 5 days (in % of test dose)	12.7	24.5	33.3	44.5
Co^{60}-B_{12} concentration in the cerebrospinal fluid after 5 days (in ng. B_{12}/ml)	< 0.5	2.6	< 0.5	23.0
Co^{60}-B_{12} concentration in serum (in ng. B_{12}/ml)				
after 2 hours	28	3	38	3
after 1 day	3	3	16	9
after 5 days	< 1	2	4-8	3

requirement, it can be calculated that a single intramuscular injection of 1000 μg. CN-DMBC will cover the vitamin B_{12} requirement for only thirty-two days, whereas the intrathecal injection
of 1000 μg. H_2O-DMBC is sufficient for about six months.

After intramuscular injection of 1 mg. CN-DMBC (522 nc)
or 1 mg. H_2O-DMBC (423 nc), it was not possible at the fifth
day to demonstrate any radioactivity in the cerebrospinal fluid
so that the vitamin B_{12} concentration was at least below 0.5 ng.
B_{12}/ml. The intralumbal injection of labeled CN-DMBC (1 mg.
= 522 nc) however resulted in radioactivity in the cerebrospinal
fluid at the fifth day which corresponded to a vitamin B_{12} concentration increase of 2.6 ng. B_{12}/ml. (Fig. 8). The intrathecal
injection of 1 mg. H_2O-DMBC (423 nc) was followed by a vitamin B_{12} concentration increase in the cerebrospinal fluid of 23 ng.
B_{12}/ml. on the fifth day, and after five weeks 3.5 ng. B_{12}/ml. were
still measured.

Since intrathecal injections of larger amounts of pure H_2O-
DMBC (1-5 mg. aquocobalamin-acetate in 0.9 per cent NaCl
solution at pH 5.8) are well tolerated by patients without any
irritation, we can highly recommend the intrathecal vitamin B_{12}
therapy with the physiological vitamin B_{12} depot-form H_2O-

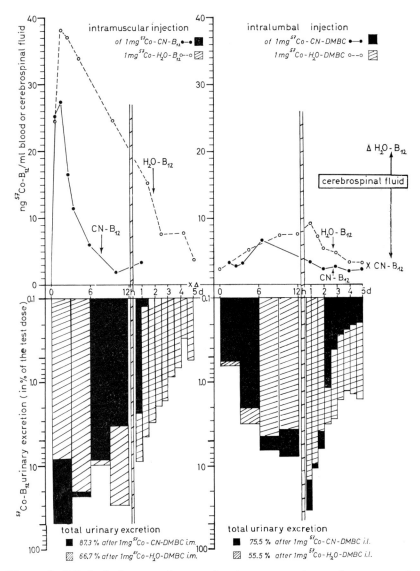

Figure 8. Whole body retention, total urinary excretion and serum and cerebrospinal fluid concentrations of Co^{60}-B_{12} after intramuscular and intrathecal injection of 1 mg. Co^{57}-CN-DMBC and Co^{57}-H_2O-DMBC, respectively in patients with severe subacute combined degeneration of spinal cord.

DMBC in cases of severe subacute combined degeneration of the spinal cord. Incorporation of larger amounts of the labeled vitamin B_{12} into the brain and spinal cord, where the degeneration changes are located in the posterior and lateral columns near the surface and the cerebrospinal fluid, was only obtained after intrathecal injection of large amounts of the vitamin. It is possible that the vitamin B_{12} reaches the places of degeneration in the spinal cord by direct diffusion from the surrounding cerebrospinal fluid. The degenerative changes can be expected to be still reversible if large enough amounts of the vitamin B_{12} arrive when only the demyelination has occurred and the axis cylinders are still intact.

In several cases with severe subacute combined degeneration of the spinal cord which did not respond to high dose, long term intramuscular or intravenous vitamin B_{12} therapy, a considerable improvement of the neurological status was observed after the intrathecal injection of 1 to 5 mg. H_2O-DMBC weekly for a few months.

BIOLOGICAL HALF LIFE AND METABOLIC TURNOVER RATE OF VITAMIN B_{12} IN MAN

It is possible to follow the whole body retention of Co^{60} label in humans even after absorption or injection of only about 10 nc over more than two years if a sensitive 2π or 4π whole body detector is available. From the long time whole body retention the biological half life and turnover rate can be calculated.

Such measurements can be performed in the 2.0 to 2.4 Mev Co^{60} sum peak area (2.5 Mev initial γ-energy) if a 4π detector with considerable sum peak sensitivity is used. Such measurements are not influenced by fluctuations of the K^{40} or Cs^{137} content of the human body. If only a 2π detector is available the low Co^{60} sum peak sensitivity has to be compensated by larger test radioactivity (100 to 200 nc instead of 10 nc).

The whole body K^{40} content remains constant over years if the weight does not change significantly (Fig. 9). The Cs^{137} content of the human body is, however, determined by the daily nutritional Cs^{137} uptake since the biological half life of Cs^{137} in man

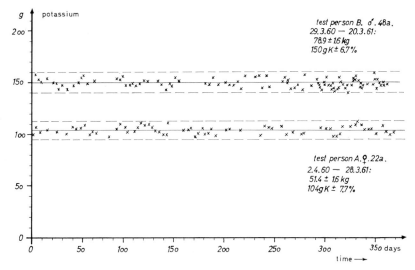

Figure 9. Constant whole body potassium content of two human volunteers as measured via K^{40} γ-radiation in the K^{40} channel of the 2π GENCO over one year.

is 130 to 150 days. The Cs^{137} content of man therefore shows considerable fluctuations which follow the nuclear weapon test activity. The Cs^{137} energy range of the multiple Compton spectrum has to be excluded for long time Co^{60} retention studies. In our earlier studies with a 2π detector, the Co^{60} long time retention measurements were performed in a Co^{60} energy channel which included the K^{40} plus the Co^{60} sum peak energy range, but not the Cs^{137} range (4, 5).

The relative whole body retention of the Co^{60} label after intestinal absorption from an oral test dose of 0.50 nMol (= 10.1 nc) Co^{60}-CN-DMBC is presented in Figure 10a for the first 200 hours and in Figure 10b for 700 days. In Figure 10a the 100 per cent value for whole body retention represents the maximum value for the patient's net count rate increase after about twenty hours (with a 2π detector), whereas the 100 per cent value in Figure 10 b represents the Co^{60} whole body retention on the 5th day after the oral Co^{60}-CN-DMBC uptake and completion of the fecal excretion of the unabsorbed Co^{60}-CN-DMBC.

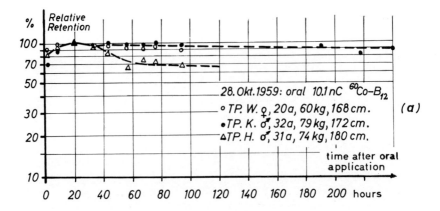

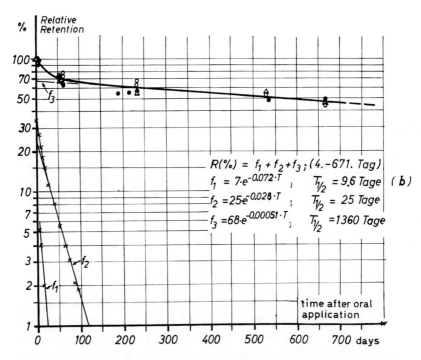

Figure 10. (a) Relative whole body retention in normal human volunteers during the first ten days after oral uptake of 0.50 nMol (10.1 nc) Co[60]-CN-DMBC in percent of the oral test dose. (b) Exponential functions for the relative whole body retention of the Co[60] label in normal human volunteers between the 1st and 666th day after complete body incorporation of absorbed Co[60]-CN-DMBC in per cent of the absorbed and incorporated Co[60]-B_{12}.

The whole body retention curve of Co^{60}-B_{12} can be described for the 700 days by the three expontential equations $f_1 + f_2 + f_3$ (Fig. 10b). Metabolic equilibrium between the small absorbed Co^{60}-CN-DMBC test dose (65 to 91 percent from 0.50 nMol) (Table X) and the large whole body vitamin B_{12} pool of 5 mg. is obtained as soon as the semilogarithmic presentation of the whole

TABLE X

TIME DEPENDENCE OF THE BIOLOGICAL HALF LIFE AND TURNOVER RATE OF ABSORBED VITAMIN B_{12} IN MAN.

Days after Intestinal Co^{60}-B_{12} Absorption	Biological Half Life (Days)	Turnover Rate* in % of Pool per day	in μg./day
30	115	0.60	30
50	340	0.20	10
75	500	0.14	6.9
100	700	0.10	5.0
270-540	1300	0.053	2.67
540-671	1360	0.051	2.55

*Calculated for a vitamin pool size of 5 mg. and for the 30-100th day on the assumption of metabolic equilibrium.

body retention against time has reached a straight line so that the calculated daily turnover rate remains constant. This is observed in human volunteers after 300 days (Fig. 11), so that all short time studies on the biological half life and turnover rate of vitamin B_{12} in man result in false values.

From the final biological half life (BHL) of 1360 days a turnover time $(TT = \dfrac{BHL}{\ln 2} = BHL \times 1.44)$ of 1958 days and a turnover rate $(TR = \dfrac{pool}{TT})$ of 2.55 μg. B_{12}/day or 0.051 per cent of the B_{12} pool per day were calculated (4, 20). Only this final value for the biological half life and metabolic turnover rate is of biological significance since it really represents the constant whole body vitamin B_{12} turnover rate with metabolic equilibrium between the different functional vitamin B_{12} pools and the radioactive test dose.

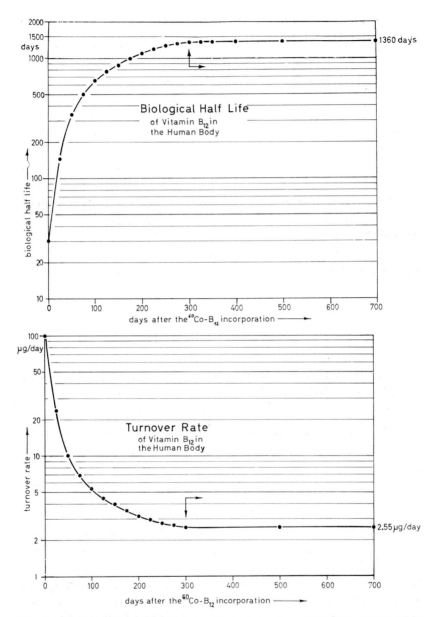

Figure 11. Biological half life (a) and turnover rate (b) of the Co⁶⁰ label in normal human volunteers during the first 700 days after complete intestinal absorption and whole body incorporation of 0.33 to 0.46 nMol $Co^{60}-B_{12}$ from an oral test dose of 0.50 nMol $Co^{60}-CN-B_{12}$. Turnover rate values are only realistic beyond the 240-300th day; then equilibrium is obtained between the $Co^{60}-B_{12}$ tracer dose and the whole body vitamin B_{12} pool ($= 5000~\mu g.$)

VITAMIN B_{12} TURNOVER RATE AS A BASIS FOR CALCULATION OF NUTRITIONAL AND THERAPEUTIC VITAMIN B_{12} REQUIREMENT OF HUMANS

Until recently it was generally believed that only an absorbed or injected amount of about 0.5 to 1.0 μg. vitamin B_{12} per day was required by adult men (21,26) This assumption was based on the observation that 0.5 to 1.0 μg. vitamin B_{12} per day was just sufficient to keep pernicious anemia patients for several months or a few years in hematological remission. This estimate did not consider the essential vitamin B_{12} requirement of the central nervous system and other tissues and organs.

Also it was never demonstrated that such a small amount of injected or absorbed vitamin B_{12} could ever normalize the whole body vitamin B_{12} pool or vitamin B_{12} metabolism (e.g., serum level and urinary excretion of vitamin B_{12}) in the treated patients with B_{12} avitaminosis (19, 27).

That such low estimations of the minimum daily vitamin B_{12} requirement which are based on the erythrocytopoetic maintenance effect of vitamin B_{12} do not represent the real whole body vitamin B_{12} requirement was also realized by clinicians. Ungley wrote "It is foolish to go on believing that 1 μg. a day is adequate therapy at any stage (28)."

Whole Body Vitamin B_{12} Turnover Rate and Nutritional Vitamin B_{12} Requirement in Man

Long time studies on the biological half life of absorbed Co^{60}-vitamin B_{12} in human volunteers resulted in a turnover rate of 2.55 μg. B_{12}/day. This amount of vitamin B_{12} is lost by the body every day via billiary, fecal and urinary excretion and must be substituted, since otherwise the biochemical and clinical symptoms of vitamin B_{12} deficiency would develop as soon as the vitamin B_{12} whole body pool is depleted to 5-10 percent of its normal value.

To get intestinal absorption of 2.55 μg. vitamin B_{12}, at least 3.64 μg. vitamin B_{12} must be within the diet per day in a concentration and form which permits the observed average absorption rate of 70 percent. The lower range of absorption in normal human volunteers is approximately 50 percent, so that in these persons 5.10 μg. vitamin B_{12} must be available with the diet. So at least 4 to 5 μg. vitamin B_{12} per day has to be in a diet of humans if the nutritional vitamin B_{12} uptake is expected to compensate for the turnover rate of 2.55 μg. vitamin B_{12}/day.

Detailed studies on the vitamin B_{12} content in an average representative human diet were not yet performed with the specific vitamin B_{12} test organisms. However, some work with the unspecific Lactobacillus leichmannii assay has shown that a high cost American diet contains 4 to 86 (average 32) μg. vitamin B_{12}/ day, whereas a low cost diet contains 1 to 76 (average 16), and a poor diet only 1 to 8 (average 2.7) μg. vitamin B_{12}/ day (29). These large differences are explained by the association of vitamin B_{12} with the more expensive food products of animal origin.

If a human can no longer absorb at least 2.55 μg. vitamin B_{12}/day from a minimum daily oral uptake of 4 to 5 μg., symptoms of vitamin B_{12} deficiency will develop when the whole body vitamin B_{12} pool size reaches less than 10 percent of the normal value. Since the whole body vitamin B_{12} content is about 5 mg., then 4.5 mg. vitamin B_{12} would be used up in 4500:2.55 = 1764 days = 4.83 years. This is in reasonable agreement with clinical observations that patients after total gastrectomy need four to seven years for development of hematologic or neurological symptoms of the B_{12} avitaminosis.

Compensation Therapy Schedule for CN-DMBC and H₂O-DMBC

A patient with B_{12} avitaminosis in relapse requires so much vitamin B_{12} by injection that the reduced whole body vitamin B_{12} pool size becomes normalized to about 5000 μg. This normalization can be obtained by sixty intramuscular injections of 1000 μg. CN-DMBC or more economically by twenty-two intramuscular injections of 500 μg. H₂O-DMBC or eleven intrathecal injections of 1000 μg. H₂O-DMBC (Table XI). It is advisable to give

TABLE XI
WHOLE BODY RETENTION AND COMPENSATION THERAPY SCHEDULE FOR 500-1000 μg. INTRAMUSCULAR
AND INTRATHECAL DOSES OF CN-DMBC AND H₂O-DMBC

Injected Doses	Mode of Injection	CN-DMBC Whole Body Retention from a Single Injection (in %)	(in μg.)	Number of Required Injections+	H₂O-DMBC Whole Body Retention from a Single Injection (in %)	(in μg.)	Number of Required Injections+
500 μg.	intramuscular	16.2	81.0	62	45.1	226	22
1,000 μg.	intramuscular	8.3	83.0	60	30.3	303	17
1,000 μg.	intrathecal	24.5	245	20	44.5	445	11

+ For normalization of the vitamin B₁₂ pool size (=5000 μg.).

those injections at intervals of at least three days to avoid losses from the later injections via increased urinary excretion.

Maintenance Therapy Schedule for CN-DMBC and H₂O-DMBC

If the patient is in remission with a normal whole body vitamin B_{12} pool size of about 5 mg., the life-time maintenance therapy can be done according to a schedule resulting from the whole body turnover rate of 2.55 μg./day and the estimated whole body retention after intramuscular injection of 20 to 1000 μg. of CN-DMBC or H_2O-DMBC (Table XII).

The results show that the superiority of H_2O-DMBC therapy is only significant for large doses of vitamin B_{12}. The vitamin B_{12} requirement of a human can be covered by approximately eleven intramuscular injections of 1000 μg. CN-DMBC per year or only three yearly intramuscular injections of 1000 μg. H_2O-DMBC (Table XII). These injections can be given either once a year at intervals of three to seven days or equally distributed over the year at intervals of one and four months (30). Under practical conditions we have not observed a single clinical decompensation within our pernicious anemia patients treated according to this therapy schedule over eight years for CN-DMBC and four years for H_2O-DMBC.

Acknowledgments

We are grateful to Dr. Ch. Rosenblum of Merck Sharp & Dohme Research Laboratories for several batches of Co⁵⁷- and

TABLE XII

Whole Body Retention and Maintenance Therapy Schedule for 20 to 1000 μg. Intramuscular Doses of CN-DMBC and H₂O-DMBC.

single injected dose (μg.)	CN-DMBC					H₂O-DMBC				
	Urinary Excretion (in %) $\overline{m}\pm s$	(in μg.) $\overline{m}$	Retention (in %) $\overline{m}\pm s$	(in μg.) $\overline{m}$	Covers daily $B_{12}\pm$ Requirement for (days)	Urinary Excretion (in %) $\overline{m}\pm s$	(in μg.) $\overline{m}$	Retention (in %) $\overline{m}\pm s$	(in μg.) $\overline{m}$	Covers daily $B_{12}\pm$ Requirement for (days)
20	7.9±4.9	1.58	92.1±4.9	18.4	7	7.5± 2.2	1.5	92.5± 2.2	18.5	7
50	31.6±6.3	15.8	68.4±6.3	34.2	13	23.5± 3.1	11.8	76.5± 3.1	38.3	15
100	45.8±7.2	45.8	54.2±7.2	54.2	21	30.1± 2.7	30.1	69.9± 2.7	69.9	27
200	64.1±3.4	128	35.9±3.4	71.8	28	45.5± 8.3	91.0	54.5± 8.5	109	43
500	83.8±3.4	419	16.2±3.4	81.0	32	54.9±11.0	275	45.1±11.0	226	89
1000	91.7±5.3	917	8.3±5.3	83.0	33	69.6± 4.0	696	30.3± 4.0	303	119

+) daily B_{12} requirement = turnover rate = 2.55 μ./day

Co^{60}-labeled vitamin B$_{12}$ and to Dr. D. Perlman of Squibb Institute for Medical Research for several Co^{58}- and Co^{60}-labeled DMBC-coenzyme concentrates.

REFERENCES

1. Heinrich: in *Radioactive Isotopes in Physiology, Diagnostics and Therapy*. Vol. II, pp. 660-696, Berlin, Springer, 1961.
2. Pfau and Heinrich: *Atompraxis*, 5:14, 100a, 1959.
3. Heinrich: 42. Deutsch. Röntgenkongre SS, No. 27, Hamburg, 16-19, IV. 1961, Strahlenforschung u Strahlenbehandlung, Band III (Sonderbände zur Strahlentherapie, Band 49), pp. 198-205, Vlg. Urban & Schwarzenberg, München, 1962.
4. Heinrich and Pfau: in 2nd European Symposium Vitamin B$_{12}$ and Intrinsic Factor, Hamburg, August 1961, Proceed. pp. 351-381 Enke, Stuttgart, 1962; *Atomkernenergie*, 6:463, 1961.
5. Heinrich: University of New Mexico Conference on Organic Scintillation Detectors, Albuquerque, N. M., Aug. 1960; Proceedings, p. 312, US-AEC, Washington, D. C., 1960.
6. Blum and Heinrich: *Vitamine ū Hormone*, 7:486, 1957.
7. Barker: in 2nd. European Symposium Vitamin B$_{12}$ and Intrinsic Factor, Hamburg, August 1961, Proceedings, pp. 82-105, Enke, Stuttgart, 1962.
8. Toohey and Barker: *J. Biol. Chem.*, 236:560, 1961.
9. Cuthbertson and Thornton: *Brit. J. Nutr.*, 6:170, 1952.
10. Taylor, Mallett, Witts and Taylor: *Brit. J. Haemat.*, 4:63, 1958.
11. Frost, Fricke and Spruth: *Proc. Soc. Exp. Biol. Med.*, 72:102, 1949.
12. Barnes and Fiala: J. Nutrit., 65:103, 1958.
13. Heinrich: *Naturwissensch.*, 45:269, 1958.
    Z. *Vitamin Hormon Ferm. Fosrchg.*, 9:385, 1958, in Vitamin Metabolism, 4th Intern. Congr. Biochem., Vienna, Sept. 1958, Proceedings, IX., pp. 150-160, London, Pergamon Press, 1960.
14. Heinrich, Friedrich, Gabbe, Manjrekar and Staak: 5th Intern. Congr. Nutrition, No. 284, Washington, D.C., 1-7, IX, 1960.
15. Gabbe and Heinrich: *Int. J. Vitam. Res.*, 31:355, 1961. In 2nd European Symposium on Vitamin B$_{12}$ u. Intrinsic Factor, Hamburg, August 1961, Proceedings. pp. 116-147, Enke, Stuttgart, 1962.
16. Heinrich: *Int. J. Vitam. Res.*, 31:369, 1961.
17. Heinrich and Gabbe: in 2nd European Symposium on Vitamin B$_{12}$ u. Intrinsic Factor, Hamburg, August, 1961, Proceedings, pp. 252-275, Enke, Stuttgart, 1962.
18. Heinrich and Gabbe: *Klin. Wschr.*, 39:689, 1961.
19. Heinrich: in *Radioactive Isotopes in Physiology, Diagnostics and Therapy*. Vol. I., pp. 1029-1141, Berlin, Springer, 1961.

20. Heinrich: Z. *Naturforschg.*, *16b*:407, 1961.
21. Bethell: in *The Vitamins*. Vol. 1, p. 522, New York, Academic Press, 1954.
22. Bethell, Meyers and Neligh: *J. Lab. Clin. Med.*, 33:1477, 1948.
23. Meacham and Heinle: *J. Lab. Clin. Med.*, 41:65, 1953.
24. Darby, Bridgforth, Le Brocquy, Clark, De Oliveira, Kevany, McGanity and Perez: *Amer. J. Med.*, 25:726, 1958.
25. Darby, Jones, Clark, McGanity, De Oliveira, Perez, Kevany and Le Brocquy: *Amer. J. Clin. Nutr.*, 6:513, 1958.
26. Will, Meuller, Brodine, Kiely, Friedman, Hawkins, Dutra and Vilter: *J. Lab. Clin. Med.*, 53:22, 1959.
27. Heinrich: *Drug Res.*, 6:305, 1956.
28. Ungley: In 1st European Symposium on Vitamin B_{12} and Intrinsic Factor. Hamburg, May 1956, Proceedings, pp. 474-486, Enke, Stuttgart, 1957.
29. Mangay-Chung, Pearson, Darby, Miller and Goldsmith: *Amer. J. Clin. Nutr.*, 9:573, 1961.
30. Heinrich and Gabbe: In 2nd European Symposium on Vitamin B_{12} u. Intrinsic Factor. Hamburg, August 1961, Proceedings, pp. 638-663, Enke, Stuttgart, 1962; *Drug Res.*, 11:1087, 1961.

23

TURNOVER OF Co^{60}-LABELED VITAMIN B$_{12}$
IN PATIENTS WITH PERNICIOUS ANEMIA[1]

Robert M. Heyssel, Richard C. Bozian, William J. Darby
and George R. Meneely[2]
Vanderbilt University School of Medicine
Nashville, Tennessee

For several years Vanderbilt University School of Medicine has conducted studies concerning the human requirements for Vitamin B$_{12}$ (1, 2,3). A large group of patients has been maintained for many years on doses of vitamin B$_{12}$, ranging from 0.50 μg. to 5 μg. per day. The availability of a human whole body counter at Vanderbilt afforded the opportunity to study the turnover of vitamin B$_{12}$ during different circumstances in patients with normal or severely depleted body stores of B$_{12}$. This work has been presented elsewhere (4).

MATERIAL AND METHODS

The study group included twenty-four persons, eighteen with pernicious anemia and six having other diagnoses. Of the eighteen with pernicious anemia, repetitive whole body counts were made on eleven subjects for a sufficient period to allow determination of turnover of Co^{60}-labeled vitamin B$_{12}$. Five subjects, three clinically healthy, one with diabetes mellitus and one with azotemia, were also studied long enough to determine turnover of vitamin B$_{12}$.

Vitamin B$_{12}$ absorption studies were done initially on all subjects. Each received approximately 0.5 μc of Co^{60} (1μc per

[1] Supported in part by the Atomic Energy Commission, U. S. Public Health Service and Army Medical Research and Development Command.

[2] Now at University of Texas M. D. Anderson Hospital and Tumor Institute, Houston, Texas.

μg. vitamin B_{12}) orally while fasting. Residual whole body Co^{60} activity was determined two to four weeks later. Subjects with pernicious anemia were then injected with 0.5 μc of Co^{60} vitamin B_{12}, and residual activity again determined. In this manner each subject served as his own control. The number of microcuries injected was determined by counting the syringe before and after injection, and the number of microcuries ingested was determined by counting the capsules before feeding. Absorption was determined by the formula

$$\frac{Ro}{R_1} \div I \times 100 = \% \text{ Absorption}$$

where Ro equals whole body cpm remaining after fed dose, R_1 equals whole body cpm per microcuries following injection, and I equals microcuries ingested.

A few of the determinations of absorption were made by counting the subject 4 hr. after ingestion of the dose and again in two to four weeks. In this instance, percent absorption is given by the formula

$$\frac{\text{cpm at 2-4 weeks}}{\text{cpm at 4 hours}} \times 100$$

Following determination of absorption, the patients were counted in the whole body counter at intervals of two to four weeks. Initially, all patients were maintained on a standard dose of B_{12}. After a suitable period (usually after more than one year of observation) the dose of B_{12} was altered for some of the patients, while whole body counting was continued.

Analysis of the slope of disappearance of Co^{60} from the whole body was done by least-squares. The first 60 to 120 days of observation after injection of Co^{60}-labeled B_{12} were analyzed separately from the remainder of the data on the assumption of a long period of equilibration. The remainder of the data was divided arbitrarily into periods depending on circumstances of dose of B_{12} and length of study in a particular patient, and slope of disappearance determined independently for each period.

Biologic half life (BHL) for Co^{60} was determined by the formula

$$EHL = \frac{BHL \times PHL}{BHL + PHL}$$

where EHL is the effective half life as determined by the slope of disappearance observed from whole body counts, PHL equals the physical half life of Co^{60} (1,923 days) and BHL is the biologic half life. Decay constant (k) for Co^{60} was determined and expressed in per cent by the formula

$$K = \frac{0.693}{BHL} \times 100$$

RESULTS

Table I summarizes absorption studies in eighteen patients with pernicious anemia, five clinically healthy subjects and one patient with megaloblastic anemia of the puerperium. The results are in agreement with those obtained by others by deter-

TABLE I

PERCENT ORAL ABSORPTION OF Co^{60} VITAMIN B_{12}

	0.5 µg./dose 0.5 µc Co^{60} B_{12}	No. Subjects
Normals	45-80% (45, 67, 77, 78, 80)	5
Patients (pernicious anemia)	0-17% Mean - 3.25%	17
Megaloblastic anemia of puerperium	85%	1

mination of fecal excretion of labeled vitamin. We did not repeat the absorption studies using intrinsic factor, but in the group with poor absorption of B_{12}, none gave evidence that a condition other than lack of intrinsic factor existed. All had had x-ray examination of their gastrointestinal tracts.

Figures 1 to 3 are typical of the data obtained by serial whole body counts in these subjects. R. R., a patient with pernicious anemia with hematologic and neurologic manifestations (Fig. 1), has now been studied for 890 days following ingestion of Co^{80}-labeled vitamin B_{12}. For the first 490 days, he was maintained on 7 µg. of vitamin B_{12} weekly by injection. Vitamin B_{12} was then discontinued. There was no observable change in slope of disappearance of Co^{60}-labeled vitamin. The calculated biologic

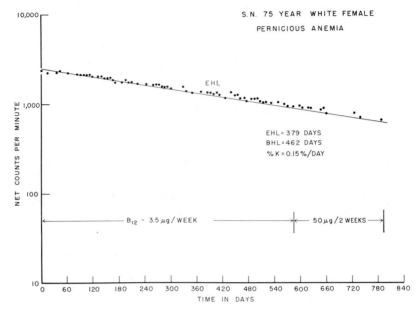

Figure 1. Turnover of Co^{60}-Vitamin B$_{12}$ in patients with pernicious anemia.

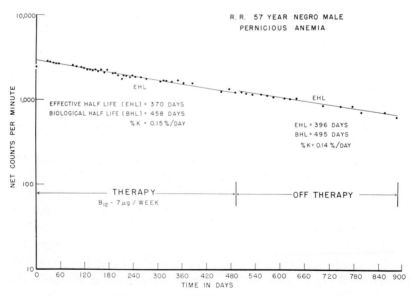

Figure 2. Turnover of Co^{60}-labeled Vitamin B$_{12}$ in patients with pernicious anemia.

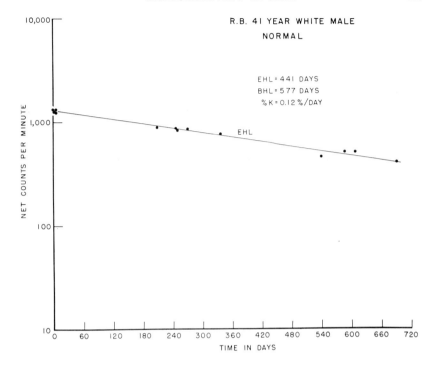

Figure 3. Turnover of Co[60]-labeled Vitamin B_{12} in patients with pernicious anemia.

half life of B_{12} is between 458 and 495 days. S. N. (Fig. 2) was similar to R. R. and received 3.5 µg. of B_{12} per week during most of the study. The calculated biological half life in S. N. was 462 days. In the normal subject, R. B., followed 441 days, the biological half life was 577 days (Fig. 3).

Table II summarizes the results obtained in all patients with pernicious anemia. The subjects are arranged in the table by size and frequency of dose of B_{12} given. Thus, R. R. and S. N. received the smallest doses, and B. V. the largest, most frequent doses. Turnover rates range from 0.11 to 0.17 percent per day. The mean turnover rate in all patients is 0.13 percent per day. Discontinuance of the dose of B_{12} had no statistically significant effect on the rate of disappearance of label in six subjects.

Table II also shows data in three normal subjects, one subject with diabetes and one subject with azotemia, anemia and

TABLE II

Biological Half Life of Vitamin B_{12} in Humans

Subjects	μg. Vit. B_{12}	During B_{12} Therapy (Post Equilibration)				Length of Period	Post B_{12} Therapy		
		Length of Period	No. of Observations	% Loss per Day	BHL* Days		No. of Observations	% Loss Per Day	BHL* Days
Normals:									
R. B.	Dietary	478	9	0.12	577	—	—	—	—
T. B.	Dietary	430	6	0.15	462	—	—	—	—
W. M.	Dietary	430	4	0.09	770	—	—	—	—
Non-Pernicious Anemia:									
R. J.**	Dietary	173	7	0.23	301	398	10	0.21	330
	+ 65/3 wks.				330	—			—
L. K.***	Dietary	487	7	0.21		—			
Pernicious Anemia:									
S. N.	3/wk.	668	61	0.15	462	—	—	—	—
R. R.	7/wk.	354	20	0.15	458	384	15	0.14	495
H. C.	30/4 wks.	420	3	0.11	630	—	—	—	—
J. C.	30/4 wks.	344	12	0.09	770	405	12	0.10	693
J. T.	45/4 wks.	152	5	0.14	495	337	7	0.11	630
M. M.	45/4 wks.	220	4	0.16	433	348	6	0.11	630
M. F.	60/4 wks.	240	5	0.17	408	—	—	—	—
J. J.	60/4 wks.	364	9	0.14	495	—	—	—	—
F. L.	60/4 wks.	420	3	0.11	630	—	—	—	—
C. H.	30/2 wks.	420	8	0.13	530	—	—	—	—
B. V.	60/2 wks.	220	6	0.12	577	345	15	0.12	577

*Biological Half Life.
**Azotemia + Purpura.
***Diabetes Mellitus.

senile purpura. R. T. was initially thought to have pernicious anemia. Subsequent absorption studies (44 percent) indicated that this was not so. L. K. had diabetes mellitus and was initially included in our normal group. Because the turnover rates in both are higher than in other subjects, they are described separately. The reasons for this difference are not clear. We plan to investigate this further. The three normal subjects have turnover rates which are similar to the patients with pernicious anemia, the mean being 0.12 percent per day.

We have selected two patients with pernicious anemia (R. R. and S. N.) on whom we have the most extensive information for closer comparisons with the three normal subjects (Table III).

TABLE III

COMPARISON OF PATIENTS WITH PERNICIOUS ANEMIA AND MARKEDLY
DEPLETED BODY STORES OF B_{12} TO NORMALS

Subject	Length of Study Period	No. of Observations	BHL (Days)	% Loss/Day
R. R. (PA)	738 Days	35	495	0.14
S. N. (PA)	668 Days	61	462	0.15
R. B.	478 Days	9	577	0.12
T. B.	430 Days	9	462	0.15
W. M.	430 Days	4	770	0.09

R. R. had hematologic and neurologic manifestations of B_{12} deficiency. Over the next six months evidence of all disability disappeared during treatment with 7 μg. of B_{12} given weekly. S. N. was in hematologic remission when initially examined, but relapsed while on 3.5 μg. of B_{12} per week. In both instances, it is certain that body stores of vitamin B_{12} were markedly reduced during observation. The body stores of B_{12} of the other subject were presumably normal. The turnover rates and biological half lives of B_{12} in normals and in these two patients do not differ significantly despite widely differing amount of B_{12} stored in the body.

DISCUSSION

We have suggested elsewhere that vitamin B_{12} turnover is principally a first order function. The rate of loss of B_{12} per day appears independent of size of body stores or the dose of B_{12}. Analysis of the data indicates that there is a decreasing rate of loss for the first 60 to 120 days. When this initial period is omitted, there is no difference in rate of disappearance attributable to the amount injected or the frequency of injection. This is further supported by the fact that stopping treatment does not alter the slope of disappearance of label when compared to periods of therapy.

There is evidence that following injection of nonlabeled B_{12} the ability to flush the labeled B_{12} from the body decreases with increasing time. The flushing effect is greater at 2 hr. than 24 hr., and at 24 hr. is greater than 48 hr. (5). Our data suggests that with longer periods the ability to increase rates of excretion of labeled vitamin practically ceases, at least in the doses used here. This suggests an early, small and labile pool of B_{12}, perhaps primarily related to the transport system.

The similar rates of loss for patients with or without pernicious anemia raises interesting questions. If one assumes normal stores (4 to 10 mg. of B_{12}) (6, 7) in the normals with disappearance rates of 0.1 per cent per day, their losses would approximate 4 to 10 μg. of B_{12} per day. In the patients cited, two (R. R. and S. N.) clearly have very small stores, probably much less than 1,000 μg. by conservative estimate. Applying similar rates of loss to the normals, they would lose 1.0 μg. or less per day.

Gräsbeck first suggested that the daily excretion rate of vitamin B_{12} approximated a first order function. He, nevertheless, concluded that the daily dosage of B_{12} should be 0.1 percent of the estimated store of the normal, or 4 to 12 μg. per day. He suggests that the many companions of pernicious anemia, such as gastric atrophy and premature greying of hair, were the result of dosage levels below the 4 to 12 μg. per day level.

Adams (10), in studies on the rates of disappearance of injected B_{12} from the blood in patients with pernicious anemia, found that serum levels fell at a rate independent of the absolute serum concentration, a finding consistent with our own observations. He concluded with Gräsbeck that higher maintenance levels were necessary. Reizenstein used both whole body counting techniques and microbiologic determination of biliary and fecel excretion, as well as B_{12} serum clearances, to estimate daily needs (11, 12, 13). He noted discrepancies between whole body counting and microbiologic techniques. He indicated that "although the rate of excretion of radioactive material was continually decreasing, after 250 days 0.1 percent of the label remaining in the body was being excreted daily, whereas only 0.04 percent of the unlabeled body stores is excreted daily." He felt these discrepancies could arise if the labeled material was slowly degraded or selectively excreted or if complete mixing of the labeled material with the body stores had not been attained. Reizenstein, acting on the latter assumption, used an analog computer to estimate the size of various body pools. He concluded that this was indeed the correct interpretation and that rates of loss as high as 0.1 percent daily overestimate B_{12} losses.

We have used a whole body counting technique similar to that of Reizenstein and have not observed the constantly decreasing rate of loss of label after the first 120 days. The argument regarding slow plasma clearance rates of B_{12} raised by Reizenstein is cogent, but it might be pointed out that the plasma system is a transport system (14) and does not necessarily reflect the over-all state of use or stores as indicated by Adams' data.

Our estimates of turnover of B_{12} are compatible with clinical observations concerning the length of time required for patients to develop signs and symptoms of B_{12} lack following total gastrectomy. It has been repeatedly observed that signs appear in one to ten years. This period for exhaustion of body stores is exactly predicted from our data. Relapse would be expected to occur when body stores are 500 μg. of B_{12} or less. If stores are 4,000 μg., then body stores would be expected to decrease to this level at about five years. If body stores are 10,000 μg., evidence of deficiency would occur at about eight to ten years. A slower turnover rate as suggested by Reizenstein does not coincide with the clinical observations and in fact would have abnormalities occurring at twenty years or more.

One reservation must be made. If using the standard chair position for whole body counting we are measuring primarily clearance rates of label from the liver and if equilibrium between liver and other sites of B_{12} deposition does not occur as suggested by Reizenstein, overestimation of turnover of B_{12} may occur. On the other hand, while 25 percent of the label is primarily in liver, the remainder is obviously in other sites. At the decay rates shown, contribution to the photopeak after a year by Co^{60}-B_{12} in body sites other than the liver should be large even if equilibrium did not occur. A change in the decay slope would be expected if this were the case, and none has been seen. There is evidence that equilibrium does occur in man and animals (17, 18, 19). If equilibrium is present, then the position of the probe with regard to any particular body site is of no importance.

We do not believe our data has any direct bearing on the correct maintenance dose of B_{12} in pernicious anemia. Further, we do not believe that the large losses of B_{12} (4 to 10 μg.) in normals are necessarily inconsistent with observations relating to a much smaller (0.5 to 1.5 μg.) minimal daily requirement of B_{12} in pernicious anemia. Gräsbeck and Adams have both indicated that they feel higher maintenance doses are necessary. Gräsbeck inferred such on the basis of changes other than the hematologic manifestations as indicated earlier; and, Adams did so on the basis of the low serum levels of B_{12} observed in patients with pernicious anemia treated with the usual dosage schedules. Such arguments are tenuous and ignore the years of clinical observations which fail to show any benefit obtained from large and frequent dosage with vitamin B_{12}. It is apparent that the body is able to operate efficiently at varying amounts of body stores of B_{12} much as with other nutrients. Our own data support these observations. One of our patients (R. R.) had consistently low (90 $\mu\mu$g. B_{12} per ml.) serum levels of B_{12} during a time of continuing clinical improvement and final complete remission of both hematologic and neurologic manifestations of B_{12} deficiency.

CONCLUSIONS

B_{12} absorption measured by whole body counting is simple and reliable.

Turnover rates of B_{12} do not vary regardless of the size of body stores, indicating that losses are primarily a first order function.

The estimated values for body turnover (around 0.1 percent of body stores per day) of B_{12} accurately predict the time that evidences of B_{12} deficiency would present in gastrectomized patients with previously normal stores of B_{12}.

Arguments concerning the correct maintenance dose of B_{12} in pernicious anemia are not answered from these studies. We believe, however, that clinical evidence suggests that there is little merit in high maintenance dosages to normalize body stores or serum levels of B_{12}.

The validity of the data with regard to turnover is dependent on the presence of a state of mean equilibrium between labeled and nonlabeled vitamin in the body.

REFERENCES

1. Darby, W. J., Jones, E., Clark, S. L., Jr., McGanity, W. J., de Oliveira, Dutra J., Perez, C., Kevany, J., and LeBrocquy, J.: The development of vitamin B_{12} deficiency by untreated patients with pernicious anemia. Amer. J. Clin. Nutr., 6:513, 1958.
2. Darby, W. J., Bridgforth, E. B., LeBrocquy, J., Clark, S. L. Jr., de Oliveira, Dutra, J., Kevany, J., McGanity, W. J., and Perez, C.: Vitamin B_{12} requirement of adult man. Amer. J. Med., 25:726, 1958.
3. Chung, A. S. M., Pearson, W. N., Darby, W. J., Miller, O. N., and Goldsmith, G. A.: Folic acid, vitamin B_6, pantothenic acid vitamin B_{12} in human dietaries. Amer. J. Clin. Nutr. 9:573, 1961.
4. Bozian, R. C., Ferguson, L., Heyssel, R. M., Meneely, G. R., and Darby, W. J.: Evidence concerning the human requirement for vitamin B_{12}. Symposium on Nutritional and Metabolic Aspects of Blood Cell Formation, Univ. Ark. Med. Center, Little Rock. Amer. J. Clin. Nutr., in press.
5. Miller, S., Corbius, H. F., Sullivan, J. F.: A modified urinary excretion test for measuring oral Co^{60}-labeled vitamin B_{12} and its application in certain disease states. Blood, 12:347, 1957.
6. Gräsbeck, R., Nyberg, W., and Reizenstein, P. G.: Biliary and fecal vitamin B_{12} excretion in man, an isotope study. Proc. Soc. Exp. Biol. Med., 97:780, 1958.
7. Adams, J. F.: Vitamin B_{12} and intrinsic factor, the measurement of the total assayable vitamin B_{12} in the body. European Symposium on Vitamin B_{12} and Intrinsic Factor, Hamburg August, 1961, Stuttgart, Ferdinand Enke Verlag, 1962.
8. Gräsbeck, R.: Calculations on vitamin B_{12} turnover in man. Scand. J. Clin. Lab. Invest., 11:250, 1959.

9. Gräsbeck, R.: *Vitamin B$_{12}$, in Advances in Clinical Chemistry,* edited by Sobotka, H., and Stewart, C. P. New York, Academic Press, 1960, 3:299.

10. Adams, J. F.: Vitamin B$_{12}$ and intrinsic factor, considerations governing the maintenance treatment of patients with pernicious anemia European Symposium on Vitamin B$_{12}$ and Intrinsic Factor, Hamburg, August, 1961, Stuttgart, Ferdinand Enke Verlag, 1962.

11. Reizenstein, P. G.: Vitamin B$_{12}$ metabolism, some studies on the absorption, excretion, enterohepatic circulation, turning over rate, body distribution and tissue-binding of B$_{12}$. *Acta. Med. Scand., 165*:Suppl. 347, 31, 1959.

12. Reizenstein, P. G.: Physiologic and pathologic loss of radiovitamin B$_{12}$ in man. *Congress Int. Soc. Hemat.,* 2 (Abstract).

13. Reizenstein, P. G., Robertson, J. S., Cronkite, E. P., and Cohn, S. H.: Relation of the behavior of tracer B$_{12}$ to that of the unlabeled vitamin in the body store. *Int. J. Vit. Res.,* Abstract.

14. Esten, S., Brody, E., Wesserman, L.: The metabolism of vitamin B$_{12}$ in pernicious and other megaloblastic anemias, *Adv. Int. Med.,* 9:11, 1958.

15. Rowland, R. A., Simpson, L. A.: Addisonian anemia following gastrectomy and gastrojejunostomy. *Lancet, 2*:1202, 1932.

16. Harvey, J. C.: The vitamin B$_{12}$ deficiency state engendered by total gastrectomy. *Surgery, 4*:977, 1956.

17. Schloesser, L. L., Desphande, P., and Schilling, R. F.: Biological turnover rate of cyanocobalarnia (Vitamin B$_{12}$) in human liver. *Arch. Int. Med., 101*:306, 1958.

18. Glass, G. B. J., and Marabaimer, W. L.: Radioactive vitamin B$_{12}$ in the liver. *J. Lab. Clin. Med., 52*:860, 1958.

19. Gräsbeck, R., Ignatius, R., Jarnsfelt, J., Linden, H.; and Mail, A.: Specific activity of radiovitamin B$_{12}$ in organs and subcellular liver fractions after injection of Co^{58}-labelled vitamin B$_{12}$. *Clin. Chem. Acta., 6*:56, 1961.

24

WHOLE BODY COUNTING TECHNIQUES IN CLINICAL DIAGNOSTIC STUDIES WITH Ca^{47}, Co^{58}-Vitamin B$_{12}$ AND Fe^{59}

E. H. BELCHER AND C. J. ROBINSON

Postgraduate Medical School of London
London, England

RECENTLY DEVELOPED whole body counting techniques using scintillation counters provide a new approach to many established diagnostic techniques with radioisotopes, and a whole body counting system can be a valuable asset to the radioisotope clinic. The measurement of the extremely low levels of natural radioactivity in the human body necessarily involves elaborate and expensive apparatus installed in heavily shielded rooms. Such installations have recently been reviewed by Spiers (1). However, in the measurement of higher body burdens of radioactivity encountered in clinical diagnostic tests, considerably less sensitive equipment is needed; and much useful work can be done with a simple system with a single uncollimated scintillation counter with a thallium activated sodium iodide crystal of moderate size installed in a moderately shielded enclosure and coupled with a single channel pulse height analyzer (2).

Such a system can be especially valuable, for example, in gastrointestinal absorption tests with radioisotopes. Direct measurement of the percentage of an oral test dose of radioactive material absorbed and retained within the body of the subject by whole body counting offers several advantages over the indirect method for the measurement of absorption based on the recovery of radioactivity from the feces or the assay of blood or urine. The whole body counting method permits a considerable reduction in the dose of radioactive material given to the subject. It avoids the inconvenience of venipuncture and the uncertainty of urine and fecal collections and can be carried out on an out-patient basis. It gives a direct measurement of absorption which is more accurate than that obtained from the fecal recovery method when absorption is small.

Whole body counting techniques are also useful in metabolic studies. The percentage of the administered dose of radioactive material remaining in the body at any time during a metabolic turnover test can be measured directly by whole body counting, thus avoiding the need for collections of urine and feces. This approach permits long duration studies which could not otherwise be carried out because of cumulative errors arising in the measurements of urine and fecal radioactivity.

However, the accurate measurement of the radioactive content of a large and irregular object such as the human body involves many calibration problems. Variations in body build between different subjects or changes in the distribution of radioactive material within the body of the subject during study may be a source of error.

In this paper, the design of a whole body counting system for clinical measurements is discussed in the light of experience with a simple system incorporating a single scintillation counter detector.

EQUIPMENT

The whole body counting system used was jointly sponsored by the Postgraduate Medical School and Hammersmith Hospital. The single scintillation counter detector consists of a thallium-activated sodium iodide crystal 7.5 cm. in diameter and 9 cm. thick coupled to a thirteen stage photomultiplier tube (E.M.I. Ltd., type 9531 B.). The detector is surrounded by a lead collimator into which it can be retracted by a rack and pinion mechanism when a collimated counter is required. For whole body counting measurements it is fully extended, the crystal being completely clear of the collimator shielding. For whole body counting, the sensitivity of the detector towards a point source of any of the gamma-emitting isotopes studied is almost independent of the direction of the source. The detector is suspended in a stirrup which is itself suspended from an overhead horizontal beam, giving a wide range of positional adjustments.

The output of the photomultiplier is fed through a cathode follower to a linear amplifier (Isotope Developments, Ltd., type 652), a single channel pulse height analyser (Isotope Developments, Ltd., type 672 A) and a scaler (E. K. Cole, Ltd., type N 530). A stable power supply unit (Isotope Developments, Ltd., type 532) energizes the photomultiplier. The pulse height analyser is aligned so that only counts in the most energetic photopeak or peaks of the gamma ray spectrum of the isotope concerned are recorded.

The detector is mounted in an enclosure 2.5 by 2.5 by 2 meters. This enclosure has an inner shielding of lead sheet 7 mm. thick and an outer shielding of chalk bricks 15 cm. thick (Unibrix Ltd., type CC) and is situated on the basement floor of the hospital. This is a brick building, and the local gamma ray background is quite high. An over-all reduction in background of about 7 times at 0.5 Mev, 4.5 times at 1 Mev and 4.5 times at 1.5 Mev is achieved by these simple and economical shielding procedures (Fig. 1).

Most of the studies described here have been made using a modification of the standard chair technique described by Miller (3). The subject is seated comfortably in a standard chair in front of the counter whose axis is horizontal 100 cm. above floor level. The distance of the front face of the crystal to the sternum of the subject is fixed at 50 cm.

RESULTS

Gastrointestinal Absorption of Co^{58}-Labeled Vitamin B_{12}

Figure 2 summarizes the studies of the gastrointestinal absorption of vitamin B_{12}, in which oral test doses of the Co^{58}-labeled vitamin were given to adult subjects (4). Doses of 0.8 μg. of vitamin B_{12} containing about 1 μc of Co^{58} were given, in some cases alone, in other cases accompanied by an intrinsic factor preparation. Absorption of the test dose was determined directly in terms of whole body counting measurements carried

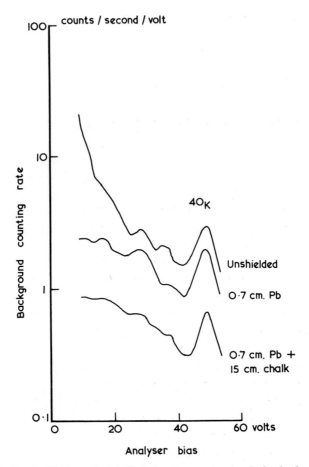

Figure 1. Unshielded and shielded background of whole body counting system.

out by the standard chair technique seven days after administration of the dose, by which time unabsorbed radioactivity can be assumed to have been cleared completely from the gastrointestinal tract and all feces passed have been collected and assayed.

The percentage of the test dose absorbed was calculated from the whole body counting measurements in two ways. In the first method, the whole body counting rate was measured immediately after administration of the dose. The counting rate

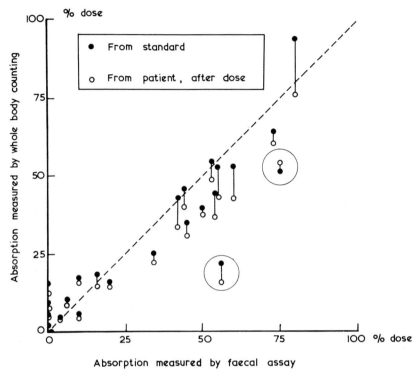

Figure 2. Gastrointestinal absorption of oral test doses of Co^{58}-labeled vitamin B$_{12}$. The ringed experimental points represent measurements in which fecal collection is known to have been incomplete.

at seven days after correction for radioactive decay could then be expressed as a percentage of this initial value. Each subject acts as his own standard, so that variations in counting efficiency due to difference in body build between different subjects are to some extent eliminated. On the other hand, the method does not take account of the changing distribution of radioactive material in the body during the test. In the initial measurement the dose is in the upper gastrointestinal tract; in the later one the absorbed material is distributed in the body tissues, largely in the liver. During the initial measurement the position of the dose is rapidly changing, and the reproducibility was found to be poor.

In the second method of calculation, the whole body counting rate at seven days was expressed as a percentage of that measured from a small standard source equal in radioactive content to the dose placed at a fixed distance from the detector. A calibration factor was included in the calculation to take account of the difference in counting geometry between the extended body of the subject and the standard source, this factor being determined from measurements on a group of subjects who received known amounts of Co^{58}-labeled vitamin B_{12} by intravenous injection seven days previously. Since the calibration factor thus determined was a mean value for the group, this method of calculation takes no account of effects due to differences in body build between different subjects. On the other hand, since it was determined from measurements which were made at seven days after injection, it relates correctly to the distribution of radioactive material remaining in the body at seven days after an oral test dose.

The agreement between the values obtained from the whole body counting measurements by the second method of calculation and those obtained from fecal radioactivity measurements is reasonably good, except in two cases where the fecal collection was incomplete. These values are slightly higher, which may in part be due to small losses of radioactivity in the urine and in part to the difficulty in making a complete fecal collection. The scatter of the observed values can be attributed in part to variations in body builds and in part to experimental errors.

On the other hand, the values obtained from the whole body counting measurements by the first method of calculation are consistently and significantly lower than those obtained from the measurements by the second method or from fecal radioactivity measurements. The mean value of the ratio of percentage absorption calculated by the second method to that found by the first method is 1.14. This ratio must be attributed to the changing distribution of radioactivity within the body during the study.

It is clear that in standard chair whole body counting measurements of the gastrointestinal absorption of Co^{58}-labeled vitamin B_{12}, the subject may be used as his own standard only if a factor is included in the calculation to take account of the changing distribution of radioactivity during the test. Even then error may be introduced by changes in the position of the dose due to peristaltic movements of the gut and gastric emptying during the initial measurement.

Gastrointestinal Absorption of Ca^{47}, Fe^{59}

Similar problems arise in any gastrointestinal absorption test, and in some tests they may be aggravated. The absorption of vitamin B_{12} is delayed until the ileum of the small intestine, so that changes in the distribution of this material during the initial measurement are restricted to movements within the lumen of the tract. Other substances, such as iron or calcium, are rapidly absorbed in the stomach or duodenum. Absorption may then be occurring even during the initial measurement.

Measurements of gastrointestinal absorption of Fe^{59} have nevertheless been carried out satisfactorily using the standard chair technique of whole body counting seven days after an oral test dose of 1 mg. Fe given to fasting subjects in the form of a ferric salt containing 1 to 5 μc Fe^{59} and accompanied by 500 mg. ascorbic acid to ensure reduction of the dose to the ferrous state in the stomach (5). However, because of the rapid absorption of this material, it was found unreliable to use the subject as his own standard. Each subject was therefore measured at seven days after administration of the dose in terms of a standard source and a calibration factor included in the calculation to take account of the difference in counting geometry between subject and standard. This method of calculation did not take account of effects due to differences in body build between different subjects.

Similar considerations were found to apply with Ca^{47}. A satisfactory test of calcium absorption was nevertheless developed in which a standard oral test dose of calcium gluconate containing 1 to 20 μc Ca^{47} was given to fasting subjects previously equilibrated for several days on a standard calcium intake (6). Absorption was determined by the standard chair technique of whole body counting at seven days, the subject again being measured in terms of a small standard source and a calibration factor used to take account of differences in counting geometry between subject and standard.

TURNOVER OF Fe⁵⁹

Further evidence of the effect of redistribution of radioactive material in the body on whole body counting rate measured by the standard chair technique is found in studies with Fe^{59}. Figure 3 shows the changes in whole body counting rate observed

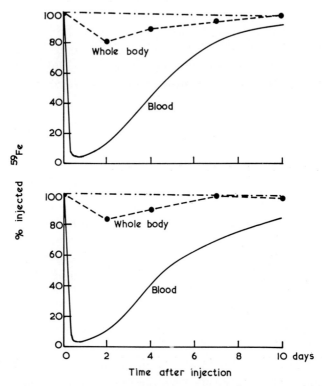

Figure 3. Whole body and blood radioactivity in two subjects given Fe^{59} by intravenous injection, O--O whole body counting rate; -.-. whole body radioactivity calculated from urinary and fecal loss.

in two subjects who received intravenous injections of Fe^{59}. The Fe^{59}, in the form of a ferric salt, was previously incubated with a specimen of the recipient's plasma to ensure binding of the radioactive iron to the plasma transferrin. For each measurement the whole body counting rate was compared to that from a small standard source. Blood samples were taken at suitable intervals and all urine and feces were assayed. Loss of radioactivity in the urine and feces was quite small during the study so body burden remained almost constant. However, as the radioactive material left the plasma and was taken up by the erythropoietic tissues, the relative counting rate fell by some 15 percent, rising again as labeled red cells were released to the circulation.

TURNOVER OF Ca^{47}

Similar effects due to major redistributions of radioactive material within the body were observed in standard chair whole body counting measurements of intravenously injected Ca^{47}. Figure 4 shows the results of studies on two subjects who re-

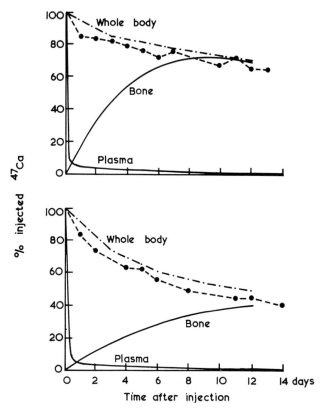

Figure 4. Whole body and plasma and nonexchangeable bone radioactivity in two subjects given Ca^{47} by intravenous injection, O--O whole body counting rate; -.-. whole body radioactivity calculated from urinary and fecal loss.

ceived 20 μc Ca^{47} intravenously for calcium turnover studies. The whole body counting rate was on each occasion compared with that of a small standard. Daily plasma samples and all urine and feces were assayed. From an analysis of the data, the fixation of Ca^{47} in bone can be calculated (6). Since there was a significant excretory loss of Ca^{47} in both urine and feces, the body burden fell continuously throughout the study. However, a discrepancy of about 10 percent is observed between the body burden measured directly by whole body counting and that determined indirectly from the cumulative urinary and fecal loss. A closer examination of the data shows that this discrepancy arises mainly during the initial mixing phase the first few hours after injection. During this period, the injected dose leaves the blood stream and equilibrates in the exchangeable calcium pool in the tissues. If the initial measurement is delayed until two hr. after injection to allow equilibration to occur, the discrepancy almost disappears and subsequent fixation of the tracer in bone does not appear significantly to influence the whole body counting rate. Rather similar effects have been observed by other workers (7-9) in standard chair measurements of intravenously injected Ca^{47}.

DISCUSSION

The results indicate that although a standard chair technique of whole body counting is satisfactory for many clinical diagnostic tests with radioisotopes, changes in distribution of radioactivity within the body of the subject can lead to changes of up to 15 percent in whole body counting rate. These changes are especially noticeable when radioactive material initially in the gastrointestinal tract or in the circulation passes into the tissues.

Such effects can be predicted from a consideration of the geometry of the standard chair technique. Figure 5 shows isocount lines for a point source placed at different positions in a typical standard chair arrangement. The counting efficiency for a point source varies rapidly with position over the body of the subject, ranging from a minimum of 50 percent at the back to a maximum of 150 percent at the front of the subject. (In

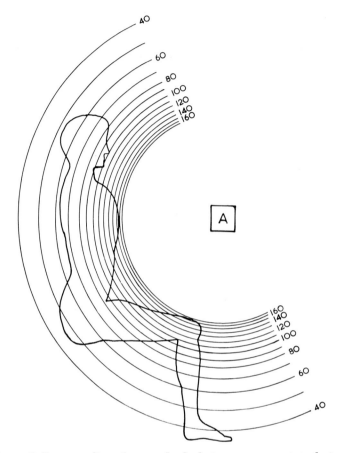

Figure 5. Isocount lines for standard chair measurement technique.

Figure 5 and those that follow, the data refer to a nonabsorbing medium; absorption of radiation within the body of the subject is not taken into account.) In these circumstances, the observation of a change in whole body counting rate of 15 percent resulting from a major redistribution of radioactive material in the body is not at all surprising. A small change in the build or position of the subject may also be expected to affect the counting rate significantly. These observations prompt a revaluation of the various techniques for whole body counting using single or multiple detectors, with special regard to their uniformity of response and freedom from positioning errors.

The alternatives to the standard chair technique are the 1 meter arc (10) and 1.75 meter arc techniques (11), both of which require a single detector, and various couch techniques using multiple detectors (12-15). The arc techniques have been considered in detail in relation to the standard chair techniques by Miller (11). They suffer from the disadvantage of low sensitivity due to the increased distance of the subject from the detector, and they are not very convenient for clinical work since not all patients can abopt and maintain the required position. Moreover, they still retain some nonuniformity of response between the front and the back of the subject. With the 1 meter arc technique, the range may be from 80 percent to 120 percent. Couch techniques are an attractive alternative. They can have high sensitivity and are well suited to clinical work with sick patients. Such techniques have been used in a number of clinical diagnostic studies, but their geometrical characteristics have not been fully explored yet.

Figure 6 shows the calculated variation in counting rate

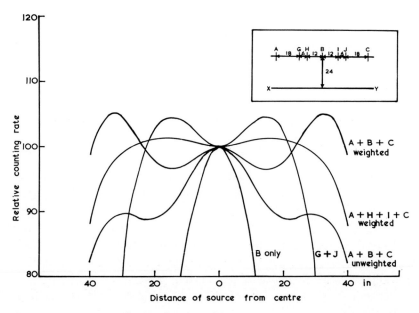

Figure 6. Variation of counting rate from a point source with position of source along the surface of a couch viewed by a single detector and by various multiple detector systems.

observed as a point source moves along the suface XY of a couch and is viewed by one, two, three or four detectors 24 in. above it. With a single detector at B, the counting rate falls off rapidly as the source moves away from the center. If two detectors at A and C are used, their counting rates being added arithmetically, the total counting rate, A + C, still shows considerable variation with position. The same is true with three detectors at A, B and C. However, if three detectors at A, B and C are used and their individual counting rates are suitably weighted before they are added together, the weighted sum of the counting rates, x (A + C) + yB, can be made almost independent of the position of the source, showing a maximum variation of ± 5 percent over the whole length of the couch. The weighting factors, x = 0.802, y = 0.506, used in these calculations are such that the weighted sum of the counting rates due to a uniformly distributed line source 72 in. long along the line XY is identical with that from a point source with the same total radioactive content at its center.

With four detectors at A, D, E and C, and even flatter response is possible, the weighted sum, x(A+C) + y (D+E) showing maximum variation of no more than ± 2 percent over the length of the couch. The weighting factors, calculated as previously, are x = 0.608, y = 0.391.

Hence, using a couch technique with three or four detectors whose counting rates are suitably weighted before addition, a nearly flat response can be obtained along the long axis of the subject. However (Fig. 7), there remains a nonuniformity of re-

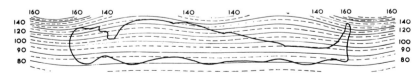

Figure 7. Isocount lines for a couch measurement technique: three weighted detectors above (A, B, C).

sponse between the front and back of the subject. With three detectors, the total range is from 70 percent to 130 percent.

The situation may be somewhat improved by placing one detector above and two below the subject, keeping the weight-

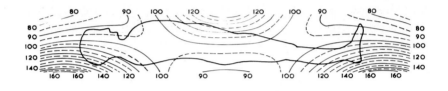

Figure 8. Isocount lines for a couch measurement technique: one detector above (B) and two below (A, C).

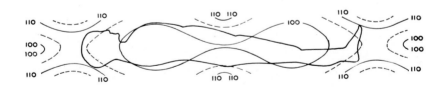

Figure 9. Isocount lines for a couch measurement technique: three detectors above (A, B, C) and three below (D, E, F).

ing factors constant (Fig. 8). The range in response over the whole body of the subject is now only 80 percent to 120 percent. With six detectors (Fig. 9), an even more uniform response is possible, the maximum variation being only 10 percent. The weighting factors for the lower three positions of measurement are identical with those for the upper three.

To make such measurements, it is not necessary to use six individual scintillation counters. It would indeed be possible to use a single detector, making measurements at each of the upper three positions of measurement in turn with the subject supine and then repeating these measurements with the subject prone. The level of the couch must be arranged so that the axis of the subject coincides approximately with the line XY for which the weighting factors have been calculated.

A more elegant method of making such measurements would be to arrange for a single detector to perform a continuous scan between A and C. The counting rates for successive increments of the scan could be separately weighted, using calculated factors, and the weighted sum computed. Alternatively, weighting could be carried out automatically by varying the scanning speed, and the cumulative counting rate determined directly. The calculation of the optimum weighting factors for a continuous scan is an interesting mathematical problem which is probably best treated by automatic computing techniques.

Such a system should considerably improve both the convenience and the accuracy of clinical whole body counting measurements. It may be expected to give results almost independent of the distribution of radioactive material within the body of the subject and should also be almost unaffected by variations in body build, small positioning errors or small movements on the part of the subject.

An important aspect of these proposed techniques is their sensitivity relative to the standard chair and arc techniques. Table I gives data relating to the sensitivity of the whole body counting system described when used for the measurement of Ca^{47} by different measurement techniques. The various couch techniques are seen to give mean counting rates lower by a factor of about two as compared with the standard chair technique, but superior to the 1 meter arc technique, and greatly superior to the 1.75

TABLE I

SENSITIVITY OF WHOLE BODY COUNTING SYSTEM TO CA^{47} IN VARIOUS
MEASUREMENT TECHNIQUES ON HUMAN SUBJECTS

Technique	Background c/s	Counting Rate c/s/μc	$\dfrac{(Counting\ Rate)^2}{Background}$
Standard chair	1.80	6.00	20.0
Couch, B only	1.80	3.99	8.82
Couch, A + B + C unweighted	1.80	3.02	5.05
Couch, A + B + C weighted	1.80	2.88	4.61
Couch, A + D + E + C unweighted	1.80	3.18	5.63
Couch, A + D + E + C weighted	1.80	3.04	5.14
1 meter arc	1.80	2.26	2.83
1.75 meter arc	1.80	0.74	0.30

meter arc technique. The improved uniformity of response of the couch techniques as compared with the standard chair would seem to outweigh the reduction in sensitivity.

REFERENCES

1. Spiers, F. W.: Proceedings of the Symposium on Whole Body Counting, Vienna, 1961. I.A.E.A., Vienna, p. 3, 1962.
2. Belcher, E. H.: Proceedings of the 5th International Symposium on Radioactive Isotopes in Clinical Medicine and Research, Bad Gastein, 1962. Munich, Urban and Schwarzenberg, p. 464, 1962.
3. Miller, C. E.: Proceedings of the Second International Conference on Peaceful Uses of Atomic Energy, Geneva, 1958. New York, United Nations, 23:113, 1958.
4. Anderson, B., Belcher, E. H., and Roblnson, C. J.: Nucl. Med. (Stuttg.) 3:349, 1963.
5. Malamos, B., Belcher, E. H., Binopoulos, D., and Constantinides, C.: Proceedings of the Symposium on Whole Body Counting, Vienna, 1961. Vienna, I.A.E.A., p. 435, 1962.
6. Fraser, T. R., Belcher E. H., and North, K.: Vienna I.A.E.A., p. 34, 1962.
7. Corey, K. R., Kenny, P., Greenberg, A., Pazianos, A., Pearson, O. H., and Laughlin, J.: Amer. J. Roentgenol., 85:955, 1961.
8. Sargent, T. W.: Proceedings of the Symposium on Whole Body Counting, Vienna, 1961. Vienna, I.A.E.A., p. 447, 1962.

9. Rinsler, M. G., Dyche, G. M., and Trott, N. G.: Proceedings of the 4th International Symposium on Radioisotopes in Clinical Medicine and Research, Bad Gastein, 1960. Munich, Urban and Schwarzenberg, p. 19, 1960.

10. Evans, R. D.: *Amer. J. Roentgenol.*, 37:368, 1938.

11. Miller, C. E.: Proceedings of the Symposium on Whole Body Counting, Vienna, 1961. Vienna, I.A.E.A., p. 81, 1962.

12. Rundo, J.: Proceedings of the Second International Conference on Peaceful Uses of Atomic Energy, Geneva, 1958. New York, United Nations, 23:101, 1958.

13. Charleston, D. B.: Proceedings of the Symposium on Whole Body Counting Vienna 1961. I.A.E.A., Vienna 1962, p. 190.

14. Eto, H., Watanabe, H., Tanaka, E., and Hiramoto, T.: Ibid., p. 211.

15. Cederquist, E. S., and Liden, K. V. H.: Ibid., p. 487.

25

WHOLE BODY COUNTING TECHNIQUES IN CLINICAL STUDIES WITH Co^{58}-LABELED VITAMIN B$_{12}$, I^{131}-LABELED ALBUMIN, Na^{22}, Fe^{59} AND Br^{82}

B. Malamos, E. H. Belcher, D. Binopoulos and C. Constantinides[1]

University of Athens and Alexandra Hospital
Athens, Greece

INTRODUCTION

W^{ITH} HUMAN gamma spectrometry, it is easy to carry out studies which previously required difficult measurements of blood and excreta and to improve the quality of these measurements. Low levels of radioactive materials can be given, the discomfort of the patients is slight and errors in the ratio analysis of blood and urine samples can be eliminated.

The five clinical studies to be presented are measurements of the rate of absorption of Co^{58}-labeled vitamin B$_{12}$, the degradation rate of I^{131}-albumin, the Na^{22} space and total exchangeable sodium, Fe^{59} absorption and extracellular fluid space with Br^{82}.

Both normal subjects and patients were studied. The results obtained by whole body spectrometry and dilution analysis were compared.

MATERIALS AND METHODS

The measurement system consisted of a single scintillation counter incorporating a thallium-activated sodium iodide crystal 7.5 cm. in diameter and 11.5 cm. thick coupled to a 256 channel

---

[1] Present address: Vanderbilt University School of Medicine, Nashville, Tennessee.

pulse height analyzer (Radiation Counter Laboratories, Inc., Type 20613) with magnetic storage, cathode-ray tube display, and pen recorder and printer write-out facilities.

The counter was surrounded by a lead collimator 6 cm. thick from which it normally projected, so that the whole of the crystal was in front of the face of the collimator. It could be retracted until the crystal was completely within the collimator. Counter and collimator were mounted on a movable light trolly, the axis of the counter being horizontal and 125 cm. above the ground. Measurements were made with the person seated comfortably in front of the counter. The horizontal distance from the front face of the counter to the subject's sternum was fixed at 50 cm. The subject's head, trunk, arms and upper legs were lying along an arc of radius 60 cm. approximately equidistant from the counter. This position of measurement (Fig. 1) is a modifica-

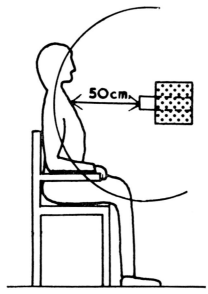

Figure 1. Standard chair technique for measurement of human subjects.

tion of the "standard chair" technique described by Miller (4). Standards were measured in small vials on the axis of the counter at a distance of 60 cm. from its front.

The 256 channels of the pulse height analyzer could be divided into four groups of 64 channels each. Only 128 of these channels are normally used in measurement. The background gamma spectrum was recorded and stored in channels 0 to 63. Gamma spectra of subjects and standards were recorded in channels 64 to 128. The background already recorded was automatically subtracted by means of the date shift and complement facilities.

The analyzer was set to operate on sixty-four channels, and the gain of the system was adjusted so that the gamma spectrum to be recorded extended over these channels. The background was first accumulated for the desired counting time on channels 0 to 63. The analyzer was then switched to channels 64 to 127, and the background already recorded and stored in channels 0 to 63 was shifted to channels 64 to 127 and complemented. The standard was then set up in position and counts accumulated for the same counting time as for the background. The accumulated net counts were then printed out. The memory of channels 64 to 127 was then cleared to zero. The background still stored in channels 0 to 63 was again shifted to channels 64 to 127 and complemented. The subject was then set up in position and counts accumulated for the same counting time. The accumulated counts, corrected for background, were again printed out. The appropriate peak or peaks were then selected on the recorded spectra, and the accumulated counts on the appropriate channels on standard and subject compared.

APPLICATION IN CLINICAL DIAGNOSIS

Gastrointestinal Absorption with Co^{58}-Labeled Vitamin B_{12}

Measurements of vitamin B_{12} absorption were made after an oral test dose of 1 μc of Co^{58}-labeled vitamin B_{12} containing 1 μgm. of the vitamin. Measurements were made seven days after administration when a large part of the injected radioactivity was present in the liver. Results from whole body counting and hepatic uptake were compared.

Vitamin B_{12} was administered to thirty-four subjects divided into five groups. In seven normal subjects the absorption ranged from 26 percent to 100 percent with a mean value of 61 percent.

Thirteen patients with gastrointestinal disease had measurements of 9 percent to 83 percent with a mean value of 37 percent. Values in seven patients with liver diseases, ranged from 50 percent to 100 percent with a mean value of 76.5 percent. Values in three patients with malignant diseases of the lymphopoetic system were 26 percent to 46 percent with a mean value of 39 percent.

In four patients, three with megaloblastic anemia and one with erythroblastosis who had histamine fast achlorydria, absorption was 0 percent.

The percentage of vitamin B_{12} absorbed varied in the group of normal subjects and in the groups of patients (Fig. 2). There was good correlation of whole body counting technique with per cent hepatic uptake (Fig. 3).

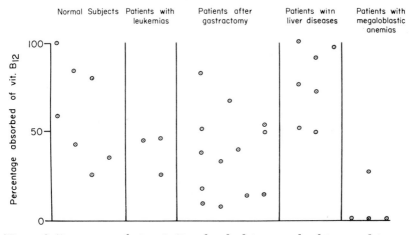

Figure 2. Percentage of vitamin B_{12} absorbed in normal subjects and in patients divided in categories.

Albumin Turnover with I^{131}-Labeled Albumin

The standard chair technique of whole body counting was also used to estimate the fraction of the administered radioactivity remaining in the body in studies of protein turnover (7).

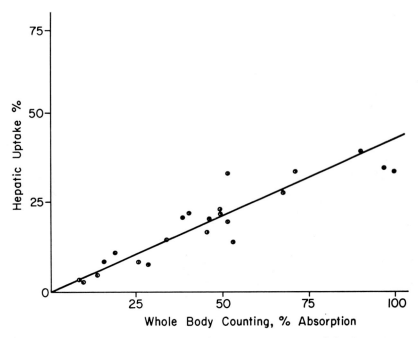

Figure 3. Correlation between B_{12} absorption as measured by hepatic uptake and by whole body counting.

In this study, 10 μc of I^{131}-labeled albumin was injected intra-
venously, and measurements were made 24 hr. after injection.
Uptake of I^{131} in the thyroid was blocked by administration of
Lugol's Solution.

We studied seventeen men and women between ages eighteen and sixty-three for fifteen days. Nine of the subjects were
clinically healthy, six had nephritis and two the nephrotic syndrome. Albumin turnover was determined by the method of
McFarlane (3) and compared to the whole body counting technique. The whole body retention at 30 min. following intravenous administration of I^{131}-labeled albumin was taken as the
100 retention value.

A reduction in the albumin pool both intravascular and ex-
travascular has been observed in nephrotic patients, but not in
nephritic.

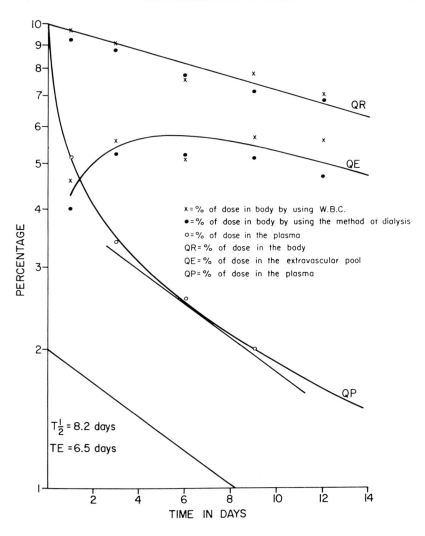

Figure 4. I[131] albumin turnover data for normal subject.

In nephrotic patients the turnover rate of albumin is increased, but due to the reduction in the albumin pool, the absolute amount of albumin daily degraded was within normal limits. In nephritic patients, both the turnover rate and the absolute amount of albumin daily degraded were reduced. Consequently the albumin half life decreased in nephrotic patients, but was normal or increased in nephritic patients.

There was good correlation between the two methods with respect to the percentage of dose remaining in the body (Fig. 4).

Measurements of Sodium Space and Total Exchangeable Sodium with Na^{22}

A dose of 20 μc Na^{22} was administered orally as sodium chloride, and measurements were made 24 hr. after administration and daily thereafter for four days.

Since only relative values of whole body radioactivity in the same subject at different times are required, differences in weight or body build introduce no errors in these studies.

In the standard chair technique used in the present study, the standard deviation of individual measurements is approximately $\pm$ 2 percent, even when great care is exercised in positioning the subject.

We studied thirty-four subjects, twelve normal individuals, and twenty-two patients with edema, diabetic acidosis, adrenal cortical insufficiency, lobar pneumonia or hypertension. The patients with edema were studied before and after administration of mercurial diuretics.

Both whole body counting and dilution analysis were used to determine the percentage of Na^{22} remaining in the body, the Na^{22} space and total exchangeable sodium (2).

The mean total exchangeable sodium of the twelve normal subjects was 44.7 $\pm$ 4.8 mEq./μgm. High values were found of total exchangeable sodium in the edematous patients. We observed a good correlation of these values with the clinical estimates of edema.

The total exchangeable sodium was decreased in patients suffering from adrenal cortical insufficiency and in diabetic patients after recovery from diabetic acidosis. Mercurial diuretics had no effect on the total exchangeable sodium in normal subjects, but caused gross reduction in patients with edema on a low salt diet. There is no correlation of the total exchangeable sodium with the serum sodium (Fig. 5).

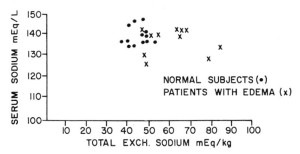

Figure 5. There is no correlation between serum sodium and total exchangeable sodium.

Gastrointestinal Absorption with Fe[59]

Measurements of gastrointestinal absorption of iron were satisfactorily made in forty-four subjects (23 normal, including 5 pregnant women during the second or third trimester) and on patients with and without diseases of blood, using Fe[59] after an oral test dose of 1 to 5 μc of the isotope containing 1 mg. of iron as a ferric salt. This dose was given with a large dose of ascorbic acid to ensure reduction to the ferrous state in the stomach. Absorption was estimated by whole body counting seven days after administration of the test dose, a value of 0.66 being assumed in all cases for the ratio of number of counts from the subject to that from the standard.

Variations in weight and body build of the subjects introduced small errors into the absorption determined in this way. Absorption was also determined by assaying a blood sample taken seven days after administration of the test dose, the percentage of the dose present in the circulation at this time being calculated, assuming a blood volume of 7.55 percent of the body weight for men and 6.65 percent for women. There was good agreement between the results of the two methods of study in normal subjects, the percentage of the absorbed dose incorporated into the circulating red cells falling within the expected limits of 60 to 90 percent (Fig. 6) (1).

Extracellular Fluid Volume with Br[82]

The standard chair technique of whole body counting was

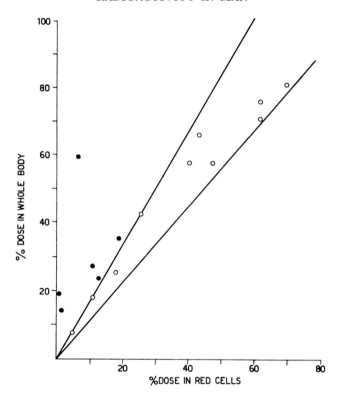

Figure 6. Measurement of absorption of an oral test dose of Fe[59] in hematologically normal (O) and abnormal (.) subjects. Abscissae: percentage of dose in circulating red cells seven days after administration. Ordinates: percentage of dose in whole body seven days after administration. The normal limits corresponding to utilization of 60 percent and 90 percent of absorbed Fe[59] are shown.

used to estimate the fraction of the administered radioactivity remaining in the body in studies of extracellular fluid volume by using Br[82] (5,6). In these studies, 20 μc of Br[82] as NH$_4$Br[82] was given orally in normal subjects and patients with edema. Measurements of extracellular fluid volume were made immediately after the administration and every 24 hr. for four days. Results using whole body counting and the method of dialysis were comparable (Fig. 7).

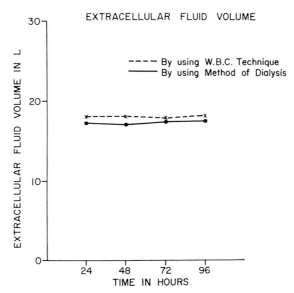

Figure 7. Extracellular fluid volume measured by using Br⁸². Correlation between whole body counting and method of dialysis in normal subjects.

CONCLUSION

Whole body counting by a standard chair technique using a single scintillation counter as radiation detector has many useful applications in clinical diagnosis with radioisotopes.

REFERENCES

1. Bothwell, T. H., Callendar, S., Mallet, B., and Witts, L. J.: The study of erythropoiesis using tracer quantities of radioactive iron. *Brit. J. Haemat.*, 2:1, 1956.

2. Forbes, G. B., and Perley, A: Estimation of total body sodium by isotopic dilution. I. Studies on young adults. *J. Clin. Invest.*, 30:558, 1951.

3. McFarlane, A. S.: the behaviour of I¹³¹ labeled plasma proteins in vivo. *Ann. N.Y. Acad. Sci.*, 70:19, 1957.

4. Miller, C. E.: Low intensity spectrometry of the gamma radiation emitted by human beings. *Proc. Second U. N. Int. Conf. P.U.A.E.* 23:113, 1958.

5. Nicholson, J. P., and Zilva, J. F.: A 6-hour method for determining the extracellular low fluid volume in human subjects. Clin. *Chiwr. Acta,* 2:340, 1957.

6. Nicholson, J. P., and Zilva, J. F.: Estimation of extracellular fluid volume using radiobromine, *Clin. Sci.,* 19:391, 1960.

7. Pearson, J. D., Veall, N., and Vetter, H.: A practical method for plasma albumin turnover studies, Radioactive Isotopes in Klinik Und Forschung III. K. Fellinger and H. Vetter, Eds. *Strablentherapie, Sonderbd.,* 38:290, 1958.

DISCUSSION

Chairman: BELTON A. BURROWS

Evans Memorial Hospital
Boston, Massachusetts

JOHN RUNDO: Dr. Belcher, I wonder if the method of positioning the counters, while giving excellent uniformity of response for point sources in air, really works for the human body. The radiation which leaves different parts of the body will have a different spectrum because of different sizes and depths of tissue.

Second, we have some evidence from our own work with patients with chronic Sr^{85} administration, where the burden at the end of the experimental period was about 0.5 μc. Up to 200 days and probably longer, there are slow, steady changes in the spectrum of radiation. The activity is much too low to be able to measure it on a $1\frac{3}{4}$ metric arc, making it difficult to determine the true retention time pattern.

The results which Dr. Jordan found, particularly the agreement with the Argonne cases, seem to confirm the ICRP figure of 120 days for insoluble materials in the lung. We have been studying one case of Co^{60} oxide inhalation for 1,250 days. It may have happened as a single exposure, or it may have been a chronic exposure of some days. There were no very short components. We know it was at least six days after inhalation, but we don't know exactly how long. We show two components. One had a half life of about thirty-eight days, similar to Dr. Miller's figure.

The second component has an effective half life of 2.9 years, which corresponds to a biological half life of 6.6 percent. We have good evidence that most of the activity is in the thorax. There may also be some in the liver. We cannot say whether it is in the lungs or whether it has migrated to the lymph nodes, which might be an explanation of the long half life. Are Dr. Jordan and Dr. Miller going to follow up their cases?

ROBERT D. JORDAN: We plan to count this man, a sailor, every month until he gets transferred. We have had the same thoughts about translocation. Some of us think that there is a good possibility that the material has moved into the lymphatic system or the liver. It is difficult to tell whether the material is in one of the lower lobes of the lungs or in the liver, because they are superimposed in the area where we think much of the material is.

Half lives, I think, are dependent upon the particle size. In our case and in Argonne's, there was almost an identical physical situation. Our people were working with slugs that had been in rabbits, — some had ruptured and some were in microscopic dust form. The oxide covered material had been brushed with a wire brush and had been lifted up into a hood vent, so we suspect that the particle sizes were approximately the same and would have about the same deposition system and clearance mechanism. The data almost turned out to be too good to be true. When we reduced the gross curve to a series of exponentials, everything fell in well.

E. H. BELCHER: It is perfectly true that the diagrams that we showed are those for point sources in air and that the distribution of the count lines would, as was indicated, be affected by observation of radiation within the tissues.

Our diagnostic studies are all carried out with the Prosslight Analyzer aligned on to the peak of highest energy gamma ray in the spectrum of the isotope concerned. Therefore, the changes in shape of the spectrum below the peak in the Compton region would not affect in any way our count area. They are only affected by absorption of primary radiation, and this will depend on the path length of radiation within the tissue. We have just begun this work and have not completed the studies, but I do not anticipate that they will show great effect, because as the point source moves away from one detector, it can approach another detector. This will tend to smooth out the differences, especially if one has six positions of measurement, three above and three below, or has a continuous scan from either side of the patient.

JOHN RUNDO: I would beg to differ. The changes are such that the low energy region does not affect the peak. The changes that we observed in our Sr^{85} studies are too broad. We see a slow, but steady decrease in the total ratio of the peak, which must be an additional absorption effect. Secondly, we see a steady increase in content of the peak ratio, which is also consistent with a steady absorption effect, so to speak.

ROBERT A. DUDLEY: The effect that Dr. Rundo has mentioned certainly occurs. This also is largely inherent in the fact that we are measuring bodies which are of appreciable thickness compared with the range of gamma rays. This will show up, perhaps not identically, but similarly with most types of measurement techniques.

We are planning to use a scanning procedure that many others have used that has magnetic tape read-outs with which your analyzers now being produced are equipped. One can, while scanning, read-out in a short time, such as 5 sec., as frequently as he would like along the scanner.

DR. STOLTZ: We have had over sixty cases of individuals with lung burdens of Ag^{110}. The particle size was about 1 μ. Some of the burdens of these boys ran as high as 1 μc. We observed an elimination rate similar to Dr. Jordan's. During the first few days there was a rapid rate of elimination, during which we were able to analyze or measure quantities of silver in great numbers of sputum samples. However, after about the first week, the elimination rate became a simple exponential elimination curve with an effective half life of about fifteen days. During this time we could detect no activity in the nose wipes or sputum. However, by having the patient clear his throat before rising in the morning, we could measure the silver coming from the sputum, indicating that it was being eliminated by a mechanism similar to what you have described. The silver was never metabolized, never showed up in the urine.

Were you able to detect anything like this in the nose wipes in the case of Co^{60}?

ROBERT D. JORDAN: We got a few sputum samples, but did not have much laboratory cooperation. We picked up small traces in samples of the urine and feces. We could never initially find anything in the blood or sputum. I think this was below the detection limit of our system.

To really learn anything from the experiment, you would have to have a technique for getting uniform particle size.

NORMAN S. MACDONALD: Is there any objective evidence that total body measurements of cobalt some 100 days after B_{12} was delivered really measures B_{12}?

H. C. HEINRICH: Work done by Rosenbloom has shown that, even one year after oral intake, Co^{60} label is retained; but with the exception of the action of bacteria in the gastrointestinal tract, we have no evidence at the present moment that vitamin B_{12} is drastically altered structurally.

We have evidence from some microbiological distribution studies that the muscle content of vitamin B_{12} is 3 mg., and that liver only contains 1.6 mg. I assume that in the chair technique we really measure liver metabolism, so I would recommend that people who have access to the whole body counters try to follow the retention of Co^{60} or Co^{58} level to find out if the values are too high. The best experiment is to inject it and to tell, with biological techniques, when B_{12} metabolism becomes normal.

ROBERT M. HEYSSEL: If 75 percent of the B_{12} is in muscle, then only 25 percent is in the liver and, therefore, we must be measuring some muscle turnover at the same time.

If I take your values for half-life, which may be right, of 360 days or 1,360 days, a patient would not become B_{12} deficient by this criteria until about sixteen years. This is not supported by the clinical data. It is a much shorter time than that, because this only makes for a loss of 2.5 mg. per day.

SESSION VIII, SEPTEMBER 6

IRON METABOLISM

Chairman: PAUL HAHN

26
ABSORPTION AND TURNOVER RATES OF IRON MEASURED BY THE WHOLE BODY COUNTER[1]

D. C. PRICE, S. H. COHN AND E. P. CRONKITE

Brookhaven National Laboratory
Upton, New York

HUMAN IRON metabolism has been extensively studied in the past twenty-five years with the radioisotopes Fe^{55} and Fe^{59}. Before the availability of the whole body counter, iron absorption studies were performed by the indirect methods of fecal assay of unabsorbed radioiron and estimation of red cell incorporation of absorbed tracer. The few long term excretion studies performed required numerous assumptions, since human iron excretion was incompletely understood.

Whole body counting provides a simple and accurate method of measuring the total body retention of administered tracer Fe^{59}, making absorption and subsequent excretion determinations possible with a single radioiron study. The energetic gamma emissions of Fe^{59} permit ready external detection with small quantities of isotope. Normal radioiron distribution is uniform throughout the circulating red cell mass, minimizing geometry influences on the counting efficiency. Only the 45.1 day half life of Fe^{59} limits long term iron turnover studies.

Measurements of Fe^{59} absorption and long term body turnover have been underway at Brookhaven National Laboratory for over two years. The present paper outlines some of the results of these studies and discusses some implications of the method.

[1] Research supported by the U. S. Atomic Energy Commission.

EQUIPMENT

The Brookhaven National Laboratory whole body counter consists of an 8 by 4 in. NaI (Tl) crystal detector mounted with three photomultiplier tubes and suspended in reproducible geometry over a flexed cot. The shielding is a room made of 6 in. laminated steel walls lined with cadmium, copper and lead, the total room size being 6 by 7 by 9 ft. Impulses from the photomultiplier tubes after linear amplification are analysed through a 100 channel Penco Model PA-4 pulse height analyser with automatic print-out, more recently replaced by a 400 channel RIDL (Model 34-12) transistorised instrument. Early studies were performed at patient-crystal distances of 0.5 and 1.0 meters. Since little difference was noted in geometry influences between the two crystal locations, all recent studies have been at the 0.5 meter distance.

The stability of the instrument is quite good. Over a one month counting period, total counts registered at the photopeak of a point source of Cs^{137} varied only $\pm$ 0.24 percent. Positional changes of the patient in the cot influenced the count rate $\pm$ 1.8 percent. The variation in repeated 10 min. background counts over 30 days was $\pm$ 1.10 percent.

In vivo efficiency of the counter for Fe^{59} distributed throughout the red cell mass, determined by counting several patients before and after phlebotomy of a measured quantity of labeled blood, is 1.16 percent at 0.5 meters and 0.39 percent at 1 meter. *In vivo* precision for a 10 min. count is 0.88 mμc at 0.5 meters and 3.2 mμc at 1 meter. Most of the radioiron studies utilized the 100 channel integral counts, the lower Fe^{59} photopeak being used only for double isotope studies with Cr^{51} and some long term excretion studies.

PATIENT PROCEDURE

After an overnight fast and a 10 min. background count, each patient is given orally 1 to 10 μc Fe^{59} in 250 μgm. carrier iron as ferrous citrate, followed by 100 cc. water. Food is withheld an additional hour. Several body counts 2 to 10 min. in duration

during the next 4 to 10 hr. establish each patient's own 100 percent activity level. Subsequent counts at intervals of days and
then weeks, corrected for isotope decay, are utilized to establish
Fe^{59} absorption (i.e., retention of unexcreted tracer) and long
term radioiron loss. The sixteen to twenty day body count is used
to calculate the patient's tracer absorption, in the absence of detectable blood loss:

$$\text{Absorption} = \frac{20 \text{ day count}}{4 \text{ hour count}} \times \frac{1}{Fe^{59} \text{ decay factor}} \times 100$$

For the purpose of comparison, radioiron excretion has been
described by a single exponential function, obtained between
days twenty and 100. During this time the regression of the retention curve in most instances appears linear.

The patients studied by the whole body counting technique
included sixteen normal persons, fourteen patients with polycythemia vera and previous phlebotomies, six women with long-
standing menorrhagia, four patients with aplastic anemia, two
patients with idiopathic steatorrhoea and other patients with
various clinical conditions.

RESULTS

General

Representative curves of total body Fe^{59} retention in several
patients during the first 10 hr. after isotope ingestion are shown
in Figure 1. In most patients the maximum counting rate immediately after radioiron ingestion is followed by a fall in total
body activity, with subsequent stabilization over the 4 to 10 hr.
interval. We have arbitrarily used this counting period to represent 100 percent radioiron activity for each subject. Other
methods of establishing 100 percent activity are possible, but
none is without its particular faults and limitations.

Figure 2 shows the curves of total body Fe^{59} retention for
ninety days in several different patients. Of particular note is the
fact that body activity does not stabilize after four to five days
after fecal excretion of most unabsorbed tracer. The retention

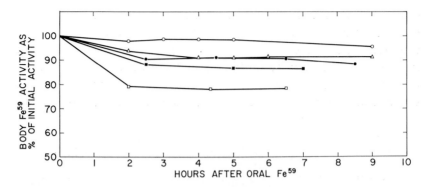

Figure 1. Several characteristic Fe^{59} studies, showing the change in body counting rate during the first 10 hr. after oral isotope ingestion. Note the uniform plateau of activity in each patient after 4 hr. (Courtesy of Grune & Stratton, Inc.)

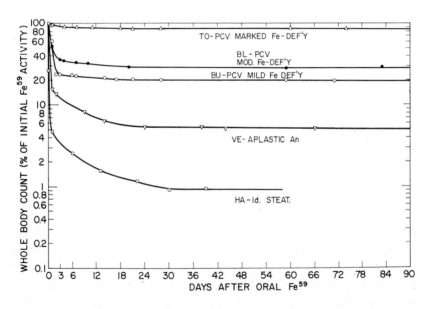

Figure 2. Changes in total body Fe^{59} activity compensated for isotope decay found in several patients. A rapid fall in activity is found during the first few days, with a continuing, but more gradual fall in activity up to day twenty, and a final slope of very gradually falling activity thereafter, used to calculate ultimate Fe^{59} loss. (Courtesy of Grune & Stratton, Inc.)

curve continues to fall less rapidly up to days sixteen to twenty in all patients except those with a marked iron deficiency. Consequently, the sixteen to twenty day level of activity is used as the final value for tracer absorption. This continuing loss of retained activity over two to three weeks probably reflects physiologic loss of iron retained only partially in mucosal cells, a theory supported by the studies of Crosby and his associates (1).

Radioiron Absorption

Normal radioiron absorption by this technique has ranged from 5.7 percent to 24.7 percent in sixteen patients studied, with a mean of 17.1 percent (Table I). Absorption in a group of iron-

TABLE I

Fe^{59} ABSORPTION IN VARIOUS CLINICAL CONDITIONS

Disease	Number Patients	Fe^{59} Absorption Mean ± 1 Std. Dev. (%)	Range (%)
Normal	16	17.1 ± 6.3	5.7-24.7
Iron Deficiency			
(a) Phlebot.			
Polycyt.	14	76.2 ± 22.3	20.6-96.9
(b) Menorrh.	6	71.0 ± 15.0	53.7-97.5
Aplastic Anemia	4	7.7 ± 1.6	5.4- 9.0
Chronic Illness	6	4.3 ± 2.7	1.1- 8.5
Steatorrhoea	2	1.8	1.2- 2.5
Rheum. Arth.	1	0.5	
Pyridox.-Resp.			
Anemia	1	69.1	

deficient patients with polythemia vera, previously phlebotomised, ranged from 20.6 percent to 96.9 percent, with a mean of 76.2 percent. It is of interest to note that the only patient with normal absorption (20.6 percent) in this latter group had normal red cell indices and normal plasma iron and had not had a phlebotomy for over two years previous to study. Six women with long antecedent histories of menorrhagia, varying degrees of microcytic hypochromic anemia and low plasma iron values absorbed 53.7 percent to 97.5 percent of the tracer, also indicating a marked degree of iron deficiency.

In aplastic anemia, and even more so in a variety of chronic illnesses, low or low normal tracer absorption was found even in the presence of considerable anemia. Idiopathic steatorrhea was found in two cases to be associated with significantly low iron absorption. One of these two patients, in fact, had an iron deficiency anemia which responded well to parenteral iron therapy alone.

The lowest radioiron absorption was found in a man with active rheumatoid arthritis, but no hematologic abnormality. A young man with massive iron stores and a striking microcytic, hypochromic, pyridoxine-responsive anemia absorbed 69.1 percent of the tracer despite his large body iron load.

Radioiron Loss

As seen in Figure 2, total body radioiron loss plotted on a semilogarithmic scale appears in most cases to be linear from day twenty to day 100. For the purpose of comparison, we have expressed this physiologic radioiron loss as a single exponential function. Table II shows normal tracer loss determined in three normal patients and two patients with aplastic anemia to range from 0.103 to 0.183 percent retained daily, with a mean of 0.136 percent per day. In contrast, ten of the iron deficient patients with polycythemia vera demonstrated radioiron loss of 0 to 0.044 percent per day, with a mean of 0.019 percent per day. The highest rate of tracer loss in this group was in the patient least depleted of iron, as might be expected (BU - 20.6 percent absorption). The patient with pyridoxine-responsive anemia also lost less than normal proportions of absorbed radioiron, 0.026 percent per day, despite a heavy body iron load. The metabolic significance of this low rate of tracer loss is undoubtedly quite different from that in the iron-deficient patients.

The lower rate of radioiron loss in iron deficiency may be a function of at least two different processes. First, these iron deficient patients incorporate almost 100 percent of absorbed radioiron into the fixed compartment of circulating hemoglobin during the first 120 days. Thus, a substantially smaller fraction of

TABLE II

FE⁵⁹ LOSS OVER THE 20 TO 100 DAY PERIOD IN NORMALS, IRON DEFICIENT PATIENTS AND A SINGLE PATIENT WITH PYRIDOXINE-RESPONSIVE ANEMIA

Disease	Fe^{59} Absorp'n (%)	20-100 Day Fe^{59} Loss (%/day)	
(1) Normal			
HR	19.5	0.110	
NE	19.0	0.110	
EG	5.9	0.182	
(2) Apl. Anemia			
VE	5.4	0.103	
AR	8.2	0.173	*0.136 ± 0.039
(3) Iron-Def'y			
MU	93.8	0	
CO	87.8	0.009	
TR	88.9	0.011	
CT	87.4	0.012	
TS	89.0	0.017	
TO	87.7	0.019	
FA	81.4	0.023	
BE	80.0	0.024	
ST	96.9	0.029	
BU	20.6	0.044	*0.019 ± 0.012
(4) Pyridox-Resp.			
Anemia	69.1	0.026	

*Mean ± 1 Std. Dev.

absorbed tracer than normal remains labile and consequently available for excretion during that period. Second, one might expect in iron deficiency a physiologic mechanism for conserving body iron by decreasing iron excretion. Whether such a mechanism exists is not known. The body may well be able to conserve iron only by removing it from the labile pool and binding it in relatively fixed compartments such as hemoglobin, thus diminishing the labile pool size (9, 10).

The earlier work of Dubach and associates (2) on fecal Fe⁵⁹ excretion (0.008 to 0.015%/day), that of Finch (3) on loss of Fe⁵⁵ from circulating hemoglobin (0.022 to 0.055%/day), and a single observation by Bonnet and associates (4) with an early body

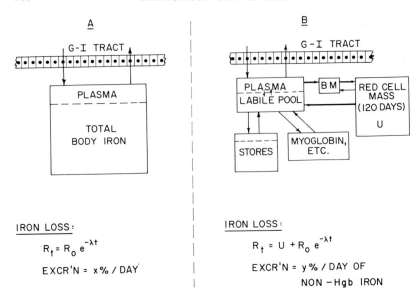

Figure 3. A. A simplified model for Fe^{59} excretion applicable only to long term studies.

B. More complex kinetic model necessary to analyze Fe^{59} loss during the first 100 days after intestinal absorption.

counter (0.14%/day) all expressed radioiron loss as a single exponential function. As shown in A of Figure 3, this mode of expression implies a single, completely miscible total body iron pool, with a constant rate of absorption and excretion. This gives the kinetic interpretation with tracer label of: $R_t = R_0 e^{-\lambda t}$, and a measurable excretion rate, X%/day ($X = 100\lambda$). As shown in B, the actual kinetics are much more complex. Considering only the 120 day fixed compartment of circulating hemoglobin in a single tracer study, the mathematical interpretation of days twenty to 100 would become: $R_t = U + R_0 e^{-\lambda t}$, where U is the fractional distribution of absorbed tracer to hemoglobin iron. In addition, there is evidence that myoglobin will bind some tracer, with a finite life span (5, 6), and that some portions of storage iron are relatively less labile than others (7). Thus, true mathematical representation of early total body radioiron activity becomes virtually impossible. Only the observation of total body activity over several years would eliminate the influence of these various pool shifts on body radioiron loss, and this becomes impossible with the 45.1 day half life of Fe^{59}. Although Finch's fifty-four month study using Fe^{55} determinations in circulating hemoglobin may have begun to approach the time of uniform body mixing, his analysis did not make allowance for the body's known capacity to conserve hemoglobin iron by efficient reutilization.

In support of this more complex interpretation of body radio-iron loss, one would expect to find increased tracer excretion beyond day 120, as hemoglobin-bound Fe^{59} from a single tagged red cell population is recycled and incompletely reutilized. Figure 4 demonstrates the fall in body radioactivity observed in one patient between 100 and 150 days and a further acceleration of tracer loss beyond 250 days when the second labeled red cell population expires. Figure 5 shows two separate studies in a pa-

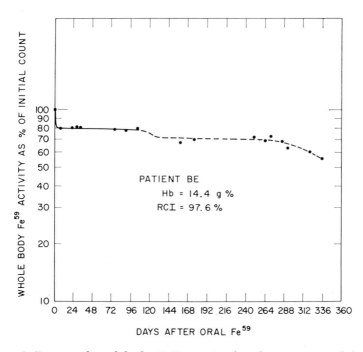

Figure 4. Pattern of total body Fe^{59} activity found in one iron deficient patient. Note the accelerated loss of label after day 100 and after day 250, suggesting greater amounts of tracer becoming available for excretion at the termination of each labeled red cell population's life span.

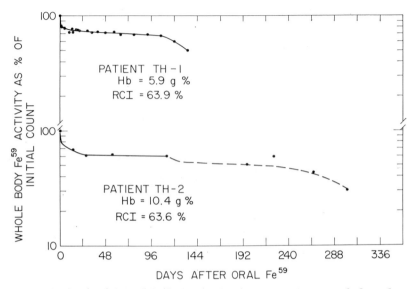

Figure 5. Pattern of total body Fe^{59} activity in a patient with hemolytic anemia and decreased red cell radioiron incorporation. Note accelerated loss of tracer after day 100 and after day 250.

tient with macroglobulinemia and hemolytic anemia. As a result of hemolysis and increased iron stores, the red cell incorporation of Fe^{59} was only 64 percent. A significant increase in Fe^{59} loss was noted in the first study beginning about day 100. In the second study, a further acceleration of radioiron loss was found beyond the 200th day.

Comparison of 300 day radioiron loss in five patients with that to day 100, compared again by expression as a single exponential function, is shown in Table III. In four of the five patients the excretion rate was greater to day 300 than to day 100, even though three of these patients were markedly iron deficient and presumably conserving iron as much as possible. Thus, there was a definite acceleration of tracer loss after day 100. The fifth patient was a man with aplastic anemia and virtually no red cell incorporation of Fe^{59} (3.5 percent). He did not have a large, long-lived compartment of stable hemoglobin with tracer recycling every 120 days.

If one considers normal radioiron loss over days 20 to 100

to be 0.14 percent/day, it is interesting to consider what size of labile iron pool this could be originating from. With 75 percent red cell radioiron incorporation, the daily loss of *nonhemoglobin* iron in such a normal individual would then be 0.74 percent per

TABLE III

Comparison of Fe^{59} Loss in Five Patients, Day 20 to 100 vs. Day 20 to 300. The Accelerated Loss after Day 100 in the Iron Deficient Patients Indicates Greater Amounts of Tracer Becoming Available for Excretion after Radioiron Release from the First Labeled Red Cell Population. In Patient V. E., with 3.5% Red Cell Incorporation, there was no Large Labeled Red Cell Compartment

Patient	Fe^{59} Absorp'n (%)	20-100 Day Fe^{59} Loss (%/day)	20-300 Day Fe^{59} Loss (%/day)
(1) Aplastic Anemia			
VE	5.4	0.103	0.034
AR	8.2	0.173	0.225
(2) Iron-Def'y			
CT	87.4	0.012	0.020
BE	80.0	0.024	0.061
ST	96.9	0.029	0.056

day. Assuming this to come from a single labile nonhemoglobin pool of iron, one concludes this pool size to be 135 mg. This conclusion is reached with many unknowns and postulates, yet the pool size corresponds well with the 133 mg. erythropoietic labile iron pool of Greenberg and Wintrobe in 1946 (8), and the 84 mg. labile iron pool of Pollycove and Mortimer (9). These postulated pools may be the same.

Studies in Blood Loss

Other more directly clinical applications of this technique of measuring radioiron loss are shown in Figures 6 to 8. Figure 6 outlines the pattern of total body activity in one of several patients with menorrhagia. Since iron deficiency in these patients leads to almost 100 percent red cell radioiron incorporation and a low rate of tracer loss, the observed fall in body activity at each menstrual period can be directly related to the proportion of total blood volume lost. Thus, in six patients studied, we found up to

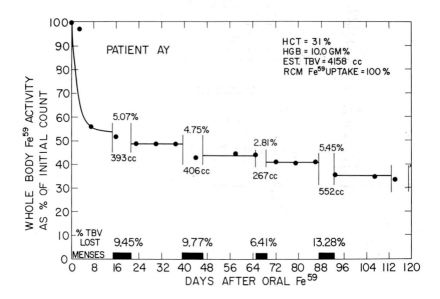

Figure 6. Monthly loss of Fe⁵⁹-labeled red cells in an iron deficient patient with menorrhagia. (Courtesy of *Canadian Medical Association Journal*.)

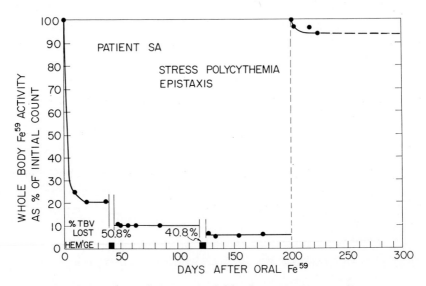

Figure 7. Massive loss of Fe⁵⁹-tagged blood in a patient with two severe episodes of epistaxis. The consequent iron deficiency was revealed by a repeat absorption study showing 94 percent radioiron absorption.

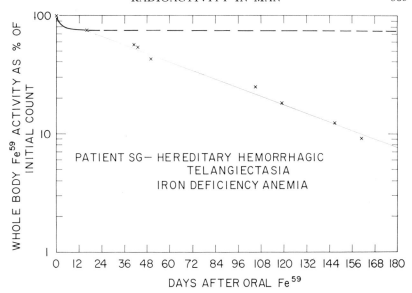

Figure 8. Continuing gastrointestinal blood loss at the estimated rate of 51 cc. per day in a patient with hereditary hemorrhagic telangiectasia and iron deficiency anemia. (Courtesy of *Canadian Medical Association Journal*).

550 ml. blood loss in a single period with marked iron deficiency resulting in all instances.

A second type of episodic blood loss is seen in Figure 7. During a single radioiron study, patient SA had two severe episodes of epistaxis with a loss of an estimated 51 percent and 41 percent of his total blood volume. As expected, a repeat iron study then showed 94 percent absorption, demonstrating his resultant marked iron deficiency.

Figure 8 shows the pattern of total body Fe^{59} loss (i.e., loss of labeled red cells) in an iron deficient patient with hereditary hemorrhagic telangiectasia and continuous gastrointestinal bleeding. With 100 percent red cell incorporation, this rate of radioiron loss represents a daily loss of 51 ml. of blood or 17 mg. of iron. Her persistent anemia is readily understandable.

CONCLUSION

The whole body counter is an excellent device for physiologic and clinical studies in iron metabolism. There is no doubt that geometry changes can greatly influence the body's Fe^{59} counting rate where there is continuing isotope redistribution. Data derived from dynamic studies consequently must be interpreted with some caution. However, there are significant advantages to this method over iron absorption studies by fecal excretion or red cell radioiron incorporation. The body's tracer content is measured directly and, therefore, there are no cumulative errors. In addition, previously unobtainable information about long term retention now may be gained rapidly. A much clearer understanding of normal and abnormal iron metabolism undoubtedly will be gained from the continuation of such studies.

REFERENCES

1. Conrad, M. E., Jr., van Hoek, R., and Crosby, W. H.: Observations on the natural history of iron deficiency and the gastrointestinal absorption of iron. *Proc. VIIIth Internat. Cong. of Internat. Soc. of Hematol.,* Tokyo, p. 1150, 1961.
2. Duback, R., Moore, C. V., and Callender, S. L.: Studies in iron transportation and metabolism. IX., Excretion of iron as measured by the isotope technique. *J. Lab. Clin. Med.,* 45:599, 1955.
3. Finch, C. A.: Body iron exchange in man. *J. Clin. Invest.,* 38:392, 1952.
4. Bonnet, J. D., Orvis, A. L., Hagedorn, A. B., and Owen, C. A., Jr.: Rate of loss of radioiron from mouse and man. *Am. J. Physiol.* 198:784, 1960.
5. Theorell, H., Beznak, M., Bonnichsen, R., Paul, K. G., and Åkeson, A.: On the distribution of injected radioactive iron in guinea pigs and its rate of appearance in some hemoproteins and ferritins. *Acta. Chem. Scand.,* 5:455, 1951.
6. Åkeson, A. V., Ehrenstein, G., Hevesy, G., and Theorell, H.: Life span of myoglobin. *Arch. Biochem. and Biophys.* 91:310, 1960
7. Duback, R., Moore, C. V., and Minnich, V.: Studies in iron transportation and metabolism and utilization of intravenously injected radioactive iron for hemoglobin synthesis and an evaluation of the radioactive iron method for studying iron absorption. *J. Lab. Clin. Med.* 31:1201, 1946.
8. Greenberg, G. R., and Wintrove, M. M.: A liable iron pool. *J. Biol. Chem.,* 165:397, 1946.
9. Pollycove, M., and Mortimer, R.: Quantitative determination of iron kinetics and hemoglobin synthesis in human subjects. *J. Clin. Invest.,* 40:753, 1961.
10. Pollycove, M.: *Ferrokinetics: Techniques in Eisenstoffwechsel:* Beitrage 3 uv Forschung und Kinik. W. Keiderling, Stuttgart, Georg Thieme Verlaf, p. 20, 1959.

27

NORMAL AND PATHOLOGICAL RADIO-IRON EXCRETION IN MAN

P. Reizenstein and I. Brann

Karolinska Hospital
Stockholm, Sweden

INTRODUCTION

ONE PURPOSE OF TRACER turnover studies is to estimate human requirements. Animal studies are of limited use, for although metabolic pathways are sometimes common for laboratory animals and man, turnover rates rarely are. Another purpose is to study metabolic differences between clinically healthy subjects and ill subjects and the effects produced by different diseases. Since both types of studies should be performed in man, they are greatly facilitated by human body counters.

Radioiron turnover was studied even without whole body counters. In 1955, Dubach et al. (1) studied fecal radioiron excretion in three women and one man and found an excretion of 0.02 to 0.03 percent per day up to twenty days after injection and 0.01 percent up to 140 days. Later, Finch (2) followed the decrease in erythrocyte radioiron for up to fifty-four months.

Whole body counter studies of radioiron turnover were started in 1959 (3-5) mainly in a group of iron-deficient patients with polycythemia vera, who lost $0.019 \pm 0.003\%$ of their radioiron daily during the three to four months after administration. These studies are extended in the present report to normal controls and to patients with menorrhagic bleeding, intestinal bleeding, aplastic anemia and hemosiderosis.

Patients were studied up to 325 days, nevertheless, the material is still incomplete, the time of study still not sufficiently long and the kinetic analysis unfinished.

METHODS

The normal controls were divided into three groups which might be expected to lose different amounts of iron. Three healthy volunteer men were followed for sixty to 194 days, nine menstruating women for twenty-one to 325 days and three menopausal women for eighty-five to 174 days. Two patients with aplastic anemia were studied, one of whom had transfusion hemosiderosis. One bled from the intestine, and another had a duodenal ulcer and iron deficiency. Four patients with menorrhagic bleeding were studied.

All got 250 μg. iron in the form of oral ferrous citrate and containing 3 to 10 μc Fe^{59}. Body counts were performed immediately before and 6 hr. after isotope ingestion, ten days later and at irregular intervals after that.

Coefficients of regression of the logarithm of retained radio-iron on time were calculated on an IBM 1610 computer. The regression coefficient = (log e)x(fraction excreted per unit time).

THE COUNTER

The body counter has been described (6). It is temporary until construction of a combined liquid scintillation and NaI counter is completed. It consists of an open iron booth, in which a patient can sit on a stool, and a crystal shielded in all directions except that facing the opening. The crystal is mounted on a trolley on rails and can be placed at fixed distances (35 to 60 cm.) from the back wall of the booth (Fig. 1, Table I).

GEOMETRY ERRORS

Variations in counting geometry due to the redistribution of the isotope in the body during the time of observation seem to affect the results obtained with all types of whole body counters. In the solid crystal type counters these variations are influenced by the positioning of the human body, the number and positioning of crystals and the metabolism of the isotope. An attempt

Figure 1. The body counter described earlier and in Tables I and II.

TABLE I

BODY COUNTER DATA

Patient shield	Weight 5.5 t
Inner dimens.:	160 by 60 by 60 cm.
Walls	10-15 cm. Fe + 3 mm. Pb
Floor	20 cm. Fe + 3 mm. Pb
Crystal shield	Weight 1 t., 10 cm. Pb
Detector	5 in. by 5 in. NaI (Tl),
	electrolytic Cu,
	5 in. EMI 6099 F.
Multichannel analyzer	Hutchinson-Scarrot,
	72 channels, 25 kev each

was made to estimate the magnitude of the errors caused by variations in geometry (Table II). Since both variations in body configuration and those in isotope distribution cause variations in the "shape" of the radioactive source, they will also cause variations in the relation between the counting efficiency and the patient-crystal distance. Therefore, the variations with time or be-

TABLE II

BODY COUNTER PERFORMANCE

Background (0.1-1.9 Mev, ch. 2-74, distance 35-60 cm.)	Empty ~ *500 cpm.* [*] Patient ~ *900 cpm.*
Efficiency, Fe^{59},	~ *1%* (35 cm.) ; *0.36%* (60 cm.)
Errors: Patient position	*7.4%* (35 cm.) ; *2.1%* (60 cm.)
Body shape	S.D. C_{35}/C_{60} *10.7%* [**]
Isotope distribution	Max. dev. (1-6 hrs after Fe^{59}) ; *24%* S.D. $C_{35/60}$ *13.6%* [***]

[*] K^{40},Cs^{137},RaC, increased background scatter.

[**] S.D. of average ratio of counts at 35 and 60 cm., respectively. 53 measurements, ten persons.

[**] S.D. from within-class-variance for five patients.

tween patients in the ratio between counts at two different distances were used as a rough measure of geometry variations.

However, such errors affect iron turnover measurements much less than the measurement of iron absorption. After the completion of iron uptake from the intestine and its incorporation into the hemin of the bone marrow and later into that of the circulating red cells, the distribution is both remarkably stable and quite homogeneous.

ABSORPTION TIME

One problem which has not been satisfactorily solved is the selection of the time at which excretion of unabsorbed iron is to be regarded as concluded, and after which the excreted radioactivity would thus derive from absorbed iron. Previously, twenty days was chosen as an arbitrary limit, (1,3-5) because there is often a change in the iron excretion curve about that time. However, normal intestinal passage takes no more than four to seven days, and in previous studies of radio-B_{12} absorption, all of the nonabsorbed radioactivity was excreted by that time (7,8). There is thus a difference in the excretion pattern between iron and, e.g., vitamin B_{12} (Fig. 2).

It is probable that the rapid excretion between ten and twenty days after administration is due to a tissue compartment

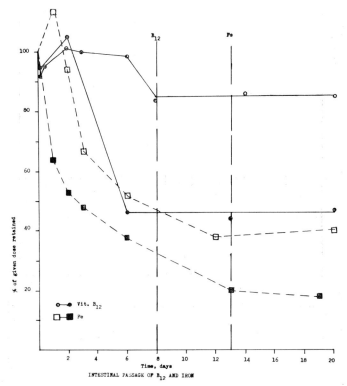

Figure 2. Difference in excretion pattern between radioiron and radio B_{12}, rapid fecal excretion after oral administration persists longer for iron than for B_{12}. Most probably, iron is absorbed into a rapidly turning-over tissue compartment and re-excreted.

with rapid turnover. Possibly, this compartment may consist of intestinal epithelium, but the rapid excretion ten to twenty days after administration was found even when radioiron was injected (1,9). Therefore, the rapidly excreted radioiron should probably be regarded as absorbed. Nevertheless, regression coefficients were calculated both with the 10th and 20th days as starting points (Table III).

RESULTS AND DISCUSSION

The results are shown in Table III and Figures 3 and 4. It

TABLE III

RADIOIRON EXCRETION IN CONTROLS AND PATIENTS

Subject Category	Case	Latest Measurement Days after Administration	No. of Measurements	% Excreted Daily† Starting Day 10	Starting Day 20	Mean ± S.D. of Day 10 Value
Male controls	K.S.	194	6	0.574 ± 0.085	0.517 ± 0.093	0.240 ± 0.165
	R.S.	138	7	0.070 ± 0.096	0.068 ± 0.02	
	B.N.	60	2	0.079	—	
Female, menstruating controls	U.L.	50	2	0.0		
	O.S.	194	6	0.147 ± 0.078	0.105 ± 0.077	
	M.L.	21**	3	0.190	—	
	M.N.	198	4	0.351 ± 0.185	0.0	0.310 ± 0.117
	F.T.	68	5	0.278 ± 0.188	0.410 ± 0.259	
	B.N.	325*	6	1.161 ± 0.424	—	
	L.G.	242*	5	0.429 ± 0.063	—	
	M.L.	90	2	0.0	—	
	E.N.	244*	6	0.230 ± 0.126	—	
Female controls, menopause	M.S.	85	5	0.252 ± 0.081	0.299 ± 0.114	0.146 ± 0.058
	E.K.	102	6	0.058 ± 0.110	0.0	
	O.O.	174	6	—	0.127 ± 0.066	
Female with menorrhagic bleeding	B.B.	69	5	0.729 ± 0.350	0.585 ± 0.579	1.332 ± 0.980
	A.G.	42	3	4.420 ± 0.619	2.770	
	M.N.	69	5	0.231 ± 0.161	0.442 ± 0.132	
	G.F.	81	4	0.129 ± 0.035	0.091 ± 0.009	
Aplastic anemia	Y.H.§§	108	4	0.0	0.0	
	A.F.§	78	7	0.0	0.0	
Iron deficiency	K.F.§	157	8	0.034 ± 0.046	0.014 ±0.040	

†) Regression coefficient/log e ± the error of the regression coefficient.
*) First measurement 90 to 100 days after administration.
**) First measurement 8 days after administration.
§) Intestinal bleeding.
§§) Hemosiderosis.

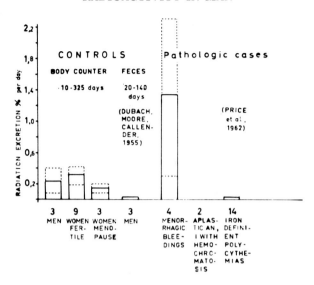

Figure 3. Radioiron excretion in different groups of subjects during the months after oral administration. - - - = mean, - - - = S.D.

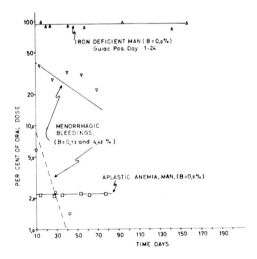

Figure 4. Examples of data obtained in four patients. Two lost very little iron although they had persistently positive stool guiacs. Two others with menorrhagic bleeding lost much. The variations in counts probably caused by geometry variations are well illustrated.

is seen that women with menstruation lose more than men or menopausal women, and women with menorrhagic bleeding lose most of all. Iron deficient patients lose less than any of these groups (3-5).

Statistically, many of the regression coefficients have large standard deviations, probably because of variations in counting geometry. Also, excretion rates vary so much within each group that the differences between the groups are not statistically significant. This is hardly surprising, in view of the possibility of undiagnosed menorrhagic bleeding in the group of control women.

Several cases have individual features of interest. Patient Y. H. had normal iron absorption and no measurable iron excretion, although his tissues were full of iron. This could have contributed to the development of his hemosiderosis.

Patient K. F. (Figure 3) had some twenty positive stool guiac test during the first twenty-one days of study and, although he probably continued to bleed, lost no significant amount of radioactivity. He had absorbed 90 percent of the test dose, and almost all of this was found in his circulating red cells. This patient illustrates the efficient intestinal reabsorption of iron after intestinal bleeding (10, 11, 12).

Male volunteer control K. S. had an unexpectedly large loss of radioactivity (0.57 percent daily), although he had repeatedly negative stool guiacs, was not a blood donor and appeared to be in perfect health.

The present figures for radioiron loss tally well with that found in a single case by Bonnet et al. (9), but they are several times higher than those found at comparable times by Dubach et al. (1). The reason for this latter discrepancy is of considerable interest. Dubach et al. injected iron and measured fecal excretion, whereas we used oral administration and a body counter. It is conceivable that excretion routes exist other than the fecal. The skin could be one (9, 13-15), although this possibility could not be confirmed by Dubach et al. It is also possible that more radioiron is excreted after oral administration than after injection. However, Bonnet et al. found a high excretion even after injection (9). Further study is required.

The present data give an idea about the relation between

iron losses in different groups of healthy and sick people. The relations between men and menopausal and menstruating women are in approximate agreement with those found by Finch (2), although the actual percentages differ. The reason is the difference in time after administration and in that between whole body turnover and red cell turnover of iron.

In contrast, the present data are not sufficient to establish the iron requirement or the loss of unlabeled iron in different groups of people.

A simple relationship between the percentage losses of labeled and unlabeled iron would exist only if isotope equilibrium, in the sense of a uniform specific activity in all compartments, were reached. Such an equilibrium has been assumed earlier (1, 2). However, it has been demonstrated that in open multi-compartment systems such an equilibrium is usually not reached (16, 17). Therefore, the percentage of unlabeled iron excreted will probably continue to differ from that for the tracer. A model satisfying the experimental results and known physiological facts must be constructed, and sufficient information collected to solve the equations describing it. Such studies are in progress.

SUMMARY

Previous studies of radioiron excretion in a group of iron-deficient patients with polycythemia vera were continued.

A simple open booth NaI body counter was used with an efficiency for Fe^{59} approximating 1 percent. Variations in patient positioning caused errors of about 2 percent of the total counts, and those caused by variations in body build and isotope distribution were about 10-15 percent.

Normal males lost 0.24 percent of the body radioiron daily during the first six months of study.

Menstruating women lost about 0.31 percent daily and were studied up to one year. Women with menorrhagic bleeding lost 1.33 percent per day.

Menopausal women lost 0.15 percent. All controls lost more than the iron-deficient patients studied earlier.

Two patients with aplastic anemia lost no iron, although one had hemosiderosis.

Two patients with intestinal bleeding reabsorbed all the iron in the intestine.

REFERENCES

1. Dubach, R., Moore, C. V., Callender, S.: Studies in iron transportation and metabolism, IX. *J. Lab. Clin. Med.*, 45:599-615, 1955.
2. Finch, C. A.: Body iron exchange in man. *J. Clin. Invest.*, 38:392-396, 1959.
3. Price, D., Reizenstein, P., Cohn, S. H., Cronkite, E. P., Wasserman, L. R.: A method for studying iron absorption and loss by whole body counting. *Clin. Res.*, 9:165, 1961.
4. Reizenstein, P., Price, D., Cronkite, E. P., Cohn, S. H., Wasserman, L.: Whole body counter studies of the absorption and turnover of iron and vitamin B_{12}. *Trans. Eur. Soc. Hematol.*, 8:237, 1961.
5. Price, D. C., Cohn, S. H., Wasserman, L. R., Reizenstein, P., Cronkite, E. P.: The determination of iron absorption and loss by whole body counting. *Blood*, 20:517, 1962.
6. Lindell, B.: An Open-Booth Body Counter. in *Whole Body Counting*. Vienna, Internat. Atomic Energy Agency, 1961, p. 235.
7. Reizenstein, P., Nyberg, W.: Intestinal absorption of liver bound radiovitamin B_{12} in patients with pernicious anemia and in controls. *Lancet*, ii:248-252, 1959.
8. Halsted, J. A., Lewis, P. M., Hvollboll, E. E., Gasster, M., Swendseid, M. E.: Recovery method for determining intestinal absorption of Co^{60}-labeled vitamin B_{12}. *J. Lab. Clin. Med.*, 48:92, 1956.
9. Bonnet, J. D., Orvis, A. L., Hagedorn, A. B., Owen, C. A.: Rate of loss of radioiron from mouse and man. *Amer. J. Physiol.*, 198:784-786, 1960.
10. Layrisse, M., Paz, A., Blumenfeld, N., Roche, M.: Hookworm anemia and erythrokinetics. *Blood*, 18:61, 1961.
11. Roche, M., Perez-Giminez, M.: Intestinal loss and reabsorption of iron in hookworm infection. *J. Lab. Clin. Med.*, 54:49-52, 1959.
12. Gerritsen, Th., Heinz, H. J., Stafford, G. H.: Estimation of blood loss in hookworm infestation with Fe^{59}. *Science*, 119:412-413, 1954.
13. Johnston, F. A., McMillan, T. J., Evans, E. R.: Perspiration as a factor influencing the requirement for calcium and iron. *J. Nutr.*, 42:285, 1950.
14. Mitchell, H. H., Hamilton, T. S.: The dermal excretion under controlled environmental conditions of nitrogen and minerals in hu-

man subjects, with particular reference to calcium and iron. *J. Biol. Chem.*, *178*:345, 1949.

15. Adams, V. S., Leslie, A., Levin, M. H.: The dermal loss of iron. *Proc. Soc. Exp. Biol. Med.*, *74*:46-48, 1950.

16. Reizenstein, P., Cronkite, E. P., Robertson, J.: Relations of the Turn-over of Tracer B_{12} to That of Unlabeled B_{12} in the Body Stores. Eur. Sympos. Vit. B_{12} and intrinsic factor (H. C. Heinrich Ed.) F. Enke, Stuttgart, p. 404-410, 1962.

17. Bergner, P. - E.E.: Tracer dynamics II. *J. Theor. Biol.*, *1*:359, 1961.

28

STUDIES OF HUMAN IRON METABOLISM WITH A WHOLE BODY COUNTER[1]

L. Clifford McKee, Joseph A. King, Robert C. Hartmann and
Robert M. Heyssel

Vanderbilt University School of Medicine
Nashville, Tennessee

THE ABSORPTION and turnover of minerals is an obvious application of whole body counting. Older methods for measuring iron absorption have disadvantages in the necessity of collecting stools over long periods or of using two isotopes of an element with multiple blood samples. These tests are time consuming for the physician and patient and require much patient cooperation. Turnover studies are even more difficult to do by conventional methods for they require long term collections of many body excreta and the use of large doses of radioactive elements or elements (Fe^{55}) which are less readily quantitated. Despite these problems, good estimates exist for absorption. The classical studies of Moore (1, 2) and others (3-5) on absorption of iron from foodstuffs and other studies on absorption of elemental iron (6-15) have fairly well delineated the extent of iron absorption under normal and abnormal conditions and some of the controlling mechanisms. Iron turnover is more controversial. Dubach, Moore, Callender, (16) and Finch (17) have estimated iron turnover to be approximately 0.5 to 1.0 mg. per day in the male. Recent studies in one subject using a whole body counter suggested that the amount lost might be higher (18). This is supported by the results of several different groups of workers who suggested

[1] Supported by Army Medical Research and Development Command, Atomic Energy Commission and U. S. Public Health Service.

that the daily loss of iron from the skin and sweat might be higher than previously estimated (19).

Using a whole body counter we have studied iron absorption in a variety of subjects and compared results to those obtained by collection of stools and measurements of Fe^{59} excreted. Seven patients with paroxysmal nocturnal hemoglobinuria presented a unique opportunity to determine total body iron turnover in a rare disease with heavy iron losses. The studies in this group are part of a more extensive investigation of this disease (20).

MATERIALS AND METHODS

The Counting Facility and Data Processing

The Vanderbilt whole body counter and methods for data processing have been described elsewhere (21). It is a large steel room (8 by 8 ft. 6 in.) which houses a 4 by 8 in. NaI thallium-activated single crystal. In these studies the crystal-subject geometrical arrangement was the standard Argonne position No. 1. Data collected are fed into a 256 channel analyzer and automatically punched on IBM cards for subsequent analysis by an IBM 650 computer. At the end of each count, printed data are also secured for manual analysis. In these studies both methods were used and checked against the other to insure accurate information.

Calibration and Administration of the Dose of Fe^{59}

It appeared desirable to attempt to measure absolute absorption of iron. Accordingly, all doses of Fe^{59} were carefully calibrated by counting a syringe containing Fe^{59} in a predetermined standard position with reference to the crystal. One microcurie was found to yield 2350 cpm integrated over the 1.28 Mev energy photopeak of Fe^{59}. All subsequent doses of radioactive Fe^{59}, either injected or ingested, were counted in an exactly similar manner and microcuries determined on the basis of the primary calibration data. Standards were utilized prior to each count, and the analyzer normalized for changes in gain or zero shift. Injected doses ranged from 1 to 5 μc, and fed doses from 2 to 10 μc. The fed dose of Fe^{59} was placed in a paper cup with 15 mg. of ferrous sulfate and brought up to 100 to 200 ml. with water. Several wash-outs of the cup were made to insure complete ingestion of the iron by the subject. The test was performed in the morning after a 12 hr. overnight fast by the subject.

Determination of Iron Absorption by Whole Body Counting

Distribution of Fe^{59} in the human with respect to the scintillation crystal could markedly affect counting rates. We had previously done extensive calibration of the steel room utilizing K^{42} to investigate the effect of body weight and height on counting efficiency of precalibrated injected doses. It had been found that unless the deviation from normal habitus (primarily with regard to obesity) was marked, efficiency for K^{42} varied by no more than 10 percent in the standard chair position (21).

Since iron is rapidly cleared from the plasma by the bone marrow, any immediate counts after intravenous injection might be falsely low due to the shielding effect of bone. On the other hand, it is known that 80 to 90 percent of an injected or fed dose of Fe^{59} is utilized in normal persons in the production of new red blood cells. Ordinarily utilization is complete in seven to ten days. It can be assumed, unless there is unusual pooling of these newly formed red blood cells within a particular tissue, that distribution of the Fe^{59} at this time will be essentially that of blood within the body and, for our purposes, uniform. Accordingly, after seven to ten days cpm/μc should be similar in any given subject after either an injected or fed dose of Fe^{59}. Further, we would not expect any gross deviation for net cpm of Fe^{59}/μc from subject to subject, unless body habitus deviated in an extreme fashion from the normal. Figure 1 shows that count rates fall immediately after intravenous injection at a rate approximating the plasma clearance rate and at seven days return to immediate postinjection levels. Table I demonstrates that efficiency varies within fairly narrow limits from subject to subject.

In fourteen subjects varying in weight from 140 to 210 lb. and in height from 5 ft. 5 in. to 6 ft. 2 in., efficiency ranged from 3,062 to 3,476 cpm. The mean value for efficiency was 3,222 cpm. This value was considered to represent 1 μc of Fe^{59} in all subjects studied. Using this factor, gastrointestinal absorption could be

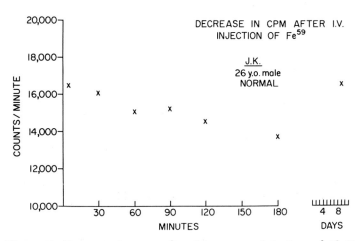

Figure 1. Decrease in cpm after intravenous injection of Fe^{59}.

TABLE I

COUNTING EFFICIENCY FOR Fe^{59}

Subject	$cpm/\mu c$ 7 Days after Injection
1	3163
2	3476
3	3179
4	3071
5	3062
6	3159
7	3197
8	3141
9	3394
10	3111
11	3442
12	3090
13	3421
14	3199

Mean   3222
Range   3062-3476

determined after appropriate half time correction for the seven day whole body count by the equation:

$$\frac{\mu c \text{ whole body}}{\mu c \text{ fed}} \times 100 = \% \text{ absorption Fe}^{59}$$

The situation could be simplified greatly by choosing some arbitrary time after ingestion of the fed dose as representative of the absolute 100 percent counting rate for the same amount of Fe^{59} in the subject had it all been absorbed. Arbitrarily it was decided to count the subject at 4 hr. after ingestion of the Fe^{59} tracer dose. Theoretically the iron should be well distributed in the gastrointestinal tract at that time; the major amount of absorption should have ensued, and utilization of absorbed iron by marrow should have occurred, at least in part. After appropriate correction for decay of the radioactive iron, iron absorption could be closely approximated by the equation:

$$\frac{\text{cpm whole body at day 7}}{\text{cpm whole body at 4 hr.}} \times 100$$

Determination of Fe^{59} Absorption by Stool Collection

On two occasions in seven subjects under metabolic ward conditions and once in two ambulatory subjects, stools were collected during the period following ingestion of the fed dose of Fe^{59} until completion of the whole body counter absorption studies. Stool collection periods were seven to fourteen days long. Stools were collected directly into No. 10 cans with a volume of approximately 2,500 ml. and brought up to standard volume with water. Small amounts of formalin were added to prevent bacterial action. Several small metal washers were added, and the cans sealed. They were shaken for 30 min. on a paint can shaker and counted in the steel room in predetermined position. Comparisons were made against standards prepared at the time of preparation of the fed dose. Absorption was determined by the formula:

$$\frac{\mu c \text{ fed} - \mu c \text{ excreted}}{\mu c \text{ fed}} \times 100$$

Total Body Iron Turnover

Three normal subjects and six patients with paroxysmal nocturnal hemoglobinuria were counted at various intervals over periods from sixty to 300 days after acquisition of a dose of Fe^{59}. Disappearance rates of Fe^{59} were determined by plotting count rates against time on semilogarithmic paper, and the resultant slopes were expressed in half times of disappearance. The biologic half life of Fe^{59} (B) was determined by the formula:

$$E = \frac{B \times P}{B + P}$$

where E equals T½ in days for disappearance of Fe^{59} determined by whole body count and P equals 45.1 days (decay constant Fe^{59}). The rate constant for iron turnover in percentage was determined by the formula:

$$\frac{0.693}{B} \times 100$$

RESULTS

Iron Absorption

In nine normal subjects iron absorption varied 2.1 percent to 13.2 percent (Table II). Determinations in this group are based wholly on the described calibration methods. Neither collection of stools nor counts 4 hr. after ingestion were done, so no comparison of results between methods is possible.

TABLE II
IRON ABSORPTION IN NINE NORMAL SUBJECTS

Subject	% Fe^{59} Retained
1	13.2
2	5.2
3	5.8
4	11.8
5	9.1
6	2.2
7	4.3
8	2.1
9	6.5

Mean 6.7

TABLE III

IRON TURNOVER IN PAROXYSMAL NOCTURNAL HEMOGLOBINURIA

Subject	Calibration Method	Stool Collection	4 Hr. Count = 100% Retention
1	31.0	37	35
2	39.0	33	49
3	38.0		

Mean Absorption of Normals = 6.7%

In three subjects who were iron deficient or in whom iron losses had been recently excessive due to repeated blood donations, absorption was higher, ranging from 31 to 39 percent (Table III). In this group, 4 hr. counts and stool collections were done. All methods agree relatively closely. In case 3 either stool collection was incomplete, or whole body counts underestimated absorption.

The most complete data are available from the paroxymal nocturnal hemoglobinuria patients (Table IV). Here studies were done on six patients on two occasions, before and after a period of therapy with iron and fluoxymesterone and once on one patient who had been on supplemental iron alone. Iron absorption varied widely in the group from a low of 16 percent to a high of 60 percent. The three methods of determination of absorption were again in reasonable agreement in most instances.

TABLE IV

% IRON ABSORPTION IN PAROXYSMAL NOCTURNAL HEMOGLOBINURIA

Subject	Calibration Method	Stool Collection	4 Hr. Count = 100% Retention
1. 1st study	26	97	—
2nd study	27	41	—
2. 1st study	43	47	—
2nd study	18	27	24
3. 1st study	60	59	—
2nd study	53	64	—
4. 1st study	18	23	—
2nd study	40	41	50
5. 1st study	59	79	—
2nd study	34	68	57
6. 1st study	21	23	—
2nd study	24	18	—
7. 1st study	—	—	—
2nd study	16	39	18

The widest deviations were in case 1, case 5 and case 7. In cases 1 and 5 there is good evidence that the patients were not sufficiently motivated to collect all stool. The differences in case 7 are unexplained. It is of interest that in eleven of the thirteen studies, determination of absorption by stool collection overestimated absorption, or the whole body counter underestimated absorption. Percent absorption determined from counting the subject 4 hr. after ingestion was in reasonable agreement in four subjects.

Total Body Iron Turnover

Total body iron turnover in normal persons was determined in only three instances. The period of study varied from sixty to 270 days. Values were from 0.06 percent per day (Fig. 2) for a study period of 180 days, 0.09 percent per day for sixty days and 0.14 percent for 270 days (Fig. 3). The high estimate for the third subject is determined from the slope of disappearance of

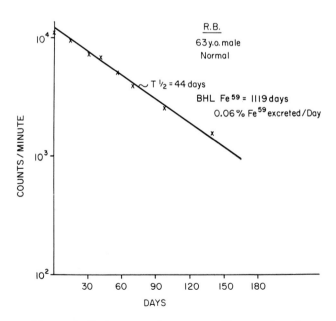

Figure 2. R. B., sixty-three year old normal male.

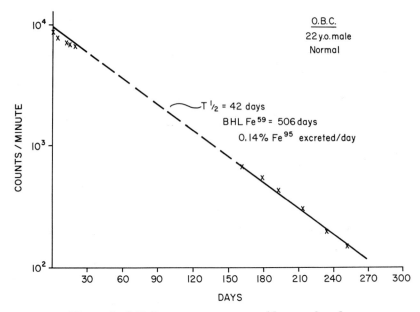

Figure 3. O.B.C., twenty-two year old normal male.

Fe[59] after 150 days, the earlier points from one to twenty-four days being disregarded.

Figures 4, 5 and 6 illustrate results obtained in patients with paroxysmal nocturnal hemoglobinuria. Turnover rates are high: 0.80 percent in patient AR, case 6 (Fig. 4); 0.21 percent per day in SM, case 5 (Fig. 5) and 0.65 percent per day in patient JB, case 3 (Fig. 6). Both patients AR and JB were placed on fluoxymesterone and supplemental oral iron during the study. In both there is a suggestion of decreased turnover following therapy. The data, however, are not complete enough for analysis of this point. Patient SM was on supplemental oral iron throughout the study and had the lowest rate of iron turnover with no suggestion of change in rate of loss. The data are summarized in Table V.

DISCUSSION

There is good general agreement between estimates of iron absorption by whole body counting and stool collections. The

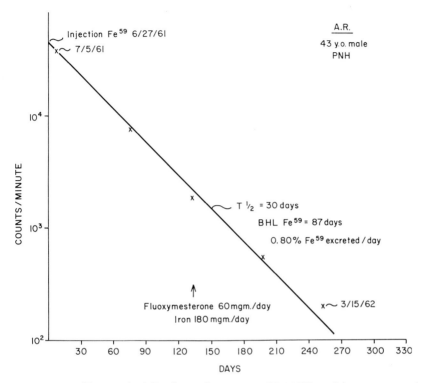

Figure 4. A.R., forty-three year old PNH male.

TABLE V
% IRON ABSORPTION IN IRON DEFICIENT SUBJECTS

Subject	Percent Fe^{59} Excreted/Day
B.G.	0.59
A.R.	0.80
J.B.	0.65
S.M.	0.21
F.C.	0.47
L.J.	0.26
3 Normals = 0.09, 0.06, 0.14	

consistently higher estimates derived from collection of stools
suggest that complete collection, even under the reasonably
rigid controlled study conditions of a metabolic ward, is difficult
to achieve or that whole body counting tends to underestimate

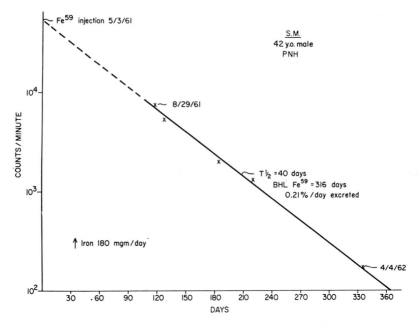

Figure 5. S.M., forty-two year old PNH male.

iron absorption. The whole body counter technique does not require metabolic ward care. Using the standard efficiency value of cpm/μc Fe^{59} for all subjects as we have done introduces an error into each determination. Since the deviation from the mean of efficiency in fourteen subjects was ± 8 percent, an error of at most of 8 percent would occur. Introduction of greater distance between the crystal and the subject or determination of each patient's efficiency value would result in more accurate values, if such were needed. While our data using the calibration factor are more extensive, a single comparison of the count 4 hr. after injection to 7 to 10 hr. after injection appears to be reliable for estimation of absorption.

Previous work has pointed out the significance of the amount of carrier iron with regard to the absolute amount of iron absorbed (7, 8). We chose arbitrarily to use 15 mg., approximately the daily dietary intake of iron. Our normal values for absorption of iron are compatible with data taken from the literature in

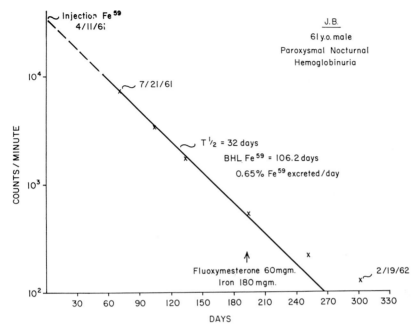

Figure 6. J.B., sixty-one year old PNH male.

which comparable amounts of carrier iron were used. The extremely high absorption of patients with paroxysmal nocturnal hemoglobinuria is consistent with collateral information regarding ferrokinetics, strainable tissue iron and urinary iron loss.

These studies also bear out the importance of careful selection of normal subjects. Two of the iron deficient subjects who absorbed by all criteria much higher amounts of fed iron were not anemic. In the one in whom serum iron determination was made subsequently, it was low. These two subjects were members of the division of hematology and subject to constant repeated blood donations of 5 to 50 ml. Since absorption determined by whole body counting and collection of stools coincided so well, there is little reason to question the results. The other normal subjects were all male medical students who had not been frequent or recent blood donors.

Total body iron turnover data have been difficult to obtain. Finch (17) calculated his results assuming that blood was in equilibrium with all body stores and followed the turnover of blood values. Dubach (16) calculated the turnover by measuring the loss from stool, urine and skin. Both methods estimated a loss of 0.5 to 1.0 mg. of iron per day. The later studies suggested that there was increased iron loss during the first twenty to twenty-five days. A recently reported study (18) using a whole body counter suggested a higher turnover with no significant loss for the first sixty days. Our preliminary data are compatible with a higher turnover than earlier studies indicated. Assuming normal body stores of iron, the turnover rate would be 2 to 6 mg. per day. The highest value is estimated from counts done after 150 days, while the lower values are from counts done before that. Theoretically, the rate of loss of Fe^{59} from the body could increase with time. Distribution between various iron compartments is unequal initially with most of the iron being used for red cell hemoglobin production. Except for minute blood loss from the gastrointestinal tract, loss of radioactivity should be minimal for the first 60 to 120 days, or until destruction of that cohort of Fe^{59} containing red cells occurs. After that time, presumably some greater portion of Fe^{59} is available for use by epithelial cells where it might be subject to external loss. Our data suggest such an occurrence, but are too limited for any conclusions.

The whole body iron turnover in paroxysmal nocturnal hemoglobinuria is far higher than in normal subjects and is explained by loss of hemoglobin iron via the kidneys. This supports other metabolic data on these patients and explains the profound iron deficiency anemia observed in one patient (20).

CONCLUSIONS

Methods for determining iron absorption in a single crystal whole body counter and comparison of results by whole body counting and stool collection are presented. There is good agreement between the two methods, and it is suggested that absorption as measured by whole body counting is probably more accurate than collection of fecal excretion except under rigidly controlled circumstances.

Normal subjects absorbed from 2 to 13 percent of a fed dose of Fe^{59} with a mean absorption of 6.7 percent. Three iron deficient subjects absorbed between 30 to 40 percent. Seven patients with paroxymal nocturnal hemoglobinuria absorbed from 16 to 60 percent of fed iron.

Total body iron turnover was determined in three normal subjects and six patients with paroxysmal nocturnal hemoglobinuria. The patients with paroxysmal nocturnal hemoglobinuria had much greater iron losses, ranging from 0.21 percent per day to 0.80 percent per day.

REFERENCES

1. Moore, C. V., Dubach, R.: Observations on the absorption from food tagged radioiron. *Asso. Amer. Physicians Trans. 64*:245, 1951.
2. Moore, C. V.: Iron metabolism and nutrition. *The Harvey Lect., 55*:67, 1961.
3. Chodos, R. B.: Ross, J. F., Apt, L., Pollycove, M., Halkett, J. A. E.: The absorption of radioiron-labeled foods and iron salts in normal and iron-deficient subjects and in idiopathic hemochromatosis. *J. Clin. Invest., 36*:314, 1957.
4. Walsh, R. J., Kaldor, J., Brading, I., George, E. P.: The availability of iron in meat: Some experiments with radioactive iron. *Austr. Ann. Med., 4*:272, 1955.
5. Schulz, J., Smith, N. J.: A quantative study of absorption of food iron in infants and children. *AMA J. Dis. Child., 95*:109, 1958.
6. Pirzio-Biroli, G., Finch, C. A.: Iron absorption: III, The influence of iron stores on iron absorption in the normal subject, *J. Lab. Clin. Med., 55*:216, 1960.
7. Bothwell, T. H., Pirzio-Biroli, G., Finch, C. A.: Iron absorption: I, Factors influencing absorption. *J. Lab. Clin. Med., 51*:24, 1958.
8. Smith, M. D., Pannacciulli, I. M.: Absorption of inorganic iron from graded doses: Its significance in relation to iron absorption tests and the mucosal block theory. *Brit. J. Haemat., 4*:428, 1958.
9. Baird, I. M., Wilson, G. M.: The pathogenesis of anemia after partial gastrectomy: II, Iron absorption after partial gastrectomy. *Quart. J. Med., 28*:35, 1959.
10. Alexander, R. S. Jr., Pirzio-Biroli, G., Harkins, H. N., Nyhus, L. M., Finch, C. A.: Iron metabolism in patients after partial gastrectomy, *Ann. Surg., 149*:534, 1959.
11. Steinkamp, R., Dubach, R., Moore, C. V.: Studies in iron transporta-

tion and metabolism: VIII, Absorption of radioiron from iron-en-riched bread. *AMA Arch. Int. Med., 95*:181, 1955.

12. Brown, E. B. Jr., Justus, B. W.: In vitro absorption of radioiron by everted pouches of rat intestine. *Amer. J. Physiol., 194*:319, 1958.

13. Hallberg, L.: Regulation of iron absorption. *Acta Heamat., 24*:29, 1960.

14. Noyes, W. D., Bothwell, T. H., Finch, C. A.: The role of the reticulo-endothelial cell in iron metabolism. *Brit. J. Haemat. 6*:43, 1960.

15. Dowdle, E. B., Schachter, D., Schenker, H.: Active transport of Fe[59] by everted segments of rat duodenum. *Amer. J. Physiol., 198*:609, 1960.

16. Dubach, R., Moore, C. V., Callender, S.: Studies of iron transport and metabolism: IX, The excretion of iron as measured by isotope tech-nique. *J. Lab. Clin. Med., 45*:599, 1955.

17. Finch, C. A.: Body iron exchange in man. *J. Clin. Invest., 38*:392, 1959.

18. Bonnet, J. D., Orvis, A. L., Hagedorn, A. B., Owen, C. A. Jr.: Rate of loss of radioiron from mouse and man. *Amer. J. Physiol., 198*:784, 1960.

19. Mitchell, H. H., Hamilton, T. S., Adams, W. S., Leslie, A., Levine, M. H., Foy, H., Kondi, A., Hussian, R., Patwardhan, V. N.: Iron content of sweat in anemias. *Nutr. Rev., 17*:295, 1959.

20. Hartmann, R. C., King, J. A., McKee, C., Heyssel, R. M.: Effects of androgens on anemia and iron metabolism in PNH. Presented in part at International Congress of Hematology, Mexico City, Sept., 1962.

21. Meneely, G. R., Ball, C. O. T., Ferguson, J. L., Payne, D. D., Lorimer, A. R., Weiland, R. L., Rolf, H. L., Heyssel, R. M.: The use of com-putors in measuring body electrolytes by gamma spectrometry. *Circulat. Res., 11*:539, 1962.

29

DETERMINATION OF ABSORBABILITY OF ORAL RADIOIRON IN HEALTH AND DISEASE IN MAN BY WHOLE BODY SCINTILLOMETRY[1]

C. C. LUSHBAUGH[2] AND D. B. HALE

University of California
Los Alamos, New Mexico

MANY PROBLEMS CONCERNING the dietary absorption of iron and its bodily utilization remain unsolved. The availability of Fe[59] and the development of radioisotopic techniques using small NaI crystals (1) have made the study of gastrointestinal iron absorption, plasma iron transport, storage, utilization and excretion relatively easy, and numerous studies concerning these problems have been reported (2).

There remains a need for a simple diagnostic procedure for determining whether or not the apparently iron-deficient anemic patient will absorb iron given orally without the collection and quantitative analysis of feces. Studies by others (3) have shown that the human body has no physiologic means (other than menstruation and necrobiotic cell loss) of excreting iron once it has been absorbed. Since, even in severely constipated persons, the unabsorbed portion of an orally administered dose of radioiron is completely excreted fecally within seven to ten days, the amount of radioactive iron remaining in the body after this time represents the portion of the dose that was absorbed from the gastrointestinal tract (4, 5). Assay by whole body scintillometry of the radioactive iron in the entire body before and after the excretory period has been found to be a facile means of measuring oral iron absorption in man without the necessity of collect-

[1] Work performed under the auspices of the U. S. Atomic Energy Commission.

[2] Now at Oak Ridge Institute of Nuclear Studies, Oak Ridge, Tennessee.

ing feces (4, 6). Determination of retention of the residual radioactive iron label by repeated whole body assay using this
method should provide a measurement of the turnover rate of
iron in individual cases of iron deficiency due to chronic hemorrhage.

METHODS

The Los Alamos liquid scintillation detectors known as
Humco I and Humco II (7,8) were used in developing this
method for measuring oral iron absorption. Humco II is now being used in clinical studies of iron demand in anemia. The development of Humco II enabled the dose of Fe^{59} to be reduced from
0.7 μc used in Humco I to 0.275 μc. In our early observations, no
nonradioactive iron was administered with the radioactive tracer
dose, but the patients and normal volunteers were encouraged
during the initial days of the studies to eat normally. Since then
the labeling technique has been changed. All persons are now labeled while fasting and given the Fe^{59} with 12 mg. of elemental
iron as ferrous citrate in 1 percent ascorbic acid solution to maintain the iron in a reduced state.

In order to determine the background radioactivity of the
person, he is assayed initially in the whole body counter before
being given the labeled iron. He is then reassayed immediately
after administration of the labeled iron to determine the effect
of self absorption on the intragastric radioactivity. A 50 kg.
phantom of sugar encased in a cardboard carton is then measured
with and without the patient's dose of Fe^{59} in its center. The ratio
between initial measurements of the radioactivity of the patient
and his standard is then used along with his radioactivity and
that of his standard on any following day to determine percent
retention of the tracer. With children, sugar or water phantoms
of appropriate weight and size are used instead of the adult
standard.

Fecal samples from the first ten patients were collected
quantitatively in plastic containers and counted in Humco I to
obtain a balance between retained and excreted iron. When cor-

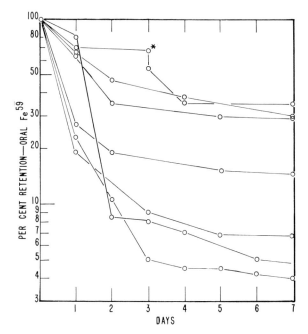

Figure 1. Whole body iron retention curves in normal and diseased persons during the first week after oral ingestion of a tracer dose (0.7 μc) of Fe^{59} measured in Humco I showing the great variability in rate of fecal excretion during the first part of the week and the ultimate leveling off by the end of the week.

rected for decay, these data revealed that even in constipated patients whole body radioactivity due to Fe^{59} (Fig. 1) was essentially constant at the end of one week. In Figure 2, the results of repeated whole body assays are shown for four subjects to show that no appreciable decrease was found in whole body radioactivity (after correction for isotopic decay) during the following month. The percent retention found after the first week was the percent of the initial dose of iron that was absorbed from the intestine and retained within the body. A routine method of analysis was established whereby the patient was counted for 200 sec. immediately before and after taking the radioactive iron and again after the seventh day. It was then possible to minimize the time required for each study.

A group of volunteers of twenty normal men and thirty normal women were studied to establish normal values. They

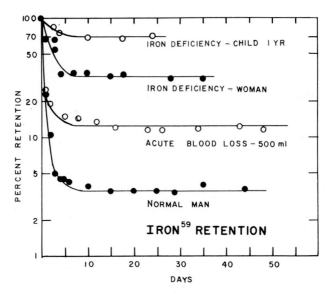

Figure 2. Whole body retention of orally administered Fe^{59}-citrate in a normal man, in the same man following acute blood loss, in an iron-deficient woman with chronic menstrual hemorrhage and in a child fed only milk during its life.

were divided into two random subgroups after a base line whole body assay. All received 0.275 μc of Fe^{59} orally with 12 mg. of elemental iron. One subgroup of men and women received radioactive ferrous iron in a solution of ferrous citrate, and the other subgroup received radioactive ferric iron in a solution of ferric sulfate. One week after the resulting initial whole body count was determined, whole body assays were repeated. The percent retention at that time was considered the amount of the orally ingested dose of iron that was absorbed. At the time of the second assay, 30 ml. of blood was drawn from each subject to determine number of erythrocytes, hemoglobin, hematocrit, reticulocyte count, serum iron content, serum-iron-binding capacity, mean corpuscular volume, mean corpuscular hemoglobin and mean corpuscular hemoglobin concentration (Table I).

In addition to the pilot group of ten and the normal group of fifty men and women, fifty-six patients were studied using Fe^{59}

TABLE I

HEMATOLOGICAL PARAMETERS FOR 50 "NORMAL" MEN AND WOMEN GIVEN
TRACER DOSES OF Fe^{59}

	Men (20)		Women (30)	
	Ferrous	Ferric	Ferrous	Ferric
RBC (million/cmm.)	6.1	5.7	5.0	4.9
Hgb (gm./100)	15.5	15.5	14.0	13.7
Hmct. (%)	51.0	52.0	45.0	45.0
Reticulocytes (%)	0.9	1.1	1.3	1.2
SI (μg./100)	139	142	115	100
SIBC (μg./100)	330	330	331	315
MCV (μ^3)	84.0	91.0	90.0	94.0
MCH ($\mu\mu$g.)	26.0	27.0	28.0	28.0
MCC (%)	31.0	30.0	31.0	30.0
Fe^{59} (% uptake)	5.3 ± 3.3	2.8 ± 1.7	11.3 ± 6.1	8.6 ± 5.4
Range (% uptake)	1.8-11.7	0.3-6.0	2.6-23.7	1.5-19.3

as ferrous citrate to define the parameters of abnormal iron absorption and to attempt to correlate this measurement with other hematologic values. The fifty-six included three subjects recovered from hypochromic anemia following parenteral iron therapy, nineteen with anemias associated with various leukemias, two with polycythemia rubra vera, one with polycythemia secondary to pulmonary disease, and twenty-eight with typical uncomplicated hypochromic microcytic anemia. Of these twenty-eight, four were children with pica who had been breast or bottle fed milk as their only source of nutriment for over one year, and one was a seven-months pregnant woman.

RESULTS

Normal ferrous iron absorption by this method is 5.3 ± 3.3% for men and 11.3 ± 6.1% for women (Table I). The ranges were 1.8 to 11.7 percent for men and 2.6 to 23.7 percent for women. The amounts of ferric iron absorbed were less in each sex, but while the ranges were similarly reduced in comparison with absorption of the ferrous salt, overlapping of the data was so great that statistically there was no significant difference in absorption of the two different ionic forms of iron. The relatively wide range of absorption by these normal persons could not be explained on the basis of the variation in the other hematologic measurements also shown in Table I.

A correlation was found with occupation in that the men with sedentary jobs absorbed 7.8 percent of the ferrous iron and 5.5 percent of the ferric iron, while those with out-of-doors occupations absorbed 5.3 and 2.0 percent, respectively. Among the women, those with a history of previous abortion and menstrual irregularities absorbed 17.5 percent of the ferrous iron and 15.5 percent of the ferric iron, while those who had had hysterectomies absorbed only 5.7 and 1.6 percent, respectively. Thus, the housewife without her uterus was remarkably similar in iron absorption to the man with a physically active occupation and no history of blood loss. It would seem from these data that normal iron demand for the most healthy active men and women without any recent blood loss is represented by the daily absorption of a little less than 6 percent of the dietary ferrous iron intake, or about 0.7 mg./day.

Iron[59] absorption determined by this method is contrasted with whole blood hemoglobin in Figure 3. A rough correlation exists between iron absorption and hemoglobin values of hypochromic patients without infection. Patients recovering or still suffering from various acute or chronic infections associated with anemia did not appear to show any increased iron absorption above that seen in the normal patients (also see Table I). The anemic leukemic patients likewise did not show increased iron absorbability. Polycythemic patients stand out remarkably because of their high hemoglobin and increased iron absorption. The one patient with polycythemia secondary to chronic bronchiectasia and degenerative emphysema did not show the same degree of iron avidity. The only pregnant woman studied had a 11.5 gm. hemoglobin and absorbed 99 percent of the Fe[59] tracer dose. At parturition two months later, the placenta was preserved so that it, the mother and the new-born child could be radioassayed in the whole body counter on the day the child was discharged from the hospital. At that time the mother was found to have retained forty-eight percent, the placenta 10 percent and the child 23 percent of the original dose. The mother hemorrhaged in

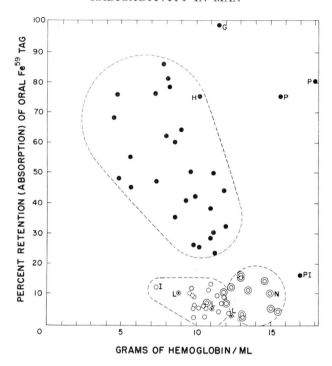

Figure 3. Absorption and retention of orally administered Fe[59] in relation to the peripheral blood hemoglobin of patients. N - normals; H - hypochromic anemias; P - polycythemias; I - postinfectious anemias; L - leukemias ; G - a seven months pregnant woman, and PI - a polycythemic man with severe pulmonary disease.

parturition and required a postpartum transfusion. This blood loss might explain the deficit of 18 percent found at re-assay. If this 18 percent loss were added to the maternal percentage, it would increase her net absorption at the time of administration of the dose from 48 to 66 percent.

The poor correlation between hemoglobin and iron absorption led to an attempt to relate absorption to serum iron content. Figure 4 shows the correlation in the first twelve patients for whom serum iron levels were obtained at the time of oral administration of the tracer. Additional studies made, along with determinations of serum iron and serum iron binding capacities, appear to support an exponential relationship, which seems to exist when hypochromia is uncomplicated and due to iron deficiency

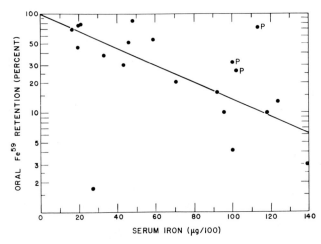

Figure 4. Relationship between oral iron absorption and serum iron content.

alone. The patient with less than 2 percent absorption and a serum iron of only 27 μg. had chronic nephritis, chronic menstrual blood loss and poor nutrition. The findings in a typical patient in relapse with polycythemia rubra vera show that the high absorption of oral iron in the true polycythemic patient is correlated with a lower serum iron. Subsequent findings showed that in remission the serum iron of the true polycythemic patient rises dramatically to higher than normal values and his increased iron absorbability returns to low normal amounts.

In Figure 5 the rate of absorbed iron loss is shown for a normal man and woman and a woman suffering from menorrhagia. The lines are extended over 500 days, although the slopes of the lines were determined from data obtained by whole body assays of these subjects at weekly to monthly intervals over only 90 to 180. The intercepts at zero time show percent of the oral dose of 12 mg. of elemental iron that was absorbed: normal man, 3.8 percent; normal woman, 10.0 percent; and woman with men-

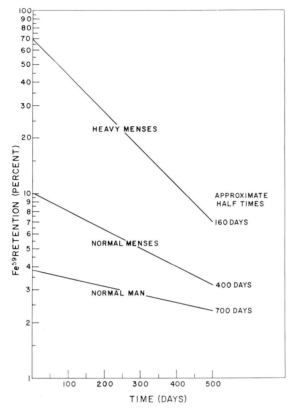

Figure 5. Whole body retention lines of orally ingested iron citrate labeled with Fe⁵⁹ in three subjects: a normal man, a normally menstruating young woman and a woman with menorrhagia. The approximate biological half times of these individuals indicate the relative rate of iron loss.

orrhagia, 69.9 percent. The rate of loss of iron from these subjects after absorption is shown by the slope of the lines and is expressed as their biological half times. The rate constants derived from these lines indicate that the normal women lost iron almost twice as rapidly as the normal men, while the women with menstrual hemorrhage lost it about 4.5 times as fast.

DISCUSSION

These data show that intestinal absorption of iron by man is easily measured by determining the whole body retention of an orally administered dose of an iron salt labeled with Fe[59]. The 0.7 mg. of iron absorbed daily by normal subjects in this study is in excellent agreement with the 0.8 mg. found by Hevesy (2) and by Sharpe *et al.* (9) with tagged test meals, but leaves unexplained the enormous percentage uptakes of normal nonfasting persons as measured by the fecal collection method of Bonnet *et al.* (10). While the use of minute amounts of iron may produce an increased absorption in normal persons when expressed as percentage and thereby disclose persons who fail to absorb iron normally, it is yet to be proven that the "mucosal blockade" of Granick (11) is a pathologic actuality and that hypoabsorbers are to be expected on this basis. The present study shows that many anemic persons fail to absorb orally ingested iron in greater than normal amounts even though their serum iron and hemoglobin levels would seem to indicate that they should. The failure of iron absorption as measured by this method to correlate with either hemoglobin or serum iron levels in these cases affords an excellent means of bringing these patients to light without the necessity of rigorous fasting, carrier-free doses and fecal collection. Whether or not this failure is due to a defect in absorption is difficult to prove. The alterations in gastrointestinal absorption of iron in the polycythemic patients in relapse and remission suggest that increased gastrointestinal absorption of iron is a measure of demand by the bone marrow for iron. The failure of iron absorption to increase during infections and leukemic diseases in the presence of anemia may likewise be correlated with suppression of erythropoiesis that is known to accompany these conditions.

Further proof that amount of iron absorption may measure bone marrow iron demand seems contained in the study of the fifty normal persons. Men in the best physical condition with nonsedentary occupations and hysterectomized housewives had the lowest iron absorption. Hemorrhoidal difficulties associated with desk jobs and normal menstruation were found to increase iron absorption in otherwise normal people. Hemorrhage of any sort dramatically increased iron demand and consequent absorption.

Determination of the chronic loss of retained iron by whole body assay of Fe^{59} should prove an excellent way to differentiate chronic blood loss iron deficiency anemia from dietary iron deficiency anemia. It should also allow therapeutic control of the deficiency by measuring the daily iron loss and, therefore, the daily amount of iron that must be absorbed to balance it. Further studies of such clinical problems as the anemia of disseminated cancer, leukemias and primary polycythemia by this method would seem warranted. Although much more investigation is required in many areas of iron metabolism, the results reported here seem to indicate that whole body assay of intestinal iron absorption is a method of great diagnostic and therapeutic potential.

REFERENCES

1. Beierwaltes, W. H., Johnson, P. C., and Solari, A. J.: *Clinical Use of Radioisotopes.* Philadelphia, W. B. Saunders Co., 1957, pp. 288-295.
2. Hevesy, G., and Lockner, D.: Iron metabolism in health and in the neoplastic state. *Arkiv f. Kemi, 19*:303, 1962.
3. Dubach, R., Moore, C. V., and Callender, S. T.: Studies in iron transportation and metabolism, IX. The excretion of iron as measured by the isotope technique. *J. Lab. Clin. Med., 45*:599, 1955.
4. Lushbaugh, C. C., and Hale, D. B.: Clinical Applications of Whole Body Scintillometry, I. Retention of Orally Administered Iron. Los Alamos Scientific Laboratory Report, LAMS-2445, 1960, p. 337.
5. Pollycove, M.: Erythrocyte kinetics in refractory anemia with erythroid hyperplasia. in Proc. 7th Int. Congr. Int. Soc. Haematol., 1, Grune and Stratton, New York, 1960, p. 465.
6. Van Holk, R., and Conrad, M. E. Jr.: Iron absorption, measurement of ingested iron^{59} by a whole body liquid scintillation counter. *J. Clin. Invest., 40*:1153, 1961.
7. Anderson, E. C., Schuch, R. L., Perrings, J. D., and Langham, W. H.: The Los Alamos human counter. *Nucleonics, 1*:26, 1956.
8. Anderson, E. C., Schuch, R. L., Kerr, V. N., and Van Dilla, M. A.: Humco II: A new four pi liquid scintillation counter. *Radioactivity in Man.* Springfield, Thomas, 1961, pp. 31-44.
9. Sharpe, L. M., Peacock, W. C., Cooke, R., and Harris, R. S.: The effect of phytate and other food factors on iron absorption. *J. Nutr., 41*:433, 1950.
10. Bonnet, J. D., Hagedorn, A. B., and Owen, C. A. Jr.: A quantitative method for measuring the gastrointestinal absorption of iron. *Blood, 15*:36, 1960.
11. Granick, S.: Iron metabolism. *Bull. N. Y. Acad. Med. 30*:81, 1954.

DISCUSSION

Chairman: PAUL HAHN

U. S. Public Health Service
Washington, D. C.

E. H. BELCHER: Whole body counting will only give a valid answer in gastrointestinal absorption tests if there is insignificant loss of labeled material in the urine or other routes during the test. Dr. McKee mentioned in his studies that Fe^{59} gave a higher result by whole body counting than by fecal recovery studies. I wonder if this might be due to losses in urine.

Concerning the carrier amount of substance in test doses of Fe^{59} which are used, the normal range of absorption will obviously depend on the amount of the carrier. Could the speakers tell us what levels of carrier they used in their studies?

CHAIRMAN PAUL F. HAHN: The amount of carrier used can make a difference in factors of 10 to 30. We ought to standardize the amount for such studies because there is such a tremendous difference.

We found many years ago that feeding at a level of 40 mg. there is about 30 percent absorption, whereas at 400 mg. there is only 5 percent absorption. As you get down to 1 or 2 mg,, the absorption goes up tremendously.

CLIFFORD McKEE: We use 15 mg.

C. C. LUSHBAUGH: We used 12 in part of the study, and in part we used as little as the laboratory would put in the bottle. We found that as long as we stayed below 15 mg. of carrier, it did not seem to make any difference in our percent absorption. I believe that Dr. Reizenstein used 250 μg. and 15 mg., and yet all of us have reported the same amount of oral absorption by the whole body retention method, where it is approximately 5 percent for a normal man.

DAVID C. PRICE: Our normal dose was as high as 25. Barnett studied several patients and was able to demonstrate that as the amount of carrier iron decreases, the proportion of tracer absorbed increases.

BENEDICT CASSEN: I have some work on this same subject which may help explain these observations. Injection into the bone marrow produces a low body count. The curve will vary a great deal depending on the condition of the patient. We have found the same range of absorption that all of the other speakers have found, between 5 and 20 percent. If you plot the amount absorbed against the total carrier dose, then the increase is almost linear.

CHAIRMAN PAUL F. HAHN: Any amount of carrier iron is important from the standpoint of therapy, and I cannot remember seeing any good guess as to what would be the optimum. Years ago, we used to balance the amount of gastrointestinal disturbance against the efficacy of the treatment. I believe that relatively small doses at frequent intervals, probably some four or five times a day, are optimal, with a dosage of 40 to 100 mg. at each time.

C. C. LUSHBAUGH: The normal diet is supposed to contain some 12 to 15 mg. of iron per day, so if you have patients who are on starvation diets, they obviously should receive 12 or 15 mg. per day carrier iron. If they are consuming normal meals during the test, then it would seem all right not to use any carrier iron, because you would be testing the amount of iron they absorbed that day in the normal diet. It was on that basis that we saw no difference when we used patients fasting on 12 mg. iron or eating normal diets during our test without carrier.

Where the man got 17 percent uptake with 250 μg. of iron, we got 7 percent on 12 mg. Actually, this is not a very linear alteration.

CHAIRMAN PAUL F. HAHN: Using material that is diagnostic, we probably are at liberty to use small amounts, as long as we are fairly consistent. But when it comes to therapy, we have to balance the total absorption versus the percent of absorption and credit both the factors.

We showed at least twenty years ago that there was a major difference in the absorption of ferrous and ferric iron under controlled conditions in dogs and in clinical anemias and in pregnancy.

C. C. LUSHBAUGH: I was surprised to see the two numbers had no statistical difference. I think that the small amount of ferric iron used in the normal person was actually converted to ferrous and absorbed only in the intestinal tract.

SESSION IX, SEPTEMBER 7

MISCELLANEOUS TOPICS
Chairman: ALEXANDER P. REMENCHIK

30

NATURAL CONTENT OF RaD (Pb^{210}) AND RaF (Po^{210}) IN THE HUMAN BODY[1]

Richard B. Holtzman

Argonne National Laboratory
Argonne, Illinois

INTRODUCTION

IN ORDER TO ASSESS the dose due to natural radiation in the human environment, the internal radioactivity of the body must be determined along with that of the external radiation. Much effort has been expended in determination of the artificial background from bomb fallout, whereas on a much smaller scale this has been done on many of the naturally occurring radionuclides, such as C^{14}, K^{40}, Ra^{226} and Ra^{228} (1-4). C^{14} accounts for little of the dose, although because of its location in the cell nucleus, it may be quite important. On the other hand, K^{40} accounts for an appreciable fraction of the internal absorbed dose in the body (5), but its biological importance is considerably reduced if an estimated RBE of 4 for alpha particles is assumed.

One purpose of these studies is to locate large human population groups which are identical to other groups, except for differences in exposure to natural radiation. Thus, there is the possibility of studying low level radiation effects on humans. Natural radiation is of particular interest because it may allow the discovery of large populations of 100,000 or more which have experienced known and constant lifetime exposures. Such groups have been found in sections of Illinois in which the Ra^{226} skeletal levels in the population are ten times those of their neighbors. The differences are caused by variations in the Ra^{226} concentrations in the drinking water (1).

[1] Work performed under auspices of the U. S. Atomic Energy Commission.

RaD is another such nuclide. It is a Ra^{226} decay product (Fig. 1), but one does not expect it to follow the parent because of their different chemistries and its long half life. The most important difference is that RaD is derived from the rare gas intermediate Rn^{222} which is easily translocated from the parent Ra^{226}.

RADIOACTIVE DECAY SCHEME OF THE Ra^{226} SERIES

$Ra^{226} \xrightarrow[\alpha]{1622\ y}$ $Rn^{222} \xrightarrow[\alpha]{3.82\ d}$ $RaA\ (Po^{218}) \xrightarrow[\alpha]{3.05\ m}$

$RaB\ (Pb^{214}) \xrightarrow[\beta]{26.8\ m}$ $RaC\ (Bi^{214}) \xrightarrow[\beta]{19.7\ m}$ $RaC'\ (Po^{214}) \xrightarrow[\alpha]{1.6\ x\ 10^{-4}s}$

$RaD\ (Pb^{210}) \xrightarrow[\beta]{21.4\ y}$ $RaE\ (Bi^{210}) \xrightarrow[\beta]{5.0\ d}$ $RaF\ (Po^{210}) \xrightarrow[\alpha]{138\ d}$ $RaG\ (Pb^{206})\ (S)$

Figure 1

Only in the last few years has naturally occurring RaD been studied. Dudley (6) estimated the body content of this nuclide to be about ten times that of Ra^{226}. Considering the amount of information available at that time, this conclusion was quite reasonable when compared to the subsequent measured values of Black (7), Hill (8) and this laboratory (9) using small sections of bone. On the other hand, Hursh (10), measuring whole body ash, found the RaD content to be only about one half that of Ra^{226}.

EXPERIMENTAL TECHNIQUE

For this study particular effort was devoted to the determination of RaD, RaF and Ra^{226} in human surgical and autopsy specimens of soft tissue and bone.

The RaD was determined by analysis of its decay product RaF (Po^{210}). The analyses were performed by first wet ashing the samples with nitric and perchloric acids. Next the nitrates were destroyed by repeated fumings with hydrochloric acid. After adjusting to pH 0.3, the Po^{210} was plated onto a silver disk at 90° C. It was then alpha counted (7, 9).

Ra^{226} was determined by the radon emanation method of Lucas (11). The ash content was determined from the calcium, expressed as calcium phosphate, which, because of a series of compensating factors, is equivalent to the ash (9).

RESULTS AND DISCUSSION

Interpretation of these measurements to obtain meaningful conclusions involved certain problems. In the sampling procedure to determine if a particular sample is representative of the whole, only small samples were available, and even if larger ones had been available, processing would have been difficult. Thus, it was necessary to determine how well they represented the entire skeleton and body. This was done with sets of bone sections, tibia, skull, mandible and either rib or joint bone, with each set from one person. Data from eight sets are shown in Table I. Within a factor of 2 or so (with a few exceptions) any given bone appears to be representative. Ra^{226} concentrations were relatively constant within a given individual, again with a few notable exceptions (Table II). Because of the fairly high probability that a given bone represents the total skeleton and for lack of a better hypothesis, it has been assumed that the distribution of RaD is uniform within the skeleton.

The second problem considered was the whole body distribution of RaD. Table III shows that about 60 percent of the activity was in the skeleton, a result in agreement with that calculated from metabolic parameters of stable lead (12, 13). Since the skeleton constitutes about 10 to 15 percent of the total body weight and contains more than 60 percent of the RaD, the dose

TABLE I

RaD Concentrations in Bone (pc/gm. ash)

SUBJECT*

Bone	40 M	43 F	49 F	52 F	63 M	68 M	77 M	90 F
Tibia	0.075	0.090	0.081	0.078 0.132	0.085	0.269 0.247	0.117	0.070
Mandible	0.105	0.049	0.081	0.077	0.055	0.093	0.225	0.061
Skull	0.102	0.092 0.146	0.110	0.366 1.33	0.091	0.201 0.419	0.191	0.086
Rib	0.142	—	0.129	—	0.150	—	0.453	0.066
Joint (Bone)	—	0.083	—	0.071	—	0.152	—	—

* Subjects identified by age and sex.

TABLE II

RA[226] CONCENTRATIONS IN BONE (pc/gm. ash)

SUBJECT*

Bone	40 M	43 F	49 F	52 F	63 M	68 M	77 M	90 F
Tibia	0.022	0.025	0.047	{0.026 / 0.030}	0.013	{0.012 / 0.019}	0.014	0.019
Mandible	0.015	0.028	0.032	0.030	0.020	0.012	0.020	0.021
Skull	0.018	{0.051 / 0.100}	0.049	{0.032 / 0.027}	0.009	{0.070 / 0.070}	0.014	0.017
Rib	0.016	—	0.053	—	0.025	—	0.020	0.025
Joint (Bone)	—	0.025	—	0.027	—	0.016	—	—

*Subject identified by age and sex.

TABLE III

DISTRIBUTION OF RAD IN VARIOUS HUMAN ORGANS

Organ (Ratio: Organ Wt. to Body Wt., %)	Average Concentration of RaD (pc/g wet)*	Fraction of Total Activity (%)
Liver (2.4%)	0.011 ± 0.003	1.7
Muscle (43%)	0.006 ± 0.004	17
Bone (Rib) (4.0% of ash) (10% of total body)	0.235 ± 0.036	63
Other tissues (45%)	0.006**	18

*Bone given per gm. ash.

**Other tissues assumed to have same average concentrations as muscle.

TABLE IV

RADIOACTIVE EQUILIBRIUM BETWEEN RAD AND RAF IN HUMAN BONE *in vivo*

Sample No.	Type of Tissue	Ratio RaF/RaD
115	Iliac Crest	0.81
131	Rib	0.77
135	Vertebra	0.79
140	Joint	1.00
186	Rib	1.43
245	Rib	1.17
Average		1.0 ± 0.2

rate to the skeleton is about ten times that to the other parts of the body.

The problem of the RaF-RaD equilibrium in the skeleton

was considered. This is important because the dose is essentially due to the alpha-emitting RaF. The results were obtained by analyzing the RaF within a few weeks after surgery and again after several months. The RaF to RaD ratio was 1.0 ± 0.2 (Table IV), thus the metabolic properties are essentially controlled by those of RaD; that is, on the average, there is little excess or deficiency of RaF over RaD.

Figure 2 is a plot of the RaD vs. the Ra^{226} concentrations in 128 samples from about 100 persons. There is little correlation, and in a given Ra^{226} interval of 0.01 pc/gm. ash, the RaD concentrations may range over a factor of 6. The RaD does appear to increase with Ra^{226} concentration; and all points, except two, lie above the line:

$$(RaD) = 0.56 \ (Ra^{226}) \ 0.71$$

where the parentheses refer to the concentration in units of pc/gm. ash of the enclosed species. The significance of this line is unknown. The two points below the curve are less significant than the others because they are data from specimens obtained from children, and there is some evidence that children have

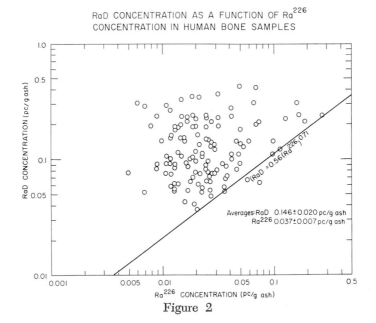

RaD CONCENTRATION AS A FUNCTION OF Ra^{226}
CONCENTRATION IN HUMAN BONE SAMPLES

Figure 2

lower RaD concentrations than do adults (9). The over-all average of RaD was 0.146 ± 0.020 pc/gm. ash, and of Ra^{226} 0.037 ± 0.007 pc/gm. ash.

The RaD concentration in the trabecular bone samples averaged 0.18 pc/gm. ash, about 75 percent greater than that in cortical bone samples (Table V). The average RaD concentration in men, 0.16 pc/gm. ash, was 35 percent higher than the 0.119 pc/gm. ash in women. While the trabecular and cortical samples are not uniformly distributed between the two sexes, the average for each respective type of bone is higher in men than in women. While there are many questions involved in the sampling procedures, these results do indicate the RaD concentration is higher in trabecular than in cortical bone and is higher in men than in women.

On a regional basis, there is no apparent correlation in the measured population (Table VI). This is a series of measurements on rib specimens from fourteen people who lived in Chicago fifteen years or more. The concentrations range over a factor of 6, but they average 0.177 pc/gm. ash, which is slightly higher than the over-all average of 0.146 pc/gm. ash, but is about the same as the average trabecular bone. The Ra^{226} values average 0.015 pc/gm. ash, which is about that expected in Chicago residents (11).

We have also tried to determine the source of RaD in the body, and six sources were considered: Ra^{226} and Rn^{222} in the

TABLE V

AVERAGE RaD CONCENTRATIONS

Bone	Sex*		
	Male (pc/g Ash Average ± E)	Female (pc/g Ash Average ± E)	All Subjects (pc/g Ash Average ± E)
Trabecular	0.196 ± 0.023 (47)	0.156 ± 0.040 (20)	0.184 ± 0.029 (67)
Cortical	0.115 ± 0.021 (36)	0.090 ± 0.020 (25)	0.105 ± 0.021 (61)
All Bone	0.161 ± 0.022 (83)	0.119 ± 0.030 (45)	0.146 ± 0.020 (128)

*The number of samples in each group is given in the parentheses. E is the 90 percent confidence interval of the mean.

TABLE VI
RaD and Ra^{226} Concentrations in Rib Bones of Chicago Residents

RESIDENCE TIME >15 YEARS

Sample	Ra^{226} (pc/g Ash)	RaD (pc/ Ash)
1	.014	.063
2	.005	.078
3	.009	.084
4	.025	.096
5	.022	.134
6	.028	.138
7	.010	.144
8	.021	.160
9	.020	.190
10	.008	.195
11	.009	.243
12	.007	.290
13	.006	.308
14	.022	.355
	.015 ± .003 (± 20%)	.177 ± .040 (± 23%)

TABLE VII
Possible Sources of the RaD Content of the Human Skeleton

Source	Contribution to RaD Concentration (pc/g Ash)
Ra^{226} in Bones	0.004
Rn^{222} Dissolved in Body (Equivalent to 50 1 of air at 3.0 pc Rn^{222}/1)	0.007
Potable Water (Maximum Observed, 0.4 pc RaD/1)	0.022
RaD in Atmosphere (0.03 pc RaD/m^3)	0.073
RaD from Short-Lived Activities (Rn^{222} daughters)	0.004
Food	0.066
Total	0.176
Total (less Rn^{222} in body and potable water)	0.148
Measured RaD Concentration (Average)	0.146 ± 0.020

body, RaD in potable water, RaD in the atmosphere, short lived Rn^{222} daughters in the air and RaD in food (Table VII).

Using the exponential model for excretion and the parameters for lead and RaD metabolism in the "Standard Man" (9, 12, 13) based on those given in the Report of the International Commission of Radiation Protection, we have estimated the contributions of these various sources to the body content. The contribution of drinking water appears significant, but the value used is extremely high (9), about ten times the average, and consequently, few people would be exposed to this. The Rn^{222} value of 3 pc/liter is also high (14). We conclude, therefore, that in most people the only significant sources of RaD to the body are food and air. The general agreement of the calculated with the measured values is significant, although because of the assumptions in the calculations and the great range of the experimental data, the close agreement is fortuitous.

The data presented here may be used to estimate the internal dose rate due to RaD and its daughters relative to that from the Ra^{226} chain. The effective dose is given by the product of the average energies of the emitted particles, an RBE of 4 for alpha particles and the fractional retention of the nuclides (15). For RaD and its daughters and for Ra^{226}, the retention is 1; for Rn^{222} and its daughters, it is 0.3. Consequently, for a given activity of each parent nuclide, the ratio of effective dose rates of RaD to Ra^{226} is 0.5. The average RaD concentration of 0.146 pc/gm. ash is equivalent to a Ra^{226} concentration of 0.073 pc/gm. ash (Table VIII). This is about twice the measured Ra^{226} in our samples. This factor of 2 is actually a minimum, since these samples include a relatively large fraction from people residing in areas with high Ra^{226} drinking water. Most people live in low level

TABLE VIII

DOSE RATES OF RaD AND Sr^{90} RELATIVE TO THOSE OF Ra^{226} AND $Ra^{226} + Ra^{228}$

Nuclide	Concentration (pc/g Ash)	Dose Rate (Relative to Ra^{226})	Dose Rate* (Relative to $Ra^{226} + Ra^{228}$)
Ra^{226} (all subjects)	0.037	1	0.5
RaD	0.146	2.0	1.0
Sr^{90}	0.5	0.3	0.15
Ra^{226} (Chicago)	0.015	1	0.5
RaD	0.146	5	2.5
Sr^{90}	0.5	0.7	0.35

*Assume Ra^{228} dose rate equals Ra^{226} dose rate.

areas, such as Chicago (11). Consequently, over the whole country the RaD dose rate levels are actually about five times those of Ra^{226}. Since the dose due to Ra^{228} in the body is about equal to that of Ra^{226} (16), the RaD dose is about two and one-half times that of the two Ra nuclides.

The radiation levels of RaD may be also compared to those of Sr^{90}. If an RBE of 4 is assumed for alpha particles relative to that of betas, and the Sr^{90} concentration is about 0.5 pc/gm. ash (17), then the RaD dose is about ten times that due to Sr^{90}.

CONCLUSION

Because of the difficulties in determining the RaD and RaF content of the skeleton, the total dose rate therein may be difficult to estimate. Moreover, because of the lack of correlation between the RaD and the Ra^{226} concentrations, the relative dose rates cannot be defined as a function of geography. The statistical uncertainties in any associated epidemiological study would thereby be increased (18). Some of the difficulties might be alleviated if further studies make other correlations apparent.

REFERENCES

1. Stehney, A. F.: *Radioisotopes in the Biosphere.* Minneapolis, University of Minnesota, 1960, p. 366.
2. Muth, H., Rajewsky, B., Hantke, H. J., and Aurand, K.: *Health Physics,* 2:239, 1960.
3. Lucas, H. F., and Krause, D. P.: *Radiology,* 74:114, 1960.
4. Krause, D. P.: Argonne National Laboratory Radiological Physics Division Semiannual Reports. ANL-6049, October, 1959, p. 51, and ANL-5967, May, 1959, p. 126.
5. Dudley, R. A.: *Low Level Irradiation.* American Association for the Advancement of Science, Washington, D.C., 1959, p. 7.
6. Dudley, R. A.: The Toxicity of Skeletal Irradiation at Naturally Occuring Radiation Levels. April, 1957 (unpublished).
7. Black, S. C.: *Health Physics,* 7:87, 1961.
8. Hill, C. R.: *Health Physics,* 8:17, 1962.
9. Holtzman, R. B.: Argonne National Laboratory Radiological Physics Division Semiannual Report. ANL-6199, August, 1960, p. 94.

10. Hursh, J. B.: *Science,* 132:1666, 1960.
11. Lucas, H. F., Jr.: Argonne National Laboratory Radiological Physics Division. ANL-6297, September, 1961, p. 55.
12. International Commission on Radiological Protection, Committee II on Permissible Dose for Internal Radiation, 1959. *Health Physics,* 3:1-380, 1960. Modifications to these data are presented in Reference 13.
13. Holtzman, R. B.: Argonne National Laboratory Radiological Physics Division Semiannual Report. ANL-6297, February, 1961, p. 67, and *Health Physics* 8:315, 1962.
14. Moses, H., Stehney, A. F., and Lucas, H. F., Jr.: *J. Geophy. Res., 65:* 1223, 1960.
15. Norris, W. P. Speckman, T. W., and Gustafson, P. F.: *Amer. J. Roentgenol.,* 73:785, 1955.
16. Lucas, H. F., Jr.: Second International Conference of Radiation Research, Harrogate, Yorkshire, England, August 5-11, 1962, p. 102 (Abstract).
17. Kulp, J. L., and Schulert, A. R.: *Science, 136:*619, 1962.
18. Marinelli, L. D.: *Amer. J. Roentgenol., LXXX:*729, 1958.

31

ECONOMIC ASPECTS OF BUILDING AND OPERATING A WHOLE BODY COUNTER

STELIOS REGAS

Metrix, Inc.
Deerfield, Illinois

THE TERM WHOLE body counter implies a gamma ray detector capable of measuring radiation from a living human body. Robley Evans named his facilities COBAFAC, which stands for "Controlled Background Facilities." This definition implies a good shield, one of the most important prerequisites of a whole body counter.

The usual whole body counters can be divided into two major categories: those using organic scintillators and those using inorganic scintillators, primarily NaI crystals.

ORGANIC DETECTORS

The two most common types are liquid and plastic scintillators. The advantage of organic detectors is their geometric efficiency and their ability to determine rapidly the amounts of gamma radiation present with some ability to identify energies as long as they differ by factor of approximately two. Their main use is the accumulation of quantitative data in as short a time as possible. When the isotopes present are known, or a gross gamma counting is needed, and the time element is important, then an organic counter is recommended.

NaI CRYSTAL DETECTORS

Sodium iodide crystal detectors have high energy resolution

capabilities. When unknown isotopes or many simultaneously used isotopes with radiation energies not differing too much from each other are to be identified, then a crystal whole body counter should be used.

Since sodium iodide crystals are expensive, the use of many sodium iodide crystals to obtain good geometric efficiency is usually prohibitive. This makes crystal detectors rather impractical when many rapid measurements must be performed. Examples would be health physics, routine biological experiments, and other instances where the isotopes being measured are known, or when a rapid screening process of possibly exposed persons is desired. The K^{40} content of a normal man can be determined with a 3 percent precision (1 sigma) is approximately 2 min. by a 2π liquid counter. The same precision will require ten to twenty times longer with a sodium iodide crystal.

COST ANALYSIS

Perhaps no other nuclear instrument varies so much in price as a whole body counter. One can have a working model for approximately $20,000. A complete installation with all the available refinements and great flexibility will cost $250,000 or more.

BUILDING FACILITIES

A building should have approximately 650 sq. ft. of floor space to be adequate to house a large shield, the associated electronics, one or two changing rooms and shower facilities, office space, laboratory space, storage area and other auxiliary areas. In most parts of the United States, an independent building of this size, including all the furniture and utilities and with good ventilation and temperature control, will cost $15,000 to $20,000.

In many cases it is wise in planning a building for housing a whole body counter to incorporate enough space for expansion and for housing other low level counting facilities. But the cost perhaps will be doubled or tripled.

SHIELDS

At this time most installations are using steel shields because of good shielding properties, availability and ease of fabrication. Local conditions might change this situation, especially when local materials are available at low cost or labor might not be charged. For example, with the chalk shields of England, low radioactivity natural chalk has given excellent shielding.

When considering new methods and techniques for creating a shield, much care must be exercised to avoid pitfalls, not only on the operational characteristics, but also on the costs. It isn't just the cost of materials which one should figure, but also all related costs necessary to complete the installation. For instance, when ore or other granular or agglomerated products are to be used, the cost of handling and transporting the materials, the cost of the framework to provide adequate support, floor loading characteristics and municipal and other regulations which must be observed are important cost factors. Some people have disregarded the cost of labor involved, although it is usually a respectable portion of the cost.

Since steel has been extensively used as a shielding material, the cost of such an installation can be used as a basis for estimating the advisability of using other materials or methods from the economic point of view.

A good steel shield with the appropriate claddings and of adequate dimensions to provide roomy facilities and to decrease the scattering effect will cost installed approximately $45,000. This is a room of outside dimensions 9 by 10 by 9 ft. with a 5 ft. door, 6 in. thick walls, lead-tin-copper cladding, proper ventilation and cable access openings. The cost includes transportation to most parts of the United States and erection of a finished product. A smaller, but adequate, room for many uses could be 50 in. wide by 50 in. high and 80 in. deep outside dimensions, with 5 in. walls. This shield will cost approximately $11,000 installed. The weight and, therefore, the cost increases rapidly with size of the steel room. The 9 by 10 by 9 ft. room weighs approximately 122,000 lbs., while the 50 by 50 by 80 in. one weighs only 26,300 lbs.

One should not overlook the expenses involved to assure radiological purity of the steel. The main potential contaminating constituents of the steel at the present time are Co^{60} and Ru^{103}. The Co^{60} is an artificially introduced isotope which through scrap recirculates even into the steel produced by mills not using this method. The Ru^{103} comes from fallout and has created great difficulties in the procurement of sufficiently clean steel to be used for low level gamma counting. In the spring of 1962, out of fifteen to twenty batches of steel tested, only two were acceptable, and only one was completely free of contamination. The cost of testing and handling large heavy samples, particularly if there are many that have to be tested, is a considerable expense. Too many shields have been built recently with decreased capabilities due to contamination. The additional expense for testing is definitely warranted and is a form of insurance.

DETECTORS

The cost of sodium iodide crystals can vary from $1,500 to $10,000 and more for a reasonable size adequate for a whole body counter. The cost is determined by the size and components of the crystal assembly, in turn determined by the intended use.

The cost of an organic detector has a wide range depending on the material, size and the number of phototubes. Approximate prices are as follows.

2π liquid detector, 6 ft. long, complete,
including phototubes, containers, supports, etc. ..$12,000-$15,000
4π liquid detector made of 2-2π as above ..$24,000-$30,000
Complete 4π liquid counter with twice the
phototubes as above (up to 24) ....$30,000-$35,000
2π plastic counter complete, made of
solid scintillation plastic ....$30,000-$35,000
Plastic blocks 12 by 12 by 6 in. with
4 multiplier phototubes ....$ 1,000-$ 1,500 each

A few successful installations have been made with the use of plastic scintillation blocks. The cost of such a system is not as high as solid plastic, but it does not have the same geometric efficiency. Resolutions of approximately 17 percent (half-width at half-height) at the Cs^{137} region have been obtained.

The choice between a liquid or a plastic scintillator is difficult and depends on many parameters, of which the most important is cost. The efficiency and resolution capabilities obtainable by the two media are very little different. Both substances have disadvantages. With the liquid there is flammability and difficulty of containment without leaks. Plastics may yellow with age, craze or crack.

INSTRUMENTATION

There is a wide range of instruments one can select from, but basically a complete single channel pulse height analyzer system including all the electronic instrumentation will cost $3,000. For a multi-channel analyzer system, depending on the readout and auxiliary equipment, one should plan to spend no less than $12,000. A good efficient system including computer capabilities will cost approximately $35,000.

ACCESSORIES

Accessories for a whole body counter include such items as crystal suspension, loading mechanisms, communications and television systems, ventilations, filters and perhaps aged air to decrease the radon and fission products effects on the background. Often these additional accessories can be added after the original installation has been completed and the counter is in operation. Early consideration should be given to the well-being and comfort of the subject. Often the subjects are volunteers who will not return if any discomfort or inconvenience is experienced during the first measurement. There are cases when people have become strongly nauseated while being measured, and if there is a case of vomiting after intake of some radio-isotopes-containing matter, then the whole counter might become contaminated.

OPERATIONAL AND MAINTENANCE CONSIDERATIONS

It is advisable that only one person be responsible for all the details involving the use of the system. For quite some time after installation such a system will have its own idiosyncrasies. An excellent approach is to have a person with sufficient knowledge to be able to give rapid interpretation of the results, to locate trouble and to intelligently present the capabilities to people who are not interested in the workings of the counter, but want to obtain results and measurements. It is much preferable from the point of view of the efficient utilization of the whole body counter to give this responsibility to a person with enough experience to be self sufficient. A person of this caliber will command a respectable salary, but it is worthwhile. This person should have two assistants; one perhaps a technician with an electronic background, the other a clerical person who can keep the records and perform the routine paper work.

Costs for power, heating, air conditioning, etc., are the normal costs found in any kind of building and are small compared with the total cost. An important expense is the maintenance of the electronic and other components. Although transistorized instruments have improved reliability over tube instruments, a certain number of difficulties are to be expected, especially from the connectors and tubes. It is advisable to have a maintenance contract with the suppliers, which will probably cost $2000 to $3000 a year, and to set aside an appropriate amount in the budget for shipping and receiving by air freight suspected components for checking, replacement or repair. Since whole body counters are not as yet mass produced, one should expect quite some downtime and quite some expenses for spare parts, improvements on cables and connectors and changes in the wiring and mechanical configurations, which will start appearing after the installation no matter how carefully the system was designed and installed.

SUMMARY

The uses of the whole body counter will dictate its size and form, and by careful selection of components one can obtain optimum results. Although $150,000 to $250,000 will be required for a sophisticated unit capable of obtaining maximum sensitivity, a working system can be acquired for a tenth of this price. Such a whole body counter can be purchased including a good steel shield ($14,000), a sodium iodide 4 by 4 in. crystal ($2,000), a single channel pulse height analyzer with all the other electronics ($3,000) and accessories including suspension, chair, ventilation, etc. ($1,000), for a total of $20,000.

32

CONTINUING USE OF THE WHOLE BODY COUNTER — THE NATURE OF THE PROBLEMS[1]

Eugene L. Saenger and James G. Kereiakes

University of Cincinnati College of Medicine

Cincinnati, Ohio

THE FUTURE DEVELOPMENT of whole body counters is at a crossroad. An important decision must be made as to whether so apparently expensive an installation will have practical clinical value or whether it will remain essentially a research device. The technique would appear to offer certain practical contributions to the armamentarium of nuclear medicine which cannot be achieved by other means. The principal utilizations will be in dose reduction for clinical isotope tests, kinetic studies of metabolism of various compounds and studies to elucidate the metabolism of certain fission products and countermeasures for them.

In order to obtain an estimate of the nature of work done with such counters up to the present time, Nuclear Science Abstracts were reviewed from January 1953 through June 1962. Of 195 reports found, 154 were abstracted between 1953 and 1961, and forty-one added in the first half of 1962 (Table I). Most of the reports dealt with design, techniques of measurement, methods of calibration, personnel monitoring, radiation accidents and nuclear safety. Nevertheless, 73 of the 195 papers (37 percent) presented some type of physiological data. In the first half of 1962, some 63 percent did (26 of 41 papers) as compared to 31 percent (47 of 154 papers) between 1953 and 1961.

[1] Supported in part by the Albertine O. Schoepf Research Fund and the National Institutes of Health.

TABLE I

ABSTRACTS OF WHOLE BODY COUNTING NUCLEAR SCIENCE ABSTRACTS 1953-1962

Subject	Total*
Technique, Design, Methods, Calibration, Reviews	127 (65%)
Potassium (chiefly K-40)	59 (30%)
Cesium	49 (25%)
Personnel Monitoring, Safety, Accidents	43 (22%)
Radium	13 (7%)
Iodine	22 (11%)
Calcium-Strontium	15 (8%)
Sodium	12 (6%)
Cobalt	10 (5%)
Iron	9 (5%)
Chromium	3 (2%)
Bromine	2 (1%)
Physiological	73 (37%)

*Percents are only those of the subject as related to the total number of papers since many papers discussed several nuclides.

There are relatively few clinical reports as yet, but the recent rapid expansion of biomedical research is impressive.

Progress in reduction of dosage in the clinical use of radio-nuclides has been relatively slow, particularly in tests which are widely used—those utilizing I^{131} for thyroid studies. The amount of the isotope of iodine used continues to be a practical compromise of the availability of certain isotopes and the availability and cost of detecting instruments. Most isotope laboratories use I^{131} and now use scintillation crystals of 1 to 3 in. diameter with varying degrees of shielding and collimation. In order to obtain an estimate of delivered dose and current practice we reviewed our laboratory's experience in the use of I^{131} in 166 children under age sixteen during 1950 to 1962. Children studied because of cancer of the thyroid were excluded. The equation

$$D_{gland} \frac{15UA \ Teff}{M}$$

Where

D = combined β and γ dose in rads

U = fractional uptake

A = I^{131} administered in microcuries

T_{eff} = effective half time in days

M = mass of thyroid in grams

as given in Hine and Brownell (1) was used after it was deter-

TABLE II

DISTRIBUTION OF AMOUNTS OF I[131] BY AGE

(1950-1962)

Age	Amount of I[131] (μc)					
	0.1-1	1.1-5	5.1-10	10.1-25	25.1-50	50-500
0-6 m	14	1	1			
7-12 m	4					
1-3 y	26	6	4	2(1)	1	1
4-6 y	5	12	6	1	1	
7-9 y		16	23	3	7	4
10-12 y		6	24	5		2
13-16 y		2	21	3	2	2
Subtotal	50	43	79	14	11	9
%	24.3	20.9	38.3	6.8	5.3	4.4

TABLE III

CALCULATED DOSES TO THYROID GLAND OF 206 TESTS BY AGE

(1950-1962)

Age	No. of Tests	Median Dose (rad)	Dose Range (rad)
0-6 m	16	6.5	0.1-85
7-12 m	4	9	9-28
1-3 y	40	20	0.1-3000
4-6 y	25	25	2-145
7-9 y	53	31	1-1290
10-12 y	38	22.5	1-89
13-16 y	30	26	2-1200
	206		

mined that it was sufficiently accurate for estimates of infant and children's thyroid dosage. An effective half time of six days was assumed, and weights of thyroid glands for various ages were taken from the data of Spector (2). Table II gives the amounts of I[131] administered by age. Of the 206 doses administered, 83.5 percent were below 10 μc. Most of the larger doses were given for scanning or chromatography and all doses above 50 μc were for such special studies. The calculated doses delivered to the thyroid are given in Table III. Because of the skewed frequency distributions, the median value is given as being the most descriptive dose for the various ages. With present equipment the median doses of 6.5 to 31 rad do not seem excessive. Although the clinical value of many of these studies has been of real value, it has been our opinion that these doses are far too high for a routine clinical test, particularly if used for screening purposes. If these doses are compared to certain routine radiographic procedures, the doses delivered to the organ of interest seems somewhat excessive for the yield of pertinent clinical data which might be obtained by other means such as chemical protein bound iodine and BMR. Also if the patient presents an interesting or puzzling problem, the clinicians tends to repeat the I^{131} studies frequently. Of the 166 children studied, twenty-three (14 percent) had multiple studies. The multiple studies included scanning and chromatography resulting in relatively high doses in certain cases of as much as 100 to 1500 rad in eight patients. Many children who were referred for multiple tracer studies have been refused by our laboratory because calculations showed that doses of several hundred rad would be received. Evidence from epidemiological studies (3) suggests that doses above 200 to 300 rad may be carcinogenic.

If one compares the median dose of 30 rad of an I^{131} tracer study to doses of radiation from roentgenographic examination, one can see readily that this dose is five to ten times greater than that of organs of interest in comparable examinations. For comparison, data of Webster and Merrill (4) for three and ten year old children was corrected for absorption to an organ of interest (Table IV). The thyroid dose exceeds doses to other organs examined by orders of magnitude of 2 to 200. These interpretations are not to be construed as an apology for our present diagnostic methods using I^{131}. It must be recognized, however, that these doses must be reduced to the same degree that other diagnostic doses have been reduced for these diagnostic methods to be widely accepted and used most profitably.

TABLE IV

ESTIMATED MIDLINE DOSES IN ROUTINE RADIOGRAPHIC EXAMINATIONS

Organ of Interest	No. Films	Midline Dose in r	
		3 Yr. Child	10 Yr. Child
Kidney (IVP)	5	.22	0.42
Stomach (UGI)*	5	3-10.0	2-7.5
Chest	2	<0.1	<0.1
Pelvis	2	0.1	0.1

*Including 5 min. fluoroscopy at 0.5-5r/min. table top dose.

TABLE V

DOSE REDUCTION FACTORS FOR POINT SOURCE & DISC.*

4 IN. RADIUS BY 4 IN. LET. NAL (TL) CRYSTAL COMPARED TO

1 IN. RADIUS BY 1 IN. CRYSTAL

Point Source Height (in.)

Photon Energy (Mev.)	6	12	18	30
0.279	.067 (0.74)**	.056	.052	.046
0.661	.048 (0.46)	.040	.036	.031
1.33	.039 (0.39)	.033	.029	.027
2.62	.038 (0.35)	.031	.026	.024

*Adapted from W. F. Miller, J. Reynolds & W. J. Snow, ANL-5902.

**Values in parenthesis are for disc having dimensions same as crystal.

TABLE VI

DOSE REDUCTION FACTORS

4 IN. RADIUS BY 4 IN. THICK VS 1 IN. RADIUS BY 1 IN. THICK

NAI (TL) CRYSTALS

Nuclide (Gamma Energy)	Point Source Height—10 in.
I-131 (.364 Mev)	.050
Cr-51 (.32 Mev)	.052
Fe-59 (1.20 Mev)	.036

It thus becomes necessary to reduce the patient dose by improving the ratio of the patient counts to the background counts. This goal may be achieved by additional shielding (iron shielded rooms) and by increasing the efficiency of detection by the use of larger crystals or liquid scintillators.

Estimated dose reduction factors are shown in Table V for 4 in. radius by 4 in. thick crystal vs. a 1 in. radius by 1 in. thick crystal of thallium-activated sodium iodide both for point sources and disc sources at various source detector distances (5). Comparing dose reduction factors at distances of 10 in. from patient to counter as used in clinical measurements, one finds reduction factors of 0.036 to 0.05 (Table VI). No estimates of counting time are discussed. At present we routinely count infants and young children for 5 to 20 min. with suitable restraints and without sedation or anesthesia.

Dose calculations for external measurement of clinical isotope tests where the detector is placed directly on the skin surface suggests that the whole body counter will be of relatively limited importance. For example, an intravenous dose of 20

μc of I^{131} labeled hippuran shows the dose to each kidney is of the order of 2 μc. The gonadal dose is about 5.5 μc if the patient does not urinate for four hours after the injection. For placentography using 5μc of I^{131} human serum albumin, the average dose to the mother is 17 mrad, and to the fetus 6 mrad. The dose to the fetus with radiography is 0.2 to 2 rad.

One may argue at this point that the expense of a whole body counter is hardly justified to obtain dose reduction of 10 to 200 in so small a group of the population. The minimal cost of a whole body counter is $30,000, and the average cost is $50,000 to $150,000. The newer radiographic fluoroscopic units which provide image intensification, high kilovoltage and the latest shielding developments range from $30,000 to $65,000. In the Cincinnati area there are at least eight such units. Thus the cost of one whole body counter seems justifiable in a hospital and available to the community for a variety of special clinical studies where it is important to minimize organ and gonad dose.

There are certain research problems which must be studied in the human on a far wider basis than has been done to date. The problem of environmental radionuclides and their relation to large populations have begun to arouse much concern on the part of scientists and politicians. It is a curious and significant fact that this controversy has revolved principally about fallout from weapons testing. Jonathon Spivak in the August 24, 1962, *Wall Street Journal* discusses the dilemma of the Federal Radiation Council in altering the interpretation of Range III levels of certain fallout radionuclides, principally I^{131}. He describes the interesting difference of opinion of the Atomic Energy Commission and Department of Defense who prefer to disregard the occasional high levels of I^{131} from fallout and of the Division of Radiological Health of the Public Health Service "who are privately eager to enforce the guides as is." According to Spivak, "The Federal Radiation Council's policy statement took a middle ground stressing that while the guides should not be ignored in judging fallout hazards, many other factors must be considered by health authorities. The dangers from I^{131} exposure were deliberately minimized."

A report of the National Advisory Committee on Radiation

to the Surgeon General of the Public Health Service of May 1962 discusses these problems in greater detail. The Committee recommends the use of evaporated or powered dry skim milk as a countermeasure for young children, lactating mothers and pregnant women against I^{131} in milk. Other measures such as the addition of iodine in various forms to the diet are not recommended. No practical countermeasures are available for Sr^{90} in foods. If the milk from a large metropolitan area such as St. Louis, Chicago or Kansas City were suddenly impounded without much prior preparation, the resulting emotional, political and economic furor by all individuals concerned would be more than mildly exciting especially for city, state and federal officials.

There has been little study devoted to the elimination of these and other fission products which might be found in the environment after a serious radiation accident. Having had some practical experience in studying relatively normal humans exposed to relatively high doses of external radiation, we predict that considerable thought is required in the design of appropriate human experiments to investigate the problems of fallout and high level contamination by fission products. Humans cannot be managed as conveniently as laboratory animals, but such studies can be successfully pursued in metabolic wards and other wards of university medical centers. Two types of study are possible. The first is the routine measurement of many persons who have been contaminated by radionuclides from fallout, and such subjects are easily available in many localities which now have whole body counters. The second type of study is considerably more difficult, but of equal or greater value. In this study a normal volunteer is given a radionuclide and is then studied on a metabolic ward. In this way various countermeasures can be evaluated in a systematic approach. It is essential that no harm be incurred by the subject, thus measuring systems of the greatest possible sensitivity are required. The amount of radionuclide to be administered should be such that the radiation level in the body is of a similar order of magnitude as radionuclides which might be present naturally. If such levels are impractical, one might use an amount of an isotope such that the yearly occupational dose is not exceeded in individuals past the reproductive period and that the yearly nonoccupational dose is not exceeded in patients who are in the reproductive period.

Thus, whole body counters in the medical centers of large communities will play an essential dual role. They will be used for improved clinical diagnosis and research and for the study of protection of populations against environmental radionuclides both at low and high levels. There should be at least one such counter in each of the major population centers of the country within the next several years to provide a network for an attack on the problems described which will continue to plague our society.

It then becomes necessary to define the further needs for utilization of whole body counters so that they can be used with maximum effectiveness to aid in the solution of the important problems which are posed. At this time it is essential that at least one large university medical center or other large medical center in each state be equipped with a whole body counter. Each of these counters should be organically linked to a general hospital which admits patients of all ages and types of illness. It is no longer adequate to endeavor to answer the important health, political and economic problems by depending solely on the counters located in federal scientific laboratories located in areas remote from large population centers. Workers in this field will continue to rely on these laboratories for new designs and concepts in techniques of whole body counting as in the past decade. But for the proper investigation of the metabolism of the several radionuclides of particular concern to the people of this country and the world, it is essential that these problems be investigated in large medical centers. In this environment the investigators in charge of the counters have the full complement of physiologists, pharmacologists, internists and pediatricians available for a team attack on each particular problem.

By locating counters widely over the country it becomes possible to investigate the many geographical, meteorological, climatological and other ecological variations to gain a better understanding of the effects of these factors in increasing or decreasing uptake of radionuclides taken up by humans.

REFERENCES

1. Hine, G. J. and Brownell, G. L.: *Radiation Dosimetry.* New York, Academic Press, Inc., 1956.
2. Spector, W. S., ed.: *Handbook of Biological Data.* Philadelphia, W. B. Saunders Co., 1956.
3. Saenger, E. L., Silverman, F. N., Sterling, T. D., and Turner, M. E.: Neoplasia in children following therapeutic irradiation for benign condition in childhood. *Radiology,* 74:889, 1960.
4. Webster, E. W., and Merrill, O. E.: Radiation hazards. II. Measurement of gonadal dose in radiographic examinations. *New Engl. J. Med.,* 257:811, 1957.
5. Miller, W. F., Reynolds, J. and Snow, W. J.: Efficiencies and photofractions for gamma radiation on sodium iodide (thallium activated) crystals. ANL-5902, Argonne National Laboratory, 1958.

DISCUSSION

Chairman: ALEXANDER REMENCHIK

Hines Veterans Administration Hospital
Hines, Illinois

JOHN A. CARDARELLI: The need for pediatric whole body counters is real. They are not nearly abundant enough.

I am sure that with the use of one isotope at a time these whole body counters can be very expensive. The cost of the shielded facilities is likewise great.

RICHARD B. HOLTZMAN: We did some work with Dr. Foche at the University of Rochester on sizes and cost. He found that a minimum sized wall, 12 in. in diameter by 30 in. long, will accommodate children up to age two. It was further indicated that the total cost of this was a little less than $20,000.

JOHN A. CARDARELLI: The survey implies reduction of the dose, and therefore, if you use one isotope at a time, I think that you can get further down.

STELIOS REGAS: The problem is: "What are you going to do to my baby?"

LESTER SKOLIL: I hate to minimize the significance of psychological factors, but I think that the use of piped-in music and television is completely unnecessary.

VOICE: I would like to agree with the importance of lowering the thyroid dose to children during the investigation. You can do this by a factor of 10 to 50 by switching to I^{132} in cases where you merely need uptake measurement which can be done in a few hours rather than in 24 hr.

EUGENE L. SAENGER: I agree with all that has been said thus far. There are peculiar factors in the United States concerned with the laboratories of doctors, as well as dual customs, particularly in many isotope centers throughout the country. I^{131} is easy to get. It is commercially available and is what the current supplier furnishes. Of course, what you have said might be the better way to do it.

459

VOICE: It is one of the values of this discussion to break up customs. What we like about I^{132} is that you can wash the color off.

EUGENE L. SAENGER: One scientist spent a great deal of time and effort coming around to all of the radiological meetings to promote this, but not many radiologists were receptive.

GERALD J. HINE: If you want to use the I^{131}, there is a new development using two crystals relatively nearby and getting a uniform field over the entire area, so that you can make use of higher sensitivity near the source and therefore can reduce your cost considerably.

EUGENE L. SAENGER: One group has been using this with a great deal of success. They can do these uptakes at quite high levels.

DR. ALLDERDICE: Dr. Jagger, did you notice any fall in serum sodium concentration when the patients were on low sodium diets, or a rise in sodium concentration when put on a high sodium diet? If you did, could you say a few words about both the quantitative and chronological relationships of the serum sodium to the total exchangeable sodium or the total body sodium loss that arises? The people in our hospital are fixed on the idea of serum sodium concentration being the answer to all total body sodium problems.

PAUL I. JAGGER: We found no uniform change in serum sodium values with changes in diet. In fact, one man's serum sodium was lower during the period of sodium loading. The two single highest serum sodium values obtained were taken during high sodium intake.

MARVIN C. BELL: Dr. Saenger, were your I^{131} levels for diagnostic purposes?

EUGENE L. SAENGER: Yes.

MARVIN C. BELL: At those levels did you observe any alteration of the thyroid function when you got up to 1,000 or 3,000 rad?

EUGENE L. SAENGER: No. These children have all been relatively well followed, and we have had no cases of hypothyroidism. Enough time has not elapsed for carcinoma to arise. We believe it may take ten years for this to occur. This is one of the problems of real concern to us.

MARVIN C. BELL: Didn't your calculations assume an end distribution of radioiodine within the thyroid?

EUGENE L. SAENGER: Yes.

MARVIN C. BELL: Studies have shown that the differences in the hot spots from the mean dose may be as much as ten times even in thyroid individuals who presumably are not concentrating in hypoplastic areas. Are you thinking of the effect on individual cells?

EUGENE L. SAENGER: It could be a good bit more.

MARVIN C. BELL: And this might add another zero?

EUGENE L. SAENGER: It might add two.

WALTER S. SNYDER: Dr. Holtzman mentioned that the children seemed to be low in Ra^{228} concentration. Do you see any suggestion of a correlation with age in the adult?

RICHARD B. HOLTZMAN: It appears to be low in the child.

There was no particular correlation in adults. There appears to be a general increase, but then it is not noticeable, because it is generally low at the lower ages.

JOSEPH RIVERA: Dr. Holtzman, how was the estimate for radium B intake for food made?

RICHARD B. HOLTZMAN: This was made from an analysis of three or four different people. Assume that most of the radium goes straight through, — there may be a 10 percent absorption. This gives a figure of 2 μc per day intake. The ICRP report says it is 8 percent absorption into the blood. From this, the calculation is made.

CHAIRMAN ALEXANDER REMENCHIK: Dr. Jagger showed a slide depicting a variable dietary sodium intake and the exchangeable sodium was less than that reported by other people after 12 days. Is that correct?

PAUL I. JAGGER: We found no increasing change of sodium on this fixed low diet. Those who have reported this slowly increasing exchangeable space on fixed diet have depended on urine excretion for determining Na^{22} retention, and this is always subject to error. Also, small sodium losses from other sources are cumulative and this introduces additional errors.

SESSION X, SEPTEMBER 7

METABOLISM OF FISSION PRODUCTS

Chairman: E. ERIC POCHIN

33

STUDIES ON METABOLISM OF Zr^{95}-Nb^{95} IN THE RAT BY WHOLE BODY COUNTING[1]

B. V. Rama Sastry, Raymond L. Weiland and Allan D. Bass

Vanderbilt University School of Medicine
Nashville, Tennessee

THE TOXIC EFFECTS of the radiation from internally deposited fallout depends on the exact nature of radionuclides in fallout, their composition and their metabolism, as well their physical half lives and the characteristics of emitted radiation. The most serious fallout hazard is internal exposure to gamma radiation. A knowledge of the metabolism of all of the gamma-ray emitting isotopes is essential in order to estimate the possible genetic damage from gamma radiation. The number of induced mutations is proportional to the radiation dose received by the gonads up to the time of reproduction regardless of isotope distribution with respect to time (1).

We have undertaken studies on the metabolism of various gamma-ray emitting isotopes present in fallout to provide a basis for estimating the extent of somatic as well as genetic damage from the total hazard of fallout.

Some preliminary studies on the metabolism of zirconium in fish (2), in mice (3) and in rats (4-7) have been reported. Studies on the metabolism of Nb and Zr indicate that bone accumulates these elements in high concentrations (3-8).

Zr^{95} is a gamma-ray emitting isotope with a half life of about sixty-five days. It decays to Nb^{95} which emits gamma rays and has a half life of thirty-five days. We have studied the metabolism of Zr^{95}-Nb^{95} in transient equilibrium in the rat in an attempt to determine the fate of these isotopes and their relationships.

[1] Supported in part by U. S. Army Medical Research and Development Command, Mead Johnson and U. S. Atomic Energy Commission.

MATERIALS AND METHODS

The Zr^{95}-Nb^{95} used was carrier-free. It was obtained from Oak Ridge National Laboratories as a solution of its oxalate and contained 4.49 mc/ml. This solution was diluted to 100 ml. with distilled water, and a theoretical amount of sodium chloride was added to make it isotonic with 0.154 M sodium chloride.

Male Sprague-Dawley rats with an average weight of 250 gm. were housed in plastic cages with a raised metal platform which supports the animal. The urine and feces collect at the bottom of the platform so that the animal has no access to the excreta. The animals were fed with Purina Rat Chow; tap water ad libitum was provided.

Rats were injected intraperitoneally with Zr^{95}-Nb^{95}, and the body burden of the isotopes was followed by external γ-ray scintillation spectrometry. To determine the tissue distribution of Zr^{95}-Nb^{95}, groups of animals were sacrificed at various intervals after administration of the isotopes. The animals were decapitated, and the blood was drained into a heparinized beaker. Bones (humerus, ulna, radius, femur, tibia and fibula), muscles (biceps, flexor, brachioradial, quadriceps femoris, adductor and gastrocnemius) and the whole liver were dissected rapidly. Bones from a single animal were combined, weighed and ground in an Omni Mixer with 15 ml. distilled water. The resulting homogenate was transferred to a ½ pt. cardboard carton (Fonda, Stanvac Standard Package Corporation). The final volume of the homogenate was adjusted with distilled water to 100 ml., and activity of the whole sample was estimated by gamma scintillation spectrometry. Muscles from a single animal were combined and prepared similarly. The homogenates of livers were prepared separately. Blood (2 to 5 ml.) was diluted to 100 ml. with distilled water for counting.

All measurements of radioactivity were made in the Vanderbilt human whole body, low level, gamma-ray scintillation spectrometer. Details of this counting facility, including the steel room, scintillation probes containing a thallium-activated sodium iodide crystal, and 256 channel pulse height analyzer have been described (9-11).

Figure 1. Vanderbilt whole body, low level gamma-ray scintillation spectro-meter. The figure shows the special lucite rat holder and its position under the crystal in the steel room.

A special lucite rat holder (Fig. 1) was used to maintain standard counting geometry under the crystal in the steel room. The three legs of the rat holder could be mounted in three sockets on a shelf in the corner of the steel room to maintain the constant position of the holder. This holder could easily be taken apart for cleaning and decontamination after counting each rat. Holes were cut in one end for ventilation.

A 250 ml. cylindrical plastic container, about the size of a

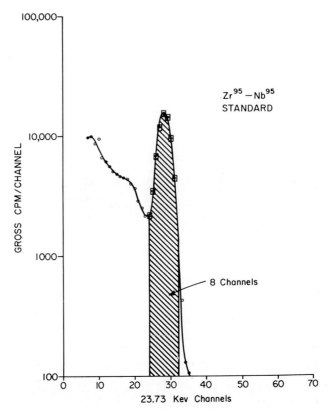

Figure 2. Spectrum of Zr^{95}-Nb^{95} with an energy calibration of 23.73 kev/ channel. Eight channels, integrated symmetrically about the photopeak, were used to determine the counts per min. on all Zr^{95}-Nb^{95} samples.

rat, was filled with a standard solution of Zr^{95}-Nb^{95} for calibration. The spectrum obtained from this, with an energy calibration of 23.73 kev/channel, is shown in Figure 2. Eight channels, integrated symmetrically about the photopeak, were used to determine the counts per minute on all Zr^{95}-Nb^{95} samples. This represents about 95 percent of the total photopeak area. All spectra were processed through the IBM computer.

Each animal was injected intraperitoneally with 35 μc/kg. of Zr^{95}-Nb^{95} and was transferred immediately to the rat holder for counting. The animal was counted within 30 to 60 min. It was assumed that the administered Zr^{95}-Nb^{95} would be absorbed

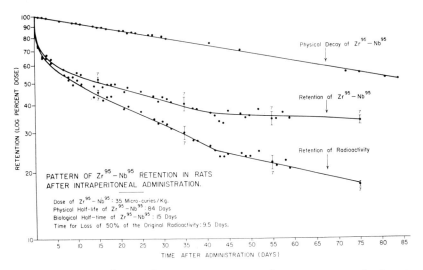

Figure 3. Pattern of Zr^{95}-Nb^{95} retention in rats after intraperitoneal administration. The vertical lines denote the standard errors. The figures on the
vertical lines denote the number of animals.

and distributed uniformly during this period. Excreta, if any, of
the animal during this period were retained in the holder for
counting. The gamma activity of the animal within 30 to 60 min.
after the administration of Zr^{95}-Nb^{95} was used to calibrate the
gamma activity of the dose of Zr^{95}-Nb^{95} in the rat. Each rat was
used as its control, and the gamma activity of any animal on the
subsequent days was expressed as percent of the gamma activity
of the dose of Zr^{95}-Nb^{95} received by the same animal. The logarithm of the percent dose of gamma activity retained by the
animal was plotted against days to obtain the retention curve of
total radioactivity due to Zr^{95}-Nb^{95} (Fig. 3).

To apply the correction for the physical decay of Zr^{95}-Nb^{95}
the decay of a standard sample of Zr^{95}-Nb^{95} was determined. The
gamma activities of the standard sample on various days were
expressed as percents of the gamma activity of the standard
sample on the first day. When the logarithm of the percent
gamma activity was plotted against days, a straight line was obtained which was used to determine the physical decay of Zr^{95}-
Nb^{95} in the animal and to estimate the Zr^{95}-Nb^{55} complex it re-

tained. The logarithm of the percent dose Zr^{95}-Nb^{95} complex retained by the animal was plotted versus days to obtain the retention curve of Zr^{95}-Nb^{95}.

During the experiments, the animals gained weight. To determine whether or not the growth of these rats influenced the counting rates, two groups of animals (group 1: average weight 250 gm.; group 2: average weight 325 gm.) were injected with identical doses of Zr^{95}-Nb^{95}, placed immediately in separate lucite holders and were counted within 30 min. There was no significant difference between the counting rates of the two groups.

Separate standards of Zr^{95}-Nb^{95} were prepared in cardboard cartons and counted at suitable intervals to estimate the Zr^{95}-Nb^{95} in tissue homogenates. There were no significant differences in the counts per minute when the standards were made in distilled water or the tissue homogenates in saline.

RESULTS

The pattern of Zr^{95}-Nb^{95} retention in rats after intraperitoneal administration is shown in Figure 3. The biological half time of Zr^{95}-Nb^{95} in rats is fifteen days. Rats lose about 50 percent of the radioactivity of the original dose in 9.5 days. The retention curve of Zr^{95}-Nb^{95} complex exhibits at least three phases: a rapid excretion phase of the first twelve days during which the animal loses about 48 percent of the administered Zr^{95}-Nb^{95} complex; a slow phase of excretion lasting twenty-nine days during which the animal loses 16 to 19 percent of the dose, and a phase during which no excretion of Zr^{95}-Nb^{95} takes place. Approximately 33 to 36 percent of the dose is retained by the animal.

From the forty-second day after the administration of Zr^{95}-Nb^{95}, the loss of radioactivity from the animal parallels the physical decay of Zr^{95}-Nb^{95}, indicating that the animal was not excreting any Zr^{95}-Nb^{95} after the forty-first day.

All concentrations of Zr^{95}-Nb^{95} complex are expressed as percent dose per gram of wet tissue. The distribution of Zr^{95}-Nb^{95} in bone, liver, muscle and blood as a function of time after intraperitoneal administration is shown in Figure 4. The highest concen-

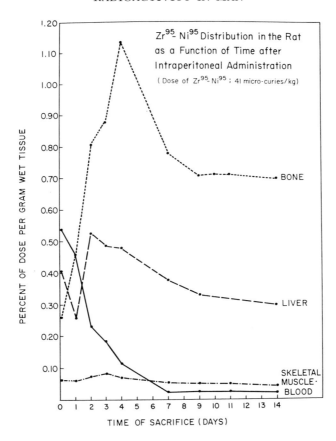

Figure. 4. Zr⁹⁵-Nb⁹⁵ distribution in the rat as a function of time after intraperitoneal administration. Each point is a mean of 3 to 5 values from equal number of animals.

tration (1.15 percent dose) was found in bone on the fourth day. This is about twelve times the concentration in the blood on the same day. At the end of the first day concentrations of Zr⁹⁵-Nb⁹⁵ in bone and blood (0.34 percent dose) are equal. This indicates that the bone accumulates Zr⁹⁵-Nb⁹⁵ against a concentration gradient. The concentration in blood falls to 0.020 percent of the administered dose per gram of wet tissue in seven days. At the end of the ninth day the concentration in bone is 0.725 percent of the dose, about thirty-six times the concentration of Zr⁹⁵-Nb⁹⁵ in the blood on the same day. These same concentrations of Zr^{95}-Nb^{95} in bone and blood were found on the seventy-fifth day.

The peak concentration in the liver (0.53% dose/gm. wet tissue) was found at the end of the second day. A concentration of 0.40 percent dose/gm. wet liver was present 1 hr. after intraperitoneal injection of Zr^{95}-Nb^{95}. This decreased to 0.25 percent by the end of the first day. The isotopes should have flooded the liver immediately after injection, with redistribution taking place in about 24 hr. Therefore, it was not surprising that the concentration of Zr^{95}-Nb^{95} decreased from 0.40 percent to 0.25 percent in about 24 hr. At the end of the first day, the liver begins to accumulate Zr^{95}-Nb^{95}. At 36 hr. concentrations in blood and liver are the same (0.36 percent dose). By the end of the second day, however, the concentration in blood falls to 0.23 percent, while the concentration in the liver increases to 0.53 percent dose, indicating that the liver accumulates Zr^{95}-Nb^{95} against a concentration gradient. The liver loses considerable amounts of Zr^{95}-Nb^{95} by the seventy-fifth day. The concentration in liver on the seventy-fifth day is only 0.062 percent dose/gm. wet liver.

Very small concentrations of Zr^{95}-Nb^{95} are found in skeletal muscle (0.04 to 0.08% dose/gm.). This concentration falls to about 0.024 percent by the seventy-fifth day, which is almost equal to the concentration in blood (0.020 percent).

The distribution of Zr^{95}-Nb^{95} in various organs on the seventy-fifth day is summarized in Table I. The highest concentrations are found in bone; other tissues containing high concentrations are the spleen, kidney and gonads. The Zr^{95}-Nb^{95} does not seem to pass the blood-brain barrier effectively. Concentrations in the brain were lower than those in blood on the fourth, seventh and seventy-fifth days.

DISCUSSION

Three important aspects of the metabolism of Zr^{95}-Nb^{95} should be evaluated to estimate the body burden of these isotopes: the rate of absorption of Zr^{95}-Nb^{95} after intraperitoneal administration, the toxicity of zirconium and niobium salts and the differential transport of Zr^{95} and Nb^{95} by animal membrances.

TABLE I

DISTRIBUTION OF Zr^{95}-Nb^{95} IN RAT TISSUES AT THE END OF THE
75TH DAY AFTER INTRAPERITONEAL ADMINISTRATION[1]

Tissue	Percent Dose/gm. Wet Tissue	
	Actual Concentration[2] M ± SE	Corrected for Growth[3] M ± SE
Bone	0.725 ± 0.058	1.077 ± 0.072
Spleen	0.377 ± 0.040	0.563 ± 0.066
Kidney	0.201 ± 0.036	0.297 ± 0.046
Gonad	0.153 ± 0.026	0.226 ± 0.034
Lung	0.093 ± 0.016	0.130 ± 0.027
Liver	0.062 ± 0.008	0.092 ± 0.012
Intestine	0.043 ± 0.001	0.066 ± 0.005
Stomach	0.034 ± 0.003	0.050 ± 0.004
Muscle	0.024 ± 0.004	0.033 ± 0.008
Blood	0.020 ± 0.015	0.031 ± 0.002
Brain	0.009 ± 0.003	0.013 ± 0.004

[1]Dose of Zr^{95}-Nb^{95}: 35 µc/kg. (i.p.).

[2]Mean weight of the rats at the time of administration of Zr^{95}-Nb^{95}: 249 gm.
Each value is a mean from three determinations.

[3]Mean weight of the rats at the time of sacrifice: 371 gm. Each value is a
mean of three determinations.

TABLE II

ABSORPTION OF ZIRCONIUM AND NIOBIUM SALTS FROM VARIOUS ROUTES
OF ADMINISTRATION IN THE RAT

Substance	Mode of Administration	Days after which % Absorption was Measured	% Absorption	Reference
Zr^{89} as $ZrOCl_2$	i.p.	2	20	Hamilton, 1943
	s.c.	6	20	Hamilton, 1943
Zr^{89} as chloride	i.m.	4	14	Hamilton, 1944
				Scott et al., 1947a
	i.m.	22	16	Scott et al., 1947a
Zr^{93} as chloride	i.m.	1	14	Scott et al., 1947a
	i.m.	32	18.5	Scott et al., 1947a
Nb^{93} as chloride	i.m.	1	35	Scott et al., 1947b
	i.m.	4	53	Scott et al., 1947b
	i.m.	84	64	Scott et al., 1947b
Zirconium citrate	i.p.	1	80-90	Schubert, 1949

The studies on absorption of zirconium and neobium salts
after various routes of administration are summarized in Table II.

Different results have been reported by various investigators. While nearly 90 percent of a dose of zirconium citrate (12) was absorbed within 24 hr., only 20 percent of zirconium chloride (13) was absorbed in two days from intraperitoneal route. The table indicates that more niobium chloride is absorbed through intramuscular route than zirconium chloride. Information on the absorption of the various salts of niobium is not available.

Our studies indicate that more than 65 percent of Zr^{95}-Nb^{95} was absorbed and excreted. Since the Zr^{95}-Nb^{95} was administered as its oxalate, our results are comparable to the studies of Schubert (12) who administered zirconium as its citrate. The discrepancies in the rate of absorption of zirconium and niobium salts can be explained partially by the chemical nature of the anion or the chelate structure with which the metal is associated. For example, when an ionizable zirconium salt is administered to an animal $Zr++++$ will be precipitated completely as $Zr(OH)_4$ at the pH of the physiological fluids because of the insolubility of the latter in water at pH 7 (14). Similarly, niobium is known to form an insoluble oxide. The zirconium or niobium ions which are not precipitated are absorbed from the intraperitoneal cavity.

The ability to form a stable complex species is at a maximum in the transitional metal ions, doubtless because of a combination of such favorable acceptor factors as small cation size, comparatively large nuclear or ionic charges and appropriate electronic arrangements (15, 16). Dicarboxylic acids (two acidic groups) and α-hydroxycarboxlic acids (one acidic group, one coordinating group) are typical chelate structures. Therefore, one might expect that zirconium and niobium as their soluble stable complexes, oxalate or citrate, would be absorbed to a greater degree from the intraperitoneal cavity than the easily ionizable chlorides would be.

There seems to be a relationship between the toxicity and the chemical nature of the anion of zirconium and niobium salts (Table III), the compounds being relatively nontoxic. However, their properties discussed in the preceding paragraphs influence their toxicity. The salts which are absorbed and excreted rapidly are the least toxic. For example, zirconium citrate, which is well absorbed and completely excreted, is the least toxic of zirconium

TABLE III

ACUTE TOXICITY OF ZIRCONIUM AND NIOBIUM COMPOUNDS

| Compound | LD_{50} in Rat[1] | | Reference |
	Compound mg./kg	Metal mg./kg.	
Zirconyl acetate	300	122	Cochran *et al.*, 1950
Zirconyl chloride	400	113	Cochran *et al.*, 1950
Zirconyl nitrate	1250	426	Cochran *et al.*, 1950
Zirconyl sulfate	175	63	Cochran *et al.*, 1950
Sodium zirconyl sulfate	4100	935	Cochran *et al.*, 1950
Potassium columbate[2]	225	86	Cochran *et al.*, 1950
Niobium chloride	40	14	Cochran *et al.*, 1950
Zirconium citrate		1750	Schubert, 1947, 1949

[1]The compounds were administered intraperitoneally.
[2]Columbium is synonymous with niobium.

compounds. The Zr^{95}-Nb^{95} is a hazard because of its gamma radiation. The rate of absorption of these isotopes after ingestion or inhalation will depend upon the form in which they are present in fallout.

In transient equilibrium activities of both parent and daughter isotopes decrease at equal rates, so that it is easy to apply the correction for total decay. In the present investigations to determine the total complex of Zr^{95}-Nb^{95}, it was assumed that the equilibrium between Zr^{95}-Nb^{95} was not disturbed by the animal tissues. From the 40th day, no Zr^{95}-Nb^{95} was excreted by the animals. Further, the physical decay line is parallel to the decay line of Zr^{95}-Nb^{95} retained by the animals. Therefore, the rate of decay of Zr^{95}-Nb^{95} retained by the animals is equal to the rate of decay of injected Zr^{95}-Nb^{95}. The Zr^{95}-Nb^{95} retained by the animals after the fortieth day is in equilibrium.

Published work indicates that zirconium and niobium behave qualitatively in a similar manner in the rat (Table IV). Although they are in the second transitional series, one can expect some small differences in their physicochemical properties and physiochemical behavior because they belong to two different groups of periodic classification. Therefore, it is reasonable to expect that rat tissue membranes show a differential transport between Zr^{95} and Nb^{95}. Some tissues may concentrate the daughter isotope (Nb^{95}), while others show preference for the parent isotope

TABLE IV

DISTRIBUTION OF Zr^{93} AND Co^{93} (Nb^{93}) AFTER INTRAMUSCULAR ADMINISTRATION IN THE RAT[1]

| Organ | % Dose/gm. or Organ | Percent Dose of Radionuclide[2] at the End of the | | | |
| | | First Day | | Fourth Day | |
		Zr^{93}	Nb^{93}	Zr^{93}	Nb^{93}
Bone	gram	0.032	0.58	0.27	0.97
	organ	(0.51)	15.01	3.62	19.74
Liver	gram	0.036	0.53	0.075	0.82
	organ	0.42	3.48	0.52	4.06
Spleen	gram	0.019	0.30	0.046	0.69
	organ	0.011	0.23	0.030	0.42
Kidney	gram	0.040	0.36	0.15	0.75
	organ	0.075	0.53	0.21	0.86
Blood	gram	0.090	0.75	0.055	0.28
	total blood	1.44	9.82	0.73	2.81

[1]Summarized from the work of Scott *et al.* (1947a, 1947b).
[2]Zr^{93}: as chloride in isotonic saline at pH 2.5.
Nb^{93}: as chloride in isotonic saline at pH 2.7.
Dose $=$ 7 μc/animal.

TABLE V

PHYSICAL HALF LIVES OF Zr^{95}-Nb^{95} ACCUMULATED BY RAT TISSUES IN FOUR DAYS

Tissue[1]	Half Life of Zr^{95}-Nb^{95} (Days)[2]
Bone	123
Standard Zr^{95}-Nb^{95}	84
Kidney	75
Liver	68
Gonads	62
Lungs	60
Spleen	55
Blood	45

[1]Tissues are pooled samples from twelve animals.
[2]The animals were sacrificed 96 hrs. after they received standard Zr^{95}-Nb^{95}.

(Zr^{95}). To study this aspect of the metabolism of Zr^{95}-Nb^{95}, Sastry *et al.* (17) determined the half lives of Zr^{95}-Nb^{95} concentrated by different tissues at the end of the fourth day, when peak concentration in the bone was reached (Table V). The half life of Zr^{95}-Nb^{95} from bone (123 days) is longer than that of the injected Zr^{95}-Nb^{95} (84 days). The half life of Zr^{95}-Nb^{95} from many soft tissues is shorter than eighty-four days. This indicates that bone shows preference for the parent isotope (Zr^{95}, half life 65 days) while the soft tissues prefer to take up the daughter isotope (Nb^{95}, half life 35 days). Further work is in progress to determine individual concentrations of the parent (Zr^{95}) and daughter (Nb^{95}) at other time intervals.

SUMMARY

The retention patterns of Zr^{95}-Nb^{95} in the rat were studied by whole body counting. The biological half time for Zr^{95}-Nb^{95} in the rat was fifteen days. The animals lost 50 percent of the original radioactivity in about 9.5 days. About 35 percent of the dose was retained permanently in the tissues.

The distribution of Zr^{95}-Nb^{95} as a function of time (14 days) was described. The concentrations in various organs on the seventy-fifth day after intraperitoneal injection were reported. Bone contained the highest concentration.

The transient equilibrium between Zr^{95}-Nb^{95} is disturbed by the rat tissues during distribution. While bone tends to concentrate more Zr^{95}, the soft tissues show preference for accumulation of Nb^{95}. The ratio Zr^{95}/Nb^{95} is larger for Zr^{95}-Nb^{95} found in the bones than the ratio Zr^{95}/Nb^{95} in the administered dose. The ratio Zr^{55}/Nb^{95} is smaller for Zr^{95}-Nb^{95} found in the soft tissue than the ratio of Zr^{95}/Nb^{95} in the administered isotope mixture.

REFERENCES

1. Quimby, E. H., and Feitelberg, S.: Radioactive Isotopes in Medicine and Biology. Philadelphia, Lea and Febiger, 1963, pp. 136-137.
2. Tomiyama, T., and Kobyashi, K.: Nuc. Sci. Abstr., 15:3328, 1961.
3. Fukuda, R. Z.: Nuc. Sci. Abstr. 15:336, 1961a.
4. Hamilton, J. G.: US AEC Reports, MDDC-1001:4, 1944.
5. Scott, K. G., Fischer, H., and Crowley, J.: US AEC Reports, MDDC-1275:109, 1947a.
6. Richmond, C. R.: Nuc. Sci. Abstr., 14:3253, 1960.
7. Fukuda, R. Z.: Nuc. Sci. Abstr. 15:2999, 1961b.

8. Scott, K. G., Fischer, H., and Crowley, J.: *US AEC Reports*, MDDC-1275:116, 1947b.

9. Meneely, G. R., Rolf, H. L., Weiland, R. L., Heyssel, R. M., and Lagemann, R. T.: In Whole-Body Counting. Proceedings of a Symposium, Vienna, June, 1961. International Atomic Energy, Vienna, p. 379, 1962a.

10. Meneely, G. R., Ball, Con O. T., Ferguson, J. L., Payne, D. D., Lorimer, A. R., Wieland, R. L., Rolf, H. L., and Heyssel, R. M.: *Circulat. Res.*, 11:539, 1962b.

11. Weiland, R. L.: *In Radioactivity in Man*. G. R. Meneely, editor. Springfield, Thomas, 1961. p. 61.

12. Schubert, J.: *J. Lab. Clin. Med.*, 34:313, 1949.

13. Hamilton, J. G.: *US AEC Reports*, MDDC-1143:3, 1943.

14. Moeller, T., and Horwitz, E. P.: *In Mineral Metabolism*. C. L. Comar and E. Bronner, editors. New York, Academic Press, 1960. pp. 101 and 115.

15. Diehl, H.: *Chem. Rev.*, 21:39, 1937.

16. Bailar, J. C. Jr.: *Chem. Rev.*, 23:65, 1938.

17. Sastry, B. V. Rama, Weiland, R. L., Ball, Con O. T.:   *Fed. Proc.*, 22:540, 1963.

18. Cochran, K. W., Doull, J. Mazur, M., and DuBoris, K. P.: *Arch. Ind. Hyg. Occupat. Med.*, 1:637, 1950.

19. Schubert, J.: *Science, 105*:389, 1947.

34

BEHAVIOR OF Sr[85] IN A NORMAL MAN FOLLOWING A SINGLE INGESTION—APPLICATION OF THE WHOLE BODY COUNTER FOR RETENTION

Susumu Suguri, Satoru Ohtani, Masao Oshino and
Kazuo Yanagishita[1]

Japan Atomic Energy Research Institute
Tokai-mura, Ibaraki-ken, Japan

INTRODUCTION

ALTHOUGH THE STUDIES of excretion and retention of radioactive strontium in a human body have been conducted by several workers (1-3), many of the data obtained are based on fecal and urinary studies. The authors completed a whole body counter (4) in March, 1961 to study the behavior of strontium in man.

Major aims of the studies were to determine the retention rate after ingestion, to determine where the strontium was mainly retained, to examine the biological constants such as f_2' and fw, and to compare the results with those from the fecal and urinary studies. The biology and chemistry group of the institute made experiments with the same subject, and the results are to be published in a separate paper (5).

TECHNIQUES

Sr[85] was used for the experiment. The solution for drinking was 2 ml. of 4.96 μc Sr[85] prepared by dilution and adding hydro-

---

[1] Visiting student from Mitsubishi Electric Manufacturing Co., Ltd.

chloric acid to the original $Sr(NO_3)_2$ in 1.03 N HNO_3 solution. This is now considered to be $SrCl_2$ solution in 0.25 N HCl. This 4.96 μc of Sr^{85} solution was put into about 150 ml. of coffee and drunk by the subject.

The subject was a fifty-three year old man, 175 cm. tall and weighing 68 kg. He had no previous contact with radioactive materials. The average urinary excretion rate of calcium during the first nine days after ingestion was 0.23 gm./day (5).

The whole body counter was slightly modified for the experiment by the use of two 5 by 4 in. sodium iodide crystals and a linear scanning collimator.

For the estimation of the body activity of the subject, a homogeneous phantom was used, consisting of thirteen rectangular polyethylene boxes filled with Sr^{85} solution. It weighed 60 kg. and was 165 cm. tall.

RESULTS

Retention of Sr^{85} in the Subject

The retention over one week is shown in Figure 1. The short and long lines shown on the upper edge of the figure indicate urination and evacuation occurring after ingestion.

Two curves are shown in the figure, and the difference between them is due to the way of estimation. Curve 1 is estimated on the basis of the intake of 4.96 μc Sr^{85}, whereas curve 2 is estimated by comparison with the phantom. The former estimation may be better during the first two days, as the Sr^{85} is localized in the gastrointestinal tract; but the latter estimation may be correct thereafter, as the Sr^{85} is distributed throughout the body. The difference between the two estimations is 0.1 μc at 45 hr. after ingestion (after second evaluation); this amount is only 2 percent of the intake amount. A large amount of Sr^{85} is discharged by evacuation during the first two days, i.e., 3.4 μc by the first evacuation and 0.76 μc by the second. Afterwards, any remarkable reduction is not noticed in each evacuation, thus most of the reduction of body activity is considered to be due to urination. From these phenomena, it is found that about 90 percent of

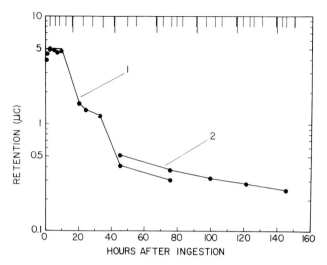

Figure 1. Retention of Sr[85] up to 145 hr. after ingestion (corrected for physical decay). Curve 1 is estimated based on the intake of 4.96 μc. Curve 2 is estimated by the comparison with the phantom.

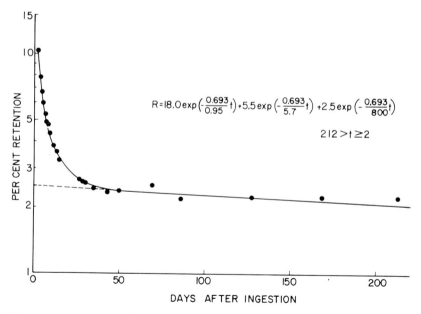

$$R = 18.0 \exp\left(-\frac{0.693}{0.95}t\right) + 5.5 \exp\left(-\frac{0.693}{5.7}t\right) + 2.5 \exp\left(-\frac{0.693}{800}t\right)$$

$$212 > t \geq 2$$

Figure 2. Retention of Sr[85] up to 212 days after ingestion (corrected for physical decay).

the ingested Sr^{85} is discharged during the first two days from the gastrointestinal tract.

A long period retention from 1.9 days (45 hr.) after ingestion is shown in Figure 2 and Table I. This curve is corrected for the physical decay of Sr^{85}. The results can be expressed in three-term exponential functions as follows:

$$R = 18.0 \exp \left(-\frac{0.693}{0.95}t\right) + 5.5 \exp \left(-\frac{0.693}{5.7}t\right) + 2.5 \exp \left(-\frac{0.693}{800}t\right), t \geq 2$$

where R is the percent retention t days after ingestion.

The retention can be also expressed in power function. Figure 3 shows the retention, for which retention and time are plotted on logarithmic scale. The result can be written in the formula:

$$R = 3.3\, t^{-0.08} + 5.5 \exp \left(-\frac{0.693}{5.0}t\right) + 10.0 \exp \left(-\frac{0.693}{1.1}t\right), t \geq 2$$

where R is the percent retention t days after ingestion.

TABLE I

RETENTION OF Sr^{85} AS A PERCENTAGE OF THE INGESTED DOSE, AFTER CORRECTION FOR RADIOACTIVE DECAY

Days after Ingestion	Per Cent Retention
1.9	10.5
3.2	7.84
4.2	6.67
5.0	5.98
6	5.30
7	4.88
8	4.76
9	4.33
11	3.81
13	3.59
15	3.27
27	2.65
29	2.59
30	2.57
35	2.41
43	2.35
50	2.38
69	2.51
85	2.20
127	2.24
168	2.25
212	2.25

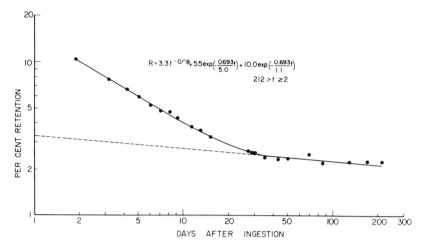

Figure 3. Plot of logarithm of percent retention against logarithm of time
after ingestion (corrected for physical decay).

The experiment shows that the parameter of the power
function is −0.08. It is of interest to compare this value with
those obtained by other workers. M. Bishop *et al.* (1) have deduced by the single injection of Sr[85] into two subjects that the
parameters of the power function are −0.24 and −0.21 for the
subjects, whose average urinary excretion rates of calcium are
0.50 gm./day and 0.28 gm./day, respectively. Their results show
that the power function can be fitted from twenty days after injection; ours can be fitted from thirty days after ingestion.

Our results seem to differ from the results of Bishop, but
when the values are plotted on semi-logarithmic scale or logarithmic scale, the shapes of the curves do not differ remarkably if the
13 percent ingested is assumed to reach into blood. Compared
with the results of Bishop, our results show that the rate of decrease of retention is somewhat larger in the earlier stage and is
smaller in the later stage. The values of retention in the later
stage are similar to those of Bishop, irrespective of the difference
of mean daily urinary excretion rate of calcium.

Distribution of Sr[85] in the Subject

The distribution of Sr[85] in the subject's body was also meas-

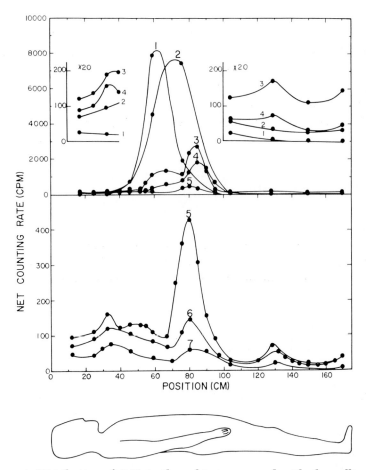

Figure 4. Distribution of Sr^{85} in the subject measured with the collimator (corrected for physical decay). Curves 1, 2, 3, 4, 5, 6 and 7 are the results of 23 min., 1.75 hr., 21 hr., 32 hr., 49 hr., 98 hr. and 364 hr. after ingestion, respectively.

ured by using the collimator. Figure 4 shows the distribution along the length of the subject's body obtained by using the collimator with a 5 by 4 in. sodium iodide crystal.

In curves 1 and 2, the measured points were so few that the curve was drawn assuming a symmetrical shape. The body activity was also measured 4 and 6 hr. after ingestion; however, the data obtained were almost similar to Curve 2. Where Sr^{58}

is accumulated will be made clear from the curves in Figure 4. Curve 1 shows that Sr⁸⁵ will mostly be in the stomach about 23 min. after ingestion. Curve 2 shows that it will be in the duodenum and the small intestine near the duodenum during 2 to 6 hr. after ingestion. Curve 3 is the data for the part of the morning beginning just after the first evacuation of the day following ingestion. This curve shows that Sr^{85} will be in the large intestine about 21 hr. after ingestion. The high concentration was also observed at the joints of the shoulder, knees and ankles.

Curve 4 shows that Sr^{85} will be in the large intestine near the anus about 32 hr. after ingestion. After the second evacuation, curve 5 was obtained. As the large peak about the waist decreased remarkably during the following 50 hr. after curve 5, a small amount of Sr^{85} seems to still remain in the intestine, about 50 hr. after ingestion. Curve 7 is for the distribution 364 hr. after ingestion, which shows that Sr^{85} will be mainly accumulated in the joints of the shoulder, waist, knees and ankles.

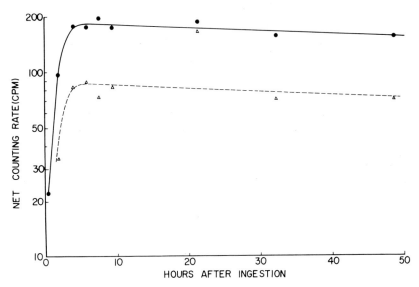

Figure 5. Accumulation of Sr^{85} at the joints of the shoulder and knees up to 49 hr. after ingestion (corrected for physical decay). Solid line shows the accumulation at the joints of the shoulder, and dotted line shows that of the knees.

The variations in the accumulation at the joints of the shoulder and knees were examined (Fig. 5). The accumulation at the joints reaches a maximum about 6 hr. after ingestion and decreases slowly thereafter. The retention at the joints of the shoulder from 6 hr. to 364 hr. after ingestion may be expressed as

$$R' \alpha \, 5.5 \exp \left(-\frac{0.693}{5.0} t \right) + 2.5 \exp \left(-\frac{0.693}{800} t \right),$$

where t is the days after ingestion.

It is of interest to compare this result with that of whole body retention. On the basis of this result, 0.95 days of half life for whole body retention would represent the deposition of strontium in soft tissue.

Biological Constants of f_1, f_2' and f_w

From the results in Figures 1 and 2, biological constants could be determined. The retention just after the second evacuation was 0.105, which was measured 1.9 days after ingestion. As no remarkable fecal excretion could be observed thereafter, this value would almost be considered as the fraction of Sr^{85} reaching the total body.

The fraction reaching the total body by ingestion, f_w, can be determined by extrapolation of the value of retention to time zero, which would be more than 0.105. From the results obtained by the biology and chemistry group, the value of f_1 was determined as 0.13 from excretion analysis (5). As for f_2' for the total body, the fraction from blood to the organ of the reference, is 1 and $f_1 \times f_2' = f_w$, f_1 become equal to f_w. As far as f_1 for the total body is concerned, the result of f_1 determined from excretion analysis would probably be correct, and we wish to take 0.13 as the f_w for the total body.

From fifty days after ingestion, the retention reduced slowly, and the biological half life was about 800 days. This stage can be considered as chronic retention, when the strontium deposits closely in the bone. The extrapolated value at time of ingestion of this chronic retention is 0.025, which can be regarded as f_w for the bone. From the formulas $f_1 \times f_2' = f_w$ and $f_1 = 0.13$, the value of f_2' for the bone is obtained as 0.20 (Table II). It is seen

TABLE II
BIOLOGICAL CONSTANTS DERIVED FROM THE EXPERIMENT

Element	Organ of Reference	Fraction from GI tract to Blood f_1	Fraction from Blood to Organ of Reference f_2'	Fraction reaching Organ of Reference by Ingestion f_w
Strontium	Total body	0.13	1.0	0.13
	Bone		0.20	0.025

from the results that there are great differences between the f_1 and f_w obtained and those of ICRP (6); the results obtained are about one third of the values of ICRP. As far as the f_2' is concerned there is no remarkable difference from the value of ICRP.

REFERENCES

1. Bishop, M., Harrison, G. E., Raymond, W. H. A., Sutton, A., and Rundo, J.: Int. J. Radiat. Biol., 2:125, 1960.
2. Stewart, C. G., Vogt, E., Hitchman, A. J. W., and Jupe, N.: Second Int. Conf. Geneva, Proc., 23:123, 1958.
3. Rundo, J., and Williams, K.: Brit. J. Radiol., 34:734, 1961.
4. Suguri, S.: Proceedings of the Symposium on Whole Body Counting, 219, 1962.
5. Fujita, M., Yabe, A., Ueno, K., Oshino, M., and Okuyama, N.: Health Physics, under publication.
6. Report of Committee II on Permissible Dose for Internal Radiation, 1959, Health Physics, 3:1, 1960.

35

CESIUM-134 IN MAN

KURT LIDÉN and INGVAR Ö. ANDERSSON
University of Lund
and AB Atomenergi
Studsvik, Tystberga, Sweden

HIGH Cs^{137} BODY burdens due to bomb fallout have been found in Laplanders and other people on a similar diet in northern Scandinavia. Values above 100 times the average Cs^{137} body contents in people on ordinary diet are frequently found. The high cesium level is mainly due to consumption of reindeer meat which has high cesium content caused by the reindeers' habit of grazing on lichens and herbs over large areas (1).

After the discovery of the high Cs^{137} body burdens of Swedish Lapps in the beginning of 1961 (1), several hundred people from northern Finland and Sweden were measured both in the laboratory and in portable whole body counters (2, 3, 4). In all these cases the whole body gamma-ray spectra have shown, besides the unusually high Cs^{137} peak at 660 kev, also a well resolved peak at 800 kev. In Figure 1 the gamma-ray spectrum of subject L. B. measured August 16, 1961, clearly demonstrates the 800 kev peak. The spectrum was obtained with a NaI(Tl) crystal 4 in. in diameter and 4 in. thick in an iron room with the subject in a calibrated chair. Figure 2 shows the average gamma-ray spectrum of twelve Swedish Lapps measured August 16-17, 1961 with each subject counted for 1 hr. The 800 kev peak has improved statistical accuracy.

As the 800 kev peak is not found in the gamma-ray spectra of Swedes from the Stockholm and Lund areas, it could be assumed that there was a relation between this peak and the increased Cs^{137} level in people on a reindeer meat diet in northern Sweden. The gamma-ray spectrum of reindeer meat was measured; it also showed a peak at 800 kev (Fig. 3). The K^{40} contribu-

Counts / hr. per 25 kev. channel

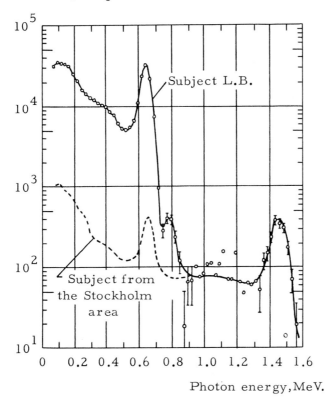

Photon energy, MeV.

Figure 1. Human body gamma spectra of a Laplander, subject L.B., and a subject from the Stockholm area. The Cs¹³⁷ body burden of subject L.B. is 0.60 μc.

tion is subtracted. The measurements from March to May, 1961, of three Lapps by means of a 5 by 4 in. crystal showed that the mean ratio of the number of pulses in the full (extrapolated) 800 kev photopeak and the full Cs¹³⁷ photopeak was (1.65±0.2):100. In reindeer meat measured March 11, 1961, the ratio was(1.42±0.07): 100. A study of twelve Lapps in August, 1961, gave a mean ratio of (1.2±0.1): 100 and no significant deviations between different human subjects. The ratio in reindeer meat extract measured October 20, 1961, was (1.10±0.05): 100. Thus in both series of

Counts / hr. per 25 kev. channel

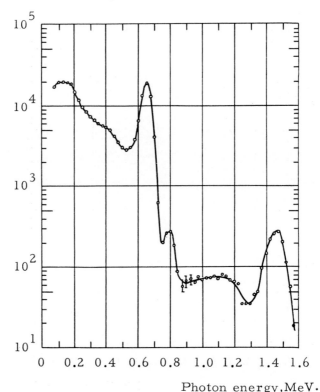

Photon energy,MeV.

Figure 2. Average gamma spectrum of 12 Swedish Laplanders measured August 16-17, 1961. Average Cs[137] body burden is 0.35 μc.

measurements the 800 kev peak to the Cs[137] peak ratio had the same value in meat and man within the statistical limits.

A number of measurements have been made to determine the physical half life of the isotope behind the 800 kev peak (5). Reindeer meat, 3 kg., was treated in a wet ashing process. The sample obtained was 1 liter of solution with colorless solid deposition. The sample was measured in an accurately defined geometry with a 4 by 4 in. NaI(Tl) scintillation spectrometer. The measurement was repeated after 130, 137 and 300 days (Table I). The half life was calculated both from the number of pulses in the 800 kev peak and from the ratio of the number of pulses in the 800 kev peak and the Cs[137] peak. In the second case one has

Counts / 200 min. per 15 kev. channel

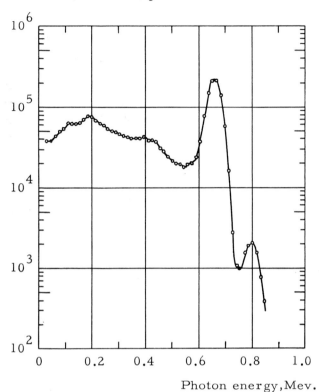

Photon energy, Mev.

Figure 3. Gamma spectrum of reindeer meat extract measured Oct. 20, 1961. K⁴⁰ contribution is subtracted. Cs¹³⁷ contents are 25 mμc/kg. of fresh weight.

TABLE I

DATA FROM THE STUDY OF THE HALF LIFE OF THE 800 KEV BAND IN THE GAMMA SPECTRUM OF REINDEER MEAT

Date	Cs¹³⁷ Band ch 52-78		Cs¹³⁴ Band ch 80-100			Time of Measurement	
	Net Counts from Sample cph	Back-ground cph	Net Counts from Sample cph	Contrib. from K40 cph	Back-ground cph	Sample Hr.	Back-ground Hr.
Oct. 20, 1961	226237	5908	2781	258	3381	3	16
March 1-2, 1962	218025	1404	2501	248	858	20	16
March 7-8, 1962	216807	1438	2452	245	859	13	16
Aug. 15-16, 1962	212111	1429	2180	242	754	9	30

TABLE II

THE HALF LIFE OF THE 800 KEV BAND CALCULATED FROM THE
DATA IN TABLE I.

Decay Period	Half Life of the Cs^{134} Band Years	Half Life of the Cs^{134}/Cs^{137} Band Ratio; Years
Oct. 20, 1961-March 1, 1962	2.2 $\begin{array}{c}+\ 0.5\\-\ 0.4\end{array}$	2.9 $\begin{array}{c}+\ 1.4\\-\ 0.6\end{array}$
Oct. 20, 1961-March 7, 1962	2.0 $\begin{array}{c}+\ 0.4\\-\ 0.3\end{array}$	2.6 $\begin{array}{c}+\ 0.8\\-\ 0.5\end{array}$
Oct. 20, 1961-Aug. 15, 1962	1.95 $\begin{array}{c}+\ 0.25\\-\ 0.20\end{array}$	2.50 $\pm$ 0.20
March 1, 1962-Aug. 15, 1962	1.95 $\begin{array}{c}+\ 0.20\\-\ 0.15\end{array}$	2.30 $\pm$ 0.20
March 7, 1962-Aug. 15, 1962	2.30 $\pm$ 0.25	2.50 $\pm$0.25

to make a correction for the decay of Cs^{137}, but an advantage is
that the result is not influenced by small changes in the geometry
(Table II). The half lives obtained by the two methods are in
satisfying agreement. The average value was 2.25 $\pm$ 0.20 years.

The information of the 800 kev peak that we had at this
stage of the investigation suggested Cs^{134} as a first tentative inter-

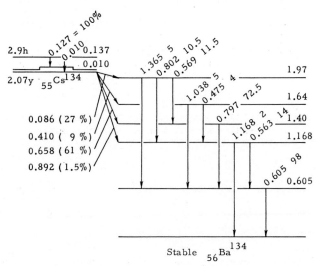

Figure 4. Level scheme of Cs^{134}.

pretation of its origin, but since there was no known yield of Cs^{134} in nuclear weapons fission this hypothesis had to be carefully tested. A direct approach in order to prove the presence of Cs^{134} was made. The level scheme of Cs^{134} recently revised (6) shows that the most intense gamma-ray lines at 605 and 797 are emitted in cascade (Fig. 4). An attempt was therefore made to study the gamma-ray spectrum of reindeer meat by a γ-γ coincidence technique. A 75 gm. sample of vacuum dried meat, corresponding to 240 gm. fresh weight, in a cylindrical container 9 cm. in diameter and 1.5 cm. high was placed between two crystals of NaI (Tl) 3 in. in diameter and 2 in. thick. One was connected to an integral discriminator (channel I), and the other to a 200 channel transistorized pulse amplitude analyzer (channel II).

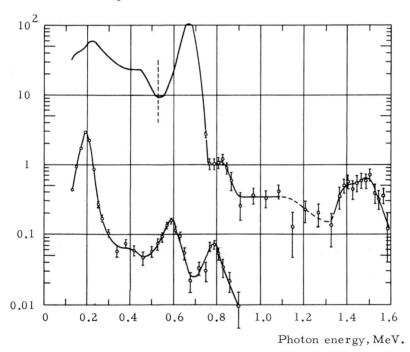

Figure 5. γ-γ coincidence net spectrum of a reindeer meat sample (lower curve, 45 hr. run) and a single crystal spectrum of the same sample in the same geometry (upper curve, 100 min. run).

The pulses from channel I corresponding to 530 kev or more opened the gate of channel II. The coincidence system had a resolving time of 1 μsec. Two successful long term runs were made, one for 45 hr. and one for 20 hr. The 45 hr. coincidence spectrum, corrected for background, is plotted in Figure 5. It shows two distinct peaks at 600 kev and 800 kev. The increased counting rate at lower energies is caused mainly by various Compton events. The random coincidence rate is negligible also at the position of the Cs^{137} peak. A test with a Cs^{134} sample of the same size and density as the meat sample resulted in a coincidence spectrum of the same shape as for the meat.

Thus these investigations have revealed the following characteristic data of the unknown isotope:

The energy of one emitted gamma-ray is 800 kev. The half life is 2.25 ± 0.20 years, compared to 2.07 ± 0.02 years for Cs^{134}.

There is a 600 kev gamma-ray peak in coincidence with the 800 kev peak; (After correction for crystal efficiency the intensity ratio for these two peaks was found to be 10:6, in accordance with the level scheme for Cs^{134} from which the ratio 100:67 for the two groups 563 + 569 + 605 and 797 + 802 kev is obtained (Fig. 4).

The metabolic behavior of the 800 kev component in reindeer meat and man is similar to that of Cs^{137}. This was concluded from the fact that we had the same ratio between the unknown photopeak and the Cs^{137} photopeak in meat and man.

Thus we believe sufficient evidence has been presented to indicate that the origin of the 800 kev peak in man's gamma-ray spectrum is a Cs^{134} contamination of human tissue.

The origin of Cs^{134} in the biosphere is not known. There seem to be no figures in the literature concerning a direct Cs^{134} yield in fission. Indirect formation in the 134 mass chain by successive beta-decay is prevented by the existence of stable Xe^{134}. Baerg et al. (8) found the independent yield of the metastable Cs^{134}, half life 2.9 hr., in thermal neutron fission of U^{235} to be less than $1.4.10^{-5}\%$. From the measurements of March, 1961 we have found the Cs^{134} activity in reindeer to be 1.6 percent of the Cs^{137} activity, assuming a total intensity of 0.8 photons per disintegration for the 800 kev lines and correcting for crystal efficiency. This corresponds to a Cs^{134} yield of about 0.01 percent.

An observation of Cs^{134} in soil samples taken close to ground zero after an atomic balloon shot in Nevada is reported (9). However, only a slight indication of Cs^{137} was found, which is rather puzzling. Neutron-induction processes are suggested as a tentative interpretation in this case.

Cs^{134} is produced in reactors by neutron activation of the stable fission product Cs^{133}. There is no direct yield of Cs^{133}, but it is created by the decay of other fission products. As this buildup of Cs^{133} is slow, it is not possible to interpret the biospheric Cs^{134} as a result of such an activation process in weapons tests. As Cs^{134} is produced in reactors, reactor release or reactor accidents might be the origin of this isotope in the biosphere. The U^{235} fission product production in a reactor as a function of thermal neutron flux, irradiation time and decay time has been calculated by Blomeke and Todd (10). If U^{235} were irradiated at a neutron flux of 10^{14} for six months the Cs^{134}/Cs^{137} activity ratio would be about 1:4.

The reactor accident at Windscale in October, 1957 was detected in Sweden (11) and Norway (12). A relatively heavy Cs^{137} fallout was found at Bergen, Norway (60.4° N, 5.3° E) during September and October 1957. Hvinden and Lillegraven reported that it might be due chiefly to the Windscale accident. From their observations it can be estimated that about 10 percent of the cumulative Cs^{137} fallout up to August 1961 could be from that accident. If we assume that the Cs^{134}/Cs^{137} activity ratio in the cesium release from Windscale was 1:4, that ratio in the cumulative cesium fallout in August, 1961 should be 0.6:100, a value which is the same, within a factor of two, as the ratio reported above. However, it should be emphasized that this is a rough and rather uncertain estimate. If the Cs^{134}/Cs^{137} activity ratio in the Windscale reactor had been 0.05 as given by Wheatley (13), our hypothesis will not hold. We would only like to show that the release of activities from reactors has to be considered when discussing the possible origin of the biospheric Cs^{134}. It remains to investigate other processes in nuclear weapons tests, for example Cs^{134} fast neutron fission yield, multiple capture, activation of nonfissionable material, etc.

Investigation of the time dependence of the Cs^{134}/Cs^{137} ratio in fresh biospheric samples and measurement of this ratio in samples from different parts of the world are in progress, and they will probably give important indications about the origin of the Cs^{134} in fallout.

REFERENCES

1. Lidén, K.: *Acta Radiol.*, *56*:237, 1961.
2. Andersson, I. Ö., and Nilsson, I.: AB Atomenergi, Sweden. *Techn. Rep. RSA-63 and SSI-2*, 1961.
3. Lidén, K., Naversten, Y., and McCall, R. C.: Whole body counting of Swedish Lapps. In preparation.
4. Miettinen, J. K., *et. al.*: Cs^{137} and potassium in people and diet — a study of Finnish Lapps. In preparation.
5. Andersson, I. Ö., Nilsson, I., and Eckerstig, K.: AB Atomenergi, Sweden. *Techn. Rep. AE-80*, 1962.
6. Nuclear Data Sheets, NRC, Washington, Set 2, 1961.
7. Wyatt, E. I., Reynolds, S. A., Handley, T. H., Lyon, W. S., and Parker, H. A.: *Nucl. Sci. Engl.*, *11*:74, 1961.
8. Baerg, A. P., Bartholomew, R. M., and Betts, R. H.: *Canad. J. Chem.*, 38:2147, 1960.
9. Krieger, H. L., and Groche, D.: *Science, 131*:40, 1960.
10. Blomeke, J. O., and Todd, Mary F.: ORNL-2127, Part 1, Vol. 1, 1957.
11. Edvarson, K., and Löw, K.: *Nature, 188*:125, 1960.
12. Hvinden, T., and Lillegraven, A.: *Nature, 192*:1144, 1961.
13. Wheatley, B. M.: *Brit. J. Radiol.*, *33*:246, 1960.

36

POTASSIUM AND Cs[137] CONTENT OF SOUTH AUSTRALIANS AGED 8 MONTHS TO 80 YEARS

Boyce Worthley

University of Adelaide
Adelaide, South Australia

INTRODUCTION

In 1959, we assembled our first high pressure ionization chamber system with a design similar to that reported by Rundo in 1955; with the advent of scintillation counters, we were at least five years behind the times instrumentally. There were four measuring cylinders set directly above the subject and four backing off chambers 1 meter above the lower chambers. The cylinders were 6 ft. long, 8 in. in diameter and contained nitrogen at a pressure of 21 atmospheres. Beneath and about the subject couch were water tanks. The differential ionization current was passed through a 10^{12}W resistor, the potential difference measured by a vibrating reed electrometer and registered by a potentiometer chart recorder. With this apparatus we could measure the potassium content of man in 2 hr. with a standard deviation of 40 gm.

This equipment was used between October, 1959, and July, 1960, to estimate the radioactive burden of fourteen males (a few with two or three repetitions) and five females. Classifying all radioactivity in terms of potassium, we found an average of 4.6 gm. potassium/kg. total body weight for men and 3.9 for women. These values were obtained by comparison with phantoms containing known quantities of potassium. By this time it was well known that the body radioactivity was being enhanced by the presence of Cs [137] from fallout, but the values seemed high.

With more substantial financial support forthcoming, we designed a gamma ray spectrometer which was manufactured for us in Edinburgh. From July, 1961, until November, 1961, we completed preliminary work, faults were eliminated from the kick sorter, spurious pulses filtered from the lines, additional mechanical and electrical features added to the equipment and calibration procedures devised and carried through.

CONSTRUCTIONAL DETAILS OF GAMMA RAY SPECTROMETER

The equipment included a circular crystal carriage which supported four 4½ by 2 in. Na I (Tl) crystals, their associated 5 in. photomultipliers and preamplification systems. The crystal positions on the circumference of the circle were adjustable, but set normally at 45° from the horizontal with two above and two below the patient's couch. The crystal distance from the center was adjustable, but was usually set at 25 cm., the maximum distance. The crystal carriage ran on a pair of rails for a maximum distance of 6 ft. being driven by a motor gear box system at a speed of 6 in. per min. A delay timer was incorporated so that the carriage oscillated between limit switches with preset pause times at the end of each sweep. By adjustment of the position of one limit switch, sweep distances between 6 ft. and 0 could be obtained.

The amplified pulses from the four crystals were taken to an adding circuit, a linear pulse amplifier, a C. D. C. 100 channel kick sorter, and to a rate meter and decade counter. There was chart reading of the pulse rate and crystal carriage position. The photomultipliers were fed with individually adjustable high tension so that pulse heights from individual crystals could be matched.

The steel room of internal dimensions 5 by 5 by 8 ft. was made of prewar solid steel plate 6 in. thick, with a motor driven sliding door of the same material. The room was lit with four 20 watt lamps and ventilated with an air extraction system set on the back wall. There is a two-way communication system and a duplicate of the door switch inside the room. So far we have had no difficulty persuading patients to spend one hour in the room. They may read unless the crystals are actually passing their shoulders, but most of them doze off. We cannot see the patients, and we have come to feel that this is a disadvantage as we cannot examine unconscious adults for potassium balance disturbance.

Most of the children examined were extremely young, eight being between eight and twelve months old, and seven others were less than six years. The babies were examined by placing them on a special small couch between the crystals with the carriage set against the back wall. A nurse sat on a chair placed almost against the sliding door, about 6 ft. from the child. Most of the other children were small enough to be examined using a crystal carriage sweep of 30 in. with a nurse near the door. Background counts were obtained with bottles of distilled water in the place of the child, and bottles of potassium and Cs^{137} solution placed on the chair and matching the nurse's body burden of this material. These counts were automatically subtracted from the measurement registration on the kick sorter. Counting times were approximately 1 hr., which with background counting meant a total measurement time per person of approximately 2½ hr., which means that only three people could be examined for natural radioactivity in a working day.

DESIGN PRINCIPLE OF MOVING CRYSTAL DETECTOR SYSTEM

To the best of my knowledge, a moving crystal detector system is unusual in body counting. One way of visualizing the system is to consider it as a cylindrical 4π shell with the curved side reduced to four lines parallel to the long axis, and the end plates represented by crystals extending part way round the circumference. This skeleton system is what our crystal sweep with end pauses endeavors to duplicate. The price one pays for relative independence of counts up on position of the radioactive material within the hypothetical cylindrical shell is that of a small decrease in counting efficiency. There is a loss of approximately 20 percent of counts by a 6 ft. sweep end pause technique when compared with the counts with the crystals stationary about the middle of a 6 ft. line source.

A simple analysis brings out the main features of the various possible modes of measurement with our crystal system, and these were confirmed in broad outline by experimental work using bottles containing Cs^{137}, Co^{60} and potassium. Rectangular polythene bottles approximately 6 by 6 by 8 in. were filled with distilled water, potassium, Cs^{137} and Co^{60} solutions. A line of eleven bottles was placed centrally on the patient's couch, ten with distilled water and one with a gamma ray emitter.

Table I shows the response of the crystals for various positions of the active bottle in the inactive line. For a 6 ft. sweep time of 12 min., the best end pause time for the three radioisotopes considered was 1.6 min., but the end pause time is not particularly critical. It is clear that almost equal response is given by all bottle positions when using this end pause sweep technique.

CALIBRATION PROCEDURE

The calibration procedure was based entirely on phantoms made up of polythene bottles of five different sizes and shapes. Using these containers, reasonably lifelike models were constructed with heads, bodies, arms and legs. The bottles gave us cheap phantoms of great flexibility. Calibration procedures were based upon the measurement of Cs^{137} in the presence of potassium at the levels found in the normal nonoccupationally exposed

TABLE I
RESPONSE AGAINST POSITION OF SOURCE ON CENTRAL AXIS

Radio-isotope	% response for position			
	1	2	3	6
Cs 137	104	107	103	100
Co 60	99	104	101	100
K 40	96	103	100	100

population. Counts were taken in the energy ranges 0.5 to 0.75 Mev and 0.85 to 1.75 Mev, using a variety of manlike models containing potassium and Cs^{137} with the end pause sweep technique. In 1 hr. the background counts in these ranges was 16,000 and 17,500, respectively.

For adults the measurement procedure entailed four 6 ft. sweeps, each lasting 12 min., with 1.6 min. pauses at each end, to a total time of 61 min. The potassium phantom consisted of a 2 percent potassium by weight solution, and the Cs^{137} phantom made using solution of approximately 1 µc Cs^{137} per 100 kg. of distilled water.

Table II illustrates calibration values obtained using this technique for phantoms weighing 30 to 90 kg., which more than covered the weight range of adults encountered. It will be observed that a weight ratio of 3 to 1 only changes the potassium and Cs^{137} counts by 10 percent, which confirms our view that this technique gave counts largely independent of the configuration of radioactive material when the activity is distributed fairly evenly throughout the volume.

Even with the sweep multicrystal technique, difficulties can arise when there is heavy localized concentration of radioactive material near the surface of the body, e.g., the difference in counts for a radium phantom made of solution and that made of distilled water with a radium impregnated "spine" was 10 to 15 percent. When this procedure was repeated measuring the bremsstrahlung from Sr^{90} solution and a plaster of paris spine containing Sr^{90}, the difference was 40 to 45 percent. The apparatus was also calibrated for childlike phantoms, using sweeps of 5,

TABLE II
CALIBRATION VALUES
FOR POTASSIUM AND Cs^{137}

	Counts/Hr./gm. K		Counts/Hr./mµ. Cs^{137}
Energy Range	0.5-0.75 Mev	0.85-1.75 Mev	0.5-0.75 Mev
Weight in kg:			
30	12.6	32.3	350
50	12.4	31.4	339
70	12.2	30.4	327
90	12.0	29.3	316

4, 3, 2.5 and 0 ft. There was marked increase in efficiency of counting as the sweep distance decreased to 0.

RESULTS

Potassium Body Burden

Table III gives the potassium concentration found on exami-

TABLE III
RELATIVE POTASSIUM BURDENS OF CHILDREN

| | Male | | | | Female | | | |
Age in Years	No.	Read-ings	gm. K/ kg.	Mean Weight	No.	Read-ings	gm. K/ kg.	Mean Weight
<1	6	8	1.44	8.1 kg.	2	2	1.47	7.7
>1	5	5	1.94	13.3	3	3	2.0	16.8

nation of sixteen children. This investigation was undertaken to see if it were possible to measure disturbances in potassium balance due to dehydration accompanying gastroenteritis. The standard deviation for the stationary crystal technique used for babies is 2 gm. potassium, and this is 20 percent of the body potassium of an 8 kg. child. It is clear that the equipment is not sensitive enough to detect real potassium fluctuations in individuals, as these would be completely masked by statistical variations. However, the average concentrations in children possess some significance. One child not listed was examined on five occasions over fifteen days, with an average potassium content of 11.7 gm. obtained with an experimental S. D. of 1.9 gm. This is close to expectations on statistical grounds. This child was physically and mentally subnormal, and although 28 months old, weighed only 8 kg. and presented the appearance of a babe in arms. The potassium concentration placed it in the category of a child less than 1 year old.

From this study it seems clear that the potassium concentration in children changes markedly at one year, and this may be connected with the body changes needed for a child to walk. This is an investigation which I commend to those of you with apparatus more sensitive than my own.

After puberty males and females seem to differentiate

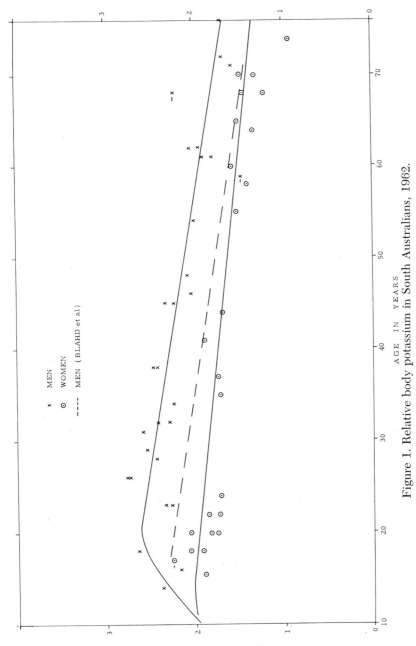

Figure 1. Relative body potassium in South Australians, 1962.

strongly in their potassium concentration (Fig. 1). Men in particular appear to rise to a peak between ages 18 and 30, corresponding fairly closely to physical prime. At great age the potassium concentration appears to return to that of babies before walking. The average concentration for males aged 20 to 60 is 2.3 gm. potassium/kg. This agrees with Suguri's values for 11 adult Japanese men, but is somewhat higher than an average from Blahd's values and the values presented by Remenchik and Miller. This variety of values indicates that potassium concentration in the human body is strongly dependent on the sample selected. Blahd's values for normal females were almost identical with our findings on Adelaide women. At this stage, however, with readings on twenty-seven men and twenty-two women, we have no clear idea of the normal range of variability in the various age groups.

Patients with a variety of diseases were examined, two with carcinoma of the bladder, one with carcinoma of the cervix, three with cardiac disorders, seven with leukemia and one with myotonic dystrophy. One subject was six months pregnant. The only variations from expectation came from one apparently healthy member of my staff, who presented with a low value confirmed by a repeat measurement, the myotonic patient with a low value, the pregnant female with a high value and one myeloid leukemia with a high value. Repeat measurements were made on six subjects with satisfactory agreement in each case.

Cs^{137} Body Burden

As a corollary to the measurement of potassium, Cs^{137} body burdens were estimated in members of the population exposed only to fallout. These figures may be of some interest, as they are

TABLE IV

RELATIVE CESIUM-137 BURDENS

IN $\mu \mu c \ Cs^{137}/$ GM. K.

Age in Yrs.	No.	Male	No.	Female
<1	5	34	2	29
1<A<14	5	33	3	24
>14	27	27.2	22	26.8

from a group of people living in the Southern Hemisphere where little nuclear weapon testing has been carried out. Table IV gives the values of $\mu\mu$c Cs^{137}/gm. potassium for all subjects examined. The averages for men and women are not significantly different. The values for children are not significantly different from adults for the small number measured. Suguri quotes a value of 29 $\mu\mu$c Cs^{137}/gm. potassium for eleven Japanese men, and this appears to be close to the Australian value.

Considering the Cs^{137} concentration in $\mu\mu$c/kg. total body weight, the males aged fifteen to fifty-four years have a value of 60, with a fall to 46 in the range of 55 to 74. Male children of all ages had a value of 65. Female children had a value of 45; females aged fifteen to twenty-four years, a value of 46; but women older than thirty-five had an average value of 35 $\mu\mu$c/kg. body weight (Table V).

The variations in Cs^{137} concentrations were much greater than those of potassium, so that average can be strongly dependent on sample.

I studied potassium and Cs^{137} burden in the elder members

TABLE V

Cs^{137} $\mu\mu$C/KG

AGE IN YEARS

	15-24		25-34		35-44		45-54		55-64		65-74		75-84	
Sex	No.	pc/ kg.	No.	pc/ kg.	No.	pc/ kg.	No.	pc/ kg.	No.	pc/ kg.	No.	pc/ kg.	No.	pc/ kg.
M	6	62	7	64	2	61	5	60	5	43	3	49	1	66
F	9	55	–	–	4	35	–	–	4	41	4	31	–	–

TABLE VI

Cs^{137} BURDEN OF W. FAMILY

Name	Sex	Age	Weight	gm. K/kg.	Cs^{137}	$\mu\mu$c/gm. K	$\mu\mu$c/kg.
B	M	45	78	2.33	7.1	39	90
L	M	18	71	2.64	5.0	27	70
N	M	14	54	2.37	3.1	24	58
R	F	44	52	1.69	1.6	18	30
S	F	20	59	2.05	4.0	33	68
E	F	16	60	1.95	3.6	31	60
					Mean	29	63

of my own family (Table VI). The Cs^{137} concentrations in the children were alike, but my own value appeared as much above average as my wife's was below. It is somewhat difficult to account for these large variations in a family sitting down to the same meal table. The mean values of concentration agree with the general average from the population sample taken.

CONCLUSIONS

More work has to be done to derive the range of normal variability in the various age groups before great confidence can be placed in measurements of body potassium as a diagnostic measure. By the same token, the time has come for a wide intercomparison of standards. Certainly a phantom containing lifelike contents of potassium and Cs^{137} would be extremely useful to laboratories like my own, which is almost completely isolated from the most active centers in the world.

REFERENCES

1. Blahd, W. H., Cassen, B., and Lederer, M.: Determination of total body potassium by K^{40} measurements in patients with muscular dystrophy and related diseases. Proceedings of I.A.E.A. Symposium on Whole Body Counting, Vienna, June, 1961.
2. Delwaide, P. A., Colard, L., Verly, W. G., and Borrlinger, R.: Measurement of the total potassium in the human system. Proceedings of I.A.E.A. Symposium on Whole Body Counting, Vienna, June, 1961.
3. Remenchik, A., and Miller, C. E.: The measurement of total body potassium in man and its relation to gross body composition. Proceedings of I.A.E.A. Symposium on Whole Body Counting, Vienna, June, 1961.
4. Rundo, J.: Some calibration problems of whole body gamma ray spectrometers. Proceedings of I.A.E.A. Symposium on Whole Body Counting, Vienna, June, 1961.
5. Suguri, S., Oshino, M., and Ohtani, S.: Measurements with a whole body counter. Proceedings of I.A.E.A. Symposium on Whole Body Counting, Vienna, June, 1961.

DISCUSSION

Chairman: E. Eric Pochin

University College Hospital Medical School
London, England

David V. Becker: Dr. Sastry, did you observe a weight change in the rats during you whole body counting experiment, and, if so, what effect did this have on continuing efficiency?

B. V. Rama Sastry: We found a change in the weight of rats, but we have not yet calculated the data.

Chester R. Richmond: How long did you wait before the tissue samples were assayed?

B. V. Rama Sastry: The tissue was sampled immediately after we treated the animals, and then we continued obtaining serial samples. The energies of parent and donor are quite similar, so while you are assaying the entire animal, you are essentially looking at both of them. After the tissues are removed, you have essentially one lement and not two, so you have to wait for the equilibrium to be achieved again. I feel that all of these tissues may disturb the equilibrium of the mixture, so that actually the ratios of zirconium to niobium are not the same.

Chester R. Richmond: You had a value of seventeen days in the biological half life for retention. We have also observed this biological change. The last component looks like a half life of about 1,700 days.

George R. Meneely: In connection with half lives and slow and fast moving components, I think that most substances disappear from the body at rates which change with time, i.e., fast at first, then more and more slowly. I find the concept of biological half life rather misleading.

Chairman E. Eric Pochin: I think that most people would be happy to agree with the idea of a single biological half life as misleading.

SESSION XI, SEPTEMBER 7
METABOLISM OF FISSION PRODUCTS
Continued
Chairman: MERRIL EISENBUD

37

RELATIONSHIPS OF RADIOCESIUM AND POTASSIUM IN THE DIET AND BODY OF FINNISH LAPPS

Jorma K. Miettinen, Paavo Roine and Kurt Lidén

University of Helsinki
Helsinki, Finland
and University of Lund
Stockholm, Sweden

IN OCTOBER 1961, the laboratories made an investigation of Cs^{137} and potassium in the diet and body of 180 inhabitants of the county of Inari, the main living area of Finnish Lapps; 149 of the persons studied were Lapps.

A cluster sampling method was used. The county was divided into nine main living areas of Lapps (Fig. 1). From each area five to fifteen healthy persons, aged ten to sixty, were invited at random. The areas 1 to 6 are mainly inhabited by settled mountain Lapps, all reindeer breeders by profession; area 7 by fisher Lapps and reindeer breeding fisher Lapps, and areas 8 and 9 by Skolt Lapps.

A smaller group of 11 inhabitants of Helsinki was studied for comparison.

The results of whole body counting are reported in this symposium by Naversten and Lidén (1).

Individual food consumption and its seasonal variations were determined by interview with the help of weighed samples of main foodstuffs and dishes. The data were collected on record forms prepared particularly for this survey. The persons studied were classified into several groups on the basis of their profession, diet and the traditional tribal grouping of the Lapps.

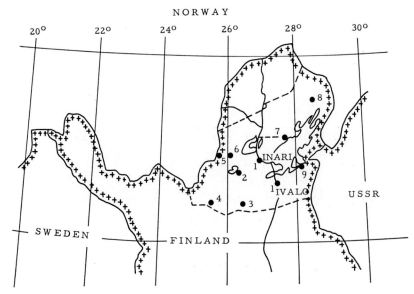

Figure 1. Main living areas of Lapps in Inari County.

1. Inari and Ivalo villages.   6. Vaskojoki.
2. Menesjärvi.   7. Partakko.
3. Kuttura.   8. Sevettijärvi.
4. Lisma.   9. Nellimö.
5. Angeli.

The results of the dietary survey are in good agreement with a recent one made on a family basis. Particularly noticeable for the Lapps are the high consumption of meat and fish — practically only reindeer meat — and the low consumption of milk products, leaf vegetables and fruit compared with people living in southern Finland.

Seasonal variation in the consumption of fish and meat is very great especially among fisher and mountain Lapps. In winter time the consumption of fish is only about 25 percent of that in summer time, but the consumption of reindeer meat is in winter five to ten times higher than in summer.

Representative samples of main foodstuffs, both locally produced and imported, were collected in Inari and analysed for Cs^{137} and potassium. From the results of these analyses and the food consumption data, it was possible to calculate the content

TABLE I

Average Content of Cs^{137} in the Body and Diet of Inari Inhabitants, Oct. 1961

	Number	Age, Aver.	Body Cs^{137} nc.	Diet Cs^{137} nc. Per Month	Main Sources of Cs^{137} in Diet, as Percentage of Total			
					Reindeer Meat	Fish	Milk	Other Foods
Men:								
Lapps,								
reindeer breeders	50	40	245	194	88.3	8.0	3.3	0.4
reindeer breeding fishers	6	38	110	186	88.3	9.3	1.8	0.6
Lapps of other professions	7	39	129	98	81.1	9.6	8.0	1.3
boarding school pupils, 16-19 y.	4	17	60	57	81.6	14.8	1.6	2.0
boarding school pupils, 10-14 y.	17	11	49	52	72.2	10.1	15.8	1.9
All Lapps	84	33	178	150	86.6	8.5	4.2	0.7
Local non-Lapps	16	39	101	96	78.7	9.7	10.4	1.2
Helsinki inhabitants	5	28	8.4	—	—	—	—	—
Women:								
Lapps,								
reindeer breeders	33	44	121	76	77.6	16.0	5.6	0.8
fishers	5	59	61	38	57.4	30.4	10.0	2.2
Lapps of other professions	6	38	49	38	75.2	11.0	13.1	0.7
boarding school pupils, 16-19 y.	9	17	49	38	70.3	19.6	8.1	2.0
boarding school pupils, 10-14 y.	12	13	40	39	74.5	10.9	12.1	2.5
All Lapps	65	35	85	57	75.3	16.2	7.3	1.2
Local non-Lapps	15	49	53	36	70.3	12.8	14.8	2.1
Helsinki inhabitants	6	32	3.2	—	—	—	—	—

TABLE II
Intake of Potassium through different Foodstuffs as Gram Per Person Per Month and as Percentage of the Total Intake and Potassium Contents of Total Body, gm./kg. Body Weight

	Cereals Gm.	Per Cent	Potatoes and other Root Vegetables Gm.	Per Cent	Milk and Cream Gm.	Per Cent	Meat Gm.	Per Cent	Sausage Gm.	Per Cent	Fish Gm.	Per Cent	Total Diet Gm./mo.	Total Body Gm./kg.
MALES														
1. Lapps														
Reindeer breeders	22	12	55	31	40	23	38	21	4.8	3	18	10	178	2.4
Reindeer breeding fishers	24	15	61	37	21	13	36	22	0.9	1	20	12	163	2.5
Lapps of other occupations	26	16	57	3	49	30	18	11	1.3	1	11	7	162	2.3
Boarding school pupils 16-19 y.	23	27	35	40	6	7	10	12	0.3	0	12	14	86	2.7
Boarding school pupils 10-14 y.	18	13	51	38	52	39	8	6	0.2	0	6	4	135	2.3
2. Local non-Lapps	26	15	56	32	65	37	17	10	0.7	0	11	6	176	2.2
3. Control group of Helsinki inhabitants	10	7	36	25	87	60	9+	6	0.8	1	2	1	145	1.9
4. Rural men in South Finland	31	19	56	34	66	40	9+	5	0.9	0	3	2	166	—
FEMALES														
1. Lapps														
Reindeer breeders	14	13	43	38	27	24	13	12	0.1	0	14	13	111	1.8
Fishers	17	19	33	36	24	26	5	5	0.3	0	13	14	92	1.7
Lapps of other occupations	20	19	39	38	32	31	6	6	0.8	1	5	5	103	2.5
Boarding school pupils 16-19 y.	17	20	31	38	20	24	6	7	0.1	0	9	11	83	2.0
Boarding school pupils 10-14 y.	20	20	42	41	29	28	6	6	0.3	0	5	5	102	2.1
2. Local non-Lapps	12	14	26	31	34	51	6	7	0.9	1	5	6	84	1.6
3. Control group of Helsinki inhabitants	9	10	22	23	59	62	5+	5	0.4	0	0	–	95	1.6

+ = beef and pork

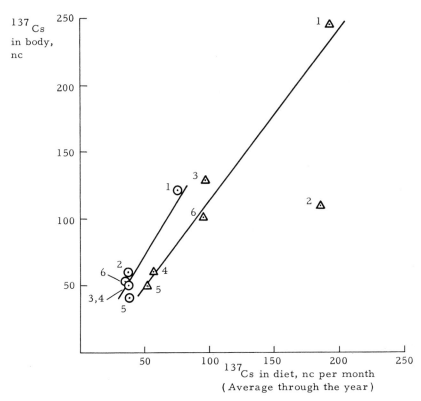

Figure 2. Correlation between the body burden and the average monthly intake of Cs^{137} in the different dietary groups at Inari.

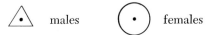   males   (•) females

1 = Lapps, reindeer breeders.
2 = Lapps, fishers (females) or reindeer breeding fishers (males).
3 = Lapps, other occupations.
4 = Lapps, boarding school pupils, sixteen to nineteen years.
5 = Lapps, boarding school pupils, ten to fourteen years.
6 = Non-Lapps, loccal.

of Cs^{137} and potassium of the average monthly diet of the different groups. The results of Cs^{137} are summarized in Table I and Figure 2; those of potassium in Table II.

The main source of Cs^{137} is reindeer meat, which is responsible for 70 to 90 percent of the intake of this nuclide. In second place is cow's milk or fish (reindeer are not milked in Finland), whereas all the other foods together contain only about 1 to 2 percent of the Cs^{137} in the diet.

In general, radiocesium in the diet and body is in direct correlation (Fig. 2). The lower body content of women is without doubt mainly due to a smaller intake in the diet. The group of male reindeer breeding fishers had an exceptionally small body burden when compared with the year-round average intake through the diet (110 nc per month). This is due to their exceptionally low consumption of reindeer meat in summer, about 0.5 kg./month, compared with the consumption in the wintertime of about 23 kg./month. In other groups this seasonal variation is much smaller.

Potatoes and cereals are important sources of potassium in addition to meat, fish and milk. People in Lapland obtain a considerably higher percentage of potassium through meat and fish and a lower percentage through milk products than people in southern Finland.

The Lapps contain considerably more potassium per kg. of body weight than the people in southern Finland; men about 2.5 gm./kg., while men in southern Finland and in other parts of the world contain about 1.9 gm./kg. The fact of a high content of potassium in Lapps is rather natural from the point of view that Lapps are very muscular and trim.

REFERENCES

1. Lidén, K., and Naversten, Y.: In this volume — High Cs^{137} Body Burdens of Lapps and Other People in Northern Scandinavia and the Food Chains Involved.
2. Jokelainen, Aili, Pekkarinen, Maija, Roine, P., and Miettinen, J. K.: The diet of Finnish Lapps. Z. *Für Ernährungswissenschaft,* 3:110-117, 1962.
3. Miettinen, J. K., Jokelainen, Aili, Roine, P., Lidén, K., Naversten, Y., Bengtsson, G., Häsänen, E., and McCall, R. C.: Cs^{137} and Potassium in People and Diet — A Study of Finnish Lapps. *Ann Acad. Sci. Finn., Ser. AII, Chemica, 120:*1-46, 1963.

38

HIGH Cs^{137} BODY BURDENS OF LAPPS AND OTHER PEOPLE IN NORTHERN SCANDINAVIA AND THE FOOD CHAINS INVOLVED

YNGVE NAVERSTEN AND KURT LIDÉN

University of Lund
Lund, Sweden

NUCLEAR WEAPONS tests have introduced long-lived nuclides, such as Cs^{137} and Sr^{90}, into the biosphere. In this paper we shall deal with some recent results concerning biospheric Cs^{137} contamination leading to a high content of this isotope in humans in Scandinavian countries.

The content of Cs^{137} in humans is closely related to the content of this isotope in the diet, which in turn to some extent depends on the local fallout level. It has been established that the distribution of statospheric fallout depends on geographic location, with higher concentrations in the northern hemisphere in the latitude range 30-60°N. The fallout is also greatly influenced by local rainfall.

However, the high body burdens in northern Scandinavia reported here are not a result of higher fallout in this region. The fallout has been evenly distributed from north to south of Sweden, being about 20 nc Cs^{137}/m^2 until September, 1961 (1). The high body burdens are a result of the extraordinary living conditions of plants, animals and humans.

Great parts of northern Scandinavia are covered with slowly growing lichens of different species. Lichens have a high capacity to retain both wet and dry deposition of radioactive fallout (2). Investigations at our laboratory have shown that Cs^{137}

content in lichens expressed in units of activity per unit area is a good measure of the integrated fallout of Cs^{137} (3). In samples of lichens (Cladonia and Cetraria species) we have found Cs^{137} contents of 10 to 30 nc/kg. standard dry weight. Even higher contents in lichens have been found in Scandinavia (2).

In northern Scandinavia hundreds of thousands of reindeers are domesticated. The adult animals eat 3 to 6 kg. of lichens a day during the winter. Cs^{137} is easily resorbed from the gut and follows the same path as potassium, so there is a high content of Cs^{137} in reindeer meat. Specific activities as high as 56 nc/kg. fresh weight in reindeer meat have been reported. The Lapps have a high consumption of reindeer products, in some cases 1 kg./day or more; and the Swedish male reindeer breeders on the average eat about 500 gm./day. It is reasonable therefore to expect high body burdens in Lapps.

In some districts cows and goats also graze on lichens, and in flooded tundra areas other plants with increased Cs^{137} contents constitute a part of their fodder (4).

In the beginning of 1961 commercially available reindeer meat was measured at our laboratory. It had 20 to 30 nc Cs^{137}/kg. fresh weight (5). By that time it became obvious to us that great populations in northern Scandinavia must have substantially higher Cs^{137} body burdens than other Swedes. The fact that reindeer meat had a high content of cesium was known earlier in Scandinavia, but this had only been reported at closed meetings. Apparently it did not result in calculation of cesium levels in humans.

The present consumption of reindeer meat in Sweden is 2 million kg./year. If this meat were equally distributed among the 7.5 million people living in Sweden, this would increase the normal Swedish human content of Cs^{137} by another 5 nc. This figure is calculated on the assumption of about 20 nc per kg. fresh weight and on the assumption of a biological half time of 70 days for Cs^{137} in human beings.

In the spring of 1961 we measured a small number of Lapps in our whole body counter at Lund. Their Cs^{137} body burdens were 150 to 300 nc. They reported a reindeer meat consumption of 200 to 400 gm./day (5).

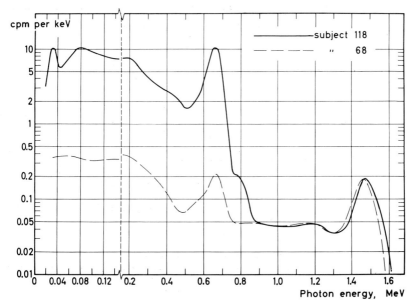

Figure 1. Spectra of two subjects with widely different body burdens of Cs¹³⁷. Subject 68 had 285 nc Cs¹³⁷, and subject 118 had 4.7 nc Cs¹³⁷.

Figure 1 shows spectra for one of these persons and for a person from Lund. One had 285 nc and the other had 4.7 nc. Above 0.15 Mev the spectrum is measured with a Ø 5 in. by 4 in. NaI crystal at 25 kev/channel. Below 0.15 Mev two Ø 110 mm. by 5 mm. NaI crystals in parallel have been used at 4 kev per channel. The Ba Kα x-ray line at 32 kev is easily recognized. To our knowledge this line had never been observed in the spectrum of a normal human being.

The stationary whole body counter as it has usually been used for Cs¹³⁷ and potassium determinations at our laboratory consisted of a conventional iron room and a 5 in. by 4 in. NaI crystal positioned in a 42 cm. chair arrangement of the Argonne type.

In 1961, a semiportable counter was constructed (6) at our laboratory. It was designed to have the same geometry as the stationary equipment and to be easily rebuilt by two persons. The shielding material consisted of lead bricks, and the total weight was about 1,500 kg. For spectrum analysis a transistorized 200 channel PHA was used. This equipment was transported by air and train to the Lapp centers in northern Sweden and northern Finland.

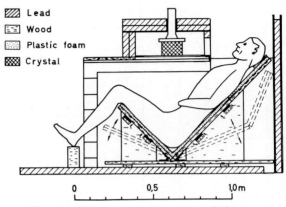

Figure 2. A profile view showing the geometry of the semiportable whole body counter.

Tables I-III give the contents for humans obtained at Jokkmokk, Sweden in September, 1961, and in April, 1962; and at Inari, Finland in October, 1961. They show a generally increased

TABLE I

RESULTS OBTAINED BY WHOLE BODY COUNTING AT JOKKMOKK (66.6°N, 19.9°E) SWEDEN, SEPTEMBER, 1961

| | | | Cs^{137} Content | |
Group	Age	Number	Average (max.-min.)* nc	nc/kg.
Lapps				
Reindeer breeders, M	40(20-64)	29	328(689-137)	5.02
F	35(16-52)	6	213(368-151)	3.77
Nonreindeer breeders, M	44(33-58)	6	172(333-48)	2.63
F	28(23-40)	4	136(207-45)	2.68
Lapp, children, M	11(10-13)	8	99(139-78)	3.20
F	15(14-16)	13	81(239-13)	1.80
F	12(11-13)	16	93(154-60)	2.52
Non-Lapps				
M	43(20-63)	12	70(121-)	0.98
F	38(20-59)	15	47(130-12)	0.76
M	16(12-19)	29	24(122-)	0.44
F	15(11-19)	20	18(44 -)	0.38
Vegetarians Mixed	(13-56)	4	18(28 -)	0.32

*Minimum detectable amount = 15 nc Cs^{137}.

Figures 3 and 4. Pictures of the semiportable whole body counter from two different directions. The bags containing 5 kg. of sugar are used for background measurements.

level of Cs^{137} body burden compared to a normal level in southern Sweden and southern Finland of usually less than 10 nc of Cs^{137}.

At Jokkmokk in September, 1961, 162 people were counted (Table I). The top values, about 700 nc Cs^{137}, were about 100 times greater than the normal Swedish level. On the average the male groups had substantially higher body activities than the female groups, except for Lapp children. The non-Lapp groups of adults showed lower values than groups of Lapp children. The highest values for non-Lapps were found among manual workers and their families.

At Inari, Finland, one month later, about the same number of people were measured (Table II). The difference between

TABLE II

RESULTS OBTAINED BY WHOLE BODY COUNTING AT INARI (69°N, 27°E) FINLAND, OCTOBER, 1961

Group	Aver. Age	Num- ber	Cs^{137} Content Average (max.-min.)* nc	nc/kg.
Lapps				
Reindeer breeders, M	40	50	245(790-86)	3.91
F	44	33	121(299-22)	2.12
Nonreindeer breeders, M	39	7	129(198-32)	2.01
F	38	6	49(93-16)	0.84
Boarding school pupils M	17	4	60(63-58)	1.04
(16-19 y) F	17	9	49(165-13)	0.94
Boarding school pupils M	11	17	49(96-13)	1.44
(10-14 y) F	13	12	40(163-19)	1.01
Local non-Lapps M	39	16	101(324-30)	1.51
F	50	15	53(162-20)	0.88

*Minimum detectable amount = 10 nc Cs.^{137}.

Lapps and non-Lapps was smaller in Finland. The Finnish Lapp groups had lower average values and the Finnish non-Lapp groups had higher values than corresponding Swedish groups. On the other hand, the highest value for the Lapps, 790 nc Cs^{137}, was even higher than in Sweden. These differences could be explained on the basis of diets. In Finland most of the meat from the winter slaughters had been consumed at the beginning of the summer. In the more civilized Swedish Lapp center, the Lapps had stored meat in freezers to be used in summer time.

It may be assumed that at Inari much higher average values could have been obtained in April or May, 1961.

In April, 1962, another 160 persons were measured in Jokkmokk, Sweden (Table III). The maximum body burden was

TABLE III

RESULTS OBTAINED BY WHOLE BODY COUNTING AT JOKKMOKK, (66.6°N, 19.9°E), SWEDEN, APRIL, 1962

| | | | Cs^{137} Content | |
Group	Age	Number	Average (max.-min.)* nc	nc/kg.
Lapps				
Reindeer breeders, M	40(20-65)	35	435(740-222)	7.08
F	43(17-56)	16	232(355-144)	4.15
Nonreindeer breeders, M	38(26-55)	6	227(478- 74)	3.64
F	27(23-41)	12	136(231- 47)	2.84
Lapp children, M	18(16-19)	4	193(325-110)	3.68
M	11(9-13)	10	78(134- 31)	2.46
F	15(14-17)	14	112(187- 34)	2.48
F	12(9-13)	11	109(172- 51)	3.02
Non-Lapps				
M	41(25-53)	16	148(363- 18)	2.17
F	38(21-56)	15	107(277- 22)	1.91
M	15(9-19)	7	78(140- 20)	1.43
F	15(11-19)	11	61(91- 42)	1.43

*Minimum detectable amount = 10 nc. Cs^{137}.

about the same (740 nc Cs^{137}) as found earlier. When comparing the results from measurements in September, 1961, to those in April, 1962, the corresponding groups in general had higher average values for the later measurement. This could be attributed to higher reindeer meat consumption in winter than in summer. For adult reindeer breeders, for instance, the average body burden increased by about 30 percent. For non-Lapps the increase was more than 100 percent. The sex difference was still about the same, — higher values for male groups than for female groups.

Control groups measured both in September, 1961, and April, 1962, showed a 10 to 15 percent increase for reindeer breeders and a 100 to 200 percent increase for non-Lapp groups (Table IV). Four women of the non-reindeer-breeding group showed constant radioactivity. This could be explained by the

TABLE IV

COMPARABLE RESULTS OBTAINED BY WHOLE BODY COUNTING AT TWO OCCASIONS AT JOKKMOKK, (66.6°N, 19.9°E) SWEDEN

| | | | | | Cs^{137} Content | | |
| | | | | Sept., 1961 | | April, 1962 | |
Group	Age	Num-ber	nc	nc/kg.	nc (Increase)	nc/kg. (Increase)
Lapps						
Reindeer breeders, M	19-65	11	418	6.35	468 (12%)	7.45 (17%)
F	16-53	6	213	3.77	233 (9%)	4.24 (12%)
Nonreindeer breeders, M	38-55	3	189	2.80	255 (35%)	3.79 (35%)
F	23-41	4	136	2.68	136 (±0)	2.63 (−2%)
Lapp children, M	10-13	8	99	3.19	88 (−11%)	2.67 (−16%)
F	11-13	10	95	2.75	110 (16%)	2.97 (8%)
F	13-17	13	95	2.12	109 (15%)	2.42 (14%)
Non-Lapps						
M	31-52	4	93	1.39	182 (96%)	2.78 (100%)
F	38-48	4	72	1.19	135 (88%)	2.52 (112%)
M	13-19	3	40	0.72	90 (125%)	1.66 (131%)
F	11-16	5	20	0.49	63 (215%)	1.55 (218%)

fact that they worked in the schools at Jokkmokk nine months of the year. During three summer months in 1961 they had a nomadic work among their relatives in the mountains. Lapp boys, aged ten to thirteen, also seemed to eat more reindeer meat during the summer vacation than at the boarding school.

Parallel to this whole body counting, investigations were carried out to determine individual food consumption and its seasonal variation. Data were collected on questionnaires prepared specifically for these surveys. In Finland the investigation was more detailed (Table V) to provide information concerning

TABLE V

THE Cs^{137} INTAKE IN FINNISH LAPPS FROM VARIOUS FOOD ITEMS

| Source of Cs^{137} | Contribution of Source to Body Content of Cs^{137} | |
	Men	Women
Reindeer meat	87%	75%
Fish	8%	16%
Cow's milk	4%	7%
All other food together	1-2%	1-2%

all the main sources of Cs^{137} in humans (4). More detailed analyzed data are reported in another paper given at this meeting

(10). The result of the diet investigation could be assumed to be roughly valid also for the Swedish Lapps. The diet investigation made by us at Jokkmokk only gave quantitative information concerning the consumption of fish and reindeer products.

Figure 5 shows a good correlation between the body con-

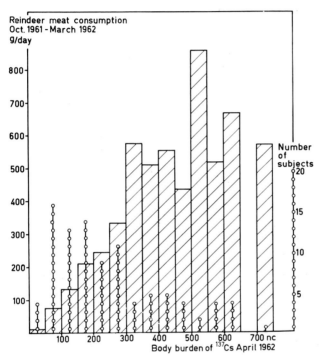

Figure 5. Body burden of Cs^{137} versus the reindeer meat consumption averaged per day from October 1961 to April 1962.

tent of Cs^{137} and the reindeer meat consumption averaged per day for the six months from October to April as obtained from the investigation at Jokkmokk, Sweden, in April, 1962.

At our laboratory special investigations have been carried out to get retention and excretion rates of Cs^{137} for humans for both intravenous and oral Cs^{137}. The excretion rate was generally about 1 per cent per day. We obtained results indicating half times of about seventy days, instead of 110 to 150 days as given by other authors (11, 12).

What is the Cs^{137} radiation dose to a human with such a high body burden? The dose has been calculated by using geometrical factors for gamma ray radiation ad modum Loevinger and collaborators (7). The doses have been calculated for persons of different sizes on the assumption of uniform distribution. Many Lapp children have about 100 nc Cs^{137} in the body. Assuming a weight of 35 kg., the dose to the subject will be 19 mrad per year. Adult reindeer breeders often have 500 nc in the body. Their dose from Cs^{137} thus will be 57 mrad per year for a body weight of 70 kg. In both cases we have assumed a constant body burden throughout the year. These figures should be compared with a natural background dose rate of about 100 mrad per year.

REFERENCES

1. Löw, K., and Edvarson, K.: Content of Cs^{137} and (Zirkonium + Niobium) —95 in Swedish soils. *Nature, 187*:736, 1960.
2. Hvinden, T., and Lillegraven, A.: Cs^{137} and Sr^{90} in precipitation, soil and animals in Norway. *Nature, 192*:1144, 1961.
3. Lidén, K., and Svensson, G.: Unpublished data.
4. Miettinen, J. K., Jokelainen, Aili, Roine, P., Lidén, K., Naversten, K. Y., Bengtsson, G., Häsänen, E., and McCall, R. C.: Cs^{137} and potassium in people and diet - a study of Finnish Lapps. *Ann. Acad. Scient. Finn. Ser. AII. Chemica, 120*:1, 1963.
5. Lidén, K.: Cs^{137} burdens in Swedish Laplanders and reindeer. *Acta Radiol., 56*:237, 1961.
6. Naversten, Y., McCall, R. C., and Lidén, K.: A semiportable whole body counter for Cs^{137} and other gamma-emitting isotopes. *Acta Radiol. Ther. Phys. Biol., 1*:190, 1963.
7. Loevinger, R., Holt, J. G., and Hine, G. J.: *Radiation Dosimetry*. G. J. Hine and G. L. Brownell, New York, Academic Press, Inc., p. 850, 1958.
8. Report of Committee II on Permissible Dose For Internal Radiation, I C R P. New York, Pergamon Press, 1959.
9. Lidén, K. and Andersson, I. Ö.: Cs^{134} in man. *Nature, 195*:1040, 1962.
10. Miettinen, J. K., Roine, P., and Lidén, K.: Relationships of radiocesium and potassium in the diet and the body of Finnish Lapps. In this volume.
11. Rundo, J., and Newton, B.: Some recent measurements of Cs^{137} and Zr^{95} in human beings. *Nature, 195*:851, 1962.
12. Richmond, C. R., Furchner, J. E., and Langham, W. H.: Long term retention of radiocesium by man. *Health Physics, 8*:201, 1962.

39
RADIOACTIVITY IN ALASKAN ESKIMOS

H. E. PALMER, W. C. HANSON, B. I. GRIFFIN
AND W. C. ROESCH

General Electric Company
Richland, Washington

MEMBERS OF THE Hanford Laboratories have participated since 1959 in a bioenvironmental study program in the Cape Thompson area of northern Alaska. The program has been part of the United States Atomic Energy Commission's Plowshare Program to develop peaceful uses for nuclear explosions. The part known as Project Chariot is a proposal to attempt excavation of a harbor by exploding nuclear devices. A comprehensive program of bioenvironmental studies was established by the commission to define the ecological structure and dynamics of the test site region near Cape Thompson to predict the biological effects of the explosions and to assist in designing the tests so that these effects would be minimal. One of the early results of these studies was the discovery of high levels of Cs^{137} in lichens and caribou (3). This stimulated interest in the body burdens of fallout isotopes in Eskimos in that area. Attempts to obtain autopsy samples of these Eskimos were of very limited success. In the fall of 1960, high body burdens of Cs^{137} were discovered in Norwegians (1) and subsequently in Swedish and Finnish Lapps (2). The latter high burdens were felt to be connected with the food chain: lichen-reindeer-man. During this period, a shadow shield whole body counter was developed at this laboratory for other purposes, which was light enough to be easily transported. During the summer of 1962, the counter was taken to various locations in northern Alaska, and the body burdens of about 700 Eskimos were measured. This paper is a description of the counter and its use and a preliminary report on the levels of Cs^{137} found.

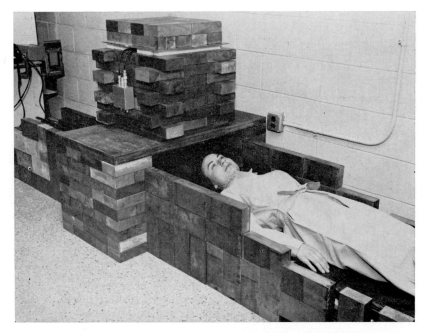

Figure 1. Shadow shield counter set up at Hanford Laboratories.

The shadow shield whole body counter (Fig. 1) has been described elsewhere (4-7). The top part of the counter contains a 9⅜ by 4 in. NaI(Tl) scintillation crystal which is shielded by 4 in. of lead on all sides except that which looks down on the subject as he passes under the detector. Beneath the subject is a blanket of lead bricks that "casts a shadow" so that no photon can enter the detector from outside the counter unless it has been scattered and thus considerably reduced in energy. Except for one iron plate, the shielding is lead bricks. This makes the counter easy to assemble, take down and transport. The system weighs five tons.

Where possible, the counter was placed on a concrete floor. At one location a floor to support the counter was not available, and it was put together outside on the ground. A hole was dug through the wet spongy tundra until gravel or permafrost was reached at 8 to 12 in. Sections of 8 by 12 in. timbers were placed in the hole, and the counter built on them. Since most of the weight of the counter is in the center section, a hole only 4 by 4

ft. was required. A floor was made from sheets of plywood placed
on the ground around the counter, and a wood framework covered with plastic was erected to protect the counter from rain and
dust. The counter could be assembled in about 6 hr. when placed
on a concrete floor and in 8 to 10 hr. outside.

The subject lies on a bed which moves under the detector at
a constant speed by a ball bearing screw driven by a motor. The
speed of the bed is changed by changing the gear ratio between
the motor and the screw. A supply of change gears was available
to permit 5, 10, 20 or 30 min. counting periods. At the start of an
examination, the top of the subject's head is 4 in. from a point
below one edge of the scintillation counter. The bed travels a distance of 84 in. At the end of the examination, the feet of a 68 in.
high subject will be about 3 in. beyond the other edge of the
counter. The feet of subjects of different heights will end up at
different positions. This is not too important because most of
the gamma ray emitting isotopes have low concentrations in the
feet.

The counter was calibrated for K^{40} and Cs^{137}. Table I shows
the calibration values for K^{40} for four subjects of different body

TABLE I

COMPARISON OF COUNTING EFFICIENCY WITH BODY SIZE FOR POTASSIUM

Subject	Weight lb.	Height	Count/Min. Per Gm. K in Body
1	185	5 ft. 7 in.	0.500
2	160	5 ft. 11 in.	0.497
3	195	6 ft. 0 in.	0.507
4	200	6 ft. 6 in.	0.505
		Average =	0.502
		Deviation from average =	±1%

size. Within the range of body size covered by the table, the
variations in sensitivity with body size are unimportant. Many of
the Eskimos measured were smaller than the subjects represented
in Table I. Many young people were measured; they were much
smaller than the calibrated subjects. It remains to investigate the
calibration of the counter for these smaller subjects. Table II
shows calibration values for Cs^{137} for two different subjects. The
agreement between them is good.

The counting efficiency is 29 percent lower than that of the

TABLE II

COUNTING EFFICIENCY FOR Cs^{137}

Subject	Weight lb.	Height	Count/Min. Per nc Cs^{137}
1	160	5 ft. 11 in.	5.73
2	195	6 ft. 0 in.	5.56
		Average =	5.65
		Deviation from average =	±1.5%

chair geometry in the Hanford iron room whole body counter. This was not a serious disadvantage in counting the Eskimos, since their body burdens of Cs^{137} were high enough that only 5 to 10 min. counting periods were required to get reliable statistics.

The background of the counter using a sugar phantom was the same as that obtained in the iron room for all energies above 0.5 Mev. Below this energy the scattering by the body of gamma rays coming from outside the counter so that they enter the detector increases the background up to 20 percent over that in the iron room.

A transistorized 512 channel pulse height analyzer* was used to analyze the pulses from the counter. A background obtained with a sugar sack phantom was stored in the analyzer and automatically subtracted from the spectrum of each subject. The data were recorded by an electric typewriter and by a punched paper tape system. The spectra on the paper tape can be inserted into the memory of the analyzer again at any later date to permit further study.

Figure 2 shows the four Eskimo villages where the counter was located and the approximate Eskimo population of each village. The counter was located at Kotzebue, Barrow, Anaktuvuk Pass, Kotzebue and Point Hope, in that order. The second stop at Kotzebue was made to count people from Little Diomede Island. They come to Kotzebue to trade every summer after the sea ice has broken up and disappeared. A few people from each of 11 villages near Kotzebue were counted when they came to Kotzebue for medical care at a Public Health Service hospital there.

The counter and equipment were shipped to Fairbanks by a

* Nuclear Data Inc., ND-130A.

Figure 2. Map of Alaska.

barge and truck route. From Fairbanks everything was carried by air freight. The shielding for two shadow shield counters was taken to Alaska. One was used at Barrow and Anaktuvuk Pass and the other at Kotzebue and Point Hope.

The Eskimos were very cooperative during these measurements. A Point Hope Eskimo was hired to help us contact the natives and to interpret for us in the few cases where the Eskimo did not speak English. At Kotzebue, subjects were obtained through personal request and through a sign placed in the village post office. At Barrow and Point Hope, each person over age twelve was sent a written invitation describing what we were doing and suggesting a time they could be counted. At Barrow, about 50 percent of those invited came in to be counted. At Point Hope, almost all those invited were counted. In the smaller village of Anaktuvuk Pass, the request was passed by word of mouth and almost everyone responded.

Table III gives the average, minimum and maximum body burdens of Cs^{137} of permanent Eskimo residents of the villages

TABLE III
Cs^{137} Body Burdens in Alaskan Eskimo Villages

Village	Number of Subjects	nc Cs^{137} Minimum	Maximum	Average
Diomede	12	8	35	22
Barrow	259	8	166	52
Point Hope	107	3	119	17
Kotzebue	132	17	518	138
Anaktuvuk	52	83	790	421

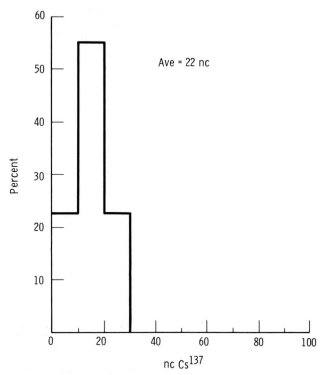

Figure 3. Permanent residents of Little Diamede Island (1962).

studied. Figures 3-7 give histograms of the amounts found. The data must be considered preliminary, subject to further sifting and adjustments of calibration factors. For comparison the average body burden of Cs^{137} of subjects counted at the Hanford whole body counter at Richland, Washington during this period

PERMANENT RESIDENTS OF BARROW, ALASKA (1962)

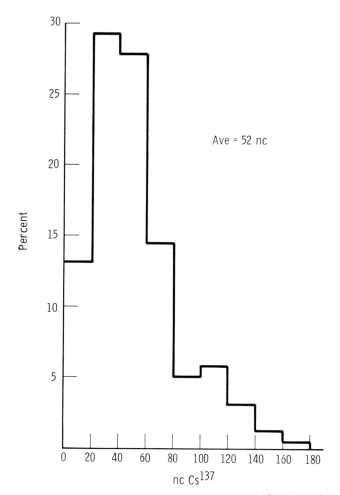

Figure 4. Permanent residents of Barrow, Alaska (1962).

was about 5 to 7 nc. The first measurements on Lapps gave as high as 361 nc. Numerous measurements made in the fall of 1961 gave 320 and 190 nc average body burdens for male and female Swedish Lapps and 243 and 123 nc for Finish Lapps, respectively (9).

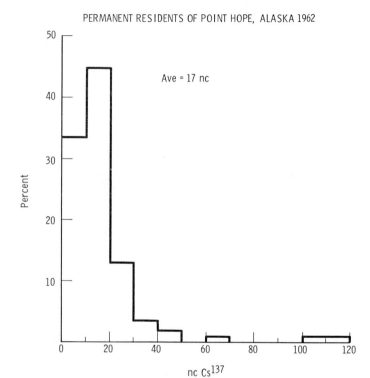

Figure 5. Permanent residents of Point Hope, Alaska (1962).

Figure 8 shows a gamma ray sum spectrum of ten Eskimos who had an average Cs^{137} body burden of 667 nc. A small peak at about 0.8 Mev from Cs^{134} is possible. Cs^{134} was found in certain groups of Swedish and Finnish Lapps in 1961 (8). The origin of the Cs^{134} in man has not been definitely established.

It is expected that the high body burdens and the differences between the body burdens of the Eskimos from different villages can be explained by differences in dietary habits. All subjects were questioned at length about their diet. Environmental and food samples were collected and were counted on special holders in the shadow shield whole body counter and are now being examined in the laboratory. It is planned to prepare a comprehensive ecological study of these Alaskan communities based on these data, the whole body counting results and data obtained in pre-

PERMANENT RESIDENTS OF KOTZEBUE, ALASKA (1962)

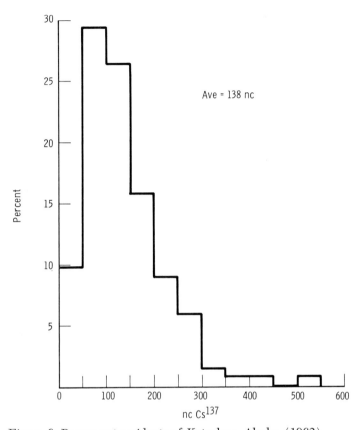

Figure 6. Permanent residents of Kotzebue, Alaska (1962).

vious years. At present, however, it appears that the high body burdens can largely be correlated with high levels of Cs^{137} in reindeer and caribou and that the latter are produced by high levels accumulated in lichens.

While at Kotzebue, natives from villages nearby were counted when they came into Kotzebue for hospital treatment (Table IV). Because of the few subjects from each village, the differences in average burden are not too significant. However, they suggest that dietary differences may exist even between neighboring villages.

PERMANENT RESIDENTS OF ANAKTUVUK, ALASKA 1962

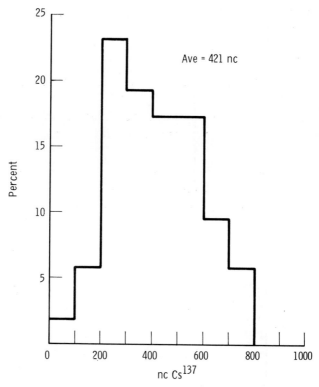

Figure 7. Permanent residents of Anaktuvuk Pass, Alaska (1962) .

TABLE IV

Cs[137] IN ESKIMOS FROM NEAR KOTZEBUE

Village	Number of Subjects	Average nc Cs[137]
Ambler	1	233
Deering	3	133
Elim	1	50
Kiana	2	212
Kivalina	3	91
Kobuck	2	273
Noorvick	3	174
Point Hope	3	45
Selawick	1	131
Shungnak	1	221
Noatak	3	

At both Barrow and Kotzebue there were significant numbers of white people who did not eat any native foods; fourteen
such people were counted at Barrow, and fifty-four at Kotzebue.
The body burdens were typical of those of people in the rest of
the United States: averages of 6 and 7 nc, respectively, at Barrow
and Kotzebue.

The school system maintained for the Alaskan Eskimos requires that children of high school age be away from home at
boarding schools from September through May of each year. Our
measurements were made when the students were at home and

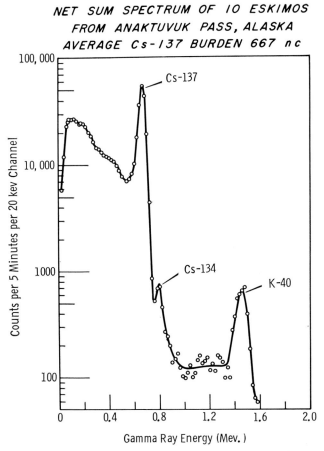

Figure 8. Net sum spectrum of ten Eskimos from Amaktuvuk Pass, Alaska.

included many of them. The average Cs^{137} body burdens of the students were lower on the average than those of the permanent residents of the same villages (Table V). This is to be expected. While at school, the students are on diets consisting almost exclusively of food shipped in from outside Alaska with a relatively low Cs^{137} content. During the school year, their body burdens would decrease (the effective half life of cesium in the body is about 100 days) and would increase again during the summer months, but on the average would be lower than if constantly on the same diet as the permanent residents.

No isotopes other than Cs^{137} and K^{40} were detected in the Eskimos except for two subjects who had a few nanocuries of Zn^{65}. These people occasionally ate canned oysters which probably led to Zn^{65} burdens. External body contamination, mainly $Zr\text{-}Nb^{95}$, was frequently noticed. There were no facilities for having the Eskimos shower, but they did change from their own clothes into a pair of paper shirts and pants. The interference from this external $Zr\text{-}Nb^{95}$ was minor and easily corrected.

TABLE V

Cs^{137} BODY BURDENS OF ESKIMO STUDENTS

Village	Number of Students	Permanent Residents	Students
Diomede	0	22	—
Barrow	44	52	11
Point Hope	9	17	14
Kotzebue	13	138	29
Anaktuvuk	4	421	227

REFERENCES

1. Baarli, J., Lidén, K., Madshus, K., and McCall, R. C.: *Nature, 19:*436-438, 1961.
2. Lidén, K.: *Acta Radiol., 56:*237, 1961.
3. Davis, J. J.: Presented at the Second Northern Meeting on Radioactive Food Chains, Helsinki, April 1-3, 1962.
4. Roesch, W. C., and Palmer, H. E.: Presented at Radiation Research Society Meeting, Washington D. C., May 15-27, 1961.
5. Palmer, H. E., and Roesch, W. C.: Presented at Health Physics Society Meeting, Las Vegas, June 13-16, 1961.

6. Roesch, W. C., and Palmer, H. E.: Research and Development Activities in the Radiological Sciences. HW-70050, Unclassified, 1961.
7. Palmer, H. E.: Research and Development Activities in the Radiological Sciences. HW-73337, Unclassified, 1962.
8. Lidén, K., and Anderson, Ingvar O.: Personal Communication, August, 1962.
9. Lidén, K., and Naversten, Y.: Personal Communication, August, 1962.

40

STATISTICAL STUDY OF THE
DISTRIBUTION OF Cs^{137} FALLOUT
BETWEEN INDIVIDUAL MEMBERS OF
A LARGE POPULATION

W. H. ELLETT AND G. L. BROWNELL

Massachusetts General Hospital
Boston, Massachusetts

IN 1957, W. F. NEUMANN (1) pointed out that an evaluation of somatic fallout hazards based on the average radioactive body burden was of little use unless the variations between individual members of the exposed population were known. He also noted along with E. Dahl (2) that Kulp's (3, 4) early data on Sr^{90} in children's bone samples could perhaps be better fitted by a log normal rather than a normal distribution curve. Subsequent data published by Kulp has tended to support this view, but such limiting factors as small sample size and lack of Sr^{90}-Ca equilibrium in the bone samples has made statistical interpretation of the data tenuous. Other investigators, notably W. H. Langham and E. C. Anderson of Los Alamos, have observed a normal distribution for total body Cs^{137}-K^{40} ratios and have based hazard predictions on a normally distributed Cs^{137} burden (5).

Since muscle tissue is the single organ of highest concentration and contains approximately half the body cesium (6), measurement of the Cs^{137} content in a large number of defatted human muscle samples seemed appropriate to determine the distribution of at least one fission fallout produce in a large population.

By confining our measurements to a single organ we avoided the variation of cesium concentration between different organs in a single individual (7). Cs^{137} has several qualities which facilitate such a study. Unlike Sr^{90}, Cs^{137} has a relatively fast turn-over in the body (about 100 days). This means the adult population is essentially in equilibrium with its radioactive environment. The convenience of counting a gamma-emitting isotope allowed us to assemble a large sample size with a minimum amount of sample preparation and risk of contamination.

Muscle samples for this study were dissected from the thigh or lower abdomen during post mortem operations at Massachusetts General Hospital. Sample collection started in November, 1958 and is still in progress. The sample size varied from 90 to 140 gm. of wet tissue. Samples from patients who had received radioisotopes for medical purposes or died from highly infectious diseases were not collected. The frozen tissue samples were dehydrated in a vacuum oven and packed in plastic test tubes for counting in a 5 in. by 5½ in. NaI well crystal. This counting apparatus uses an 18 in. by 18 in. plastic scintillator for

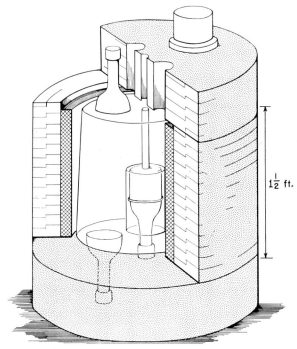

$1\frac{1}{2}$ ft.

COAXIAL ANTICOINCIDENCE WELL COUNTER
Figure 1

background and Compton suppression and is shielded by 4 in. of mercury and lead (Fig. 1) (8).

Gamma spectra were measured for 50 min. with a 256 channel pulse height analyzer. For an average sample, the counting statistics for the cesium peak were ± 15 percent. After counting, the dry samples were defatted by washing them in a mixture of methyl alcohol and chloroform and then dried to constant weight at 100°C. Final counting data is expressed in picocuries per gram of defatted dry tissue. Data from 670 individuals collected from February, 1959 to February, 1962 was coded and assembled on magnetic tape for analysis with a 7090 digital computer. Appropriate control cards allow the samples to be analyzed by sex, age at death and geographic location of the patient's home. The preliminary analysis presented is for all 670 samples and includes all ages and sexes and will be subject to change as the effects of other parameters are investigated.

The body burden of Cs^{137} as reflected in samples collected throughout 1959 was relatively constant. Starting in 1960 there was a decrease in sample activity as the amount of direct fallout material in foodstuffs declined. This decline continued until late fall 1961 when the activity of the samples showed a slight increase. Figure 2 is a scatter diagram of our counting data on 671 samples. Despite the large variation among individual samples, the downward trend is evident as is the asymmetrical nature of the distribution.

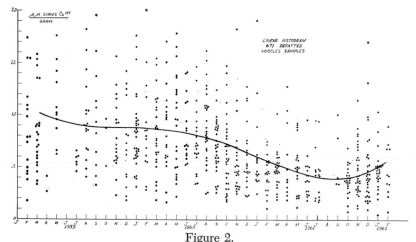

Figure 2.

The solid curve shown in Figure 2 is a 4th degree polynomial fitted to the data points by a least-square program. If the mean activity of the sample population had not changed with time, a polynomial of degree zero would give an adequate fit, and a histogram of the data could be prepared by counting all samples within a given fraction of the mean value. Because of the time-dependent nature of the data, it was analyzed in terms of subsets consisting of 50 serial data points. Each of these subsets span a relatively narrow time interval (2 to 3 months). The relative variance of each set was calculated in terms of the average value of the polynomial for the time interval during which the fifty samples were collected. A histogram (frequency distribution) of the 671 samples was prepared by summing the subsets in terms of their standard deviation intervals, s* and is shown in Figure 3. The asymmetry of this distribution is obvious; in particular, the many samples above the 3s level and the lack of samples below the -2s level would indicate that this set of data is not part of a normally distributed parent population.

To test this hypothesis, a chi-squared test was performed on the data. The usual criterion for rejecting the normal hypothesis is that a probability less than .01 exists that the sample was drawn from a normally distributed parent population (9). For

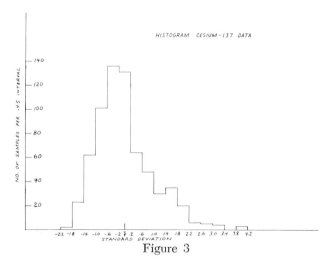

Figure 3

*s, the standard deviation of an experimental population, is analogous to σ for a theoretical gaussian distribution.

13 degrees of freedom this would correspond to a chi-squared value of less than 28. Chi-squared for this distribution is approximately 200, indicating essentially a zero probability that the parent population was normally distributed. A plot of this data on integral probability paper is shown in Figure 5. If the data were normally distributed, the indicated points would fall on a straight line.

Figure 4 shows a scatter diagram of the Cs^{137} sample data on a logarithmic activity scale and the fourth degree polynomial giving the best fit to the transformed data. In contrast to Figure

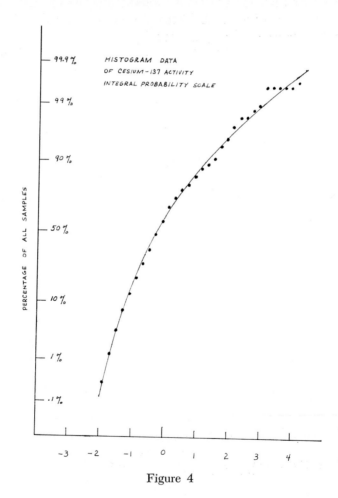

Figure 4

2, the data points are now symmetrically distributed around the polynomial values. A histogram of this logarithmically transformed data was prepared as before (Fig. 5). A comparison with Figure 3 shows that this frequency distribution is much more symmetrical. It is also within acceptable statistical limits on both

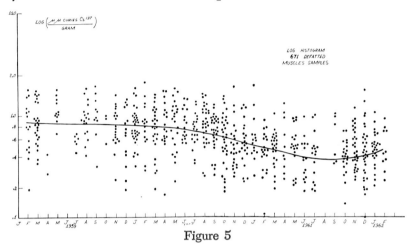

Figure 5

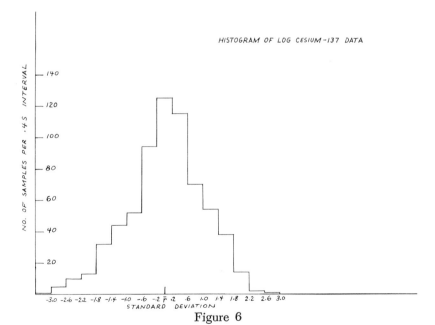

Figure 6

the high and low scales. A plot of this data on integral probability paper is shown in Figure 6. Also plotted in this figure is the straight line graph for a perfect infinite normal distribution. The logarithmically transformed Cs^{137} data gives a reasonable fit to this line between the 5 percent and 95 percent limit. However, a chi-squared test on the transformed data gave a probability of less than .01 that the parent population was normal; i.e., χ^2 equaled 22 vs 20 for $Px > .01$ and eight degrees of freedom.

Yamagata (7) has recently shown that the distribution of

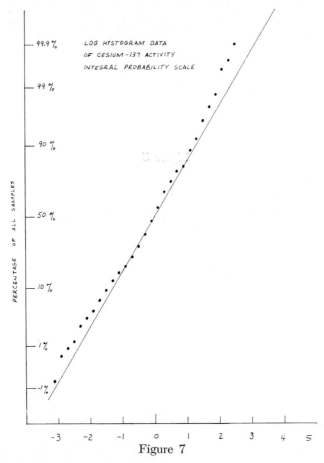

Figure 7

natural cesium also resembles a log normal distribution. However, we have been unable to prove this point conclusively even with a much larger sample size. Even without considering the time variations in the frequency distribution, Figure 5 is a summation of several distributions, men, women, race, ethnic groups, etc. The variations between these groups may be great enough to perturb the results. Another consideration is the normally distributed counting error in the sample data. The logarithmic transformation of this normally distributed error would tend to reduce the number of samples in the lower and upper tails. There are some indications in Figure 6 that this is the case. If both the counting errors and sample variations were gaussian, it would be relatively easy to prepare a net histogram with the counting error removed. Since the parent population is not normally distributed, preparing the histograms of this type will be extremely difficult and perhaps impossible. The Cs^{137} sample data can also be analyzed in terms of nonparametric statistics. This method of analysis allows predictions to be made on the number of individuals which will exceed the maximum activity concentration found in the original sample as the sample size is increased. It is an accurate prediction method and assumes nothing about the parent population except that it is continuous between any two values, say zero and some noninfinite upper limit. The most active sample in our data group exceeded the mean activity by a factor of four. We have calculated the number of samples which would be in another set of 670 tissue samples (Table I).

The following model of radioactive intake and excretion patterns is an adaptation of one presented by Aitchison and Brown

TABLE I

NONPARAMETRIC ANALYSIS OF THE COUNTING DATA

No. of Samples 4 x the Mean Activity	Probability of Occurrence in another Set of 670 Tissue Samples
0	. 5
1 or more	.15
2 or more	.25
3 or more	.12

(10) to show the genesis of log normal growth distributions in biological systems. It indicates that a log normal distribution of Cs^{137} is consistent with some of the facts concerning isotope intake and excretion and might be expected on theoretical grounds.

Fundamental to the notion of a normal distribution is the fact that Y_i a single measurement of a value is composed of a true value Y_o and a series of additive elementary errors which are both plus and minus:

$$Y_i = Y_o + \epsilon_1 + \epsilon_2 \ldots \epsilon_m$$

Because of the binomial addition of these elementary errors, a sample of n independent observations of Y will be normally distributed about Y_o. This is essentially Hagen's derivation of the normal frequency distribution (9). The total absorption peak from a NaI spectrometer is an example. In this case fluctuation in luminous efficiency, lightpath, gain, etc. for the same elementary event are additive and give rise to the well-known gaussian peaks.

Consider an inhomogeneous population group, each with a body burden B_o. The many causes of the inhomogenuities in the group need not be specified or independent if they all operate simultaneously. After a reasonable time, assuming there are no gross changes in dietary habits or other factors which influence the inhomogenuity of the population, some members of the population group will have a larger body burden of Cs^{137} than others. It seems reasonable to assume that through dietary habits members of the population with larger body burdens will take in more Cs^{137} activity in a short time interval, Δt, than those individuals with smaller body burdens. That is, the assumption is made that positive elementary changes in the body burden of individual members of the population group are, to a first order, proportional to B_o, the individual's body burden at the beginning of the short time interval Δt. Negative changes in the body burden following the exponential excretion laws will also be, to a first order, proportional to B_o.

The Aitchison Brown model assumes that changes take place in steps, each step is very small and randomly distributed between $\pm$ values; if this is so, the change in the body burden after the jth step is:

$$B_J - B_{J-1} = (\epsilon_j) B_{J-1}$$

$$\frac{B_j - B_{j-1}}{B_{j-1}} = (\varepsilon_j)$$

where (ε_j) is a set independent from the set (B_j).

After n steps

$$\sum_{J-1}^{n} \frac{B_j - B_{j-1}}{B_{j-1}} = \sum_{1}^{n} \epsilon_j$$

now if the effect of each step is small

$$\int_{o}^{Bn} \frac{dB}{B} = \sum_{1}^{n} \epsilon_j \text{ and } l_n B_n = B_o + \epsilon_1 + \epsilon_2 + \epsilon_3 \ldots \epsilon_n$$

that is the log of B_n is normally distributed and B_n is an asymmetrical log normal distribution into two parameter form.

REFERENCES

1. Neumann, W. F.: *Bull. Atomic Scientist, XIV, 1*:31, 1958.
2. Dahl, E.: *Teknisk Ukeblad*, July, 1957.
3. Turekian, K. K., and Kulp, J. L.: *Science, 124*:405, 1956.
4. Research Branch, Division of Radiological Health, USPHS: *Radiol. Health Data*, Vol. II, No. 5, 1961.
5. Langham, W. H., and Anderson, E. C.: *Health Physics, 1*:30, 1959.
6. I.C.R.P. Committee II on Permissible Dose for Internal Radiation: *Health Physics, 3*:1960.
7. Yamagata: *J. Radiat. Res.* (Japan), *1*:9, 1962.
8. Ellett, W. H., and Brownell, G. L.: *Nucl. Instr. Methods, 7*:56, 1960.
9. Worthing, A. G., and Geffner, J.: *Treatment of Experimental Data.* New York, John Wiley & Sons, 1943.
10. Aitchinson, J., and Brown, J. A. C.: The Lognormal Distribution, Monograph No. 5. Cambridge University Press, 1957. American Branch, New York, N. Y.

41
CESIUM-137 BURDENS IN A DEFINED POPULATION SAMPLE[1]

George R. Meneely,[2] Robert M. Heyssel, Raymond L. Weiland,
Howard L. Rolf, Con O. T. Ball, John L. Ferguson, A. Ross
Lorimer, C. Constantinides and E. U. Meneely

Vanderbilt University School of Medicine
Nashville, Tennessee

THERE IS WORLDWIDE concern regarding the effects of chronic low dose irradiation on humans. The emphasis has been primarily on internally deposited radionuclides from fallout of nuclear weapons tests. The dose-response relationship of radiation is difficult to evaluate since the incidence of long term somatic effects is low. In estimating risk from internal emmitters it has been the custom to average dose over a large (nationwide or worldwide) population. Our observations show that individual burden and hence individual dose varies over a wide range even among people living in the same environment. Some of this variation can be associated closely with age, sex, race and socioeconomic factors. Even within defined categories the individual variation is still large, often by a factor of four or six or even more.

METHODS

Radioactivity Survey: Population Measured, Environment, Community Participation

To assess the variations in Cs^{137} burdens in the population of

[1] Supported by Army Medical Research Development Command, U. S. Atomic Energy Commission, U. S. Public Health Service and National Science Foundation.

[2] Present address: University of Texas M. D. Anderson Hospital and Tumor Institute.

550

Nashville, Tennessee, attributable to age, sex, race, individual and environmental differences, a subsample was randomly selected from a geographic and socioeconomic stratified sample of occupied dwellings in 1959 (1). About one third of the residents are Negro and few are foreign born. Nashville is located halfway between the Great Lakes and the Gulf of Mexico, and the Atlantic coast and the Great Plains of the West, in the north central part of Tennessee on the Cumberland River. The city is topographically situated in a basin with hills to the south, west and north which rise to a height of 300 to 400 ft. above the basin. The climate is moderate, with a normal monthly average of 80° F in July, the warmest month, and 50° F in January, the coldest month. Precipitation is ample and fairly evenly distributed throughout the year. The average annual snowfall and sleetfall of about 8 in. seldom interfere with outdoor occupations more than a few days in a season. Industry is diversified as to products and size of industrial plants. Manufacturing of chemicals and allied products, shoes, clothing, river transport equipment, appliances and furniture are the principal industries.

Before initiating the Radioactivity Survey in June 1960, the staff held a planning conference attended by the mayor of Nashville, the county public health officer, the superintendent of schools, the president of the Academy of Medicine, the deans of the medical schools, the executive secretary of the Chamber of Commerce and representatives of the local newspapers, television and radio stations. The survey was widely and favorably publicized initially, and feature stories appeared at intervals. Interviewers accompanied by medical students carried identification cards from the County Health Department. One respondent, usually the mother, in each selected household was interviewed as to length of residence in the area, occupation, age, sex, race, education, illnesses, operations and daily milk consumption of household members. Appointments for measurements at the Vanderbilt low level counting facility were made for each household member over seven years old able to sit in the whole body counter for 30 min.

Whole Body Counter Calibration for Body Potassium and Cs[137] Burdens

The Vanderbilt University whole body counter consists of a 4 in. by 8 in. NaI thallium-activated crystal positioned over an Argonne type chair (2) in a room shielded with 8 in. of steel and lined with ¼ in. of lead and ⅟₁₆ in. of stainless steel. Signals from the crystal are delivered to a multichannel pulse height analyzer with a magnetic core memory. Gamma ray spectra over 0 to 3 Mev energy range were printed on tape and IBM cards automatically punched at the end of each run. A standard Na[22] spectrum was recorded before each background and subject spectrum for exact energy per channel and zero position calibration. Electronic data processing machine methods were used for all calculations (3 - 6). Total body potassium estimations were made from integrated K[40] ptotopeaks after calibration using K[42] (5 - 7). Body configuration influenced calibration principally as related to stature and habitus of the subject as an extended radiation source (of which $\sqrt{WH}$ is a measure) and by self absorption in relation to subject thickness (of which $\sqrt{W/H}$ is a measure). When these together with the inherent physical properties of the system were taken into account, a calibration factor for each subject could be calculated by fitting the hypothetical calibration equation to K[40] and K[42] observations coupled with the calibration principle of Miller and Marinelli (2):

$$\text{Factor} = \frac{27.43}{\sqrt{WH}} \exp 1.091 \sqrt{W/H} \qquad \begin{array}{l} W = \text{Weight} \\ H = \text{Height} \end{array}$$

This factor multiplied by the integrated photopeak area in counts per minute gives total body potassium in grams and substantially reduces variation in results due to differences in stature and habitus among subjects. The validity of this factor has been established by a variety of observational methods with point sources, phantoms and human subjects (3 - 5).

The factor used in determining total body potassium is:

$$F_{K\text{-}40} = \frac{27.43}{\sqrt{WH}} \exp{-1.091} \sqrt{W/H}$$

where the counting rate used is the integrated net counting rate over the ten channels located symmetrically about the K^{40} photopeak. This may be expressed in grams per cpm at the peak channel by multiplying the right side of the equation by the ratio of 10 channel photopeak area to peak channel photopeak area. The 10 channel photopeak area at K^{40} energy represents 95.84 percent of the total photopeak area. The peak channel represents only 16.34 percent of the total photopeak area. Therefore, this ratio is

$$\frac{95.84}{16.34} = 5.87$$

The factor then becomes

$$F_{K-40} = (5.87) \frac{(27.43)}{\sqrt{WH}} \exp\text{-}1.091 \sqrt{W/H} = \frac{161.01}{\sqrt{WH}} \exp\text{-}1.091 \sqrt{W/H}$$

The efficiency for K^{40}, in peak channel cpm/gm. is the reciprocal of the factor, or

$$E_{K-40} = \frac{1}{F_{K-40}} = \frac{\sqrt{WH}}{161.01} \exp\text{-}1.091 \sqrt{W/H}$$

Since there are 3.451 K^{40} gammas per second emanating from 1 gm. of potassium, then the K^{40} efficiency expressed in photopeak channel cpm/gamma per second is

$$E_{K-40} = (\frac{\sqrt{WH}}{161.01}) (\frac{1}{3.451}) \exp\text{-}1.091 \sqrt{W/H} = \frac{\sqrt{WH}}{555.64} \exp\text{-}1.091 \sqrt{W/H}$$

The mass absorption coefficients for K^{40} and Cs^{137} in tissue are respectively 0.056 and 0.082 cm^2/gm.

The efficiency expression for the steel room is $E = KU^{-1.055}$ where E is in counts at the photopeak channel per grams of an energy U in Mev, K is a geometry constant.

From the above, an efficiency expression for Cs^{137} may be derived for humans from K^{40} as follows:

$$E_{\text{Cs-137}} = \left(\frac{\sqrt{WH}}{555.64}\right)\left(\frac{K\ 0.66^{-1.055}}{K\ 146^{-1.055}}\right)\exp-(1.091)\left(\frac{0.082}{0.056}\right)\sqrt{W/H}$$

$$= \left(\frac{\sqrt{WH}}{555.64}\right)\left(\frac{1.49}{0.645}\right)\exp-1.596\ \sqrt{W/H}$$

$$= \frac{\sqrt{WH}}{240.53}\ \exp-1.596\ \sqrt{W/H}$$

where the efficiency is expressed in Cs^{137} photopeak channel cpm/gamma per second.

One microcurie of Cs^{137} emits 3.05×10^4 gammas per second. The above efficiency expression may be changed to photopeak channel cpm/μc by the following:

$$E_{\text{Cs-137}} = \left(\frac{\sqrt{WH}}{240.53}\right)(3.05 \times 10^4)\exp-1.596\ \sqrt{W/H}$$

$$= \frac{\sqrt{WH}}{78.86 \times 10^{-4}}\ \exp-1.596\ \sqrt{W/H}$$

A factor by which the net cesium peak channel counting rate (in cpm) may be multiplied to obtain total microcuries of cesium is simply the reciprocal of the above efficiency expression:

$$F_{\text{Cs-137}} = \frac{1}{E_{\text{Cs-137}}} = \frac{78.86 \times 10^{-4}\ \exp-1.596\ \sqrt{W/H}}{\sqrt{WH}}$$

Since it is more normal to use an integrated counting rate of six channels located symmetrically about a Cs^{137} photopeak, the factor F must be changed to take this into account.

Six channels represent 95.28 percent of the total area under a cesium photopeak. The peak channel represents 26.6 percent of the total photopeak area.

The cesium factor, expressed in millimicrocuries per cpm, where the counting rate has been obtained by integrating six symmetrical channels is

$$F_{Cs\text{-}137} = \left(\frac{78.86 \times 10^{-4}}{\sqrt{WH}}\right) \left(\frac{26.6 \times 10^3}{98.28}\right) \exp{-1.596} \sqrt{W/H}$$

$$= \frac{2.202}{\sqrt{WH}} \exp{1.596} \sqrt{W/H}$$

RESULTS

There was good agreement in age and sex distributions of both races between a survey of occupied dwellings of 1959 from which the sample was drawn (1) and the 1960 census (Fig. 1). Over 90 percent of the eligible persons participated.

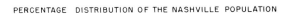

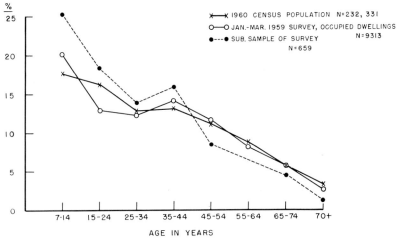

Figure 1

Observations of total body potassium as related to age and sex correlated well with those of Anderson and Langham (8), but there were significant differences between races. Negroes of both sexes in the survey had significantly higher body potassium than whites (Table I) (5, 7).

In contrast the median cesium burden was significantly higher in the white race (Fig. 2). Average cesium burdens per kilogram of body weight (Table II, Fig. 3) were significantly

TABLE I

Gm. K/Kg. Body Weight, $\bar{x} \pm SEM$

Age	White		Negro	
	Male	*Female*	*Male*	*Female*
8	2.22 ± 0.04	2.16 ± 0.02	2.33 ± 0.05	2.33 ± 0.08
9	2.16 ± 0.05	2.10 ± 0.02	2.23 ± 0.04	2.28 ± 0.08
10	2.07 ± 0.05	2.01 ± 0.01	2.16 ± 0.04	2.11 ± 0.10
11	2.04 ± 0.06	1.95 ± 0.05	2.17 ± 0.09	2.06 ± 0.09
12	2.09 ± 0.05	1.84 ± 0.04	2.21 ± 0.03	1.86 ± 0.03
13	2.13 ± 0.05	1.83 ± 0.04	2.24 ± 0.14	1.81 ± 0.09
14	2.12 ± 0.06	1.78 ± 0.05	2.27 ± 0.04	1.73 ± 0.08
15	2.15 ± 0.08	1.78 ± 0.05	2.15 ± 0.08	1.70 ± 0.07
16	2.21 ± 0.11	1.72 ± 0.06	2.19 ± 0.08	1.69 ± 0.07
17	2.21 ± 0.09	1.75 ± 0.03	2.22 ± 0.19	1.63 ± 0.07
18	2.29 ± 0.08	1.72 ± 0.03	2.43 ± 0.05	1.75 ± 0.09
19	2.22 ± 0.06	1.74 ± 0.02	2.46 ± 0.06	1.73 ± 0.08
20-29	2.11 ± 0.02	1.70 ± 0.03	2.40 ± 0.08	1.74 ± 0.04
30-39	2.10 ± 0.03	1.62 ± 0.03	2.19 ± 0.05	1.73 ± 0.04
40-49	1.92 ± 0.05	1.59 ± 0.03	2.15 ± 0.06	1.54 ± 0.05
50-59	1.98 ± 0.04	1.51 ± 0.03	2.02 ± 0.04	1.55 ± 0.07
60-69	1.76 ± 0.06	1.47 ± 0.05	1.80 ± 0.04	1.61 ± 0.09
70+	1.70 ± 0.07	1.44 ± 0.02	1.50 ± 0.08	1.55 ± 0.02

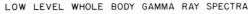

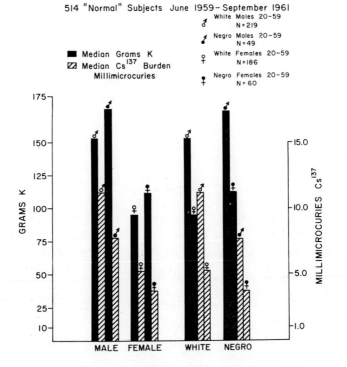

Figure 2

TABLE II

Mmc Cs/Kg. Body Weight, x̄ ± SEM

Age	White		Negro	
	Male	Female	Male	Female .
8	0.083 ± 0.013	0.067 ± 0.010	0.043 ± 0.008	0.035 ± 0.008
9	0.079 ± 0.008	0.069 ± 0.008	0.053 ± 0.008	0.047 ± 0.012
10	0.076 ± 0.007	0.068 ± 0.007	0.049 ± 0.007	0.063 ± 0.013
11	0.079 ± 0.008	0.067 ± 0.006	0.053 ± 0.006	0.064 ± 0.012
12	0.078 ± 0.007	0.061 ± 0.006	0.049 ± 0.006	0.045 ± 0.007
13	0.097 ± 0.009	0.074 ± 0.007	0.055 ± 0.006	0.047 ± 0.007
14	0.110 ± 0.013	0.077 ± 0.009	0.074 ± 0.007	0.041 ± 0.006
15	0.118 ± 0.012	0.080 ± 0.007	0.082 ± 0.008	0.048 ± 0.008
16	0.123 ± 0.016	0.070 ± 0.007	0.081 ± 0.007	0.041 ± 0.010
17	0.115 ± 0.016	0.080 ± 0.007	0.072 ± 0.011	0.060 ± 0.020
18	0.150 ± 0.020	0.102 ± 0.014	0.082 ± 0.016	0.055 ± 0.019
19	0.157 ± 0.022	0.095 ± 0.014	0.086 ± 0.018	0.071 ± 0.016
20-29	0.134 ± 0.007	0.080 ± 0.006	0.100 ± 0.010	0.062 ± 0.005
30-39	0.158 ± 0.017	0.077 ± 0.006	0.104 ± 0.008	0.065 ± 0.006
40-49	0.145 ± 0.011	0.094 ± 0.010	0.100 ± 0.009	0.053 ± 0.004
50-59	0.111 ± 0.009	0.077 ± 0.008	0.098 ± 0.009	0.060 ± 0.007
60-69	0.086 ± 0.016	0.056 ± 0.010	0.085 ± 0.010	0.070 ± 0.015
70+	0.075 ± 0.009	0.065 ± 0.090	0.070 ± 0.009	0.046 ± 0.008

MEAN NANOCURIES OF CESIUM-137 PER KILOGRAM OF BODY WEIGHT

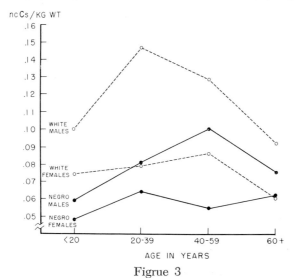

Figrue 3

MEAN NANOCURIES OF CESIUM-137 PER KILOGRAM BODY WEIGHT

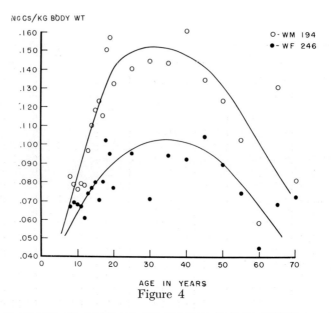

AGE IN YEARS

Figure 4

MEAN NANOCURIES OF CESIUM-137 PER KILOGRAM OF BODY WEIGHT

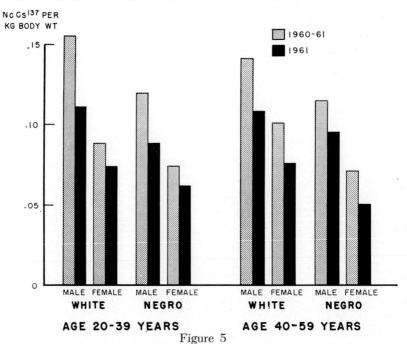

Figure 5

higher in the white race than in the Negro (9). White males had a significantly higher burden than white females (Fig. 4). Similar findings were reported by Onstead, Oberhausen and Keary in 1960 and 1962 (10, 11). The mean cesium burden was significantly higher in Negro males than in Negro females at ages forty to fifty-nine. The differences approached the 5 per-cent level in the eight to twenty age groups (Table II). Cesium burdens were significantly higher from July 1960 to January 1961 than from February to November 1961 (Fig. 5), comparable to the Onstead, Oberhausen and Keary findings. Distribution of persons measured in the two time periods were similar in age, sex, race and occupation.

Cesium burdens were higher in both races in both sexes among the families of professional, technical, managerial, crafts, clerical and sales personnel than among operatives, service work-ers, domestic servants and laborers. The proportion of the Negro households where the principal wage earner's occupation was service or labor, 54 percent, was significantly larger than the 11 percent heads of households similarly employed in the white race. There was no apparent association between the occupation of the principal wage earner of the household and the reported daily milk consumption. The proportion of the white population drinking milk, 72 percent, was significantly larger than the Negro, 44 percent. However, the reported consumption of milk was not associated with the magnitude of the cesium burden in either race.

CONCLUSIONS

Quantitative study of human radiation effects requires that one take cognizance in detail of the kind and amount of internal radioisotope burdens rather than of averages.

It is clear that the observed wide range of Cs^{137} burdens must be paralleled by similar wide individual variation in popu-lation burdens of other radioisotopes which are more difficult or impossible to measure. Any effort to relate genetic or late so-matic effects or ionizing radiation to the magnitude of isotope burdens must take into account wide individual variations.

These relate to race, sex, age and socioeconomic factors, as well as geographic and meteorologic influences. Those persons most likely to have their isotope burden assessed under the usual circumstances represent a particular segment of the population. The studies presented here indicate that averaging the burden for the population as a whole *even in a restricted geographic setting* may be misleading.

REFERENCES

1. Zeidberg, Louis D., Schueneman, J. J., Humphrey, P. A. and Prindle, R. A.: Air pollution and health. General description of a study in Nashville, Tennessee. *J. Air Pollution Control Ass.*, 11:289 (June) 1961.

2. Miller, C. E., and Marinelli, L. D.: Low intensity spectrometry of the gamma radiation emitted by human beings. *Prog. Nucl. Energ.*, *(Med.)*, Vol II, Bugher, J. C., Coursaget, J., and Loutit, J. F., (eds.). New York, Pergamon Press, 1959, pp. 87-104.

3. *Radioactivity in Man, Whole Body Counting and Effects of Internal Gamma Ray-Emitting Isotopes.* G. R. Meneely (ed.). Springfield, Thomas, 1961.

4. Meneely, G. R., Rolf, H. L., Weiland, R. L., Heyssel, R. M., and Lagemenn, R. T.: The use of computers in whole body counter data processing. *Whole Body Counting.* Proceedings of a Symposium, Vienna, June 13-16, 1961, International Atomic Energy Agency Press, Vienna, 1962, pp. 379-387.

5. Meneely, G. R., Ball, C. O. T., Ferguson, J. L., Payne, D. D., Lorimer, A. R., Weiland, R. L., Rolf, H. L., and Heyssel, R. M.: Use of computers in measuring body electrolytes by gamma spectrometry. Presented at the Symposium on Application of Computers in Cardiovascular Disease (Heart Association of Southeastern Pennsylvania), Philadelphia, February 28, 1962. *Circulat. Res.*, 11:539, 1962.

6. Meneely, G. R., Heyssel, R. M., Ferguson, J. L., Parrent, O. C., Jr., and Weiland, R. L.: Whole body potassium measurements in humans. *The Physiologist*, 3:112, 1960.

7. Meneely, G. R., Heyssel, R. M., Ferguson, J. L., Weiland, R. L., Ball, C. O. T., Lorimer, A. R., and Meneely, E. U.: Low level gamma ray NaI scintillation spectrometer studies of total body potassium

in 1000 normal humans and effects of potassium feeding in volunteers. Abstract no. 647 in Proceedings of the International Union of Physiological Sciences, Vol II: 22nd International Congress, Leiden, 1962 — Abstracts. International Congress Series No. 48. Excerpta Medica Foundation, Amsterdam, Holland, 1962.

8. Anderson, E. C., and Langham, W. H.: Average potassium concentration of the human body as a function of age. *Science, 130*:713 (Sept. 18), 1959.

9. Meneely, G. R., Weiland, R. L., Rolf, H. L., Ball, C. O. T., Ferguson, J. L., Lorimer, A. R., Constantinides, C., and Meneely, E. U.: Variations in cesium-137 burdens in a defined population sample attributable to age, sex, race, individual and environmental differences. Abstract submitted to the Second International Congress of Radiation Research, Harrogate, England, August 5-11, 1962.

10. Onstead, C. O., Oberhausen, E., and Keary, F. V.: *Atompraxis, 6*:337, 1960.

11. Onstead, C. O., Oberhausen, E., and Keary, F. V.: Cesium-137 in man. *Science, 137*:508, 1962.

DISCUSSION

Chairman: MERRIL EISENBUD

New York University
New York, New York

JOHN RUNDO: I wanted to take the opportunity of presenting some results which may help to clarify some of the points made in papers this afternoon.

When the mean test ratios were plotted of a small group of subjects living within ten to twenty miles from one another from 1956 to 1962, the two curves showed great variability. I discovered that one subject drank 2 pints of milk a day and the other a $\frac{1}{2}$ pint of milk a day. It is quite obvious that the content of one subject is more than that of the other because he drank so much more milk.

Also in 1959, I suddenly realized that by making a comparison between body content of cesium and the daily excretion of cesium and of the mean day intake, that you can make an assessment of the biologic half life.

In one man who became contaminated in 1957 with 3.5 μc of Cs^{134}, we were able to make measurements for 1,044 days. There was an effective half life of 124 days, which when corrected for a radioactivity which gives a biologic half life of 146 days.

Another individual had only 0.6 μc. We followed him for over 100 days and found an effective half life of ninety-five days and a biologic half life of 108 days.

There were two cases of contamination with Cs^{137} where we had to correct for the fallout level. In one case, where the original content was only 29 μc, we estimated subsequently that 5 μc were due to fallout. The fallout level loss was deduced from the original or average values, indicating a half life of 113 days. The second Cs^{137} case is being followed for another 1,000 days. It has now given us about 120 days.

Therefore, we have four cases of single acute exposure with exponential release from the body and a half life ranging from 108 to 146 days. The average biological half life of all of these subjects is about 122 days.

I know of twenty other cases, and if you take the average value for the whole 28, it comes to 110 or 112 days.

The lowest value for our subjects is forty-eight days and the highest is 200 days.

I suggest that this is a consequence of biological variation among individuals which may account to some extent for the variation you see in the sum contents of people, even members of the same family sitting down to the same table.

R. R. NEWELL: Much has been made of small doses which are useful in clinical investigation when you have a low background room. The large shielded room offers a chance to do standard tests with much less radiation dose to the subject.

Many people write as if the irradiation were a regrettable necessity in order to get the needed clinical information. The best that they can say for it is that it is a good bargain for the patient. However, this does not match the clinical intuition of the men who have a lifetime of experience in radiating people.

Radiologists are unaware of any injury done by clinically administered diagnostic doses. Based on personal experience, I believe that clinical diagnostic radiology has not been doing any radiation injury.

Then I add that I produced many radiation injuries, and so has every other conscientious therapist.

The official and popular estimate of the wickedness of radiation is based on the National Committee's maximum permissible dose and the parallel federal radiation guides.

It is certain that every gamma or every x ray absorbed in living tissue does some disruption of some molecules. Some of them will be living molecules, and one of them may be a vital molecule. In our imagination we see vital molecules knocked out in numbers proportional to the absorbed dose, and we say that the only completely safe place to draw the line is at zero dose, but we will let the conscientious physician use radiation if he can predict a positive balance of good to the patient.

The maximum permissible dose has been progressively lowered through the years. One might suppose that this was because the earlier permissible level has been found to be too generous, has led to too many injuries. Such is not the case.

The propaganda for radiation protection has, of necessity, advertised the M.P.D. and the federation guide. It should have been predictable that the M.P.D. would come to be understood as the safety limit, but it is not in fact the boundary of radiation injury. It should not be understood as a health standard, but is an operating prescription, just like the automobile federal limit.

The M.P.D. is designed to make the users of radiation behave themselves. It is a blunder to use the M.P.D. to guide the recipients of radiation. This distinction becomes important when the users are beyond our control, as in radioactive fallout.

George R. Meneely: Dr. Rundo, what were the routes whereby these people became contaminated.

John Rundo: These were accidental intakes, and we do not know the method of injury to the body. Subsequent experience suggests that most of these are minor intakes which we see in inhalation cases.

In both of the 134 cases there was fairly severe hand contamination at the outset. I do not have enough data to know if any of the activity on the hands did get through the skin, but in one case it might have caused a lot of body contact.

SESSION XII, SEPTEMBER 7

SOCIAL AND INDUSTRIAL ASPECTS OF INTERNAL
RADIOISOTOPE BURDENS

Ctairman: RUSSELL H. MORGAN

42
OCCURRENCE OF LEUKEMIA AND LYMPHOMA IN PATIENTS GIVEN THERAPEUTIC DOSES OF RADIOIODINE[1]

George E. Thoma, Jr., and Robert K. Dorton

Saint Louis University School of Medicine
Saint Louis, Missouri

FOR THE PAST SEVERAL years there has been considerable interest in the possible leukemogenic effect of radioiodine used therapeutically for thyroid cancer and hyperthyroidism.

Six cases of leukemia have been reported (1-6) among a relatively small number of patients who have been treated with I^{131} for thyroid carcinoma with doses of fifty to several thousand millicuries. In one case the leukemia appeared in less than one year after the first dose of radioiodine. In the other cases the latent period was from two to four years. There have also been four cases of "leukemia or aplastic anemia" reported in patients treated for carcinoma of the thyroid with doses of radioiodine ranging from 250 to 1,710 mc (7).

It is estimated that the radiation dose to the hematopoietic tissue from orally administered I^{131} is about 0.5 to one rad per mc (8). Green *et al.* (9) in trying to correlate I^{131} therapy and the eventual development of leukemia measured the dose in 191 thyrotoxic patients after a single therapeutic dose of I^{131}. They found that the average dose to the bone marrow was 1.4 rad per mc.

In 1960, Pochin (10) attempted to determine the incidence of leukemia among an estimated 59,200 patients treated for hyperthyroidism with radioiodine during the preceding twenty years. These were compiled from data in response to question-

[1] This work was supported by the U. S. Public Health Service and National Cancer Institute.

naires returned from most of the major thyroid treatment centers in the United Kingdom, United States, Canada and Austria. He estimated that 221,900 patient years were at risk and, using the appropriate national leukemia rates, determined that the expected number of cases of leukemia that would arise by chance in such a population was twenty-one, with a range of fourteen to twenty-eight cases. He added ten cases of leukemia and one of lymphosarcoma to the eight cases of leukemia previously reported. Later Solomon and Rubenfeld (11) reported one case of chronic lymphocytic leukemia and another of giant follicular lymphoblastoma following I^{131} therapy for thyrotoxicosis. In addition Burns et al. (12) reported two cases of acute leukemia following radioiodine therapy. One of these cases was included in Pochin's report as chronic monocytic leukemia (Case 16, Table VIII of Pochin's report). These cases have recently been summarized by Wald, Thoma and Broun (13). Since their compilation, Choeng and Bourne (14) reported the first case of acute leukemia in Australia after I^{131} treatment for hyperthyroidism. Recently Johnson (15) and Moore (16) each reported a case of acute leukemia. This makes a total of twenty-three cases of leukemia and two cases of lymphoma that have been reported after I^{131} therapy for thyrotoxicosis. In our group of hyperthyroid patients treated with I^{131} we have thus far found two cases of acute lymphoblastic lymphoma. These occurred approximately four years after therapy. The cases reported to date and the two from Saint Louis University series are summarized in Table I.

Although the total number of reported cases of leukemia or lymphoma is increasing, it is still difficult to show a positive correlation between radioiodine therapy and leukemia. The total population of patients treated for hyperthyroidism from which the reported cases have been collected is crudely estimated to be 100,000. The twenty-three cases of leukemia and four of lymphoma are probably within the expected incidence. In view of the low doses of radiation to the blood-forming organs resulting from treatment with 8 mc or less of I^{131}, the lack of any evidence clearly indicating an increase over the expected incidence of leukemia is not surprising. There are, however, certain features about the leukemia group that should be considered. Of the

TABLE I

LEUKEMIA AND LYMPHOMA FOLLOWING RADIOIODINE THERAPY FOR HYPERTHYROIDISM

Case	Author	Age at Time of 1st Dose	Sex	Total Dose (mc)	Latent Period in Months—1st Dose to:		Type of Leukemia
					Symp-toms	Diag-nosis	
ACUTE							
1	Pochin *et al.* (17)	41	F	7.1	19	24	Acute
2	Abbatt *et al.* (18)	67	F	17.0	18½	19	Acute myeloid
3	Childs (19)	46	M	5.3	?	14	Acute granulocytic
4	Werner and Quimby (20)	28	F	2.1	17	18	Acute granulocytic
5	Blomfield *et al.* (21)	50	F	4.9	17	17	Acute monocytic
6	Vetter and Hofer (22)	50	M	7.1	18	18	Acute stem cell
7	Kennedy and Fish (23)	38	M	5.5	22	22½	Acute granulocytic
8	Burns *et al.* (12)	64	F	8.0	6	12	Acute monocytic
9	Burns *et al.* (12)	67	M	14.0	64	84	Acute monocytic
10	Pochin (10)	65	M	3.9	38	43	Acute
11	Pochin (10)	73	M	8.9	35	36	Acute
12	Pochin (10)	64	M	8.5	?	60	Acute
13	Pochin (10)	?	M	4.0	?	(4 yr.)	Acute blast cell
14	Pochin (10)	54	M	3.5	52	54	Acute myeloblastic
15	Pochin (10)	58	M	46.0	32	33	Acute monocytic
16	Choeng and Bourne (14)	62	F	8.0	15	15	Acute myeloblastic
17	Johnson (15)	55	M	19.2	22	26	Acute myelomonocytic
18	Moore (16)	70	F	11.83	39	42	Acute myelomonocytic
CHRONIC							
1	Chapman (24)	65	M	4.0	?	26	Chronic monocytic
2	Solomon & Rubenfeld (11)	66	M	7.5	31	31	Chronic lymphocytic
3	Pochin (10)	60	M	14.3	?	86	Chronic monocytic
4	Pochin (10)	60	M	28.0	?	3	Subchronic lymphocytic
5	Pochin (10)	?	?	?	?	(4 yr.)	?
MALIGNANT LYMPHOMA							
1	Solomon & Rubenfeld (11)	65	F	11.4	40	40	Giant follicular lymphoblastoma
2	Pochin (10)	69	F	12.5	?	51	Lymphosarcoma or aleukemic lymphatic
3	Thoma and Dorton	65	M	6.9	52	56	Acute lymphoblastic lymphoblastic
4	Thoma and Dorton	52	F	6.0	46	46	Acute lymphoblastic lymphoma

twenty-three cases of leukemia, eighteen were acute and five were chronic. Although the characteristics of the population at risk have not been completely established, it appears that the proportion of acute leukemia is higher than would be anticipated. However, this may not prove to be the case since the mean age of this group (Table II) is above that of hyperthyroid patients in general. This probably reflects the conservative use of I^{131} in the younger population.

TABLE II
RANGE AND MEAN AGE AT TIME OF FIRST DOSE OF I^{131}

	Males	Females
Acute leukemia	55	55
	(38-73)	(28-70)
Chronic leukemia	64	
	(60-66)	
Lymphoma	65	62
		(52-69)

TABLE III
NUMBER AND PERCENT OF MALES AND FEMALES

	Males	Percent	Females	Percent
Acute leukemia	11	61	7	39
Chronic leukemia*	4	100	0	
Total leukemia	15	68	7	32
Lymphoma	1	25	3	75
Total	16	62	10	38

*Sex not recorded in one case in Pochin's report (10).

Table III shows that 68 percent of the cases of leukemia in which the sex was recorded occurred in men. This suggests a heightened sensitivity of males, since it is estimated that only about 20 percent of the thyrotoxic patients treated with I^{131} were males.

Seven of the twenty-three cases of leukemia were diagnosed in less than two years after the first therapeutic dose of radio-iodine. In one case the symptoms of leukemia were manifested within six months after the first dose. Only five were diagnosed more than four years later. This latest period distribution is in marked contrast to the four to eight year peak that is generally thought to occur in radiation leukemogenesis. These latent period data suggest that these causes of leukemia occurred by chance.

However, there is insufficient information about the relationship of hyperthyroidism to leukemia to rule out the possibility that under these clinical circumstances the latent period of radiation-related leukemia was shortened.

The four reported cases of malignant lymphoma also may have occurred by chance, but there is possibly more basis for implicating radioiodine in the lymphoma cases than in the leukemias. Germinally active lymphoid cells are occasionally formed in thyroid tissue. The radiation dose to the hematopoietic tissue from 8 mc of I^{131} is about 10 rad, whereas the beta dose to the hyperactive thyroid from 8 mc of I^{131} is several thousand rad.

SUMMARY AND CONCLUSIONS

From a crudely estimated total of approximately 100,000 patients treated for thyrotoxicosis with radioiodine during the past twenty years, twenty-three cases of leukemia and four cases of lymphoma have been reported after I^{131} therapy. Although there is an increasing number of cases of leukemia and lymphoma being reported, it is still difficult to show a positive correlation between the radioiodine therapy and leukemia. There are, however, certain atypical features about the small leukemia group. Although the characteristics of the population at risk have not been completely established, it appears that the proportion of acute leukemias is higher than would be anticipated. However, this may not prove to be the case since the mean age of this group is above that of hyperthyroid patients in general.

It is estimated that approximately 20 percent of the hyperthyroid patients treated with I^{131} were men. In contrast 68 percent of the cases of leukemia in this group occurred in men, suggesting a heightened sensitivity of men to radiation-related leukemia. Seven of the twenty-three cases were diagnosed in less than two years after radioiodine therapy, and only five were diagnosed more than four years later. The latent period distribution differs from the four to eight year peak that is said to occur in radiation leukemogenesis. These facts would suggest either that these cases of leukemia and lymphoma occurred by chance or that under these clinical circumstances the latent period of radiation-related leukemia was shortened. Further clarification will have to await the results from studies of larger populations.

REFERENCES

1. Delarue, M. J., Tubiana, M., and Dutreix, J.: Cancer de la thyroid traite par l'iode radioactif. *Bull. Acad. Franc. Pour L'Etude du Cancer, 40*:263, 1953.
2. Seidlin, S. M., Yalow, A. A., and Siegel, F.: Blood radiation dose during radioiodine therapy of metastatic thyroid carcinoma. *Radiology, 63*:797, 1954.
3. Blom, P. S., Querido, A., and Leeksma, C. H. W.: Acute leukemia following x-ray and radioiodine treatment of thyroid carcinoma. *Brit. J. Radiol., 28*:165, 1955.
4. Seidlin, S. M., Siegel, F., Melamed, S., and Yalow, A. A.: Occurrence of myeloid leukemia in patients with metastatic thyroid carcinoma following prolonged massive radioiodine therapy. *Bull. N. Y. Acad. Med., 31*:410, 1955.
5. Jelliffe, A. M., and Jones, K. M.: Leukaemia after I^{131} therapy for thyroid cancer. *Clin Radiol., 11*:134, 1960.
6. Ozarda, A., Ergin, U., and Bender, M. A.: Chronic myelogenous leukemia following I^{131} therapy for metastatic thyroid carcinoma. *Amer. J. Roentgenol., 85*:914, 1961.
7. Halnan, K. E.: Problems of thyroid cancer and its treatment by radioiodine. *Nucl. Med., 1*:1, 1959.
8. Sinclair, W. K.: In Proceedings of the Conference on Radioiodine, Nov. 5 and 6, 1956. Argonne Cancer Research Hospital, Chicago, The University of Chicago Press, p. 9, 1957.
9. Green, M., Fisher, M., Miller, H., and Wilson, G. M.: Blood radiation dose after I^{131} therapy of thyrotoxicosis. *Brit. Med. J., 2*:210, 1961.
10. Pochin, E. E.: Leukaemia following radioiodine treatment of thyrotoxicosis. *Brit. Med. J., 2*:1545, 1960.
11. Solomon, S., and Rubenfield, S.: Chronic lymphatic leukemia and giant follicular lymphoblastoma after I^{131} therapy. *Arch. Int. Med., 106*:428, 1960.
12. Burns, T. W., Vickers, R., and Lowney, J. F.: Acute leukemia after radioactive iodine (I^{131}) therapy for hyperthyroidism. *Arch. Int. Med., 106*:97, 1960.
13. Wald N., Thoma. G. E., and Broun, G. O. Jr.: *Progress in Hematology: Hematologic Manifestations of Radiation Exposure in Man*, Vol. III. New York and London, Grune and Stratton, pp. 1-52, 1962.
14. Choeng, M., and Bourne, R. G.: Acute leukemia after I^{131} treatment in thyrotoxicosis, *Med. J. Aust., 11*:555, 1961.

15. Johnson, R. E.: Acute myelomonocytic leukemia after radioiodine therapy hyperthyroidism. *JAMA, 179*:572, 1962.
16. Moore, M.: Acute leukemia following I^{131} therapy. *Southern Med. J., 55*:81, 1962.
17. Pochin, E. E., Myant, N. B., and Corbett, B. D.: Leukaemia following Radioiodine treatment of hyperthyroidism. *Brit. J. Radiol., 29*:31, 1956.
18. Abbatt, J. D., Farran, H. E. A., and Greene, R.: Acute myeloid-leukaemia after radioactive-iodine therapy. *Lancet, 1*:782, 1956.
19. Childs, D.: In Proceedings of the Conference on Radioiodine, Nov. 5 and 6, 1956. Argonne Cancer Research Hospital, Chicago, The University of Chicago Press, p. 33, 1957.
20. Werner, S. C., and Quimby, E.: Acute leukemia after radioactive-iodine (I^{131}) therapy for hyperthyroidism. *JAMA., 165*:1558, 1957.
21. Blomfield, G. W., Eckert, H., Fisher, M., Miller, H., Munro, D. S., and Wilson, G. M.: Treatment of thyrotoxicosis with I^{131}: a review of 500 cases. *Brit. Med. J., 1*:63, 1959.
22. Vetter, H., and Hofer, R.: Acute leukaemia following radioiodine-therapy of thyrotoxicosis. *Brit. J. Radiol., 32*:263, 1959.
23. Kennedy, W. M., and Fish, R. G.: Acute granulocytic leukemia after radioactive iodine therapy for hyperthyroidism. *New Engl. J. Med., 260*:76, 1959.
24. Chapman, E. M.: In Proceedings of the Conference on Radio-Iodine, Nov. 5 and 6, 1956. Argonne Cancer Research Hospital (line 9 in the statement erroneously attributed to Dr. Werner), Chicago, The University of Chicago Press, p. 33, 1957.

43

DEMOGRAPHIC FACTORS IN RELATION TO INTERNAL EMITTERS

EDWARD S. WEISS

U. S. Public Health Service
Washington, D. C.

INTRODUCTION

RADIOACTIVITY IN MAN is well within the sphere of interest of the student of population statistics. He traces his professional lineage back to the men who carried out the special census ordered by the Lord on the first day of the second month in the second year after the exodus. The Lord said to Moses, "Take ye the sum of all the congregation of the children of Israel, after their families, by the house of their fathers, . . . every male . . . from twenty years old and upward, all that are able to go forth to war . . . " The job was done in a day and Moses knew that he could raise an army of over 600,000 men.

Since that time, population census have become much more elaborate, but by no means as efficient and economical as the first. Our own census of 1960 will occupy 15 to 20 ft. of shelf space when publication is completed.

The Bureau of the Census of the Department of Commerce reports the results of its decennial canvass under several major subdivisions, of which we will consider only one: Characteristics of the Population. For the whole United States, each of the fifty states and six other areas, extensive tabulations are provided under number of inhabitants, general population characteristics, general social and economic characteristics and detailed characteristics.

The first provides "head counts" for the thousands of incorporated and unincorporated places, counties, urban areas, standard metropolitan areas, etc. The general characteristics are restricted to age, race, sex, relationship to head of household and marital status. An example of some summary data extracted from the U. S. Summary volume is given in Table I.

Some of the social and economic characteristics refer to nativity, school enrollment, fertility, veteran status, employment transportation. Of course, not every characteristic is cross-tabulated with each of the others or for each small geographical or political unit. This extensive cross-tabulation for selected areas is available in the series designated as "detailed characteristics."

The second major source of official demographic data is the Department of Health, Education and Welfare.

From its National Center for Health Statistics come the annual tabulations of births, deaths, marriages and divorces reported by the states and other registration districts. Although barred from imposing regulations governing quality and completeness of reporting, this federal agency has achieved a magnificently high level of uniformity in registration and reporting by encouraging the passage of model legislation and providing consultant services to local and state registrars.

USE OF BASIC CENSUS COUNTS

One of the most frequent questions asked is for an "average." I am not sure that this is always the *right* question to ask, but it is a common one.

After last year's Russian tests, the question put to me was what was the average I^{131} intake of an American child who consumed a liter of milk per day during the four or five months that short lived nuclides were present.

My response is summarized Table II.

USE OF MORTALITY STATISTICS

In his Janeway lecture a few years ago, Marinelli made a rather sophisticated use of bone cancer mortality data in connec-

TABLE I

SUMMARY OF POPULATION CHARACTERISTICS FOR THE UNITED STATES BY REGIONS: 1960

Region	Number	Percent In- crease 1950 to 1960	Percent Non- white	All Persons			Fer- tility Ratio[1]	14 Years and over		18 Years Old and over
				Percent under 18 Years Old	Percent 18 to 64 Years Old	Percent 65 Years and over		Male Percent Married	Female Percent Married	Percent Male
Northeast	44,677,819	13.2	7.1	32.9	57.0	10.1	441	68.7	63.7	47.6
North Central	51,619,139	16.1	7.0	36.0	54.2	9.8	513	69.9	66.6	48.5
South	54,973,113	16.5	20.9	37.8	53.9	8.3	500	69.2	66.1	48.3
West	28,053,104	38.9	7.9	36.2	55.2	8.6	498	68.4	67.6	49.7
U. S. (total)	179,323,175	18.5	11.4	35.8	55.0	9.2	488	69.1	65.9	48.4

[1]Children under five years old per 1,000 women fifteen to forty-nine years old.
Source: Table 55, PC(1)—1B

TABLE II

AVERAGE DAILY INTAKE OF IODINE[131] FROM INGESTION OF ONE LITER OF MILK
PER DAY FROM SEPTEMBER 15, 1961 TO JANUARY 30, 1962

Region	1960 Population ($x10^6$)	Average Daily Intake ($\mu\mu c$)
Northwest States	5	62
California	16	27
North Mountain States	2	63
South Mountain States	5	53
West North Central States	15	129
East North Central States	36	76
West South Central States	17	100
East South Central States	12	66
Northeast States	45	54
Southeast States	26	43
Continental U. S.	179	(66)*
Alaska	0.2	151
Hawaii	0.6	15
All United States	180	(66)*

*( ) Population weighted average

TABLE III

Location	Water Concentration $\mu\mu c/l$	Bone Cancer Mortality*			Ra^{226} Burden 10^{-10}
		Male	Female	Ratio, F/M	
Illinois	>0.4	1.91	1.62	.85	>1.1
Chicago	0.03	1.97	1.59	.81	0.4
Joliet et al.	4.8	1.77	2.57	1.45	7.0

*1940-1950, per 10^5 pop.
From Marinelli: (AJRRT Nov. 1958).

tion with radium concentrations of public water supplies. A portion of one of his tables is given in Table III.

The skeletal burden estimate for the three smaller cities is fifteen times higher than for Chicago (7.0/0.4). But the male death rate (1.77) is lower (cf. 1.97). On the other hand, the female death rates seem to be directly related to the body burdens (in a mathematical sense).

Among other observations and conclusions, Marinelli makes use of these data to support a nonlinear, threshold model for radiation effects.

PLANNING

In the preface to the proceedings of the first symposium on *Radioactivity in Man,* Dr. Meneely said, "One of our major enterprises at the present time is an attempt to characterize the cesium burden of a community, namely, Nashville, Tennessee, which we propose to do by studying the cesium burden of a very carefully drawn sample of this population. This sample has been organized on the basis of geographical distribution throughout the community of race, of sex, of economic status and the study has been guided by other appropriate sociological criteria. Then, following this analysis, a random number technique was employed to select households. All of the members of these particular households are in the process of being assayed for their cesium burden. If we are able to persuade a substantial fraction of this sample to submit to the counting process, we should be able to generalize our observations to characterize the burden of the citizens of our city."

If this kind of planning can be introduced into data collection at state, national and international levels, we may some day understand the interaction of man with one portion of his environment.

WHOLE BODY COUNTERS AND PUBLIC HEALTH

GEORGE W. GAFFNEY

Division of Radiological Health
U. S. Public Health Service
Washington, D. C.

WE WILL CONSIDER some of the possible roles which whole body counters can fulfill in a continuing study and attempt to relate them to other techniques.

The most direct and reliable measurements of organ and whole body burdens of specific radionuclides in human population groups are those which are made by the most direct and reliable means feasible. In some cases this means external counting, such as of radioiodine in the thyroid gland, or of radiocesium in the whole body or of radium in the bodies of some watch dial painters. Sometimes the most direct and reliable means feasible is the assay of breath samples after suitable equilibrium conditions have been established, such as for measurement of relatively low radium burdens. Sometimes the most direct means is the assay of radionuclide in tissue obtained surgically or at autopsy to determine radioiodine in the early fetal thyroid gland or radiostrontium in bone. In other instances, assay of blood plasma or of excreta may be the best direct means for obtaining useful information. All of these alternative approaches are based on measurements made on man, his tissues, breath, fluids or excreta.

The Public Health Service's activities in measurements or radioactivity in man, built in many cases on work sponsored by the Atomic Energy Commission and university groups in this country and abroad, will become increasingly meaningful for public health purposes in the months and years to come. The basic information will be from estimates of radioactivity burdens

579

in man, as opposed to measurements made on various components of the human environment. There will, of course, be every effort to relate the human and environmental data, but the basic frame of reference will be people rather than environment.

Some of the approaches to be used in the human studies have the advantage that a minimum of assumptions are involved in estimation of the organ or body burdens of specific radionuclides, in contrast to techniques based on levels in various components of environment and on assumptions regarding amounts, times and routes of intake.

From determination of levels of some radionuclides in the environment and a knowledge of the daily intake by all routes from this environment, one can gain information related to the body burden of the radionuclide. This is most useful for certain radiation protection purposes as recognized in the guidance of the Federal Radiation Council in establishing various ranges of intake for radiation protection purposes. In applying the guidance, however, it is not possible to immediately determine the amount in each component of the dietary and other sources of intake, particularly at any substantial number of sampling points. For this and other reasons, wide use has been made of the radionuclide content of milk as a relatively quick indicator of the level of the radionuclide in the total diet. Accordingly, it is most important that the calculated values for organ and whole body burdens based on levels measured in milk be compared, where possible, by direct and reliable means. Such data should include information on age groups from early fetal to adult, on urban and rural populations and on populations widely distributed geographically. It should be kept in mind that demonstrating the validity of a relationship between organ or body burden and the level of a nuclide in an indicator food for one set of conditions does not guarantee that such validity exists for all sets of conditions which might be encountered now or in the future. Much more should be learned about the variability in organ and whole body burdens of radionuclides in individuals and population groups and the factors affecting them. When the average level and variability in level of a radionuclide in human population groups is to be determined, the estimates must be based on measurements made on suitable samples drawn from those population groups.

Identifying and obtaining measurements on representative samples of human populations is certainly not easy, but some of the groundwork has been laid in the statistical sampling processes used in health surveys conducted in cooperative studies by the Public Health Service, state and local health departments, the Bureau of the Census, various university groups and others.

For measurements on people to determine certain organ and body burdens directly by *in vivo* techniques, considerably more external counting will be done. This will include, but will not necessarily be limited to I^{131} in the thyroid gland and Cs^{137} distributed in the whole body. For certain important gamma-emitting nuclides, this tool, unlike *in vitro* techniques, permits periodic determination of organ or body content of the nuclide in the same person. Thus it is particularly appropriate for doing frequent studies in subjects from whom the amounts, times and routes of intake are known.

In some instances, of course, *in vivo* counting simply will not work or, at least, cannot be considered to be a promising approach in the light of existing information. The possibility of measuring I^{131} in the fetal thyroid *in vivo* has not been ruled out. For information on the level of radioiodine in the fetus, however, the direct approach certain to prove feasible is radioassay of tissue obtained following accidental deaths. In cases in which adequate information will be available to permit such study, investigation will be made of the relationship of the level of radioiodine in the fetal thyroid to the level in the dietary intake of the mother.

It is also not feasible at the present to use the *in vivo* counting approach for population studies of some radionuclides at the current levels in large population groups. Assessment of the level of radium deposition in humans, when possible at all, can be done by analysis of radon in breath (after equilibrium conditions are established) at much lower levels than can be attained with existing whole body counting systems. In the study of radiostrontium in man, the best estimates would seem necessarily to be based on assay of bone samples excised surgically or made available at autopsy.

Thus it is as clear to those associated with the Division of Radiological Health as to others that existing whole body counters have limitations which do not make them suitable for all the tasks which many should like to be able to assign to them. The basic requirement of a good tool, however, is that it serves to do well at least one important task. Whole body counters provide the means of making direct and reliable periodic determinations in the same individuals of some of the most important short and long lived radionuclides in living humans in population groups. The technique immediately lends itself to the testing of the validity of estimates of certain burdens of radionuclides based on measurements of levels in the environment. It offers promise in the establishment of a network for estimation of body and organ burdens of several important nuclides in suitable population samples, independent of information on, or assumptions related to, amounts, times and routes of intake. Thus the *in vivo* external counting technique will have applicability under widely varied conditions important from the public health standpoint.

For most of the types of studies to be done, facility requirements include heavily shielded chambers or rooms, the choice of material depending on whether there is interest in the portion of spectrum below 70 kev, and on such considerations as bulk and cost. Also required are high resolution detectors—which now means crystal detectors—fed into multi-channel analyzer systems with provision for several hundred channels. There must be adequate provision for data processing, and operation must be by suitably trained staff. The most useful of the facilities will be those accessible to young subjects, including premature infants. Within 95 percent confidence the minimum detectable levels in 30 min. counts should be for I^{131} in the thyroid less than about 20; for Cs^{137} in the whole body of an infant, less than 100; and in the adult, less than 500.

Within its requirements and budgetary limitations, the Public Health Service is initiating arrangements for studies involving counting time on existing whole body counting facilities appropriately distributed geographically and with relation to population centers. In a center established for the purpose, the available data from *in vivo* counting will be collated, analyzed and evaluated in terms of health implications.

In attaining the public health objectives the Division of Radiological Health welcomes your active cooperation and assistance. It cannot hope to succeed without it. For those of you associated with hospitals, your understanding is needed of the efforts to obtain thyroid, bone and other tissue specimens at your institutions. For you associated with institutions with suitable existing whole body counter installations, we have been in contact with many of you and will be attempting to reach the rest. Probably not to exceed one facility in any one city or town, it is hoped that arrangements can be initiated for *in vivo* counting at all existing facilities at which counting time can be made available. Funds are quite limited. It is hoped, nevertheless, that you and your institutions in understanding the public health goals can find it possible to cooperate in an attempt to establish a network, independent of calculation based on measurement of levels in man of important isotopes in radiological health, and of some of the factors affecting these levels.

DISCUSSION

Chairman: RUSSELL H. MORGAN

Johns Hopkins Hospital
Baltimore, Maryland

CHAIRMAN RUSSELL H. MORGAN: Dr. Thoma, are there any data giving the incidence of leukemia-lymphoma among patients who have had hyperthyroidism not treated with radioactive materials?

GEORGE E. THOMA: These data are not yet available. All patients with a diagnosis of hyperthyroidism are going to be seen at intervals, the controls being those who were treated with antithyroid drugs or by surgery as opposed to I^{131}.

RICHARD B. HOLTZMAN: Dr. Thoma said he found two cases of lymphoma in his practice. This, it seems to me, is a high probability. It is quite possible that in these other studies some of the records had gotten lost, particularly on people who had leukemia.

GEORGE E. THOMA: We did not find these two lymphomas in the course of normal follow-up of these patients. The patients with hyperthyroidism when treated with I^{131} generally recovered and are well. It is difficult to carry on long term studies of well patients. They do not come back to the clinic or hospital. The two persons were discovered in a deliberate follow-up of the records. There are many patients in our service whom we have not contacted as yet, and there well may be many more than were reported.

RICHARD B. HOLTZMAN: The point that I was trying to make is that lymphoma is not much more common than leukemia, which is extremely rare, in the order of 1 to 100,000 per year. Therefore, if in 5,000 or 6,000 man-years you found two of these cases, this implies a high probability right there. There is a certain probability of finding one of these cases anyway.

GEORGE E. THOMA: There is a great danger in the individual reporting of all of these cases, such as if a man has treated ten cases with radioiodine and finds leukemia in one, and then ten years later reports that this is a one in ten incidence. That is why we have to study a large, well defined population and cannot take any individual case reports and draw conclusions from them. Perhaps from 500 patients treated, the occurrence of two lymphomas is extremely high, but I don't think this means anything.

GEORGE R. MENEELY: Speaking on behalf of the A.M.A. and on behalf of Northwestern University and all of the other sponsoring organizations, I would like to say that we are all extremely grateful to our speakers, chairmen and the audience.

NAME INDEX

A

Abbatt, J. D., 569, 573
Adams, J. F., 338, 339, 340, 341, 342
Adams, V. S., 401
Adams, W. S., 416
Aitchinson, J., 547, 548, 549
Albert, R. D., 5, 14
Alexander, R. S., Jr., 415
Allderdice, 431, 460
Allen, T. H., x, 201, 231, 262, 264, 268, 269, 271
Alsopp, C. B., 231
Anderson, B., 358
Anderson, Ernest C., v, xi, 69, 87, 103, 118, 121, 152, 153, 159, 161, 162, 164, 165, 166, 167, 168, 169, 170, 171, 172, 173, 175, 177, 179, 185, 201, 202, 209, 211, 230, 231, 250, 261, 262, 265, 266, 268, 269, 271, 427, 540, 549, 555, 561
Andersson, Ingvar Ö., v, 463, 488, 496, 526, 539
Andrews, Howard, 285
Appleby, D. B., 231
Apt, L., 415
Armstrong, Fred G., xxxvi
Aurand, K., 201, 441
Austin, James B., v, xxxvi, xxxviii

B

Baarli, J., 231, 538
Baerg, A. P., 494, 496
Bailor, J. C., Jr., 478
Baird, I. M., 415
Ball, C. O. T., v, xxxvi, 234, 248, 261, 416, 478, 509, 550, 560, 561
Ball, Margaret, R., 231, 272, 276
Ballou, N. E., 134
Barker, 329

Barnes, 329
Barnett, H. L., 185, 428
Bartholomew, R. M., 494, 496
Bass, Allen D., v, 463, 465
Bauer, F. K., 271
Baum, J. W., 52, 63
Becker, David V., 507
Becker, K., 463
Becquerel, xliii
Behnke, Albert R., ix, x, xiii, 177, 225, 231, 232, 234, 264, 271, 273, 275, 276
Beierwaltes, W. H., 427
Belcher, E. H., v, 121, 134, 153, 279, 343, 358, 360, 371, 372, 375, 428
Bell, Marvin C., 431, 460, 461
Bell, P. R., 5, 6, 14
Bender, M. A., 572
Benedict, C., 375
Bengston, G., 516, 526
Berg, L., 269, 271
Bergner, P., 401
Bernstein, Lionel, xxxvi
Bethell, 330
Betts, R. H., 494, 496
Billewicz, W. Z., 231
Binopoulos, D., v, 134, 279, 358, 360
Bishop, M., 483, 487
Black, D. A. K., 262
Black, S. C., 343, 441
Blahd, William H., v, 234, 262, 263, 271, 276, 277, 503, 504, 506
Blasingame, F. J. L., v, xxxvi, xlv
Blaw, H., 180, 185
Blom, P. S., 572
Blomeke, J. O., 495, 496
Blomfield, G. W., 569, 573
Blum, 329
Blumenfeld, N., 400
Boling, E. A., x, 231, 271
Bonnet, J. D., 383, 398, 400, 416,

SUBJECT INDEX

B

Blood volume distribution
  determination of by whole body
    counting, 48-51
      experiments to study accuracy
        and limitations of, 48-49
      illustration principle of, 48-49
      positioning patient, 49-50
      results of, table, 50
      separation thorax and abdomen
        for, 67-68
      study accuracy of technique,
        table, 49
      study limitations of technique,
        table, 49
      summary, 50-51
      technique, 49
  study effect tilting on, 66-67
  use of term blood volume, 67
Bromine
  extracellular fluid volume with Br^{82},
    367-368
    results, graph, 369

C

Calcium
  gastrointestinal absorption Ca^{47};
    349
  turnover of Ca^{47}, 351-352
  whole body counting measurements
    after Ca^{47} injected, graphs, 351
Cardiac failure
  potassium balance measured in pa-
    tients with, graph, 254, 255
  whole body potassium determina-
    tion, 253-257
    interpretation of data, 256-257
Cesium^{134}
  approach to prove presence of in

Laplanders, 492-494
  calculation half life of, table, 492
  half life in gamma spectrum rein-
    deer meat, table, 491
  level scheme of, 492
  origin of in biosphere, 494, 495
  production of in reactors, 495
  use coincidence system to study,
    493-949
  yield of in fission, 494-495
Cesium^{137}
  accuracy and precision measure-
    ment of by whole body counter,
    157-76
    approach to, 157
    calibration with K^{42}, 162
    coefficient of variation of in-
      dividuals studied, 159
    comparison calibration phantom
      and living person, 174-175
    contamination of laundry used on
      subjects, 165-166
    disadvantage use mannikins, 163-
      164
    factors influencing calibration,
      159-160
    meteorological patterns as a fac-
      tor, 169
    need for point source, 171-173
    need for standard intercalibra-
      tion method, 163
    objective of, 157
    possible use fixed dietary intake,
      164
    possible use large dose Cs^{137},
      164
    race as variant, 169-170
    radon daughter products as
      problem, 162
    standard deviation error of popu-
      lation averages, 170

596

methods determination iron absorption, 408-409
percent iron absorption in iron
deficient subjects, table, 411
percent iron absorption in paroxysmal noctural hemoglobinuria, table, 409
results, 407-410
total body iron turnover, 407,
409-410
total body iron turnover in normal persons, graph, 409, 410,
411, 412, 413
whole body counter studies radioiron turnover, 391-394
body counter data, table, 393
body counter performance, table,
394
counter used, 392
early radioiron turnover studies,
391
geometry errors, 392-394
methods, 392
photograph of body counter, 393

L

Lean body mass, defined, 273, 275
Leukemia
in patients given therapeutic doses
radioiodine, 567-572
age at time first dose I^{131}, table,
570
average dose to bone marrow, 567
cases reported, table, 569
conclusions, 571-572
features of, 568, 570
need to study large population,
584-585
number and percent men and
women, table, 570
number cases reported, 567
studies of incidence, 567-568
summary, 571-572
time between treatment and appearance leukemia, 567
incidence, 584
Lymphoma, in patients given therapeutic doses radioiodine, See Leukemia

M

Muscular dystrophy
distribution body potassium concentration, graph, 266
distribution potassium relative of,
graph, 267, 268
interrelation body potassium and
body water in patients with, 263-
271
Muscle disease
body potassium measurements procedure, 264-265
interrelation body potassium and
body water in patients with, 263-
271
body potassium concentration
family of dystrophic patients,
267
conclusions, 269
data of subjects studied, graph,
269
discussion of, 268-270
distribution body potassium concentration, graph, 266
distribution potassium relatives
dystrophic patients, graph, 267,
268
mean regression curves potassium
concentration, graph, 265
procedure and methods determinations, 264-265
results of study, 265-268
summary, 270
use radioactive K^{42} to study, 263
use whole body counter to study
unaffected family members, 263-
264
role potassium in muscle metabolism, 263
Myotonia atrophica
distribution body potassium concentration, graph, 266
interrelation body potassium and
body water in patients with, 263-
271

N

Niobium, See Zirconium

daily requirements of humans of, 325-326

development B₁₂ avitaminosis after total gastrectomy, 326

gastrointestinal absorption with Co⁵⁸-labeled, 362-363

administration test dose, 362-363

correlation absorption measured by two methods, graph, 364

percentage absorption normal subjects, 363

percentage absorption patients studied, graph, 363

half life and deficiency of, 374

maintenance therapy schedule for CN-DMBC and H₂O-DMBC, 327

table, 328

metabolic turnover CN-DMBC and DMBC-Coenzyme in rats, 304-315

biological half life after oral uptake, graph, 313

biological half life and turnover rate absorbed, 310-314

biological half life and turnover rate of intraperitoneally injected, 305-310

biological half life of intraperitoneal injected, graph, 308

comparison absorbed and injected, table, 309

exponential functions for relative whole body retention after oral uptake of, graph, 312

exponential functions for relative whole body retention of injected, graph, 307

intraperitoneal injection of Co⁶⁰-label, 305

method of study, 304-305

nutritional requirement and turnover rate, 314-315

oral administration analogues for study, 310

purposes of study, 304

relative whole body retention and excretion after oral intake of, graph, 311

relative whole body retention and fecal excretion of, graph, 306

results studies, 314

summary biological half life absorbed and injected, table, 312

summary turnover rate absorbed and injected, table, 312

summary turnover time absorbed and injected, table, 312

turnover rate after oral uptake, table, 313

turnover rate of intraperitoneal injected, graph, 308

percent depletion to cause symptoms deficiency, 325

structure specificity in vivo retention and excretion molecule of, 316-317

turnover rate and nutritional requirement of in rats, 314-315

use turnover rate to calculate requirements of for humans, 325-327

compensation therapy schedule for CN-DMBC and H₂O-DMBC, 326-327

maintenance therapy schedule for CN-DMBC and H₂O-DMBC, 327

nutritional requirement daily, 325-326

previous method used, 325

Vitamin B₁₂ avitaminosis

compensation therapy schedule for CN-DMBC and H₂O-DMBC, 326-327

development symptoms after total gastrectomy, 326

W

Water shield whole body counter, 71-86

comparison water and steel shields, 78-81

Argonne National Laboratory comparisons, 80-81

Argonne National Laboratory comparisons, graph, 80

Argonne National Laboratory comparisons, table, 81

basis of, 78

shielding effectiveness, table, 79

water shield backgrounds, graph, 79